PEARSON
Saskatchewan
SCIENCE 9

PEARSON

On the Cover

Northern Lights reflection on Moose Jaw River

Auroras are most commonly seen near Earth's magnetic poles. These natural light displays can be green, red, blue, or a mixture of these. According to scientists, the aurora borealis (the Northern Lights) and the aurora australis (the Southern Lights) are caused by charged particles from the Sun as they enter Earth's magnetic field and collide with the atmosphere.

Auroras are significant to many cultures throughout history and around the world. The First Nations and Métis peoples of Saskatchewan respect the Northern Lights and understand them to be spirits.

PEARSON
Saskatchewan
SCIENCE 9

Camille Hounjet
Rosetown Central High School
Sun West School Division

Bob Kvamme
Estevan Comprehensive School
South East Cornerstone School
Division No. 209

Penny Mohr
Bjorkdale School
North East School Division

Kelly Phillipchuk
Estevan Comprehensive School
South East Cornerstone School Division
No. 209

Ted View
École St. Mary
Regina Catholic Schools

Donald Lacy
Heather A. Mace
Kirsten Mah

Igor Nowikow
Joanne Neal, Ph.D.
Lionel Sandner

PEARSON

Pearson Canada Inc.
26 Prince Andrew Place
Don Mills, ON   M3C 2T8
1-800-361-6128

ISBN-13: 978-0-13-209054-4

PUBLISHER: Reid McAlpine
MANAGING EDITOR: Lee Ensor
RESEARCH AND COMMUNICATIONS MANAGER: Martin Goldberg
PRAIRIE REGIONAL SALES MANAGER: Doug Franke
PROJECT MANAGER AND DEVELOPMENTAL EDITOR: Jessica Fung
DEVELOPMENTAL EDITORS: Eileen Pyne-Rudzik, Ph.D., Rachelle Redford, Winnie Siu
COPY EDITOR: Ruth Peckover
PROOFREADER: Linda Szostak
INDEXER: May Look
COORDINATING AND PRODUCTION EDITOR: Ellen Davidson
EDITORIAL ASSISTANT: Marissa Murray
PHOTO RESEARCHERS: Derek Capitaine, Dominic Farrell, Mary Rose MacLachlan
PRODUCTION COORDINATOR: Cheri Westra
COVER DESIGN: Alex Li, David Cheung
INTERIOR DESIGN: Alex Li, David Cheung
COMPOSITION: Heather Brunton/ArtPlus Ltd.
ART DIRECTION: ArtPlus Ltd.
COVER PHOTOGRAPH: © Mark Duffy/Alamy
ILLUSTRATORS: ArtPlus Ltd., Deborah Crowle, Kevin Cheng, Crowle Art Group, Mark Foerster, Stephen McMath, Allan Moon, Jane Whitney
MANUFACTURING COORDINATOR: Karen Alley
VICE-PRESIDENT, PUBLISHING: Mark Cobham

1 2 3 4 5   CC   15 14 13 12 11

Printed and bound in the United States.

PEARSON

www.pearsoncanada.ca

Message from the Minister of Education
The Honourable Donna Harpauer

On behalf of the Government of Saskatchewan, I am pleased to present *Saskatchewan Science 9*.

This resource was developed by Saskatchewan writers and teachers with Saskatchewan students in mind. This allows our students to better understand how the information they learn applies to the world around them.

This material aligns directly with curriculum outcomes and includes Saskatchewan content, pictures, profiles, and First Nations and Métis ways of knowing, knowledge and perspectives.

As a government, we are committed to providing a high quality education for Saskatchewan students. This new resource will support teachers across Saskatchewan and help students succeed inside and outside of school.

Donna Harpauer

Honourable Donna Harpauer
Minister of Education

The authors and Pearson Education Canada would like to thank the staff of the Saskatchewan Ministry of Education for their guidance in the development of this program.

TEACHER REVIEWERS

Lanna Abbott
Lumsden High School
Prairie Valley School District #208

Corrinne Arnold
Bruno Central School
Horizon School Division #205

Larry Bogdan
Avonlea School
Prairie South School Division #210

Renée Boyko
Churchill Community High School
Northern Lights School Division #113

Dawn Marie Goosen
Humboldt Collegiate Institute
Horizon School Division #205

Heather Haynes-Macdonald
Miller Comprehensive High School
Regina Catholic Schools

Sheila Jensen
Star City School
North East School Division #200

Terry Johanson
Caswell School
Saskatoon Public Schools

Teresa Koop-Hunter
Martensville High School
Prairie Spirit School Division

Cecile Laberge
St. Mary High School
Prince Albert Roman Catholic Separate
School Division # 6

Norman G. Lipinski
Holy Cross High School
Greater Saskatoon Catholic Schools

G. Dean Loberg
Meadow Lake Tribal Council

Bill Mantyka
Evan Hardy Collegiate
Saskatoon Public Schools

Karen D. MacDonald
Campbell Collegiate
Regina Public Schools

Cameron McBain
Kerrobert Composite School
Living Sky School Division # 202

Tegan McGregor
McNaughton High School
South East Cornerstone School
Division #209

Lindsay Morhart
Holy Trinity Catholic School Division

Heidi Paterson
Preeceville School
Good Spirit School Division

Kate Renwick
St. Walburg School
Northwest School Division #203

Greg Taylor
Regina Public Schools

Michelle Wallace
W.F. Ready School
Regina Public Schools

EXPERT REVIEWERS

Dr. Glen S. Aikenhead
Professor Emeritus
University of Saskatchewan

Dr. William Brooks
Partner
eclecthink International

Dr. Stephen Cheng
Lecturer in Chemistry/Supplemental
Instruction Coordinator for Science
University of Regina

Yue Ding
Department of Physics and
Engineering Physics
University of Saskatchewan

Carey Hydamacka
Electrical Engineer
Canadian Light Source Inc.

Dr. Vett Lloyd, Ph.D.
Associate Professor
Mount Allison University

Dr. Melissa Mirosh
Department of Obstetrics, Gynecology,
and Reproductive Services
University of Saskatchewan

Roger A. Pierson, MS, Ph.D.
Department of Obstetrics, Gynecology,
and Reproductive Services
University of Saskatchewan

Tracy Walker
Educational Outreach Coordinator
Canadian Light Source Inc.

FIRST NATIONS AND MÉTIS CONTENT ADVISORS AND REVIEWERS

Elder Peter Bishop
Métis Nation, Green Lake

Elder Velma Goodfeather
Dakota First Nation
Standing Buffalo Reserve

Elder Ken Goodwill
Dakota First Nation
Standing Buffalo Reserve

Elder Alma Kytwayhat
Makwa Sahgaiehcan First Nation

Elder Danny Musqua
Keeseekoose First Nation

Elder Isador Pelletier
Pasqua First Nation

Elder Julie Pitzel
Métis Nation

Elder Mary Ruelling
Clearwater River Dené First Nation

Jeanne Auramenko
Knowledge Keeper
Clearwater River Dené First Nation

Judy Bear
Traditional Knowledge Keeper
Sweetgrass Cree First Nation

Mary Lee
Knowledge Advisor
Chitek Lake First Nation

Sandy Pitzel
Knowledge Keeper
Métis Nation

Albert Scott
Knowledge Trustee
Kinistin Saulteaux Reserve

FIRST NATIONS AND MÉTIS CONTENT ADVISORS

Dr. Herman Michell
Associate Professor
First Nations University

Delvin Kanewiyakiho
Traditional Knowledge Keeper
Cree First Nation, Little Pine Reserve

Welcome to Pearson Saskatchewan Science 9!

You are about to begin a journey exploring Reproduction and Human Development; Atoms and Elements; Characteristics of Electricity; and Exploring our Universe.

You will be investigating the natural phenomena of the world around you and the technological responses of our society to this world. As you do so, we will help you by:

- building on your own experiences of scientific phenomena

- providing you with examples of scientific achievement that people like yourself have undertaken

- providing you with different types of activities that suit different types of thinkers

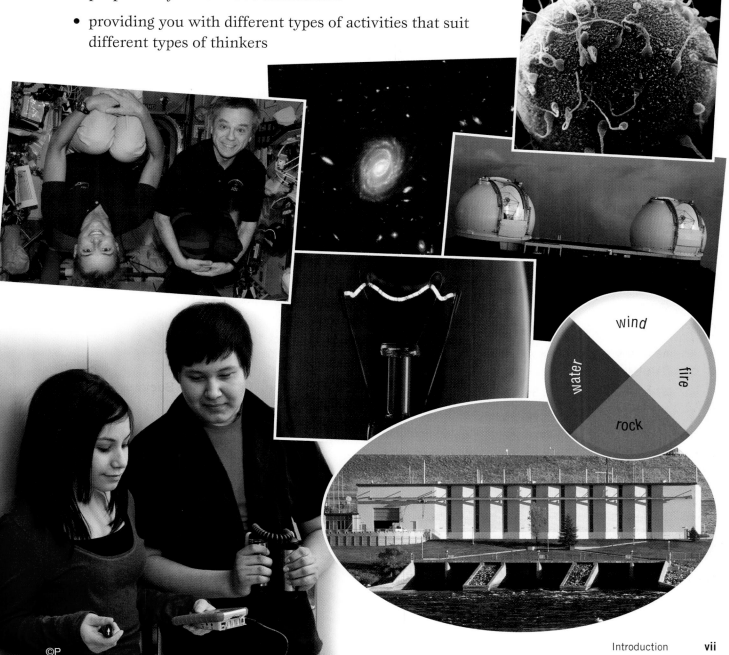

©P

UNIT A — Reproduction and Human Development   2

©P

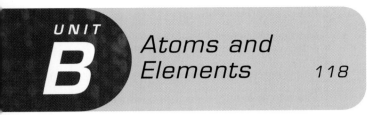

UNIT B
Atoms and Elements 118

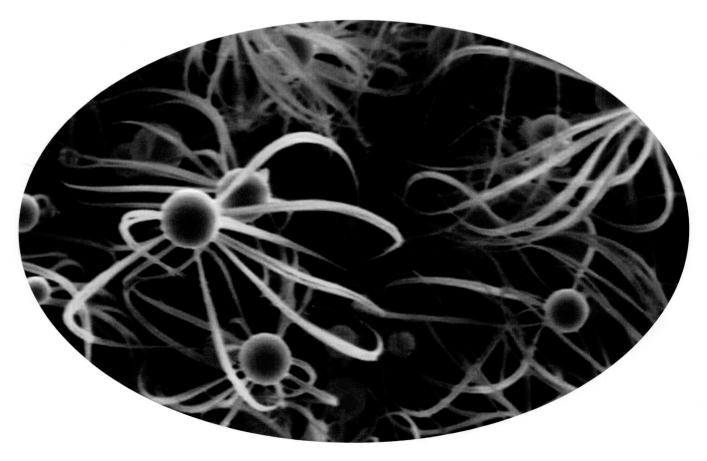

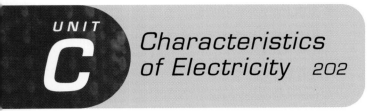

UNIT C Characteristics of Electricity 202

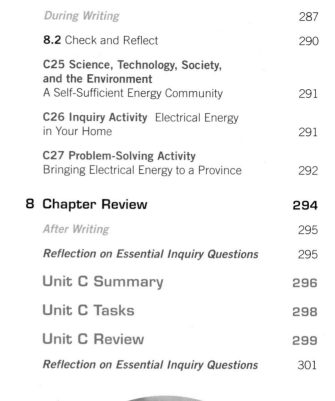

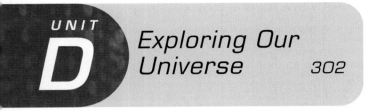

UNIT D
Exploring Our Universe 302

Welcome to *Saskatchewan Science 9*

You are about to begin a scientific exploration using *Saskatchewan Science 9*.
To assist you in your journey, this book has been designed with the following features.

1. Unit Overview — what you will learn

The book is divided into four units. Each unit opens with a large photograph that captures one of the ideas that will be covered in the unit.

The unit **Contents** lists the chapters, Big Ideas, and sections in the unit. The orange DI box indicates essential lessons that have additional differentiated instruction support in the Teacher's Resource.

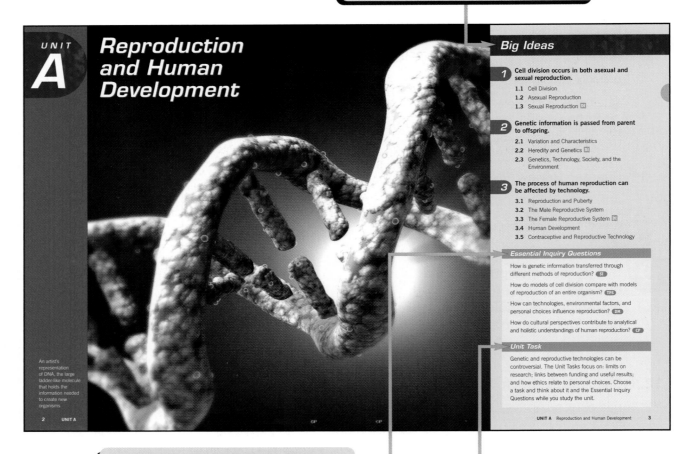

There are four **Essential Inquiry Questions**. These questions guide your learning through the unit in four areas of study: scientific inquiry, technological problem-solving, STSE decision-making, and cultural perspectives. You will be able to answer these questions by the end of the unit.

An introduction to the **Unit Task** is provided below the unit contents. This task is revisited at the end of each chapter, providing you with an opportunity to review key ideas covered in the chapter that will be required to successfully complete the Unit Task.

©P

2. Chapter Introduction — organizes the topics

Each chapter starts with an engaging visual designed to motivate your interest and provide discussion opportunities for the class.

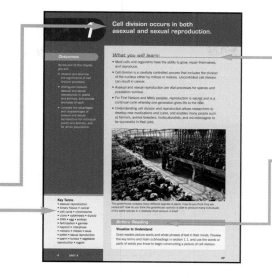

The chapter introduction provides learning support by listing what you will learn in the chapter.

A **Before Reading** or **Before Writing** strategy starts the Before, During, and After literacy activities for each chapter.

The **Big Idea** is a key concept that you should remember when the unit is done.

The **Key Terms** lists the vocabulary terms you will be learning in the chapter.

3. Sections — engaging information on the topics

There are two to five sections in each chapter. Each section starts with a reading and a Quick Science activity.

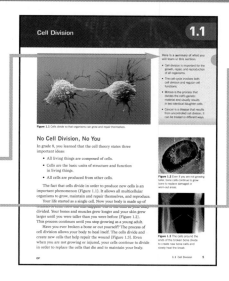

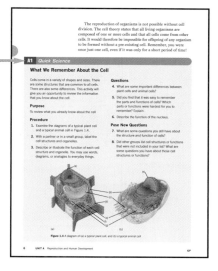

Each section includes a summary of what you will learn in the section.

The **Quick Science** activity is a short, informal learning experience using simple materials and equipment.

The **infoBIT** features are quick tidbits of information that add to your knowledge of the concepts in the unit.

The **Suggested Activity** icon tells you when to perform an activity.

The **Learning Checkpoint** allows you to check your understanding of what you just read.

During Reading and **During Writing** literacy activities provide you with an opportunity to consolidate your understanding.

reSearch is an additional way to study one of the ideas in the section.

First Nations and Métis content is an important part of *Saskatchewan Science 9*. As you read through the sections, you will see how First Nations and Métis ways of knowing provide an alternative way of looking at the world.

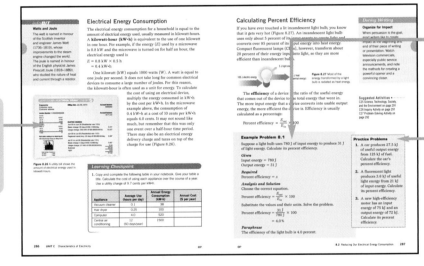

You will find many photos and illustrations to help explain or clarify many of the ideas in the unit.

Check and Reflect questions provide opportunities for you to review the main ideas you learned in each section.

Skill Builder Activity reviews or reinforces certain skills necessary for completing some of the activities.

Example Problems show the detailed steps in solving problems.

Practice Problems model the example problem and provide opportunities for further practice. Use these problems to check if you understand the concept being discussed.

The **Chapter Review** contains questions relevant to the whole chapter. Answering the questions will help you consolidate what you learned in the various parts of the chapter.

After Reading or **After Writing** literacy activities provide you with an opportunity to consolidate your understanding.

The **Reflection on Essential Inquiry Questions** prompts you to consider what you learned in the chapter and how it relates to the Essential Inquiry Questions at the beginning of the unit.

The **Unit Task** provides you with an opportunity to review key ideas covered in the chapter that will be required to successfully complete the Unit Task.

There are six main types of activities: Quick Science; Science, Technology, Society, and the Environment; Inquiry Activities; Problem-Solving Activities; Decision-Making Analyses; and Inquire on Your Own. The Quick Science was discussed on page xvii.

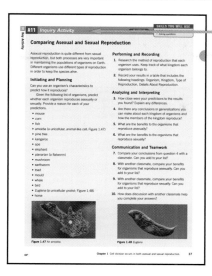

Inquiry Activity: These activities provide the oportunity for you to work in a lab setting. You will develop scientific skills of predicting, observing, measuring, recording, inferring, analyzing, and many more. In these activities, you will investigate many different phenomena found in our world.

Science, Technology, Society, and the Environment: These are short decision-making activities that ask you to research an issue related to the chapter and state your opinion based on the evidence you collect.

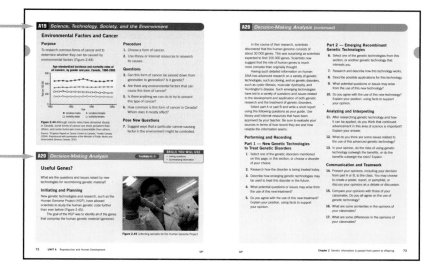

Decision-Making Analysis: These activities present issues or questions related to everyday life. You will need to analyze the issue and develop an opinion based on the evidence you collect and make an informed decision. In many instances, you will present your findings and decisions to your classmates.

Problem-Solving Activity: These activities provide a challenge to meet a need through design and construction. In a group, you will brainstorm, research, and build a prototype device. You will then test and evaluate how well your design meets agreed criteria and present your results in a report or presentation.

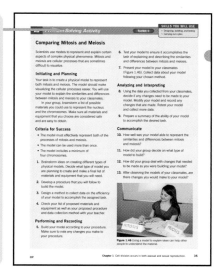

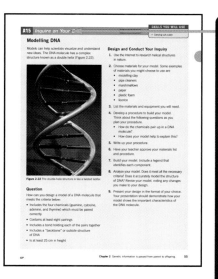

Inquire on Your Own: These open-ended activities provide an opportunity to apply the skills you learned to investigate a question related to a concept. You will research, plan, and carry out your own investigation or design a technological solution. After collecting data from your experiment, you will draw conclusions and report on your findings.

5. Unit Summary — a review of what you learned

At a glance, you can find all of the key concepts you learned in the unit. You can also read the summary of ideas in each section of the unit as well as review vocabulary and key visuals. These pages can help you organize your notes for studying.

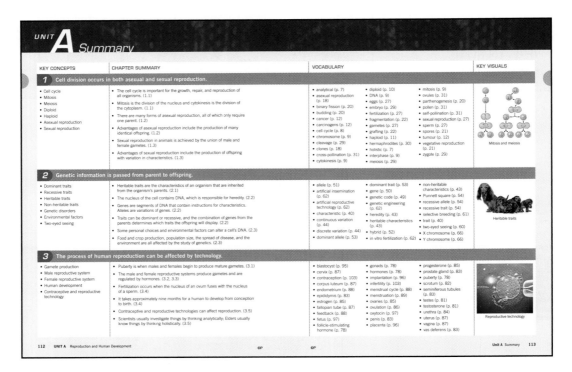

6. Unit Task — lets you demonstrate learned skills

A task at the end of each unit presents an opportunity for you to demonstrate what you learned. Choose one of the Unit Tasks. You will work in a group or individually. The task requires you to apply some of the skills and knowledge that you acquired during the unit.

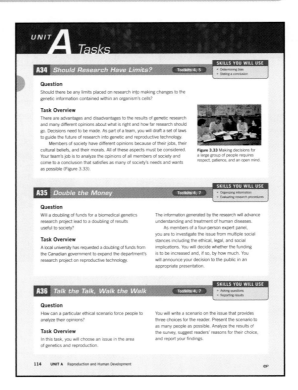

The Unit Review is an opportunity to review the concepts, skills, and ideas you learned in the unit.

Using Key Terms
This is a chance to review the important terms in the unit.

Reviewing the Big Ideas
Questions designed to review your basic understanding of the key concepts in each chapter of the unit

---

UNIT **A** Review

Using Key Terms

1. Create a concept map that illustrates your understanding of the following terms and how they relate to reproduction.
   - mitosis
   - meiosis
   - gametes
   - eggs
   - sperm
   - asexual reproduction
   - sexual reproduction
   - heredity
   - characteristics
   - traits
   - DNA
   - genes
   - alleles

Reviewing the Big Ideas

2. What is the function of cell division?

3. Explain the difference between a haploid cell and a diploid cell.

4. Describe the reason gametes contain only half the DNA of body cells.

5. List three environmental factors that can cause changes in a cell's DNA that may lead to cancer.

6. What is the difference between mitosis and cytokinesis?

7. Describe how a hybrid black cat differs from a purebred black cat.

8. What is a zygote? How is it formed?

9. Outline the path of development in animals from gamete to embryo.

10. Sketch the parts of a flower that are involved in reproduction. Describe how each part functions in cross-fertilization.

11. Summarize how bacteria cells divide by binary fission.

12. Explain the difference between asexual and sexual reproduction and the advantages and disadvantages of each.

13. How does binary fission differ from meiosis?

Question 13

14. Briefly list the costs and benefits of asexual and sexual reproduction in terms of diversity.

15. What is similar about egg and sperm cells? What is different?

16. Differentiate between heritable and non-heritable characteristics. Provide two examples of each type.

17. Use a diagram to compare the inheritance of dominant and recessive traits.

18. What is meant by the term "genetic code"?

19. What is the general structure of the DNA molecule?

20. Explain the relationship among DNA, chromosomes, genes, and alleles.

21. Sketch a simple diagram of a human cell and include information about the roles of chromosomes, genes, and DNA.

©P

Unit A Review   115

Using the Big Ideas
Opportunities to apply what you learned in the unit to the world around us and everyday life

---

UNIT **A** Review (continued)

22. Explain the effect that technology such as artificial insemination, that is used in the livestock industry, has on the genetic variation of domesticated animals such as cattle and sheep.

23. Compare and contrast genetic engineering with other types of reproductive technology. List possible advantages and disadvantages of each.

24. Describe three examples of genetic engineering.

25. Compare and contrast gamete formation in male and female humans.

26. What is the main function of the male and female reproductive systems in humans?

27. Write out the path that mature sperm cells take from the testes to the outside of the body.

28. Describe the function of the follicles in the production of egg cells.

29. Compare the roles of LH and FSH in regulating the female reproductive cycle.

30. Name and state the function of the four hormones discussed in Chapter 3.

31. Describe positive and negative feedback using two hormones in the female reproductive system.

32. Write out the path that a mature egg cell takes from the ovary to the outside of the body.

33. Where in the body is an egg usually fertilized by sperm?

34. What is the difference between fertilization and implantation?

35. Explain cleavage in terms of zygote development.

36. What is the placenta and what is its function?

37. Explain the relationship between technology and reproductive technologies.

38. Describe how four of the methods of contraception discussed prevent pregnancy from occurring. Be sure to explain what part of the regular reproductive process is interrupted.

39. Describe a situation where in vitro fertilization might be used and explain what in vitro fertilization is.

40. Elder Lemaigre understands that human reproduction is sacred. In what way, if any, does a scientific understanding of human reproduction involve the idea of sacredness?

Connecting the Big Ideas

41. Explain how the three Big Ideas are related. You can write a description, use a concept map, or draw an illustration to show the relationships.

42. Which type of reproduction, sexual or asexual, is responsible for an increased amount of genetic variation in plants and animals? Support your answer with examples.

43. What impact does the cloning of domesticated animals have on genetic diversity? Would cloning of wild animals ever be a possibility? Explain your answer.

44. Describe the similarities and differences between cell division and human reproduction. How are these connected?

Using the Big Ideas

45. Imagine that your gonads were exposed to a high dose of radiation. Explain some of the possible consequences, including any impact on future generations.

46. Explain how you would create a new breed of dog.

47. List reasons you would or would not be concerned about drinking milk from cows treated with a growth hormone.

48. Describe how you would conduct research to identify issues arising from the development of new reproductive technologies.

49. Suppose someone is making a personal choice on an issue related to human reproduction. Suggest an advantage to them of using two-eyed seeing.

50. A student states that genetic engineering is "perfectly safe." What safety and ethical issues do you think might arise from the use of genetic engineering?

51. As a society, how should we make decisions about the uses of technology such as genetic engineering and cloning?

Reflection

52. Describe three things about reproduction that you did not know before you started working on this unit.

53. List questions for further study that you have about the transmission of genetic material in sexual reproduction or asexual reproduction.

54. Based on your unit work, describe three ways in which technology has been developed to meet human needs and wants.

55. Write a paragraph about the balance among the physical, emotional, mental, and spiritual dimensions when two people have a baby.

56. Describe at least one career choice that would be related to what you have learned in this unit. Research the education required, average salary, and average job duties of this career.

57. Describe a human being from two points of view as studied in this unit: (a) a scientific way of understanding, and (b) a holistic way of understanding.

Reflection on Essential Inquiry Questions

How is genetic information transferred through different methods of reproduction?

How do models of cell division compare with models of reproduction of an entire organism?

How can technologies, environmental factors, and personal choices influence reproduction?

How do cultural perspectives contribute to analytical and holistic understandings of human reproduction?

Human Development

Connecting the Big Ideas
Questions that require you to use the ideas in more than one chapter in your answers

Reflection
Opportunities to express your thoughts about ideas you discovered in the unit

Reflection on Essential Inquiry Questions
This is a chance to revisit and answer the Essential Inquiry Questions from the beginning of the unit.

Here are other features you will find in each unit. Each one has a different purpose and is designed to help you learn about the ideas in the unit.

Ask an Elder

Ann Marie Lemaigre: Niotlsini's gift

For Saskatchewan's Dené people, as for all First Nations and Métis peoples, all life is sacred. Ann Marie Lemaigre, an Elder from the Clearwater River Dené Nation, describes her people's views on the sacredness of life. Further teachings and contributions were provided by Elder Mary Ruelling, also from the Clearwater River Dené Nation. This profile was written through the help of Jeannie Auramenko, a teacher and Dené interpreter.

According to Elder Ann Marie, "It is from the Creator that all created things come." From that perspective, all life is sacred. She sums up the Dené beliefs by saying, "Niotlsini (Creator) is [creating] all things, including human [beings] [recogniz]ed as the absolute force of [life. The sa]credness of life stems from [the life-]giver and the preserver of all [life. In Dené prayers, we acknowledge [God] for thanksgiving, for our way [of life,] in to each one of us, living in [all] [living things, and respect for all." [We believe] that all living things are interdependent. The Dené people [in their tr]aditional ways show respect for [life and t]raditional land management. [They] harvest only what they need. Some of the Dené still travel along the traplines, snaring animals for their furs to earn a living (Figure 3.32). Trappers carefully monitor and observe that their way of life is in harmony with the land.

"Human beings are dependent upon all growing matter. We are a part of the puzzle. However, we are the most needy of all living things. We cannot survive without our natural brothers and sisters. These include the plants, animals, birds, and fish. The Dené make offerings to the natural brothers and sisters. The offering will consist of what they have as their sustenance.

This is followed by a prayer. For example, when travelling by boat or canoe, before you enter the water, you say a prayer to the water spirit asking for protection, thanksgiving, and safe travel. Some will touch the water and recite a prayer. The land is here to look after us, as well as the water," says Elder Ann Marie Lemaigre.

Elder Lemaigre's words illustrate a holistic way of thinking.

Figure 3.32 The Dené people who practise the traditional way [show] respect for the land through traditional land managem[ent]

108 **UNIT A** Reproduction and Human Development

Ask an Elder
This feature gives you access to the wisdom of a First Nations or Métis Elder or Knowledge Keeper who shares an oral story related to the content of the unit.

Ask an Expert
This feature introduces a person in an occupation or activity related to the unit's content. You may learn the steps needed to become an expert in that field.

Ask an Expert

Sheila Flynn: Growing a Greenhouse

Sheila Flynn became interested in gardening and planting, or horticulture, at a very young age while working with her mother, who was an avid gardener. She extended her knowledge by working at greenhouses, attending classes, asking many questions, and doing a lot of research.

When Sheila decided to try growing some of her own plants, she had her husband build her a small 2 m × 2.5 m greenhouse. She really enjoyed it and decided to buy a bigger greenhouse so that she could grow enough plants to sell the following year. After attending the Saskatchewan Greenhouse Growers Convention in the fall of 2004, she began ordering plants with other local greenhouse operators.

Her hobby has now turned into a full-time job. Today, Sheila operates a 9 m × 30 m greenhouse in Beechy, Saskatchewan, and sells her plants to customers from all over the province (Figure 1.35).

Figure 1.35 Sheila's greenhouse in Beechy, Saskatchewan, is full of healthy, beautiful plants for customers to take home to their gardens and yards.

[...th] year of growing and selling plants. She has [learned what] it takes to produce a good-quality plant that will [keep com]ing back, year after year. She looks for a variety of [plants that are re]sistant and have proven performance records. She [looks for] new varieties that are developed each year. Sheila [buys plants tha]t have grafted onto sturdier roots and stems [to ensure the] survival of the top-heavy plant. She also buys [seeds to grow] beautiful plants. She has used the seeds produced [from the] flowers for herself, but always buys good-quality [seeds, tes]ted for disease to grow flowers for her customers.

[work with] something I love," says Sheila. "It gives me a lot [of satisfactio]n opening day each year when there is a [crop of beautif]ul, good-quality plants."

[...]d Human Development

Careers and Profiles

Dawn McGowan: Neonatal Nurse

Dawn McGowan, a Métis woman of Saulteaux (Nakawē) and Swedish descent, is a nurse who practises neonatal medicine in the city of North Battleford. Dawn has been a nurse for 31 years. For the first 20 years of her career, she worked as a licensed practical nurse in the field of maternity in Whitehorse, Yukon Territory. Then, after four years of additional training in the Nursing program at the University of Saskatchewan, she earned her nursing degree, graduating with Distinction. She worked at the Royal University Hospital in Saskatoon in Neonatal Intensive Care. Dawn now works as a registered nurse in the neonatal unit at the Women's Health unit, which includes newborns, at Battleford's Union Hospital.

As a neonatal nurse, Dawn assists with the delivery of premature babies and cares for them in the early weeks of life. These premature babies, often born at only 24 weeks, have many complications such as infections. They may require intubation to breathe and extensive attention until they are old enough and strong enough to leave the hospital at 40 weeks. "The smallest baby I ever cared for weighed no more than one pound," Dawn said proudly. "Life, no matter how small, has meaning." (Figure 3.21)

In addition to her duties as a neonatal nurse, Dawn serves on a medical team that performs emergency transport of sick babies, either by plane or by ambulance. She is the person responsible for resuscitation procedures and life support, if needed by the patient. The range of this specialized team extends from as far north as La Ronge down to the southwestern corner of Saskatchewan near Swift Current.

Figure 3.21 Even the smallest forms of life have a lot of meaning.

Q: Who inspired you to become a nurse?
A: I don't remember wanting to be anything but a nurse. My mother had a drive to care for other people. Her caring ways inspired me.

Q: What challenges do you face as a neonatal nurse?
A: Sometimes, rarely, we lose a baby, but you have to see the positive side even in tragedy. The resilience we need must outweigh the grief we feel. To be a nurse means that you have to have a different kind of belief system, a kind of strength and caring that allows you to continue to advocate and to care for people despite the tragedies.

100 **UNIT A** Reproduction and Human Development

Careers and Profiles
This feature describes the background and some of the interests of the person being profiled.

©P

9. Toolkits — provides skills information and practice

These pages provide references to lab safety and other basic scientific skills that will help you as you do the activities. Remember to check the Toolkits when you need a reminder about these skills.

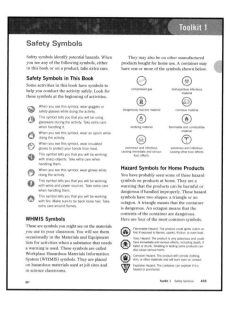

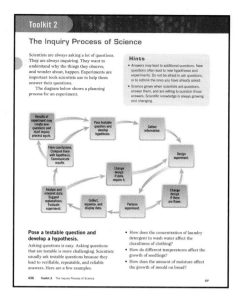

10. Glossary — provides definitions for all key terms

The Glossary is a list of all the important vocabulary terms that you learn in the different units. The terms are listed in alphabetical order. The page on which a term is defined is at the end of each definition.

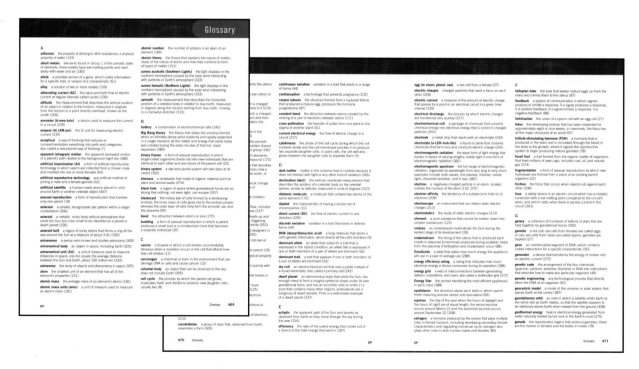

Now it is time to start. We hope you will enjoy your scientific exploration using *Saskatchewan Science 9*!

There is much to learn in the science you are studying this year. The Big Ideas that organize each unit can be used to help you develop your understanding of science.

Unit A: Reproduction and Human Development   2

1 Cell division occurs in both asexual and sexual reproduction.

2 Genetic information is passed from parent to offspring.

3 The process of human reproduction can be affected by technology.

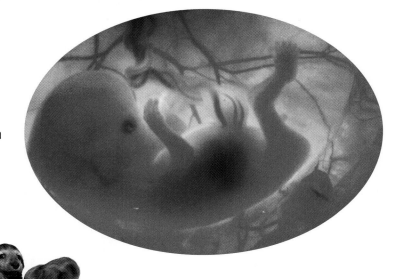

Unit B: Atoms and Elements   118

4 People of all cultures investigate matter according to various properties.

5 The periodic table is a tool for organizing scientific understanding of the elements.

©P

Reproduction and Human Development

An artist's representation of DNA, the large ladder-like molecule that holds the information needed to create new organisms

©P

Big Ideas

1 Cell division occurs in both asexual and sexual reproduction.

1.1 Cell Division

1.2 Asexual Reproduction

1.3 Sexual Reproduction **DI**

2 Genetic information is passed from parent to offspring.

2.1 Variation and Characteristics

2.2 Heredity and Genetics **DI**

2.3 Genetics, Technology, Society, and the Environment

3 The process of human reproduction can be affected by technology.

3.1 Reproduction and Puberty

3.2 The Male Reproductive System

3.3 The Female Reproductive System **DI**

3.4 Human Development

3.5 Contraceptive and Reproductive Technology

Essential Inquiry Questions

How is genetic information transferred through different methods of reproduction? **SI**

How do models of cell division compare with models of reproduction of an entire organism? **TPS**

How can technologies, environmental factors, and personal choices influence reproduction? **DM**

How do cultural perspectives contribute to analytical and holistic understandings of human reproduction? **CP**

Unit Task

Genetic and reproductive technologies can be controversial. The Unit Tasks focus on: limits on research; links between funding and useful results; and how ethics relate to personal choices. Choose a task and think about it and the Essential Inquiry Questions while you study the unit.

©P

Outcomes

By the end of this chapter, you will:

- observe and describe the significance of cell division processes

- distinguish between asexual and sexual reproduction in plants and animals, and provide examples of each

- compare the advantages and disadvantages of asexual and sexual reproduction for individual plants and animals, and for whole populations

What you will learn:

- Most cells and organisms have the ability to grow, repair themselves, and reproduce.

- Cell division is a carefully controlled process that includes the division of the nucleus either by mitosis or meiosis. Uncontrolled cell division can result in cancer.

- Asexual and sexual reproduction are vital processes for species and population survival.

- For First Nations and Métis peoples, reproduction is sacred and is a continual cycle whereby one generation gives life to the next.

- Understanding cell division and reproduction allows researchers to develop new medications and cures, and enables many people such as farmers, animal breeders, horticulturalists, and microbiologists to be successful in their jobs.

This greenhouse contains many different species of plants. How do you think they are produced? How do you think the greenhouse operator is able to produce many individuals of the same species in a relatively short amount of time?

Key Terms
- asexual reproduction
- binary fission • cancer
- cell cycle • chromosome
- clone • cytokinesis • diploid
- DNA • egg • embryo
- fertilization • gamete
- haploid • interphase
- meiosis • mitosis • ovule
- pollen • sexual reproduction
- sperm • tumour • vegetative reproduction • zygote

Before Reading

Visualize to Understand

Good readers picture words and whole phrases of text in their minds. Preview the key terms and main subheadings in section 1.1, and use the words or parts of words you know to begin constructing a picture of cell division.

©P

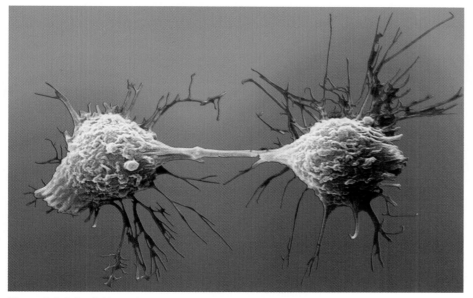

Figure 1.1 Cells divide so that organisms can grow and repair themselves.

Here is a summary of what you will learn in this section:

- Cell division is important for the growth, repair, and reproduction of all organisms.

- The cell cycle involves both cell division and regular cell functions.

- Mitosis is the process that divides the cell's genetic material and usually results in two identical daughter cells.

- Cancer is a disease that results from uncontrolled cell division. It can be treated in different ways.

No Cell Division, No You

In grade 8, you learned that the cell theory states three important ideas:

- All living things are composed of cells.

- Cells are the basic units of structure and function in living things.

- All cells are produced from other cells.

The fact that cells divide in order to produce new cells is an important phenomenon (Figure 1.1). It allows all multicellular organisms to grow, maintain and repair themselves, and reproduce.

Your life started as a single cell. Now your body is made up of trillions of cells. How did that happen? All of the cells in your body divided. Your bones and muscles grew longer and your skin grew larger until you were taller than you were before (Figure 1.2). This process continues until you stop growing as a young adult.

Have you ever broken a bone or cut yourself? The process of cell division allows your body to heal itself. The cells divide and create new cells that help repair the wound (Figure 1.3). Even when you are not growing or injured, your cells continue to divide in order to replace the cells that die and to maintain your body.

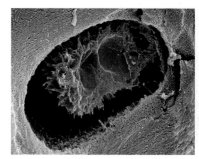

Figure 1.2 Even if you are not growing taller, bone cells continue to grow bone to replace damaged or worn-out areas.

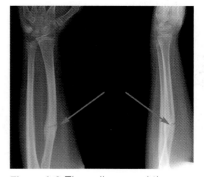

Figure 1.3 The cells around the ends of the broken bone divide to create new bone cells and slowly heal the break.

The reproduction of organisms is not possible without cell division. The cell theory states that all living organisms are composed of one or more cells and that all cells come from other cells. It would therefore be impossible for offspring of any organism to be formed without a pre-existing cell. Remember, you were once just one cell, even if it was only for a short period of time!

A1 *Quick Science*

What We Remember About the Cell

Cells come in a variety of shapes and sizes. There are some structures that are common to all cells. There are also some differences. This activity will give you an opportunity to review the information that you know about the cell.

Purpose

To review what you already know about the cell

Procedure

1. Examine the diagrams of a typical plant cell and a typical animal cell in Figure 1.4.

2. With a partner or in a small group, label the cell structures and organelles.

3. Describe or illustrate the function of each cell structure and organelle. You may use words, diagrams, or analogies to everyday things.

Questions

4. What are some important differences between plant cells and animal cells?

5. Did you find that it was easy to remember the parts and functions of cells? Which parts or functions were hardest for you to remember? Explain.

6. Describe the function of the nucleus.

Pose New Questions

7. What are some questions you still have about the structure and function of cells?

8. Did other groups list cell structures or functions that were not included in your list? What are some questions you have about those cell structures or functions?

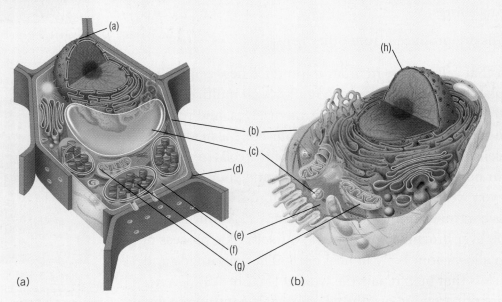

(a)   (b)

Figure 1.4 A diagram of (a) a typical plant cell, and (b) a typical animal cell

Holistic and Analytical Ways of Thinking

For many First Nations and Métis people, everything in Mother Earth is related. Everything has Spirit and is therefore sacred, for instance, rain, animals, wind, soil, plants, rocks, lightning, rivers, and humans. People are related to everything they can see, hear, taste, smell, and feel. Through Spirit, a person is connected to the oneness of everything. People see themselves related to this *whole* oneness. This is a **holistic** way of thinking. It has proven to be a powerful way of understanding the physical world for Indigenous people who depended upon it to survive over tens of thousands of years in harsh environments, by living in harmony with those environments.

A completely different approach to thinking comes from analyzing everything into parts and categories. Rain is thought of as a collection of water molecules. People are thought of as molecules, cells, organs, and systems. The night sky is thought of as planets, stars, and galaxies. This scientific way of thinking is **analytical**; it reduces or compartmentalizes everything into parts and categories, which scientists then study in detail. For this reason, it is also called a reductionist way of thinking. For about 400 years, analytical thinking has proven to be a powerful way to understand and control the physical world to benefit humans.

In this chapter, you will learn powerful ideas about reproduction from a scientific or analytical point of view.

The Advantage of Microscopes

Many centuries ago, scientists and Greek philosophers such as Aristotle (Figure 1.5) believed that new organisms appeared suddenly from non-living or rotting material. This idea was called spontaneous generation. One example of this idea is a recipe for producing mice: Wheat and sweaty underwear were placed in an open container and left for three weeks. It was thought that the sweat mixed with the wheat to produce mice!

The belief in spontaneous generation was widely held for many centuries. It was disproved in 1688 by Francesco Redi, an Italian physician. According to spontaneous generation, maggots appeared from meat. To test this belief, Redi placed meat in jars. Some jars were sealed, some were covered with cloth, and others were left uncovered.

Figure 1.5 Aristotle (384–322 BCE) formally stated the idea of spontaneous generation as a theory. His theory was believed for almost two thousand years.

Figure 1.6 Hooke's microscope. The appearance and functionality of microscopes changed as technology advanced over the years. Do you think microscopes will always look the way they do now?

As he predicted, the meat that was sealed or covered with cloth did not "grow" maggots. The meat that was left in the open eventually had maggots, which Redi determined came from eggs left by flies. These experiments were early ways of trying to figure out how new organisms arise.

Our scientific understanding of cells and how new organisms appear was further advanced by an important technological development: the microscope. Scientists were very excited that they were able to use this instrument to make observations about the world around them! In 1665, Robert Hooke used a primitive form of compound microscope to look at very thin slices of cork (Figure 1.6). He observed that cork was made up of air-filled spaces, which he later called cells. In 1674, Antoni van Leeuwenhoek used a microscope to observe living micro-organisms and animal cells. Both Hooke's and van Leeuwenhoek's observations expanded our knowledge of the variety of living things, but because neither of them was able to observe cell division, scientists still did not understand how organisms reproduced.

By 1833, further advancements in microscopy allowed Robert Brown to observe and describe cell structures and the nucleus of plant cells. Shortly after this, in 1838, German biologists Matthias Schleiden and Theodor Schwaan recognized that *all* plant and animal cells have similar cell structures, including a nucleus. They theorized that all living things are made up of cells and that the cell is the basic unit of life. This important idea formed part of the cell theory. Additional observations of cells led Rudolf Virchow to develop the third principle of the cell theory in 1855: All cells arise from other cells. The development of the cell theory and our understanding of cells would not be possible without the development of newer microscope technologies. The microscope changed the way we look at life and understand how new life is formed.

The Cell Cycle

Many cultures, including First Nations and Métis peoples, often understand the world as constantly changing in cycles and processes, such as the seasons of the year. Scientists describe the **cell cycle** as a process by which the parent cell grows, duplicates itself, and divides to produce new daughter cells, usually two.

Scientists describe these three major phases of the cell cycle as interphase, mitosis, and cytokinesis.

During **interphase**, a cell performs its normal cell functions, grows, and prepares for cell division. During **mitosis**, the nucleus divides to produce an exact copy of itself. During **cytokinesis**, the rest of the cell contents divide to produce two separate daughter cells (Figure 1.7).

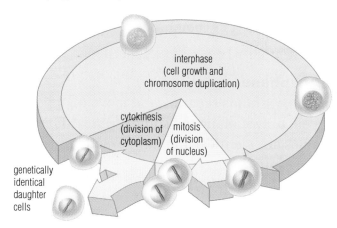

Figure 1.7 A cell grows and divides into new daughter cells.

Interphase

Interphase is the longest phase of the cell cycle, during which the cell performs its normal cell functions, grows, and prepares for division. The nucleus contains information for cellular activity, which is also referred to as genetic information. A cell's genetic information directs all the cell's functions and is stored in the form of long molecules of **DNA** (deoxyribonucleic acid). According to scientific models of the cell, each double-stranded DNA molecule is packaged into a structure called a **chromosome**. In preparation for cell division, the chromosomes are duplicated and then condense. Once the chromosomes are duplicated, each chromosome is made up of two identical copies of the DNA (Figure 1.8). Duplicating the chromosomes is important because without an exact copy, the new cells will not be able to perform their normal cell functions.

The Stages of Mitosis

The next phase of the cell cycle is mitosis. During this phase, the nucleus divides. The nuclei produced are identical to each other and to the parent nucleus. Mitosis has four stages: prophase, metaphase, anaphase, and telophase (Figure 1.9). Mitosis is a continuous process.

chromosome duplication

Figure 1.8 A diagram to show how, at the end of interphase, each duplicated chromosome is made up of two copies of the genetic information

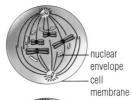

nuclear
envelope
cell
membrane

Figure 1.9 Mitosis happens in a series of four stages.

Stage 1: Prophase

The chromosomes, which were duplicated during interphase, condense and shorten. They can be seen through a microscope. The membrane around the nucleus (the nuclear envelope) begins to dissolve and disappear. The mitotic spindle forms.

Stage 2: Metaphase

The doubled chromosomes line up in the middle of the cell on the mitotic spindle. The membrane around the nucleus is completely dissolved.

Stage 3: Anaphase

The chromosome strands separate and move to opposite ends of the cell, drawn along the spindle fibres. The two sets of chromosomes are identical and have exactly the same genetic information.

Stage 4: Telophase

The separated chromosomes arrive at opposite sides of the cell. The mitotic spindle disappears. A new nuclear envelope begins to form around each set of chromosomes, forming two new nuclei. The chromosomes begin to lengthen and become less condensed and are no longer visible under the microscope.

Cytokinesis

The last phase of the cell cycle is cytokinesis. In animal cells, the cell membrane pinches in to divide the nuclei, cytoplasm, and organelles to form two daughter cells (Figure 1.10). In plant cells, a cell wall forms between the two nuclei, dividing the cytoplasm and forming two daughter cells (Figure 1.11). The arrow highlights the formation of the cell wall.

After cytokinesis, the daughter cells are in interphase and the cell cycle begins again. Figure 1.12 summarizes the phases of the cell cycle and the stages of mitosis.

According to scientists, most cells are produced through mitosis. All daughter cells produced through mitosis have the same number of chromosomes as the parent cell. In sexually reproducing species, the body cells contain two sets of chromosomes, one set received from the male parent and one set received from the female parent. Cells that have a double set of chromosomes are called **diploid** cells. Mitosis in a diploid cell produces two daughter cells that are also diploid.

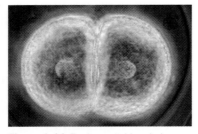

Figure 1.10 During cytokinesis in an animal cell, the cell membrane pinches in to form two daughter cells.

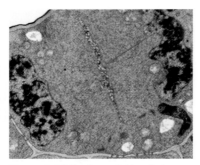

Figure 1.11 During cytokinesis in a plant cell, the cell wall divides the cell into two daughter cells.

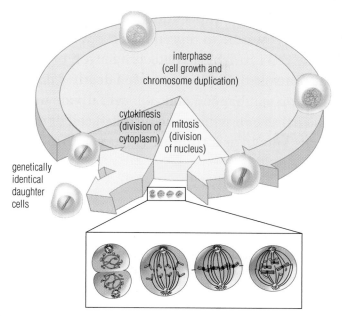

Figure 1.12 The cell cycle is composed of interphase, mitosis, and cytokinesis.

In section 1.3, you will learn about sex cells, also called eggs and sperm, which are produced through a special form of cell division, called meiosis, and contain half the number of chromosomes as the parent cell. You will also learn about a process called fertilization, in which two sex cells join together. For now, just keep in mind that cells that contain a single set of chromosomes are said to be **haploid** and that two haploid cells join together in the process of fertilization.

Suggested Activities •·········
A2 Skill Builder on page 15
A3 Skill Builder on page 16
A4 Inquiry Activity on page 16

During Reading

Picture Mapping

As you read about the cell cycle, draw pictures with arrows to confirm your understanding of how the stages and phases of cell division connect.

Learning Checkpoint

1. Compare two different general ways to understand a human—a scientific way and a First Nations and Métis way.

2. In your own words, describe the cell cycle. Make sure to include a description of each phase.

3. What is the difference between mitosis and cytokinesis?

4. Describe the four stages of mitosis. Include diagrams in your description.

5. Briefly explain the difference between diploid and haploid cells.

Cell Division and Cancer

Normally, a cell's DNA controls the cell cycle and ensures that cells reproduce only as needed. It also makes sure that the cells die as they age or if they are damaged. Sometimes, the complicated process of cell division encounters or creates errors in the duplication of chromosomes.

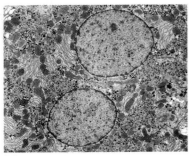

(a)

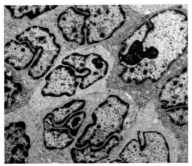

(b)

Figure 1.13 Healthy cells (a) and cancer cells (b) often appear different and differ in how cell division is controlled.

reSearch

When Henrietta Lacks's physician removed cells from her body in 1951 to test for cervical cancer, neither of them could have imagined that these cells would still be reproducing today. Usually, human body cells can divide only about 50 times in the laboratory before they die. So what made Henrietta's cells so special? Research the history of the HeLa cell and write a paragraph to summarize what you have learned. Begin your research using the library or the Internet. Include information about Henrietta Lacks and her family. Explore any issues that may have arisen from the use of her cells for research.

Usually when an error in duplication is detected, the cell destroys itself. It does not continue to reproduce cells with incorrect DNA. However, if the cell is unable to detect the error, or if the section of DNA that controls the cell cycle or cell death is damaged, the opposite situation can happen and cells will divide uncontrollably. **Cancer** is the disease in which uncontrolled cell division creates a clump of cells known as a **tumour** (Figure 1.13).

Benign and Malignant Tumours

There are two main types of tumours: malignant and benign. Benign tumours may grow quickly and physically crowd the surrounding cells or organs but otherwise do not cause any damage. Benign tumours do not spread throughout the body and are considered non-cancerous.

Malignant tumours can grow very quickly and invade and damage the surrounding cells or organs by interrupting their normal function. Cells of malignant tumours can separate from the main tumour and, by travelling through the bloodstream, spread to a different part of the body and start growing a new tumour. For this reason, malignant tumours are very dangerous and are considered cancerous. The many types of cancer result from uncontrolled cell division of specific cells. For example, lung cancer involves uncontrolled cell division in the lungs, whereas bone cancer involves uncontrolled cell division in bones.

Whether malignant or benign, tumours can endanger the health of the organism. As tumours in the body grow larger, they can crowd surrounding cells and organs, thereby interfering with the normal functioning of the body systems. Anything that interferes with the normal functioning of the body systems can be dangerous because all of the body systems work together to ensure the overall health of the organism. Also, like any other type of cell, tumour cells require nutrients and oxygen to survive. If tumour cells begin to use up the nutrients and oxygen that healthy cells need, the healthy cells will not be able to survive.

Causes of Cancer

Research into the causes of cancer has shown that in some cases, cancer is caused simply by errors in replicating the cell's DNA. In other cases, cancer occurred after an organism was exposed to certain harmful environmental factors. Scientists call chemicals or toxins in the environment that can damage DNA in cells and cause cancer **carcinogens**.

It has been shown that the use of tobacco can cause numerous types of cancer, including lung cancer and cancer of the mouth and throat. Ultraviolet (UV) rays, such as those produced by the Sun and by tanning beds, have been shown to cause various forms of skin cancer. You will learn more about how carcinogens and UV rays cause cancer in section 2.3.

It is important to be aware of the results of scientific research and take action to try to protect your cells from unnecessary damage. Trying to prevent cancer from developing in your body, such as by avoiding tobacco products or not using tanning beds, is easier than treating cancer once it has developed (Figure 1.14).

Figure 1.14 Covering up is the most efficient way to help reduce exposure to UV rays and your risk of developing cancer. Sunscreen is also effective.

Cancer Treatment

Treating cancer is difficult because healthy cells and cancer cells are very similar. Most treatments kill healthy cells in addition to cancer cells, causing the patient to feel tired and ill. Despite this problem, it is usually necessary to treat cancer to prevent it from spreading and causing damage to the body.

There are risks and benefits to each type of treatment. Doctors consult with patients to weigh the risks and benefits of different treatments and decide on the best course of action. One treatment option is surgical removal of the tumour. Surgery can be effective for benign tumours and when used with another form of cancer treatment.

Chemotherapy is a combination of drugs that are taken orally or injected into the body to kill fast-growing cells, which include cancer cells. The death of healthy cells is what causes a cancer patient's hair to fall out. Hair-making cells are one of the first types of healthy cells to respond to chemotherapy because they grow quickly.

Another way to treat cancer is radiation therapy. Radiation therapy involves the use of radiation energy to damage cancer cells in order to prevent them from reproducing. However, radiation can also damage healthy cells. To minimize this risk, radiation beams are carefully aimed at the tumour to try and minimize the exposure to healthy cells (Figure 1.15). In about half of all cancer cases, both radiation and chemotherapy are used.

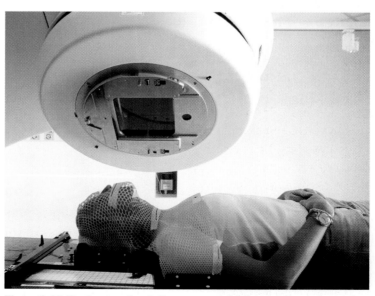

Figure 1.15 The beams of radiation are carefully aimed at the cancer cells to reduce damage to the surrounding healthy cells.

reSearch

Investigate how different types of cancer are caused and how they are treated. Prepare a poster to display your findings.

A Holistic View of Cancer

Cancer and cancer treatment are viewed differently by the First Nations and Métis peoples of Saskatchewan. Many traditional people, like the Cree, the Dené, and the Dakota understand illnesses in a holistic way. They examine the entire being of a person and understand that the physical, mental, spiritual, and emotional parts of the body need to work together to function properly in a healthy person.

Many First Nations and Métis groups do not have the word "cancer" in their language but every First Nations group has a substitute word instead. Cancer, often called "the great sickness," is known by other names in the diverse languages of the Saskatchewan First Nations such as the Cree, Nakawē (Saulteaux), and Dakota. In Cree, cancer is called *manicōs* or *mancōs*, which means "like a bug that multiplies under the skin." This traditional name describes the rapid and uncontrolled multiplication of cancer cells in the human body. Dakota people call cancer *Po'pi ohinni icaǧa*, which means "growth or clump." In Nakawē, cancer is described as *kāzanagak-akoziwin* or "powerful illness or sickness that recurs." The Nakawē see cancer as an illness that, if left untreated, can recur.

A traditional remedy used today to treat cancer involves not only the healer and the patient but the patient's family and community. This remedy that Elders and healers use to treat cancer involves all aspects of a person's being and is often a combination of traditional medicines and herbs, prayers, and ceremonies. To treat the physical aspect of the body, herbs and medicines are used. Ceremonies and prayers are used to treat the spiritual aspect of the patient. Elders and healers then provide the patient with teachings on how to care for their body and address the mental aspect of the healing process. Lastly, the emotional part of the healing involves family and community support.

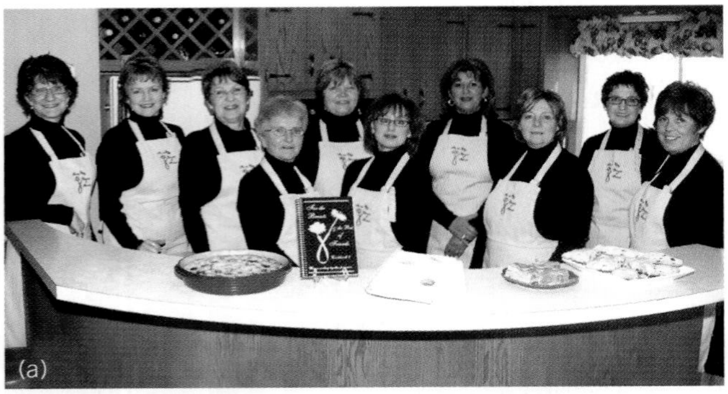

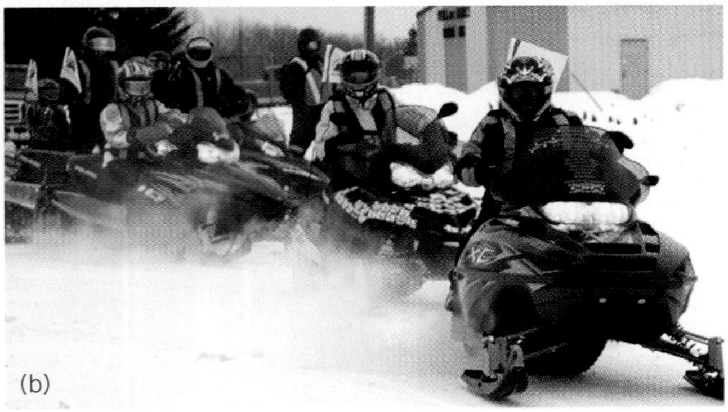

Figure 1.16 (a) The Breast Friends have raised more than $1 million for patient needs, equipment, and research through the production and sale of cookbooks. (b) Prairie Women on Snowmobiles conduct annual 8-day snowmobiling Missions to create awareness of breast cancer, riding approximately 1800 km across Saskatchewan. They have raised more than $1.4 million for breast cancer research.

Community Involvement

Saskatchewan communities support cancer patients in emotional, physical, and financial ways. Groups provide services to help with daily living, such as transport to treatment, discussion groups, workshops, and retreats. Others raise funds for cancer causes (Figure 1.16.)

1. Describe how the development of the microscope affected the scientific understanding of the cell. Give one other example of technology that has helped advance scientific understanding of the world around us.

2. List the phases of the cell cycle and describe what happens in each phase.

3. List the stages of mitosis and describe what happens in each stage. Include a diagram of each stage.

4. A friend says cells do nothing during interphase. Do you agree or disagree? Explain why.

5. Explain what cancer is, using your understanding of the cell cycle.

6. Describe the difference between a benign tumour and malignant tumour. Which is more dangerous? Explain why.

7. What are some ways you can reduce your risk of cancer? Give two examples.

8. Recall a time that you had an injury such as a cut or a scrape. From a scientific point of view, describe how the process of cell division affected the healing of your wound.

9. Describe a holistic view of cancer and cancer treatment.

10. List the substitute words that First Nations and Métis groups have for cancer and include their meanings. How accurately do these describe cancer? Explain.

A2 Skill Builder

Using the Microscope

A microscope is a powerful scientific tool. In grade 8, you learned how to use a microscope. Complete this Skill Builder to refresh your skills.

1. Always carry a microscope with two hands, with one hand on the arm of the microscope and the other hand under the base.

2. Always start with the lowest-power objective lens in place.

3. Place the slide on the stage and fasten it in place using the stage clips.

4. Move the slide from side to side in order to get the specimen under the lens. Keep in mind that all images are upside down and backward when you are trying to move the slide.

5. Adjust the mirror or diaphragm so that the optimum amount of light shines on the slide.

6. Use the coarse adjustment knob to move the lens up or the stage down, until the specimen comes into focus.

7. Use the fine adjustment knob to focus more clearly on the specimen (Figure 1.17).

8. Change to the next power objective lens to get a closer look at the specimen.

9. Repeat steps 7–8 until you have the best image possible.

10. When you are finished, remove the slide and move the lowest-power objective lens into place.

Figure 1.17 Careful focussing of the microscope at each power will reveal the details of the specimen.

Cell Drawings

A scientific drawing can help you record your observations and communicate your findings. Cell drawings should be clear, simple, and easy to understand (Figure 1.18).

1. Using a pencil and a sheet of paper, draw the cell membrane or cell wall using clear, firm lines. Do not sketch. You can shade darker areas if necessary.

2. Draw the nucleus.

3. Draw any other organelles that are present. Remember to draw only what you see.

4. Use a ruler to draw label lines pointing to each cell structure. Make sure the lines do not cross. Label all structures clearly.

5. Title your drawing with the name of the specimen. Record the objective lens you used to observe the image.

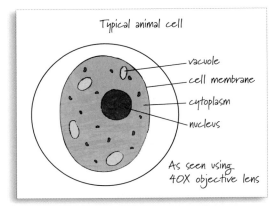

Figure 1.18 A cell drawing should clearly show your observations.

SKILLS YOU WILL USE
- Using appropriate equipment and tools
- Observing and measuring

Observing Mitosis

In this activity, you will be observing different phases of the cell cycle and stages of mitosis in onion root tip cells. The slide of onion root tip cells was prepared by slicing through a live root tip, staining the cells, and preserving it for future observation (Figure 1.19). When you look at cells on a prepared slide, keep in mind that the cells are no longer living. What you see is a snapshot of the cells that were dividing when the slide was prepared.

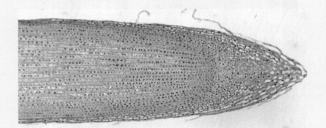

Figure 1.19 Root tips have areas of rapidly dividing cells. The phases of the cell cycle and stages of mitosis can be easily observed.

Initiating and Planning

How can we recognize the phases of the cell cycle and distinguish between the stages of mitosis?

Materials & Equipment

- compound microscope
- prepared slide of onion root tip

Performing and Recording

1. Set up the microscope and ensure that the lowest-power objective lens is in position and the diaphragm is open to the widest position.

2. Obtain a prepared slide of an onion root tip and place it on the stage of the microscope. Move the slide around until you see the coloured area of the slide through the lens. Use the coarse adjustment knob to bring your specimen into focus.

©P

3. Centre the image of the root tip in your field of view, and then carefully switch to the medium-power objective lens. Use the fine adjustment knob to focus the image. Look for cells undergoing cell division. The cells' chromosomes are stained to make them easier to observe. Carefully switch to the high-power objective lens and use the fine adjustment knob to focus the image.

4. Identify cells that are in interphase. Make a sketch of a cell in interphase.

5. Identify cells that are in each of the four stages of mitosis: prophase, metaphase, anaphase, and telophase (Figure 1.20). Make a sketch of a cell in each stage of mitosis.

6. Identify cells that are in cytokinesis. Make a sketch of a cell in cytokinesis.

7. Count the total number of cells in the field of view. Record this number in your notebook.

8. Create a table similar to Table 1.1 and record the number of cells in each phase of the cell cycle and stage of mitosis. The total number of cells should equal the sum of the number of cells at each phase or stage.

Table 1.1

Cell Phase or Stage	Number of Cells
Cytokinesis	
Interphase	
Prophase	
Metaphase	
Anaphase	
Telophase	

9. Be sure to put the low-power objective lens back into place when putting away the microscope.

Analyzing and Interpreting

10. Calculate a percentage for the number of cells at each phase or stage.

11. Assume that the percentage of cells in each phase or stage represents the relative amount of time it spends in that phase or stage. Create a graph that shows the percentage of time spent in each phase or stage.

12. In what stage of mitosis were the majority of the cells?

13. Based on your observations, does cell division occur as a continuous process or as a series of separate events? Explain.

14. Did you observe any stages of mitosis that were difficult to identify or classify? Explain how you decided in which phase or stage it was.

15. As with all living organisms, the onion plant began life as a single diploid cell. If the original cell had 16 chromosomes, how many chromosomes were in each of the cells you observed?

Communication and Teamwork

16. Compare your results with another lab group. Were your percentages of the number of cells at each phase or stage similar? Explain.

17. How well did you and your lab partner(s) work together? How did you decide on a role for each group member?

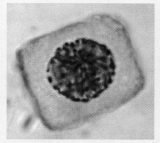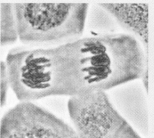

Figure 1.20 Onion root tip cells in each stage of mitosis

Here is a summary of what you will learn in this section:

- Asexual reproduction involves only one parent.

- Plants can reproduce asexually by binary fission, spore production, vegetative reproduction, fragmentation, or grafting. Animals can reproduce asexually by budding or parthenogenesis.

- Asexual reproduction can produce lots of identical individuals very quickly but produces entire populations of individuals that may not survive if the environmental conditions are not optimal.

- Asexual reproduction is a fundamental part of the agriculture and forestry sectors in Saskatchewan.

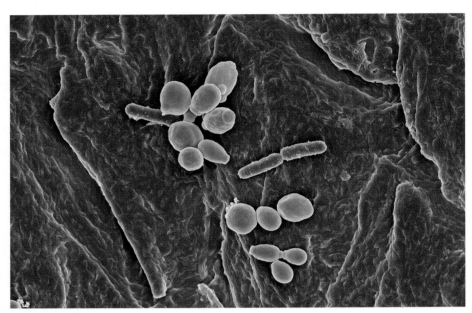

Figure 1.21 Bacteria are organisms that can reproduce asexually.

What Is Asexual Reproduction?

Asexual reproduction is reproduction that involves only one parent. All the offspring that result from asexual reproduction are genetically identical to that parent because the parent makes an exact copy of itself. Offspring that are identical copies of the parent are called **clones**. There are several different forms of asexual reproduction, and each form is important to the survival of organisms.

In some cases, asexual reproduction can produce lots of identical individuals very quickly. Over a 12-hour period, a single bacterium can divide to produce 10 million copies of itself. This is a great advantage in environments that do not change very much. For example, bacteria that live in the gut of an animal will always have a warm, moist environment to live in while the animal is alive. Producing many copies of a bacterial cell that is suited to that environment is a safer bet for survival than producing a smaller number of bacteria with many variations that may never be needed. Species that reproduce asexually invest energy to produce as many identical copies of themselves as possible to build a large population quickly (Figure 1.21).

The main disadvantage of asexual reproduction is that all the offspring are identical to the parent. Any factor that negatively affects the parent, such as a disease or drug, will also affect all the offspring.

If environmental conditions become unfavourable, the entire population may be wiped out. For example, every single one of those 10 million identical bacteria could be killed if they have no resistance to an antibiotic that is applied to them.

Growing a Potato

There are many different types of plants that reproduce asexually. Potatoes are an example of this type of plant. Can you use a regular potato to grow more potatoes?

Purpose

To try growing a potato from an existing potato

Materials & Equipment

- potato with many "eyes" or dark spots
- knife
- cutting board
- 2 flowerpots or other containers
- potting soil
- masking tape
- pen
- water

CAUTION: Use caution when handling the knife. Always use a cutting board and cut downward.

Procedure

1. Carefully cut the potato into pieces. Make sure that some of the pieces have eyes, while others do not (Figure 1.22).

2. Fill each flowerpot with potting soil. Do not pack the soil tightly.

3. In one flowerpot, plant 5–7 pieces of potato with eyes at least 5 cm apart. Label the flowerpot.

4. In the other flowerpot, plant 5–7 pieces of potato that do not have eyes. Make sure to plant the pieces at least 5 cm apart and to label the flowerpot.

5. Place the plants in a sunny location such as next to a window or outdoors. Water the plants every 1–2 days, ensuring that the soil is moist but not soaking.

Questions

6. Did any of your potato pieces grow? If so, which pieces grew?

7. What is an "eye" on a potato?

Pose New Questions

8. Suggest a question that could extend your learning about how a plant can grow more plants.

Figure 1.22 The spots on a potato are often referred to as "eyes."

Types of Asexual Reproduction

Binary Fission

Binary fission occurs when single-celled organisms, such as bacteria, amoebas, and some algae, divide into two identical daughter cells to produce two new individuals that are identical to each other and are clones of the parent cell. In bacterial cells, which do not have a nucleus to separate the single chromosome from the rest of the cell, the parent cell duplicates its DNA, then the cell membrane grows inward and divides the parent cell and the two copies of DNA into two new daughter cells

In amoeba and other unicellular organisms that do have a nucleus, the DNA is duplicated and the nucleus undergoes mitosis. Binary fission follows as the cytoplasm pinches in and pulls apart completely, to produce two separate new individuals (Figure 1.23).

Figure 1.23 Amoebas are single-celled organisms that can reproduce through binary fission.

Budding

Organisms such as hydra and yeast reproduce asexually by budding. During **budding**, the parent produces a small bud, or a miniaturized clone. In some organisms, such as hydra and yeast, the buds eventually detach and become separate individuals (Figure 1.24(a)). In other animals, such as coral, the offspring remains attached to the parent, forming a large structure composed of many identical individuals (Figure 1.24(b)).

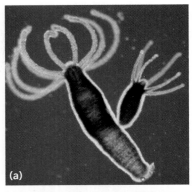

Figure 1.24 Many organisms reproduce through budding, such as hydra (a) and coral (b).

Parthenogenesis

Some species of animals, particularly social insects, such as ants and bees, use a unique method of asexual reproduction that scientists call parthenogenesis. **Parthenogenesis** is the process by which unfertilized, haploid eggs mature into new organisms (Figure 1.25). Parthenogenesis is also observed in more complex animals, such as certain species of snakes and lizards. In bees, unfertilized eggs become male drones, whereas fertilized eggs become female workers and queens. You will learn more about eggs and fertilization in section 1.3.

Figure 1.25 Aphids are insects that can reproduce asexually through parthenogenesis.

©P

Spores

Many fungi, green algae, some moulds, and non-flowering plants such as ferns reproduce by producing spores (Figure 1.26). **Spores** are haploid cells that can develop into new organisms. Production of offspring through spores is similar to parthenogenesis because both processes produce offspring from haploid cells. However, parthenogenesis involves unfertilized eggs. Spores, on the other hand, are not sex cells but simply haploid reproductive cells. They cannot be fertilized to produce offspring.

Spores are similar to seeds in that they contain and protect the DNA of the organism against unfavourable environmental conditions. The spores remain in a state of suspended animation—they are alive but do not grow—until environmental conditions, such as temperature, sunlight levels, or water levels, are suitable for growth. One individual will produce many spores, and each spore can develop into a new individual.

Figure 1.26 Spores can survive unsuitable growing conditions because they remain dormant, which is an inactive state of rest. When conditions improve, spores can produce new individuals.

Vegetative Reproduction

Most plants are able to reproduce through vegetative reproduction. **Vegetative reproduction** is described by scientists as the asexual production of identical offspring, or clones, from the parent plant. It does not involve the formation of a seed.

There are many methods of vegetative reproduction. If you take a cutting from a coleus plant and place it in water, the cutting will grow roots and eventually develop into a whole new plant.

Other forms of vegetative reproduction use specially modified stems. Many plants, such as strawberries or spider plants, grow modified stems that run horizontally over the ground. These are called runners and they produce new plants along their length (Figure 1.27 (a)). Rhizomes are similar to runners except that they grow underground. The rhizomes have nodes from which new individuals can grow (Figure 1.27 (b)).

Figure 1.27 Runners (a) and rhizomes (b) both produce new individuals along modified stems.

Recall the Quick Science activity in which you cut up a potato and each piece grew into a new individual. The potato is an example of a tuber. Tubers and bulbs, such as onions or tulip bulbs, are also forms of vegetative reproduction (Figure 1.28). New individuals can develop from pieces of the tuber or bulb.

Figure 1.28 Pieces of a bulb can produce new plants. Lilies and onions are examples of bulbs.

Match the Story to the Picture

You may read paragraphs where there are so many new terms that you cannot understand all of them. Do not forget to check the diagrams and other pictures included in the text. Reread the text, matching the words you are reading to the pictures to get a better understanding of the ideas.

Suggested Activity •··········
A6 Inquiry Activity on page 24

Figure 1.30 Grafting allows two or more plants to grow together as a single plant.

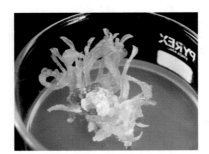

Figure 1.31 These cells can grow into a clone of the parent plant.

Fragmentation

In **fragmentation**, new individuals are formed from a piece of the existing parent organism. Some animals, such as some species of worms, can grow two identical individuals after being cut into two pieces (Figure 1.29). Starfish have this same ability, as they can grow a whole new organism from one part of an arm that has been removed from the parent. Individuals produced through fragmentation are identical clones of the parent.

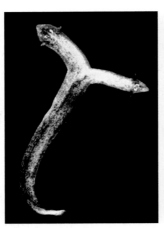

Figure 1.29 Organisms can repair limbs and produce new individuals through fragmentation.

Grafting

Grafting is a process in which a part of one plant is joined with another plant, called the parent tree or the root stock. The two plants heal together and grow as a single plant, but the two plants maintain their own characteristics. This process is commonly used by gardeners to produce flowers with certain colours or trees that grow different types of apples on different branches (Figure 1.30). It is also used to strengthen the stem of a plant to ensure that it grows and develops a strong, healthy stem.

Plant Tissue Cultures

Plant cells can be placed in a petri dish or in a bottle containing nutrients and other chemicals and grown into new individuals. This is known as a plant tissue culture. Once these cells have developed into seedlings, they can be transplanted into soil and grown like a normal plant. Because the starting point is a cell rather than an entire part of the plant, many more clones can be produced from a single plant (Figure 1.31). Plant tissue culture is often used to clone plants that have desirable features such as disease resistance or good fruit production. It can also be used to conserve endangered plant species.

©P

Asexual Reproduction and Agriculture

Potatoes are an excellent example of how different methods of asexual reproduction are used in agriculture in Saskatchewan. First, a parent plant with desirable features is selected. Cuttings are taken from the parent plant and are either grown directly or used to create plant tissue cultures. The resulting clones are grown and produce seed potatoes. Seed potatoes are potatoes that are grown for replanting, instead of for eating.

Suggested Activity •············
A7 Science, Technology, Society, and the Environment on page 25

The seed potatoes are replanted the following year. Each seed potato is usually cut into pieces prior to planting so that each piece can grow a new plant (Figure 1.32). The plants grown from seed potatoes then produce potatoes sold for eating. It is also possible to replant the potatoes grown from seed potatoes, but there is a seven-year limit on how many generations can be produced from the original seed potato. This limit helps ensure good seed quality and minimizes the risk of diseases.

Figure 1.32 A single seed potato can be cut up and planted to produce many new plants.

1.2 CHECK and REFLECT

1. Define asexual reproduction. List three examples of asexual reproduction.

2. What is a clone?

3. Define binary fission. Compare binary fission in bacteria and amoeba.

4. Describe how an animal can reproduce by budding. Explain one advantage of this type of reproduction.

5. An individual produced by asexual reproduction may be identical to its parent. Do you agree or disagree with this statement? Support your answer.

6. How are parthenogenesis and spores the same? How are they different?

7. What practical applications might we gain if we furthered our scientific understanding of fragmentation?

8. In grafting, a branch from one tree is joined to a parent tree. Will fruit grown from the grafted branch have the DNA of the original plant or the new parent plant? Explain.

9. What might be some advantages of using plant tissue culture to produce new plants?

10. Identify the methods of asexual reproduction used to produce potatoes. Give some reasons why these methods might be used.

11. Select two methods of asexual reproduction. Use a graphic organizer to compare and contrast the two methods.

12. What are some advantages and disadvantages of asexual reproduction? Add to your list as you continue through the unit.

A6 *Inquiry Activity*

Observing Asexual Reproduction

Asexual reproduction in plants and animals can happen in many different ways. You will perform four activities in this inquiry and determine which type of asexual reproduction took place in each.

Initiating and Planning

Which type of asexual reproduction do yeast, bread mould, spider plants, and planarians (flatworms) use?

Materials & Equipment

Part 1:
- 10-mL graduated cylinder
- yeast in solution
- sugar solution
- petri dish
- warm water
- scoopula
- microscope slide
- cover slip
- compound microscope

Part 2:
- medicine dropper
- water
- bread

- sealable plastic bag
- magnifying glass

Part 3:
- spider plant
- clear container
- water

Part 4:
- 2 Petri dishes
- pond water
- planarian
- razor blade
- cotton swab
- microscope slide
- microscope

Performing and Recording

Part 1

1. Place 2 mL yeast solution and 1 mL sugar solution in a Petri dish.
2. Add 4 mL of warm water.
3. Let the Petri dish sit for 10 min, then use the scoopula to place some of the mixture on a microscope slide.
4. Cover with a cover slip, being careful not to crush the yeast.
5. Observe the yeast under a microscope. Record your observations and include a diagram.

Part 2

6. Place 10 drops of water on a piece of bread.
7. Seal the bread in the bag.
8. Store the piece of bread in a warm area.
9. Observe the bread every day for 5 days. Record your observations and include diagrams of any changes you observe.

Part 3

10. Obtain a cutting of a parent spider plant (Figure 1.33) from your teacher.
11. Fill a container with water.

Figure 1.33 Spider plants are a familiar example of organisms that have asexual reproduction.

12. Place the plant cutting in the water.
13. Observe the plant every day for 5 days. Record your observations and include diagrams of any changes you observe.

©P

Part 4

14. Prepare two Petri dishes by half-filling them with pond water.

15. Obtain a planarian (Figure 1.34) and a razor blade from your teacher.

> **CAUTION:** Use extreme care when using a razor blade.

16. Place the planarian in a Petri dish. Once it stretches out, cut it in half widthwise so that there is a head half and a tail half.

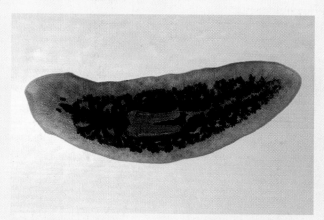

Figure 1.34 A planarian

17. Use the cotton swab to transfer one of the halves to the other Petri dish.

18. Label each Petri dish to indicate which half of the planarian it contains.

19. Observe each half of the planarian every day for 5 days, making sure to add more pond water if necessary. Record your observations and include diagrams of any changes you observe.

Analyzing and Interpreting

20. Describe the changes that took place in each of the four activities.

21. Using the definitions and examples of each type of asexual reproduction that were presented earlier in this section, which type do you think most likely occurred in each of the four activities? Explain your answers.

Communication and Teamwork

22. Write a summary of each activity that includes how you decided which type of asexual reproduction occurred in each.

A7 *Science, Technology, Society, and the Environment*

Asexual Reproduction and Agriculture

Potatoes are an important food source throughout the world. Before contact with Europeans, Indigenous peoples of South and North America developed many types of potatoes, some of which gave rise to the varieties popular today.

Potato agriculture in Saskatchewan uses different methods of asexual reproduction. What other forms of asexual reproduction might be used in agriculture?

1. Select a method of plant asexual reproduction described in this section.

2. Using library or Internet resources, research an agricultural crop that is produced using your selected method of asexual reproduction. Find out how the crop normally reproduces in the wild.

3. Create a pamphlet for the public that summarizes your findings. Be sure to explain how your method of asexual reproduction works, and include a description of how it applies to agriculture.

Sheila Flynn: Growing a Greenhouse

Sheila Flynn became interested in gardening and planting, or horticulture, at a very young age while working with her mother, who was an avid gardener. She extended her knowledge by working at greenhouses, attending classes, asking many questions, and doing a lot of research.

When Sheila decided to try growing some of her own plants, she had her husband build her a small 2 m × 2.5 m greenhouse. She really enjoyed it and decided to buy a bigger greenhouse so that she could grow enough plants to sell the following year. After attending the Saskatchewan Greenhouse Growers Convention in the fall of 2004, she began ordering plants with other local greenhouse operators.

Her hobby has now turned into a full-time job. Today, Sheila operates a 9 m × 30 m greenhouse in Beechy, Saskatchewan, and sells her plants to customers from all over the province (Figure 1.35).

Figure 1.35 Sheila's greenhouse in Beechy, Saskatchewan, is full of healthy, beautiful plants for customers to take home to their gardens and yards.

Sheila is now in her sixth year of growing and selling plants. She has learned a lot about what it takes to produce a good-quality plant that will keep her customers coming back, year after year. She looks for a variety of plants that are disease resistant and have proven performance records. She also enjoys trying out the new varieties that are developed each year. Sheila sells a lot of fruit trees that have been grafted onto sturdier roots and stems in order to guarantee the survival of the top-heavy plant. She also buys cuttings to grow into full, beautiful plants. She has used the seeds produced from her flowers to grow flowers for herself, but always buys good-quality seeds that have been tested for disease to grow flowers for her customers.

"I make a living doing something I love," says Sheila. "It gives me a lot of pride and satisfaction on opening day each year when there is a greenhouse full of beautiful, good-quality plants."

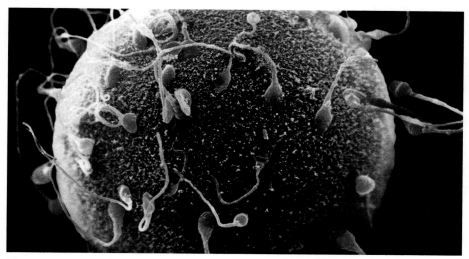

Figure 1.36 Only one of the many sperm cells surrounding the egg will fertilize the egg.

Here is a summary of what you will learn in this section:

- Sexual reproduction in animals is achieved by the union of male and female gametes.

- Gametes are produced through the process of meiosis.

- Sexual reproduction produces individuals with many variations of characteristics, so they are very rarely identical; this form of reproduction may require a large amount of energy to produce only a small number of offspring.

What Is Sexual Reproduction?

Sexual reproduction usually involves two individuals. You might think that sexual reproduction always involves a male and a female, as it does in humans and other mammals. However, sexual reproduction also occurs in species that we may not think of as having males and females, such as plants and coral.

Sexual reproduction in plants or animals is the union of two sex cells, also called **gametes**, to produce a new individual. Sex cells from females are called **eggs** or ova (singular: ovum), whereas sex cells from males are called **sperm**. A sex cell has one role only, which is to join with another sex cell during reproduction to form a new individual (Figure 1.36). The union of the sperm cell with the egg cell occurs during mating and is called **fertilization.**

Most species of animals and flowering plants reproduce sexually. The offspring of sexual reproduction will have a mix of traits, or features, from both parents (Figure 1.37). Producing offspring that have a mix of traits from both parents is important for biological diversity.

For First Nations and Métis peoples, sexual reproduction is not simply a process whereby sex cells join. Elders teach that sexual reproduction bears sanctity as sexual reproduction produces life. Elder Velma Goodfeather explains that in the Dakota culture, sexual reproduction is seen as a healthy, sacred, and very natural means that enables living things to grow again.

(a)

(b)

Figure 1.37 Sexual reproduction produces offspring that have some traits from one parent and some traits from the other. Both plants (a) and animals (b) can reproduce sexually.

Reproduction as seen by traditional Dakota people is a continual cycle whereby one generation gives life to the next and promotes the propagation of life. Most First Nations and Métis peoples believe that all living things are sacred and that no one organism, be it plant, insect, or human, is more important than another.

A8 *Quick Science*

Variations in Characteristics Within Our Class

Look around your classroom at your peers. Everyone looks different, and you are able to tell everyone apart just by looking at them. Some traits are more common than others.

Purpose

To observe the variations in characteristics within a group of people

Procedure

1. Look at Figure 1.38. Predict which of the following traits you think will be most common in your class:
   Hairline: widow's peak versus straight
   Thumb: hitchhiker's versus straight
   Tongue: able to roll versus not able to roll
   Earlobes: attached versus unattached

2. Create a table similar to Table 1.2 in your notebook. Make sure to include all the characteristics you will be observing. Allow enough rows for every student's data.

3. Observe each student in your class and record which traits they exhibit.

4. Add up the total number of students that exhibit each trait. Calculate the percentage of students that exhibit each trait.

Questions

5. Which traits are most common in your class?

6. Were your predictions correct?

7. Do you think that your results are similar to the results you would find if you tested a larger group of people? Explain.

Pose New Questions

8. Suggest a question that would allow you to investigate why certain traits are more common in your class.

9. Write a question that investigates the relationship between traits and sexual reproduction.

Table 1.2

Characteristic	Hairline		Thumb		Tongue		Earlobes	
Variation	Widow's peak	Straight	Hitch-hiker's	Straight	Roll	No roll	Attached	Unattached
Student 1								
Student 2								

Figure 1.38 (a) widow's peak, (b) hitchhiker's thumb, (c) tongue roll, and (d) attached earlobes

Meiosis

Gametes are produced through a cell division process called **meiosis**. In meiosis, the parent cell goes through interphase, during which chromosomes are duplicated. In the first division of meiosis, the chromosomes pair up. Only one of each pair goes to each daughter cell. As a result, each cell has only half the number of chromosomes of the parent cell. In the second division of meiosis, those daughter cells each divide once more without duplicating their chromosomes. The result is four daughter cells each with half the number of chromosomes of the parent cell (Figure 1.39).

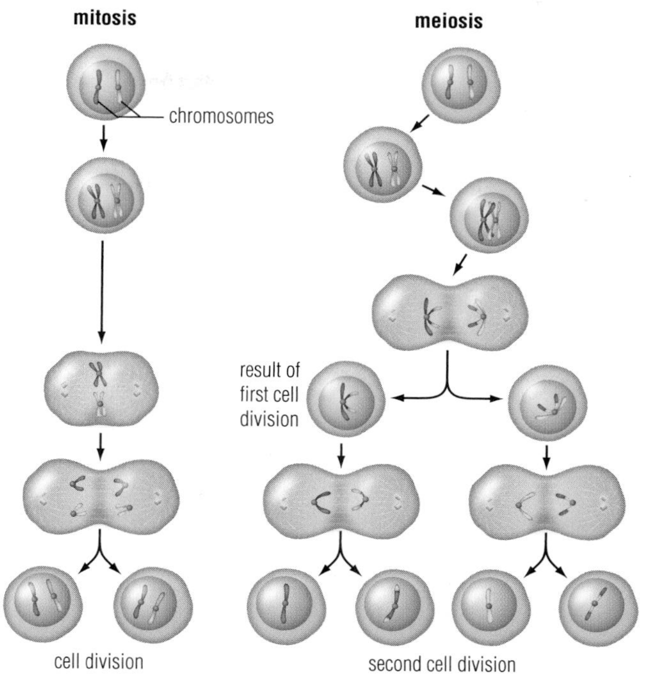

Sexual Reproduction in Animals

Most animal species, from dragonflies to salmon to bears, reproduce sexually (Figure 1.40). The joining of the two gametes creates a new single cell known as a **zygote**. The zygote has a full set of chromosomes and is the first cell of a new individual. The zygote then divides into two cells, beginning a process called **cleavage**. A new multicellular life form, referred to as an **embryo**, develops through continued mitotic division.

mitosis

chromosomes

result of first cell division

cell division

meiosis

second cell division

Figure 1.39 Mitosis produces two daughter cells with the same number of chromosomes as the parent cell. Meiosis produces four daughter cells that have half the number of chromosomes of the parent cell.

Suggested Activity • • • • • • • • • • •
A9 Problem-Solving Activity on page 35

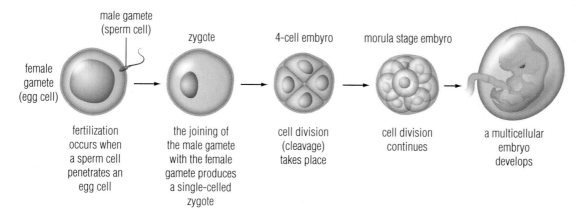

male gamete (sperm cell)

zygote

4-cell embyro

morula stage embyro

female gamete (egg cell)

fertilization occurs when a sperm cell penetrates an egg cell

the joining of the male gamete with the female gamete produces a single-celled zygote

cell division (cleavage) takes place

cell division continues

a multicellular embryo develops

Figure 1.40 A diagram of sexual reproduction showing fertilization, zygote formation, and some of the stages of embryo development

Depending on the species, the development of the embryo may occur inside the female parent, which happens in most mammals, or outside, in an egg, which happens in most other types of animals.

The new individual will show some of the traits of its female parent and some of its male parent. Although the new individual may resemble one parent more than the other, it will not be identical to either parent.

The Critical Role of Meiosis in Sexual Reproduction

During sexual reproduction, the male and female gametes unite to form a zygote, which then develops into a new individual. Gametes are haploid; they have half the number of chromosomes of a normal cell. If the sex cells contained the same number of chromosomes as every other cell—that is, if the gametes were diploid—then the zygote would inherit twice as many chromosomes as it needs. An incorrect number of chromosomes can cause problems with normal cell function and growth.

Hermaphrodites

Most animals have distinct sexes; individuals are usually either male or female. Some animals, however, are hermaphrodites. **Hermaphrodites** can produce both male and female gametes. Common garden worms and slugs are examples of hermaphrodites. Although hermaphrodites usually mate with other individuals of their species, in times of environmental stress, members of some species can fertilize themselves.

Sequential hermaphrodites are species that are born as one sex, but then become the opposite sex. One example is the clownfish. Clownfish travel in packs that consist of a large, reproductive female, a smaller reproductive male, and numerous smaller non-reproductive males (Figure 1.41). If the female dies or leaves, the reproductive male becomes a female and the largest of the non-reproductive males becomes the new reproductive male.

Figure 1.41 It is easy to tell which of the clownfish is female. Her larger size helps ensure reproductive success.

Learning Checkpoint

1. Explain what a gamete is and how it is formed.

2. What is a zygote and how is it formed?

3. What is similar about sperm cells and egg cells? What is different?

4. List the steps of fertilization and embryo development in animal sexual reproduction. Be sure to include the words "gametes" and "zygote" in your description.

©P

Sexual Reproduction in Plants

As in animals, sexual reproduction in plants requires the joining of a male gamete with a female gamete to produce a zygote and an embryo. Most plants produce both male and female gametes. However, some produce only female gametes and others only male.

Figure 1.42 shows the structures of a flower that are involved in reproduction. Most flowers have all of these structures, although the shapes and sizes of each flower vary. Some flowers are large and showy. Others are hardly noticeable. **Pollen** contains the male gametes of a plant and is found on the stamen, or male structure, of the plant. **Ovules** contain the female gametes of a plant and are found in the pistil, or female structure, of the plant.

During Reading

Create a Picture Glossary

To learn unfamiliar terms, create a three-column table in your notebook. Write the new term in the first column on the left. Add a definition in the middle column. In the third column, draw a picture that will help you to remember the term.

Suggested Activity • · · · · · · · · · · ·
A10 Inquiry Activity on page 36

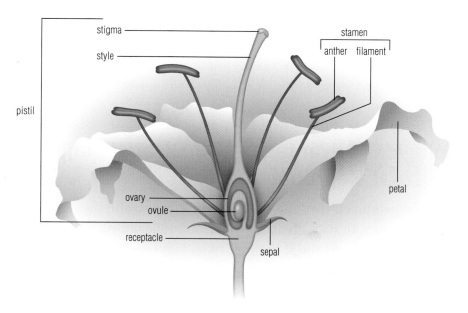

Figure 1.42 Flower parts involved in sexual reproduction of plants

Pollination occurs when pollen is transferred from the anther of the stamen to the stigma of the pistil. **Self-pollination** occurs when the transfer is within the same plant. **Cross-pollination** occurs when the pollen of one plant is carried to the stigma of another by wind, water, or animals, such as bees or butterflies (Figure 1.43). Fertilization occurs when the male and female gametes unite, whether in self-fertilization (within the same plant), or in cross-fertilization (between plants). A grain of pollen produces a long tube that eventually grows down the style into the ovary that contains the ovules. A gamete in the pollen grain and a gamete in an ovule join and, as in animals, a zygote is formed. The zygote then begins a series of divisions to produce an embryo.

Figure 1.43 Unlike roses and lilies, the flowers of prairie cord grass are very small and hardly noticeable. Grasses like this depend on wind for pollination.

The embryo will eventually develop into a new individual. In most plants, the embryo is produced inside a protective covering known as a seed. The seed protects the embryo and stores food for the embryo to use when it begins to grow into a new individual. The new embryo may not begin to grow for some time, but stay dormant within the seed until growing conditions are favourable. A plant produced from cross-fertilization will show some of the characteristics from the parent that provided the female gamete and some from the parent that provided the male gamete. It will not be identical to either parent.

Learning Checkpoint

1. Make a table to compare the male and female gametes in plants. Indicate where each are found.

2. List three ways in which pollination can occur. Give an example of each.

3. How is sexual reproduction in plants similar to sexual reproduction in animals?

Biological Advantages and Disadvantages of Sexual Reproduction

Offspring produced through sexual reproduction show variation: they have a mix of traits from both parents. Variation helps a species survive by giving it the ability to survive changes in its environment.

Sexual reproduction has the advantage of creating lots of variation, which helps species survive environmental change. It also has some disadvantages. Gametes must be produced, which requires different amounts of energy in different species. Gametes must meet. This problem is solved in various ways. For example, flowering plants produce lots of pollen to be blown by the wind, or attract pollinators, which transfer the pollen. The embryo must be protected and nurtured during development. This problem also is solved in a variety of ways. The most extreme form of protection occurs in mammals where the embryo grows within the body of the female parent. Because of the large amount of time and energy needed for this development, only a limited number offspring can be produced (Figure 1.44).

Figure 1.44 Sexual reproduction in mammals takes time to produce a limited number of offspring that show variation in characteristics.

Organisms That Reproduce Both Sexually and Asexually

Some species have the ability to reproduce both sexually and asexually. Most plants that produce seeds by sexual reproduction can also reproduce asexually, either from cuttings or by producing structures such as bulbs or runners.

Some plants can use their seeds to reproduce both asexually and sexually. In the asexual method, embryos develop in the seeds without the contribution of sperm cells. These seeds will grow into plants that are genetically identical to the parent plant. Some species of grasses, sunflowers, and roses can do this.

Some animal species can also reproduce both ways. Aphids are small insects that feed on the sap of certain plants. Throughout the growing season, females produce live female young through parthenogenesis. These female young mature and also reproduce asexually. Over the summer, several generations are produced. In the fall, when days shorten and the temperature drops, the females produce a generation that includes both males and females. These males and females reproduce sexually and lay eggs that will hatch in the spring to produce new colonies. Sponges can also reproduce both sexually and asexually (Figure 1.45).

reSearch

Some animals, such as the jellyfish, alternate between sexual and asexual reproduction. Use library or Internet resources to research other examples of life forms that fall into this category. Write a paragraph about the advantages and disadvantages of alternating between different forms of reproduction.

Suggested Activity •••••••••••
A11 Inquiry Activity on page 37

Figure 1.45 To reproduce sexually, sponges release sperm cells into the water. Water currents carry the sperm to other sponges, which take the sperm into the body to fertilize the egg cells.

1. Compare the processes of mitosis and meiosis. Use a graphic organizer to list the similarities and differences.

2. Explain what happens to the chromosomes during cell division to produce both diploid and haploid cells. Use diagrams to illustrate your answer.

3. How are gametes different from zygotes? Compare the number of chromosomes in each.

4. If the number of chromosomes in a gamete of an organism is n, is the amount of DNA in the body cells of that organism equal to $\frac{1}{2}n$, n, or $2n$? Explain.

5. Organisms of the same species have the same number of chromosomes, but different species have different numbers of chromosomes. Copy Table 1.3 into your notebook and complete it to compare chromosome numbers in some common species.

6. What is a hermaphrodite? Use an example to illustrate your answer.

7. Explain what happens to male and female gametes during sexual reproduction in plants and animals.

8. Using a graphic organizer such as a Venn diagram, compare and contrast sexual and asexual reproduction.

9. Use a simple sketch to illustrate the process of fertilization in plants.

10. A flower produces a seed. Explain how this can be an example of both asexual and sexual reproduction.

11. Which type of reproduction, sexual or asexual, is responsible for an increased amount of genetic variation in plants and animals? Support your answer with examples.

12. Explain how sexual reproduction plays a role in the Saskatchewan agriculture industry.

Table 1.3

Organism	Number of Chromosomes in a Cell at the End of Mitosis	Number of Chromosomes in a Body Cell	Number of Chromosomes in a Gamete	Number of Chromosomes in a Zygote	Number of Pairs of Chromosomes
Cabbage	18				
Black bear					38
Human			23		
Peanut	40				

A9 *Problem-Solving Activity*   Toolkit 3

SKILLS YOU WILL USE
■ Designing, building, and testing
■ Carrying out a plan

Comparing Mitosis and Meiosis

Scientists use models to represent and explain certain aspects of complex physical phenomena. Mitosis and meiosis are cellular processes that are sometimes difficult to visualize.

Initiating and Planning

Your task is to create a physical model to represent both mitosis and meiosis. The model should make visualizing the cellular processes easier. You will use your model to explain the similarities and differences between mitosis and meiosis to your classmates.

In your group, brainstorm a list of possible materials you could use to represent the nucleus and the chromosomes. Make sure all materials and equipment that you choose are considered safe and are easy to obtain.

Criteria for Success

- The model must effectively represent both of the processes of mitosis and meiosis.
- The model can be used more than once.
- The model includes a minimum of four chromosomes.

1. Brainstorm ideas on creating different types of physical models. Decide what type of model you are planning to create and make a final list of materials and equipment that you will need.

2. Develop a procedure that you will follow to build the model.

3. Design a method to collect data on the efficiency of your model to accomplish the assigned task.

4. Check your list of proposed materials and equipment as well as your proposed procedure and data collection method with your teacher.

Performing and Recording

5. Build your model according to your procedure. Make sure to note any changes you make to your procedure.

6. Test your model to ensure it accomplishes the task of explaining and describing the similarities and differences between mitosis and meiosis.

7. Present your model to your classmates (Figure 1.46). Collect data about your model following your chosen method.

Analyzing and Interpreting

8. Using the data you collected from your classmates, decide if any changes need to be made to your model. Modify your model and record any changes that are made. Retest your model and collect more data.

9. Prepare a summary of the ability of your model to accomplish the desired task.

Communicate

10. How well was your model able to represent the similarities and differences between mitosis and meiosis?

11. How did your group decide on what type of model to build?

12. How did your group deal with changes that needed to be made as you were building your model?

13. After observing the models of your classmates, are there changes you would make to your model?

Figure 1.46 Using a model to explain ideas can help other people to understand the material.

DI
Key Activity

A10 *Inquiry Activity*

Toolkits 1, 10

SKILLS YOU WILL USE
- Using appropriate equipment and tools
- Organizing information

Investigating Flower Reproductive Structures

Initiating and Planning

What are the reproductive structures of a flower?

Materials & Equipment

- lily
- small scalpel with sharp blade
- magnifying glass
- piece of dark cloth
- probe
- microscope slide
- cover slip
- water
- medicine dropper
- microscope
- labelled diagram of parts of a flower (in text)
- 5 recipe cards
- white glue
- poster board

CAUTION: Use care when handling the scalpel and the probe.

Performing and Recording

1. Obtain a lily and carefully use the scalpel to cut it in half from top to bottom.

2. On a piece of blank paper, sketch a cross section of the flower as it appears now, before you dissect it. You may need to use the magnifying glass to closely examine the flower. Label the parts.

3. Shake the lily gently over the piece of dark cloth. If pollen does not fall onto the cloth, carefully rub the anthers over the material. Using the probe, gently separate the grains of pollen.

4. Prepare a wet-mount slide to examine the pollen under the microscope. What do you see at each level of magnification? Record your observations on a recipe card labelled "pollen."

5. Carefully remove the petals. Label a card "petals" and use a small amount of glue to affix the petals to the card.

6. Gently pull away the stamens from the base of the pistil. Label a card "stamen" at the top and then draw two lines leading away from the word. At the base of one line, write the word "anther," and at the base of the second line, write the word "filament." Carefully separate the two parts of the stamen and glue them under the correct headings.

7. Dissect the pistil, cutting lengthwise from the stigma through the style, then through the ovary at the bottom. Label a card "pistil" and glue one-half of the cross section to it. Label the parts of the pistil.

8. Using the magnifying glass and probe, examine the ovule inside the ovary. Record your observations on a card labelled "ovary."

Analyzing and Interpreting

9. Review the recipe cards that you have assembled as you dissected the flower. How do you think these separate pieces work together to reproduce a new plant?

10. Go back to your sketch of the parts of the flower. In pencil, show the process of reproduction as you think it occurs.

11. What characteristics do a pollen grain and an ovule have that help them carry out their roles in sexual reproduction?

Communication and Teamwork

12. Review your work with a partner or other group, and then share ideas with the whole class. Revise your sketch as necessary.

13. Arrange your recipe cards and sketch on a piece of poster board to create a display of your work.

14. In a paragraph, summarize the roles each of the plant parts play in sexual reproduction and how these parts have characteristics that help them perform their roles.

DI Key Activity

Comparing Asexual and Sexual Reproduction

Asexual reproduction is quite different from sexual reproduction, but both processes are very important in maintaining the populations of organisms on Earth. Different organisms use different types of reproduction in order to keep the species alive.

Initiating and Planning

Can you use an organism's characteristics to predict how it reproduces?

Given the following list of organisms, predict whether each organism reproduces asexually or sexually. Provide a reason for each of your predictions.

- mouse
- corn
- fish
- amoeba (a unicellular, animal-like cell; Figure 1.47)
- pine tree
- kangaroo
- ape
- elephant
- planarian (a flatworm)
- mushroom
- earthworm
- toad
- mould
- whale
- bird
- *Euglena* (a unicellular protist; Figure 1.48)
- horse

Performing and Recording

1. Research the method of reproduction that each organism uses. Keep track of what kingdom each organism belongs to.

2. Record your results in a table that includes the following headings: Organism, Kingdom, Type of Reproduction, Details About Reproduction.

Analyzing and Interpreting

3. How close were your predictions to the results you found? Explain any differences.

4. Are there any conclusions or generalizations you can make about each kingdom of organisms and how the members of the kingdom reproduce?

5. What are the benefits to the organisms that reproduce asexually?

6. What are the benefits to the organisms that reproduce sexually?

Communication and Teamwork

7. Compare your conclusions from question 4 with a classmate. Can you add to your list?

8. With another classmate, compare your benefits for organisms that reproduce asexually. Can you add to your list?

9. With another classmate, compare your benefits for organisms that reproduce sexually. Can you add to your list?

10. How does discussion with another classmate help you complete your answers?

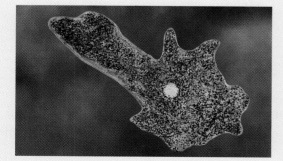

Figure 1.47 An amoeba

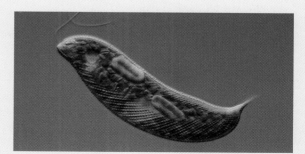

Figure 1.48 *Euglena*

Key Concept Review

1. What are the phases of the cell cycle?

2. What is the difference between mitosis and cytokinesis?

3. List the four stages of mitosis. Draw diagrams to help explain what is happening to the chromosomes at each stage.

4. What form of asexual reproduction do yeast cells use and how does it work?

5. An amoeba reproduces by binary fission. Briefly describe the process of binary fission. Explain whether it is an example of sexual or asexual reproduction.

6. Describe a type of cell division that occurs during the asexual reproduction of a unicellular organism.

7. What is the key difference between mitosis and meiosis?

8. What process is shown in the figure below? What type of reproduction is this process associated with? Provide an example of an organism that uses this method of reproduction to produce offspring.

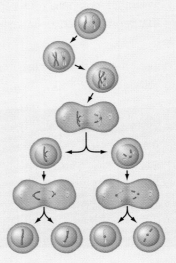

Question 8

9. How does sexual reproduction contribute to genetic variation?

10. Make a table to compare the advantages and disadvantages of sexual and asexual reproduction.

11. What type of cell division is required for sexual reproduction? How does it differ from cell division during asexual reproduction?

12. What is the difference between pollen grains and ovules?

13. Use a table or Venn diagram to compare two different forms of asexual reproduction.

Connect Your Understanding

14. Suppose a single bacterial cell got into your nose at 10:00 a.m. If bacterial cells are able to divide once every 10 min, how many of them will there be in your nose at noon that day? How many will there be by 8:00 p.m.?

15. How is the DNA of a parent inherited by offspring in asexual reproduction? What about in sexual reproduction?

16. Why does meiosis produce cells with only half the amount of DNA? How does this aid in the formation of a healthy zygote?

17. You have a job that involves growing a large number of identical plants for a gardener. The plants can be grown from seeds or cuttings. Which method would you use? Give reasons for your choice.

18. Which type of reproduction, sexual or asexual, is responsible for an increased amount of genetic variation in plants and animals? Support your answer with examples.

©P

19. List the steps of fertilization and embryo development in animal sexual reproduction. Be sure to include the words "gametes" and "zygote" in your description.

20. Compare the process of fertilization in plants and animals.

21. Using a diagram, explain how a zygote forms in a flowering plant.

22. Describe the steps of vegetative reproduction that occur when a plant is grown from a cutting. Why is this process considered to be an example of asexual reproduction?

23. Using diagrams, explain what happens to the DNA during cell division to produce gametes.

24. When a cell divides during asexual reproduction, it divides its cell contents between the two resulting cells. Describe what happens to the DNA of the cell during this type of cell division. Explain how this process ensures that the same characteristics are passed from generation to generation.

25. Why does sexual reproduction produce offspring with characteristics that are different from their parents, whereas offspring produced through asexual reproduction are identical to their parents?

26. Imagine an organism that lives where there are often big changes in environmental conditions. What type of reproduction would be more advantageous for this organism? Explain your answer.

27. If you were researching plants to grow in colder climates, why would an understanding of the variations within a plant species be important?

28. Describe one possible cause of cancer from an Elder's viewpoint, and one from a scientist's viewpoint. Could both viewpoints be used together to provide a fuller description of cancer than that produced by using just one viewpoint?

Reflection

29. Why is it important to understand the advantages and disadvantages of both sexual and asexual reproduction?

30. Based on what you have learned in this chapter, what are three questions you have that are related to the information presented?

After Reading

Reflect and Evaluate

How did the use of visualization and picture mapping help you to understand new ideas and terms? Share with a partner one of the diagrams or picture maps that you drew, and explain the concept or terms that it illustrates.

Reflection on Essential Inquiry Questions

Write notes on the ways that mitosis and meiosis are important to asexual and sexual reproduction. **SI**

The single cell of the zygote is the link between two adult organisms and their offspring. Suggest a way to model the importance of the zygote. **TPS**

What did you learn in this chapter about ways that technology can affect cellular reproduction? **DM**

Re-read pages 13 and 14 and make notes on ways that the scientific and holistic treatments of cancer may work together to help the patient. **CP**

Unit Task

In this chapter, you learned about cell division and different forms of reproduction. Genetic and reproductive technologies can alter the genetic information in cells or change how organisms reproduce. How can you apply your new knowledge to the unit task you have chosen?

Genetic information is passed from parent to offspring.

By the end of this chapter, you will:

- examine ways that genetic information is transferred and factors that may influence the process
- examine the impact of genetics on society past and present

What you will learn:

- According to the currently accepted molecular model, the DNA molecule holds the instructions for the characteristics of every organism.
- There are analytical and holistic ways of understanding how characteristics are passed on to the next generation.
- From a scientific perspective, some genetic traits are harmful and can even be fatal. From First Nations and Métis perspectives, there are reasons why these traits exist.
- Humans can make choices that can affect the genetic material in the cell.
- The study of genetics and technological developments in this field are changing how food is grown and produced, how humans have children, and how we detect and treat diseases.

A greenhouse displays many plants of different species. Different types of characteristics are easily seen. How does the greenhouse operator know what characteristics to expect? The study of heredity and genes enables us to predict the characteristics of the offspring of organisms.

Key Terms

- allele • artificial reproductive technology • artificial insemination • characteristic
- continuous variation • discrete variation • dominant allele
- dominant trait • gene
- genetic code • genetic engineering • heredity
- heritable characteristics
- hybrid • in vitro fertilization
- non-heritable characteristic
- recessive allele • recessive trait • selective breeding
- trait

Before Reading

Asking Questions of the Text and of Ourselves

Good readers use active reading strategies. They think as they read and evaluate the information, often asking questions about the different ideas in the text. They also question their own and others' actions and decisions that may have contributed to a particular situation. Skim the subheadings in Chapter 2 and turn them into questions that begin with "What is/are . . . ?," "How can we . . . ?", or "How do we . . . ?" Keep an ongoing list of these questions to use as a study guide later on in the chapter or unit.

Here is a summary of what you will learn in this section:

- Variation can be discrete or continuous. Variation can be affected by heredity and the environment.

- Heritable characteristics are the traits of an organism that are inherited from the organism's parents.

- Non-heritable characteristics are traits that are learned or developed during an organism's life.

- The First Nations and Métis ways of understanding heredity include the transmission of personality traits as well as physical traits.

Figure 2.1 Although these emperor penguins look almost identical, they vary from one another in subtle ways.

Variation, Characteristics, and Traits

In Chapter 1, you learned that offspring produced through sexual reproduction inherit a combination of both parents' features or characteristics. In everyday language, the words "characteristics" and "traits" are used interchangeably. So far, we have used the terms in a general way. In the study of genetics, however, they have very specific meanings. A **characteristic** is a feature such as eye colour or wing shape. Some characteristics, such as leaf colour, can vary among offspring of the same species. A **trait** is a variation of a characteristic, such as brown eye colour versus blue eye colour, or long wing shape versus round wing shape. It is variation that accounts for diversity. Look at the emperor penguins in Figure 2.1. In what ways could these penguins show variation?

Not all traits are visible. For example, Jack pines exhibit variation because some individuals can resist drought better than others. Magpies show variation because some individuals can fly longer distances. Different individuals of the same species of bacteria can vary, making some more resistant to antibiotics.

Measuring Variation in the Human Hand

Variation within a species may not be something that is immediately noticeable. In this activity, you will measure the amount of variation within one human characteristic—hand span.

Purpose

To determine the amount of variation in human hand span

Materials & Equipment

- sheet of blank paper
- pencil
- ruler

Procedure

1. On the sheet of paper, spread your left hand as wide as you can on a flat surface so that the tips of your thumb and your little finger are as far apart as possible.

2. Use a pencil to carefully trace your hand. Be sure your pencil is pointing straight down and not at an angle.

3. Use a ruler to measure your hand span in centimetres (Figure 2.2). Record your result.

4. Create a frequency distribution table similar to Table 2.1. Collect the data from the entire class and record it in your table.

5. Graph the data in a line graph. Draw a line of best fit or a smooth curve that best fits the data points.

Table 2.1

Hand Span (cm)	≤ 12	13–16	17–20	21–24	25–28	≥ 29
Number of Students						

Question

6. Describe and explain the shape of the curve of hand spans from your class.

Pose New Questions

7. Compare the distribution of numbers for hand span and thumb shape (page 28) in your class. Suggest a possible reason for the differences.

Figure 2.2 Measure your hand span from tip to tip.

Heritable and Non-Heritable Characteristics

Look at your classmates and recall activity A8 Quick Science that you did in Chapter 1. What are some different features that distinguish you from your classmates? You are all humans, but it is easy to tell each other apart just by looking at your differences. You might describe someone as being tall, with brown hair and brown eyes. You might choose to describe classmates by their talents. Maybe someone is an excellent guitar player or a record-breaking high jumper. Maybe someone is able to memorize the entire periodic table after looking at it for only a few minutes. All of these descriptive features are characteristics of people, but are they all passed down from parents?

Heredity is the transmission of characteristics from one generation to the next. From a scientific viewpoint, **heritable characteristics** are characteristics that are passed from parent to offspring. Some examples of inherited characteristics are eye colour, hair type, and skin colour. Figure 2.3 shows some examples of heritable characteristics in pea plants. **Non-heritable characteristics** are characteristics that cannot be passed on to other generations. If someone dyes his or her hair a different colour, his or her children will not inherit the dyed colour (Figure 2.4).

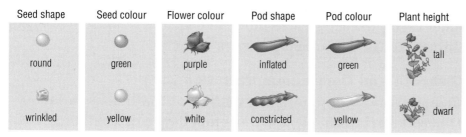

Figure 2.3 Some of the characteristics of pea plants that scientists have studied include seed shape, seed colour, flower colour, pod shape, pod colour, and plant height.

Figure 2.4 Members of the same family often resemble each other because they share similar heritable characteristics. Non-heritable characteristics, such as dyed hair or ear piercings, are not passed on to the next generation.

From a cultural perspective, heredity is viewed differently by many First Nations and Métis peoples, particularly for personality traits. The Dakota people believe that traits are inherited through a spiritual means. When a woman is pregnant, she looks for a wise relative who leads a healthy and humble lifestyle; often an Elder is chosen. This person is called when the woman is giving birth so that he or she can be present for the delivery. The candidate is the first to take the baby and to clean the baby's ears, eyes, and mouth. Prayers are said and ceremonies performed for the baby. It is believed that the fontanelle, the soft spot on a baby's head, is a point of entry for the baby's spirit (Figure 2.5). Through the fontanelle, the traits and characteristics of the candidate also enter the child. The Dakota call a trait or characteristic *Oȟaŋ Tawa*.

Among the Dené, traits are believed to develop when a baby is conceived. The pregnant woman is encouraged to act and speak in a fashion that would promote desirable traits in her child. She would practise patience, stay calm, and help in her community.

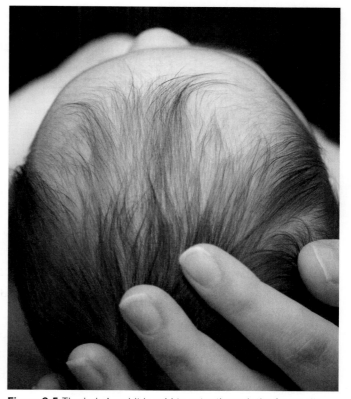

Figure 2.5 The baby's spirit is said to enter through the fontanelle, or soft spot, on a baby's head.

The belief that positive traits promote the inheritance of similar traits in the child is so strong that the entire family and community become involved in the process. The community treats a pregnant woman well to help her maintain a positive frame of mind and keep her in happy spirits.

The Nakawē possess similar beliefs. They believe that the behaviour and actions of the parents and relatives in the child's life impact the baby in the womb. For example, if the parents argue when the woman is pregnant, the child might be born rebellious. This is why traditional Nakawē take care when they speak near a pregnant woman. Often, the mother sings to her unborn child. Later in life, the child learns different characteristics from teachers through songs, dance, and stories.

Discrete and Continuous Variation

Characteristics can show either discrete or continuous variation. **Discrete variation** refers to traits that have a defined form. You can think of discrete variation as being the "either/or" form of a characteristic. For example, a particular species of plant may produce only white or purple flowers. Your earlobes are either attached or they are not (Figure 2.6). **Continuous variation** refers to traits that have a range of forms. They are not one form or another. For example, the height of average adult humans ranges from 1.2 m to 2.1 m.

Variation and the Environment

Some variations in individual organisms result from interactions with the environment. Imagine you have two plants that are completely identical. If you put one plant in a sunny window and the other in a dim closet, they would soon begin to look very different. The one in the sunlight would be green and bushy, but the plant in low light would be pale green and spindly. Figure 2.7 shows the effects of soil acidity on hydrangeas.

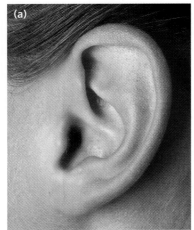

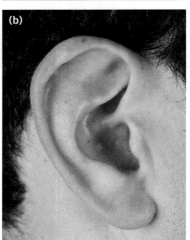

Figure 2.6 Earlobes can be (a) attached or (b) free.

Figure 2.7 Environmental factors can affect variation. Acidic soil produces blue flowers, whereas alkaline or basic soil produces pink flowers.

Another example of a characteristic that can be affected by the environment is height. Height is a characteristic that is inherited, but it can also be affected by diet. In general, North Americans are taller than they were in the 19th century because of better nutrition and access to a wider variety of foods. There have always been shorter people and taller people, but on average, North Americans living in the 19th century would have been somewhat shorter than North Americans living today.

Variations caused by interactions with the environment usually cannot be passed from parents to offspring. You would not expect the offspring of a plant grown in dim light to look like this parent unless they too were grown in low-light conditions. Similarly, if a child of tall parents does not receive proper nutrition, he or she probably will not be as tall as his or her parents.

Suggested Activity • · · · · · · · · · · ·
A13 Quick Science on page 46

During Reading

Making Inferences

By asking the question "Why?" you may be able to make inferences or calculated guesses about the factors that affect variation. As you read about each factor, ask the question "Why?" and make note of your answers. Draw conclusions about how humans might control these factors.

2.1 CHECK and REFLECT

1. Explain the difference between a characteristic and a trait. List three characteristics. For each characteristic, give two examples of traits.

2. Explain the difference between a heritable characteristic and a non-heritable characteristic. Give one example of each, using examples that are different from those in the text.

3. Describe how the inheritance of traits is viewed by some First Nations and Métis peoples.

4. List some non-heritable characteristics that you have. Use your understanding of First Nations and Métis perspectives of heredity to explain how you might have developed these characteristics.

5. Using your own words, explain the difference between discrete and continuous variation. Give an example of each.

6. How might variation help a species survive? Use examples to illustrate your answer.

7. Some characteristics are heritable but can also be affected by the environment. Explain how the size of a plant such as a pine tree can be affected by both inherited characteristics and the environment so that variation results.

Question 7

Super Dogs

Humans and dogs have had a close relationship since the end of the Ice Age, roughly 12 000 years ago. Descended from grey wolves, many of the approximately 400 modern dog breeds we see today still share many physical characteristics with wolves (Figure 2.8). Some scientists think that humans chose and bred canids with desirable characteristics that help them perform specific tasks. One of the extraordinary abilities of dogs is their capacity to learn and be trained.

Purpose

To research different dog breeds and their characteristics to discover what tasks or functions each breed performs

Procedure

1. As a class, brainstorm a list of specific dogs, such as TV show dogs, or dogs that perform special tasks, such as police dogs.

2. Determine the breed of each dog.

3. Choose one dog and, in pairs, brainstorm a list of the traits that your "super dog" displays that help it to do its job.

4. Infer which traits are typical of the breed.

5. Research any additional traits that your dog's breed typically displays.

6. Using a graphic organizer of your choice, compare and contrast the traits of your dog with those of a typical dog of the same breed.

Questions

7. Imagine you are a breeder and wish to breed a dog for a specific task. Select a task. What are some desirable characteristics that your ideal dog should have? What are some undesirable characteristics?

8. What questions would you suggest that someone ask themselves before deciding on a particular dog breed for a pet?

Pose New Questions

9. What questions do you still have about dog breeds or a particular breed of dog?

Figure 2.8 Grey wolves were the ancestors of domesticated dogs. By selecting parents with desirable characteristics, such as size or ear shape, different dog breeds with an immense variety of traits were eventually produced over many generations.

Figure 2.9 Traits are passed from parent to offspring through DNA. This is why the pups resemble their parents.

Here is a summary of what you will learn in this section:

- The nucleus of the cell contains DNA which has the genetic information that is required for cells to divide.

- DNA is packaged in the form of chromosomes.

- A gene is a segment of DNA that provides information for a characteristic. An allele is a variation of a gene that provides information for a trait.

- Traits can be dominant or recessive. The combination of alleles from the parents determines which traits the offspring will have.

DNA: Skinny Molecule, Big Impact

People have taken advantage of heritable characteristics to produce many breeds of domestic plants and animals. Having many breeds of the same species ensures that there is variation of characteristics within a population. The breeding of purebred dogs was not intended to promote variation but to develop breeds that displayed specific, desired traits (Figure 2.9). This has made dogs one of the most physically varied species on Earth.

Why do the puppies of chihuahua dogs turn out to be chihuahuas? How are heritable characteristics passed from parent to offspring? The reason is that the chihuahua parents pass on DNA to their offspring that acts as a "chihuahua blueprint"; each puppy receives a complete set of instructions for growing into a chihuahua dog.

From a scientific point of view, DNA directs the mechanism of heredity. Recall that DNA molecules are macromolecules that contain the information that tells the cell what to do. DNA also tells the cell what type of cell it should become and what type of organism will be formed by the groups of cells. Canadian-born scientist Oswald Avery furthered our understanding of DNA and heredity when he proposed that DNA is responsible for an organism's inherited characteristics. It is incredible to think of the impact that these molecules of DNA have on the entire organism.

What We Remember About the Nucleus

Purpose

To create a graphic organizer that summarizes what you already know about the cell's nucleus.

Procedure

1. Examine Figure 2.10. Identify the nucleus of each cell in the micrographs of the animal cell and the plant cell.

Questions

2. Was it easy to identify the nucleus in each of the animal and plant cell micrographs?

3. What is the function of the nucleus?

4. What important material does the nucleus contain?

Pose New Questions

5. What are some questions you still have about the nucleus and its function? As you read through this section, check back to see if your questions are answered.

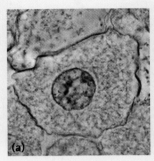 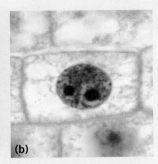

Figure 2.10 (a) micrograph of animal cell; (b) micrograph of plant cell

re*Search*

Research the work of scientists, such as Oswald Avery and Irene Ayako Uchida, and their contributions to our knowledge of inheritance and genetics. Write a short script for a documentary about their achievements.

DNA and the Genetic Code

The existence of DNA was discovered in 1869, but little was known about the structure of the molecule or its role. In 1944, Oswald Avery and his colleagues confirmed that DNA was genetic material, the material that determined how traits were passed from one generation to the next. This led to a new question: How could the blueprints for so many different organisms be passed on by what seemed to be exactly the same molecule? Solving this puzzle was one of the greatest scientific achievements and involved many scientists. Two scientists in particular played a major role: James Watson and Francis Crick, but Rosalind Franklin and Maurice Wilkins were also important to the project. Franklin was a chemist who used X rays to investigate the structure of DNA (Figure 2.11). In 1953, Watson and Crick built on what was known about the molecule and on their interpretation of Franklin's X ray studies. They completed a model of the DNA molecule that indicated how the same chemical building blocks could carry the wide range of instructions needed for the diversity we observe in the living world.

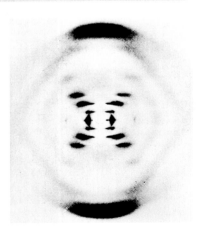

Figure 2.11 Rosalind Franklin produced this image of DNA using X rays. It greatly helped others to propose a structure for the DNA molecule.

The Watson–Crick model of the DNA molecule can be compared to a ladder that has been twisted into a continuous spiral, a shape known as a double helix (Figure 2.12). The uprights of the twisted molecular ladder are identical all along its length. However, the rungs vary in composition. Each individual rung pairs up just two of the following four chemicals: guanine, cytosine, adenine, and thymine, or G, C, A, and T, for short. Guanine can only pair with cytosine and adenine can only pair with thymine.

The arrangement of these four chemicals, G, C, A, and T, forms a code that cells can "read." The 26 letters in our alphabet can be rearranged to form the thousands of words we can read. Similarly, the **genetic code** is based on arranging the four chemical "letters" into "words," or instructions that describe how to make any particular organism. In other words, all the blueprints for almost all life forms on Earth are written in the same language!

Chromosomes

If the DNA from one typical human body cell were stretched out, it would be about two metres long, more than 1 000 000 times longer than the cell it came from! To fit such a length of DNA into their cells, organisms coil and supercoil their DNA into chromosomes, which you learned about in Chapter 1.

You could think of one chromosome as a single volume of a set of encyclopedias, and the set of chromosomes as the complete set of encyclopedias. If you were missing a single volume of the set, you could be missing information you might need at some time in the future. This is also true for our chromosomes. One chromosome contains only part of the instructions for making a human. All of our nuclei, except for those in gametes (which are haploid) must have a complete set of chromosomes.

A complete set of human DNA is made up of 46 chromosomes, arranged in 23 pairs. One chromosome of each pair comes from the mother, and one of each pair comes from the father (Figure 2.13).

Suggested Activity • • • • • • • • • • • •
A15 Quick Science on page 55

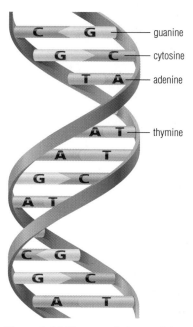

Figure 2.12 The overall shape of the DNA molecule is a double helix. Paired chemicals form the genetic code.

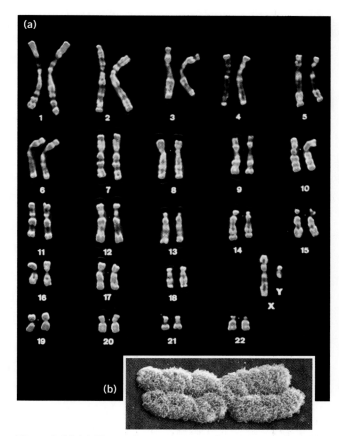

Figure 2.13 (a) These chromosomes are from a human male. A photo of a complete, organized set of chromosomes is called a karyotype. (b) A close-up of the X chromosome.

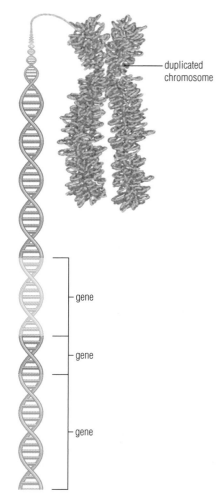

duplicated chromosome

gene

gene

gene

Figure 2.14 Each gene is an uninterrupted segment of DNA in a chromosome.

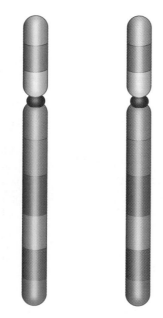

Figure 2.15 Gene pairs occupy matching locations on paired chromosomes.

In most sexually reproducing organisms, the chromosomes are organized into pairs. For dogs, a complete set has 78 chromosomes (39 pairs), and for cats, the number is 38 chromosomes (19 pairs). It is important to note that the number of chromosomes an organism has does not determine how large or how complex the organism will become.

Genes

Recall the analogy of encyclopedias. A cell's genetic information is organized into many volumes of encyclopedias, or chromosomes. The information in the encyclopedias is made up of letters, or the DNA chemicals guanine, cytosine, adenine, and thymine. In this analogy, a gene would be words that make up a section of the encyclopedia. The DNA "letters" G, C, A, and T have no meaning as individual letters, but when they are put together into genes or words, they provide information about a specific topic.

So what exactly is a gene? A **gene** is thought to be an uninterrupted segment of DNA, which contains coded instructions for a specific characteristic (Figure 2.14). Genes are responsible for the inheritance of an organism's characteristics.

Much of the early research into genes was carried out on the fruit fly. Scientists consider that

- Genes are located on chromosomes.

- Each chromosome contains many genes.

- Like chromosomes, genes come in pairs.

- Gene pairs occupy matching locations on paired chromosomes (Figure 2.15).

- Both genes in a pair carry DNA instructions for the characteristic.

- The DNA code may not be exactly the same in both genes of the pair, so they may produce different traits, or variations, of a characteristic.

You know that offspring produced through sexual reproduction inherit a set of genes from both parents, but the inherited genes may not be identical. For example, a fruit fly inherits one gene for leg length from its mother and one from its father. However, there are two possible versions of the leg-length gene: long leg or short leg. The wing-shape gene also has different possible forms. Examples are: long; rounded, called dumpy; and very small, called tiny.

Each possible version of a gene is called an **allele**. So, while a gene is the coded information for a characteristic, such as leg length, an allele is the coded information for a specific trait, or version of a characteristic, such as short or long leg. Most genes in most species have a variety of alleles that differ in their exact DNA sequence. Figure 2.16 shows a pair of chromosomes with the same genes but different alleles.

To understand how chromosomes, genes, and alleles are linked to heritable characteristics, let us return to the example of dogs. All dogs belong to the same species, and most dog breeds have a hairy coat. So we could begin by thinking of "hairy coat" as an example of a heritable characteristic. The characteristic "hairy coat" would be coded for by a gene, which is a sequence of DNA located on a chromosome. But, when we observe dogs, we see many different versions of "hairy coat." The different variations would be coded for by alleles, or different versions of the gene. The hair may be straight or curly, short or long, coarse or fine, and the different versions of coat colour are almost too numerous to count (Figure 2.17).

Figure 2.16 In this chromosome pair, each chromosome carries the same genes but different alleles may be present.

Figure 2.17 Although all dogs belong to the same species, the characteristic of hairy coat has an incredible variety of traits. Each trait is coded for by alleles.

Observing this variation, we can make three inferences. First, "hairy coat" is almost certainly more than just a single characteristic and must involve a combination of several characteristics. Second, more than one gene pair may be involved in determining the individual details of a dog's hairy coat. For example, there could be one gene pair for hair length, a second gene pair for waviness, and another gene pair for texture. Third, there may be several possible alleles for each gene pair. For the coat-colour gene alone, there must be ten or more possible alleles, all in just one species!

Patterns of Inheritance

Long before research scientists understood DNA and genes, plant and animal breeders were conducting experiments in selective breeding (Figure 2.18). In the hopes of producing ideal offspring, only animals with the most desirable traits were allowed to reproduce. By keeping written records of failures as well as successes, the breeders began to detect certain basic patterns of inheritance.

Suggested Activity •···········
A16 Problem-Solving Activity on page 56

Figure 2.18 The Saluki may be the oldest domesticated dog breed, with records dating back to 6000 BCE.

A breeder who wishes to produce albino cats, which have a white coat, should choose purebred parents—cats whose ancestors have produced only albino offspring for several generations. The term "pure breeding" is applied to such a group. Similarly, a breeder who wishes to produce black cats should choose purebred parents from different pure-breeding lineages of black cats. This way, a breeder can be confident that the parents will produce black kittens.

An individual produced by crossing two purebred parents that differ in a trait such as coat colour is known as a **hybrid**. Now, suppose a purebred black cat is crossbred with a purebred albino cat. What pattern of inheritance will be observed in the hybrid offspring?

Dominant Traits

Figure 2.19 shows the result of crossbreeding a purebred albino female cat with a purebred black male cat. Notice that every kitten in the resulting litter has a black coat. Crossing a purebred black female with a purebred albino male will produce the same result. No matter how many times the experiment is repeated, all of the offspring will have black coats: never white, never grey, only black.

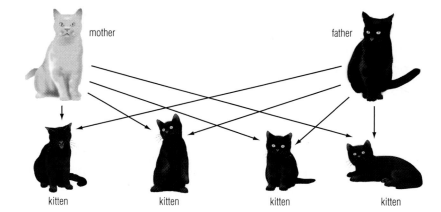

Figure 2.19 A cross between a purebred albino female cat and a purebred black male cat produces black kittens.

By definition, the kittens are hybrids, but they show no outward sign that their mother is a purebred albino cat. We know that the hybrid kittens have inherited an allele for black-coat colour from their father. We can infer that the hybrid kittens must also have inherited an allele for the albino white-coat colour because only albino alleles are present in the mother's lineage. However, the DNA information from the albino allele has somehow been ignored or suppressed. Only the DNA instructions from the black-coat allele have actually been carried out.

©P

Mating unlike purebred cats has revealed that the DNA instructions carried by the black-coat allele are dominant over the DNA instructions carried by the albino allele. We say that the allele for black fur is an example of a **dominant allele** and that black-coat colour is a **dominant trait**.

Recessive Traits

Will the albino allele be dominated by the black-coat allele in all future generations? To find out, a second experiment can be conducted in which adult hybrids are crossed.

In this new experiment, each hybrid parent possesses one black-coat allele and one albino, white-coat allele. When the hybrid cats are crossed, each parent can only pass on half of its genes to the offspring. This means that each parent passes on one of two possible alleles for coat colour to each kitten.

Figure 2.20 shows the average results of this experiment: Three out of every four kittens will have black coats, whereas one will be albino. If the experiment is repeated hundreds of times, you could expect approximately 75 % of the cats to be black and about 25 % to be albino.

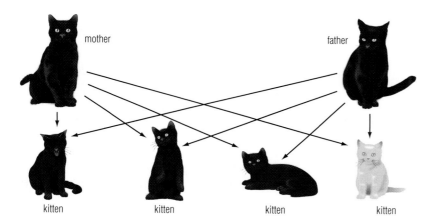

Figure 2.20 The hybrid cats are the parents in this cross.

How can we explain the production of white kittens? Two hybrid parents can produce a kitten with four possible combinations of alleles:

1. One black-coat allele from its father and one black-coat allele from its mother. The kitten will have black fur.

2. One black-coat allele from its mother and one albino allele from its father. The black-coat colour is a dominant trait, so the kitten will have black fur.

During Reading

Drawing Conclusions

When we ask questions, we can analyze ideas and draw conclusions. Use a three-column table to help you draw conclusions from the reading you have done about heredity. Label the first column "I read" and record a phrase or sentence from the text. Label the second column "I asked" and write down your question(s). Label the final column "Therefore" and record your conclusion.

infoBIT

Genetic Analysis

In analyzing the results of genetic crosses, a common convention is to assign letters to the alleles of a gene. The dominant allele is assigned the upper case form of the letter while the recessive allele is assigned the lower case form of the same letter.

For the example of the coat-colour gene in cats, the black-coat allele would be written B and the albino allele would be written b. Gametes carry only one allele and so gamete makeup will be written either B or b, as shown in the Punnett square in Figure 2.21.

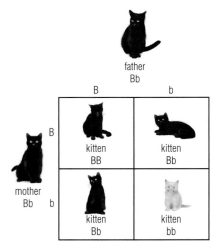

Figure 2.21 A Punnett square showing all possible results of the cross of two cats hybrid for coat colour

3. One albino allele from its mother and one black-coat allele from its father. Again, the black-coat colour is a dominant trait, so the kitten will have black fur.

4. One albino allele from its mother and one albino allele from its father. There is no black-coat allele to mask the effect of the albino allele, so the kitten will have white fur.

A diagram called a **Punnett square**, named after the geneticist who devised it, can be used to predict the results of a particular cross. The diagram of the cross of hybrid cats in Figure 2.21 shows all possible combinations of genes in the offspring kittens as a result of combinations of all possible gametes in the cross.

The albino condition, which produces white fur, is an example of a **recessive trait**, and the albino allele is an example of a **recessive allele**. A recessive trait appears in the offspring only if both inherited alleles are recessive alleles. In contrast, even one dominant allele will cause the dominant trait to appear.

2.2 CHECK and REFLECT

1. Which of the following contain DNA? Explain your answer.

   (a) chromosome

   (b) nucleus of a cell

   (c) gene

2. What four chemicals make up the genetic code? Describe how these chemicals are arranged in a DNA molecule.

3. Define the following terms in your own words and explain their function:

   (a) DNA

   (b) chromosome

   (c) gene

   (d) allele

4. Explain why chromosomes are considered to be the "source of diversity" in organisms.

5. Explain how DNA, chromosomes, genes, and alleles are related. What is their role in storing genetic information?

6. How do alleles fit into the analogy of chromosomes as encyclopedias? Explain your answer.

7. Explain how dominant and recessive traits differ from each other.

8. How does a purebred individual differ from a hybrid individual?

9. How could two black cats produce an albino kitten? Use a diagram to explain your answer.

10. If you wanted to be certain that a trait would appear in the offspring of the plants or animals that you were breeding, what would you have to find out about the parents? Explain your answer.

11. The term "reductionist" is sometimes used to describe the analytical way of looking at the world around us. Do you think this term is applicable to the scientific study of heredity? Explain why, and compare it to the holistic way of understanding heredity.

Modelling DNA

Models can help scientists visualize and understand new ideas. The DNA molecule has a complex structure known as a double helix (Figure 2.22).

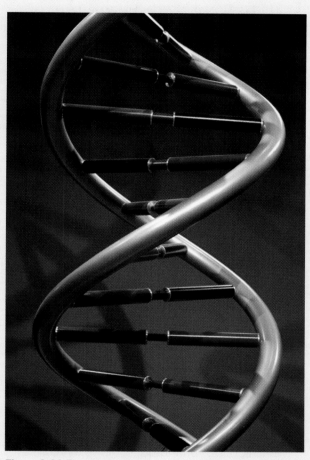

Figure 2.22 The double-helix structure is like a twisted ladder.

Question

How can you design a model of a DNA molecule that meets the criteria below:

• Includes the four chemicals (guanine, cytosine, adenine, and thymine) which must be paired correctly

• Contains at least eight pairings

• Includes a bond holding each of the pairs together

• Includes a "backbone" or outside structure of DNA

• Is at least 25 cm in height

Design and Conduct Your Inquiry

1. Use the Internet to research helical structures in nature.

2. Choose materials for your model. Some examples of materials you might choose to use are
   • modelling clay
   • pipe cleaners
   • marshmallows
   • paper
   • plastic foam
   • licorice

3. List the materials and equipment you will need.

4. Develop a procedure to build your model. Think about the following questions as you plan your procedure.
   • How do the chemicals pair up in a DNA molecule?
   • How does your model help to explain this?

5. Write up your procedure.

6. Have your teacher approve your materials list and procedure.

7. Build your model. Include a legend that identifies each component.

8. Analyze your model. Does it meet all the necessary criteria? Does it accurately model the structure of DNA? Revise your model, noting any changes you make to your design.

9. Present your design in the format of your choice. Your presentation should demonstrate how your model shows the important characteristics of the DNA molecule.

SKILLS YOU WILL USE
■ Carrying out a plan
■ Designing, building, and testing

A16 *Problem-Solving Activity*

Toolkits 3, 7

Showing the Relationships

A grade 8 class has just studied the structure of cells and the students are interested in learning more about genetic material and how it is organized. Their science teacher has asked you to explain to them the relationships among DNA, chromosomes, genes, and alleles.

Initiating and Planning

Design a way to summarize the relationships among DNA, chromosomes, genes, and alleles (Figure 2.23). Be creative. It could be a poster, Web page, model, skit, story, song, or any other method you choose to convey the information.

Materials & Equipment

You may use any materials necessary to complete your design. All materials must be checked with your teacher.

Criteria for Success

To be successful, your presentation must meet the following criteria:

- solve the problem described above
- show the relationships accurately
- be appealing and understandable for grade 8 students

Brainstorm Ideas

1. Work with a partner or in a small group. Brainstorm ways to convey the information. All ideas should be considered. You may wish to perform some research to get some preliminary ideas.

2. Look for ways to blend the best of the group's suggestions.

3. Select one solution to the problem.

4. Plan out your presentation. Write your plan in detail or use diagrams to illustrate your procedure.

5. Check your procedure with your teacher.

Performing and Recording

6. Follow your procedure to create your presentation.

7. As a group, go through your presentation from start to finish. Identify any problem areas. If necessary, make adjustments to your presentation and record any changes to your procedure.

8. Make your presentation. Ask your classmates to evaluate it based on the Criteria for Success.

Analyzing and Interpreting

9. Does your presentation meet all of the criteria?

10. Based on the feedback you received from step 8, how effectively does your presentation convey the information?

11. How does your work compare with that of your classmates?

Communicate

12. Share and compare your design with others in the class. Highlight the features that make your presentation both accurate and effective.

13. Are there ways you might improve your design?

14. As you were completing your presentation, did you have any questions about the relationships among DNA, chromosomes, genes, and alleles?

15. Assess your group's effectiveness. What did you do well? What could you improve?

Figure 2.23 Planning a presentation to explain the relationships among DNA, chromosomes, genes, and alleles

©P

Exploring Genetic Possibilities

In sexual reproduction, the offspring inherit genes in pairs: one from each parent. In an offspring, the combination of alleles determines what the offspring is like. The fruit fly is a common animal used to study heredity (Figure 2.24).

Purpose

To predict the traits of fruit fly offspring

Procedure and Questions

1. In fruit flies, suppose that there are two possible alleles for leg length: long-leg and short-leg.

   (a) Suppose a fruit fly inherits two long-leg alleles. Will this fruit fly have long legs or short legs? Explain your reasoning.

   (b) Suppose a second fruit fly inherits two short-leg alleles. Will this fruit fly have long legs or short legs? Explain your reasoning.

   (c) Suppose a third fruit fly inherits one short-leg allele and one long-leg allele. Can you be sure what leg length this offspring will have? Explain why.

2. In fruit flies, two possible alleles for body colour are tan/beige body and ebony body.

   (a) List three possible ways to pair these alleles in an offspring. Use a Punnett square to illustrate your answer.

   (b) For each pair, can you be sure what body colour an offspring will have? Explain why.

3. In fruit flies, two possible alleles for wing shape are long-wing and dumpy-wing.

   (a) List three possible ways to pair these alleles in an offspring. Use a Punnett square to illustrate your answer.

   (b) For each pair, can you be sure what wing shape an offspring will have? Explain why.

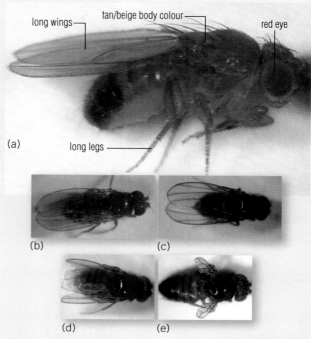

Figure 2.24 Fruit flies have characteristics that show discrete variation, which helps scientists identify patterns of inheritance. (a) A normal, wild type fly showing typical traits for wing length, body colour, eye colour, and leg length (b) A normal fly, in dorsal view (c) A fly with normal wings but ebony body colour (d) A fly with dumpy wings, which are shortened and indented, and normal body colour (e) A fly with tiny wings and ebony body colour

4. A hybrid fruit fly has long wings, tan/beige body colour, and long legs.

   (a) Based on this hybrid fly, which traits are dominant?

   (b) Use your answer to (a) to revisit your answers to questions 1–3.

5. What combinations of leg length, body colour, and wing shape are possible? Make sketches to illustrate your answer.

Pose New Questions

6. Suggest a situation similar to the ones you just answered questions about. You can choose any organism you like. Ask the same types of questions. Switch situations with a partner, and see if you can answer each others' questions.

Here is a summary of what you will learn in this section:

- Genetic conditions are passed down from parent to offspring.
- Some personal choices and environmental factors can alter a cell's DNA.
- Developments in the study of genetics have a major impact on society.
- Saskatchewan plays a major role in the study of genetics.

Figure 2.25 Cows can have their genes modified, or changed, in order to produce more milk, and resist diseases such as mastitis, a condition that reduces the amount of milk produced.

Figure 2.26 Genetically modified canola can improve production and, therefore, the monetary value of a crop.

Improving What We Have

Some people spend time thinking of ways to improve what we have. Have you ever thought about how something could be better than it already is? Maybe a video game would be better if it had more characters. Or maybe a computer would run better if it had more memory. Food could be better if it were sweeter, or more flavourful, or easier to ship long distances to market. Scientists and engineers are always trying to improve what we have. By analyzing heredity into molecules of DNA, scientists found that they could actually change the DNA of organisms to make them different. If you could change one food, how would you change it? If you could change one animal, how would you change it? How would you be ethically responsible in making such a decision to change DNA?

Scientists alter the genes of many different organisms in order to improve their use to some people in society. There are now crops that are more tolerant to drought, excessive heat, and frost. Crops can also be altered to be resistant to certain chemicals so that farmers can spray their fields with herbicides to kill weeds without harming crops. There are animals that are genetically altered to be more productive (Figure 2.25). However, if all the individuals of one species have exactly the same or very similar DNA, then there is little variation among individuals and, overall, biological diversity is reduced.

©P

One example of an improved agricultural crop is canola (Figure 2.26). An agricultural chemical company has developed a type of canola with specially modified DNA that makes it resistant to a popular herbicide. The herbicide can be applied to kill weeds without harming the canola plant. This technology was costly to develop, so anyone who wants to grow this type of canola must purchase a technology use agreement (TUA). At this time, the agricultural chemical company owns the patent and the rights to the modified DNA in the seed.

A18 *Quick Science*

Design a Species

Some plants and animals are bred from two species in an attempt to combine the characteristics from each of the parents (Figure 2.27).

Purpose

To explore the idea of changing the traits of an organism

Procedure

1. Choose a living organism that you would like to change in some way.

2. Make three or more changes to the traits that the organism displays.

3. Create a drawing or computer-generated poster of your new and improved organism.

Questions

4. Give a reason for each of the changes you made to the original organism.

5. Give an example of something positive that could come from changing the DNA, and therefore the traits, of plants and animals.

6. Give an example of a negative impact on society that could happen as a result of being able to change an organism's DNA.

Pose New Questions

7. Suggest a question you have about altering the DNA in organisms.

Figure 2.27 A liger has some of the characteristics of a tiger, and some of the characteristics of a lion.

Two-Eyed Seeing

In the previous activity, you designed a species from a scientific point of view. An analytical thinker breaks down phenomena such as the inheritance of characteristics into smaller and smaller parts: cells, chromosomes, and DNA molecules. If you can understand and control DNA molecules, then you can probably change the living thing itself, such as altering round tomatoes by growing cube-shaped tomatoes.

A holistic way of thinking is followed by most First Nations and Métis peoples, who pay great attention to the whole environment or to the natural world. To change anything, such as killing a rabbit to eat or catching a fish, there is a prayer or offering to give in order to keep a balance within the whole environment and the whole world. Harmony and balance of everything is most important in First Nations and Métis cultures. From this perspective, people are not made up of parts such as chromosomes and DNA. People are part of the whole of creation, and as such, they have relationships and responsibilities with everything in creation. A holistic person would not even think of changing human beings, other than to help them gain physical, emotional, mental, and spiritual balance within themselves. Offering a prayer or a gift to Spirit or to Mother Earth is a simple example of one's responsibility. To live responsibly in harmony means to help your whole family, your whole community, and the whole world. Holistic thinking is common sense for First Nations and Métis peoples who live by traditional values.

People are not necessarily locked into one type of thinking. Everyone has the potential of moving out of their preferred way of thinking to understand how others think. Sometimes, analytical thinking seems better in one situation; at other times, holistic thinking seems better. What if someone could see out of one eye analytically and out of the other eye holistically? That person would have the power of using the best from analytical science and the best from holistic ways of knowing. Mi'kmaq Elder Albert Marshall from the Eskasoni First Nation in Nova Scotia calls this **two-eyed seeing** (Figure 2.28). He has given you something to think about as you finish this chapter.

Figure 2.28 Elder Albert Marshall's idea of two-eyed seeing helps us understand and respect both analytical and holistic ways of thinking.

Biotechnology

Biotechnology is a scientific term that describes the use or modification of living things to improve our lives in areas such as medicine, agriculture, and engineering. Although biotechnology has successfully produced most of our world's crops and livestock, it takes a very long time—many generations of the plants and animals—to produce offspring that consistently have the desired combination of traits. Scientists and breeders have, therefore, developed technologies that can speed up this process. These technologies can range from "low tech" to extremely "high tech."

©P

Selecting Desirable Traits

Selective breeding is the process of selecting and breeding individuals with desirable traits to produce offspring that also have these desired traits. The grains and fruits you ate for breakfast, in addition to many other foods, are probably products of selective breeding (Figure 2.29).

Figure 2.29 Selective breeding of plants and animals for food is one of the many ways in which biotechnology affects our lives.

Figure 2.30 These horses have been bred for their size.

Consider the example of horse breeding. By combining the genes of champion parents, breeders hope to create offspring that have the prized traits of both parents. Selective breeding increases the chances of producing the desired traits in succeeding generations (Figure 2.30).

Some cultures have practised selective breeding since humans first began to farm about 10 000 years ago. After many generations of selective breeding, most of our plants no longer resemble the original species from which they were bred. Corn, for example, was bred by Indigenous peoples from species of grasses called teosinte. Teosinte produced much smaller cobs and far fewer seeds than modern-day corn (Figure 2.31).

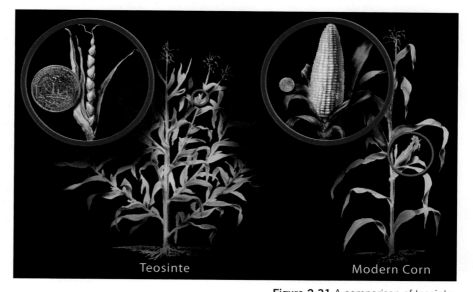

Teosinte

Modern Corn

Figure 2.31 A comparison of teosinte and modern corn shows the difference in seed number and cob size.

Source: National Science Foundation, USA.

In Saskatchewan, the First Nations and Métis peoples were mostly hunter–gatherer societies. They did not practise agriculture but did domesticate and selectively breed dogs and horses. Some Elders such as Mary Ruelling and Velma Goodfeather agree that their ancestors did not breed their horses or dogs for pedigree or for attractiveness but for other physical qualities, such as strength or endurance, and to prevent breeding by closely related individuals (inbreeding). According to Mary Ruelling, a Dené Elder from the Clearwater Dené Nation, northern communities did not selectively breed dogs, which served as the main form of transportation. Instead, trappers routinely exchanged dogs with other groups to ensure that no inbreeding occurred. This Dené practice promoted strong genetic diversity in their domesticated dog populations.

infoBIT

Stronger Wheat

A Saskatchewan farmer by the name of Seager Wheeler was able to produce a variety of wheat that was ideal for the short growing seasons and cold, harsh winters of Saskatchewan.

Artificial Reproductive Technology

Artificial reproductive technology refers to any artificial method of joining a male and a female gamete. Most livestock in Canada are produced by some method of artificial reproduction. In **artificial insemination** (AI), sperm are collected from a chosen male and inserted into many females. The advantage of this technology is that the sperm can be used to inseminate many females at once. It is also faster and safer because the animals do not interact.

Another reproductive technology is **in vitro fertilization** (IVF). The term *in vitro* means "in glass." In this technology, sperm from a male and eggs from a female are collected. In a laboratory, the eggs and sperm are combined in a Petri dish to fertilize the eggs. This produces many more embryos than could be produced naturally. Each embryo is implanted into a different female. If implantation is successful, the females will eventually give birth to the offspring, all of which will be brothers and sisters (Figure 2.32).

Scientists can also determine the sex of the embryos before they are implanted. By choosing only female embryos, dairy farmers can guarantee that all the calves produced will be female. This embryo selection conserves resources.

Figure 2.32 The beef industry relies on artificial reproductive technology to produce cattle with specially selected traits that provide us with high quality meat. How do these beef cattle compare with the dairy cows shown earlier?

Genetic Engineering

Genetic engineering refers to any technology process that directly alters the DNA of an organism. Genetic engineering is a rapidly developing science and industry, and every new advance increases our ability to control the characteristics of organisms.

Much genetic engineering involves inserting a gene from one species into another species. One example is bacteria that are genetically engineered to produce medicines such as insulin. Insulin is a substance that many diabetic people use to control the level of sugar in their blood. Just 20 years ago, insulin had to be extracted from the pancreas of cattle, and it was expensive to produce. Today, the human insulin-producing gene is inserted into a bacterium's DNA. Because bacteria reproduce so rapidly, bacterial colonies can produce insulin quickly and cheaply. Now, most of the world's supply of insulin comes from genetically engineered bacteria (Figure 2.33).

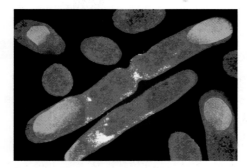

Figure 2.33 These bacteria are genetically modified to produce insulin. In this artificially coloured photo, the bacteria are magenta and the insulin production parts are orange.

©P

Another example involves a micro-organism called *Bacillus thuringiensis*, which produces a toxin commonly called Bt. Bt is poisonous to many insects. Scientists have isolated the gene that contains the instructions for making Bt toxin and have inserted it into the DNA of plants. These genetically engineered plants now produce Bt toxin! When insects eat the Bt-producing plants, they die and growers never need to apply pesticides to the engineered plants. Since the 1990s, cotton, corn, and potatoes have been engineered to produce Bt toxin. Figure 2.34 shows another example: that of inserting an insect's gene into a plant to produce a luminous, glowing plant.

Biotechnology and Society

Development of technology that allows us to select or introduce traits of the organisms around us has given humans some important benefits. However, as with any technology, we need to use these technologies responsibly and be aware of the possible risks as well as the benefits. We also need to be aware of who benefits and who lives with the risks.

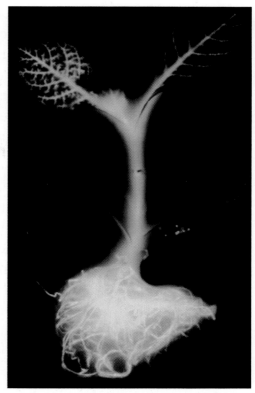

Figure 2.34 This plant was grown from cells that had a firefly gene inserted into them. When the gene is activated, the plant glows.

Risks in Animals

In agriculture, most individuals in a crop or livestock population are extremely genetically similar as a result of generations of selective breeding. Artificial reproductive technologies can reduce the genetic variation in breeding lines of livestock. In artificial insemination, sperm from just a few males are used to impregnate many females. With in vitro fertilization, many embryos are created from the eggs and sperm of just two individuals.

Now, scientists and breeders can produce an identical copy (a clone) of a single animal. The most famous example of this is a sheep named Dolly (Figure 2.35). Dolly was produced in Scotland in 1996, and was an exact duplicate of her mother.

Animals like Dolly have been cloned for a variety of reasons. Some, like the rhesus monkey ANDi (a backward abbreviation of "inserted DNA"), have been genetically altered as part of research programs into human diseases. Other animals, such as cattle, are being cloned as potential large-scale producers of meat and milk. One risk is that herds of genetically identical individuals may be far more susceptible to disease than more genetically varied herds.

Figure 2.35 Dolly's cells appeared the same age as her mother's, even though Dolly was six years younger.

During Reading

Asking Questions of the Author

As you read, consider what the author has included and omitted. What questions would you ask the author about how information is chosen and why it is included?

Cloning and genetic engineering have been fraught with difficulties. Cattle cloners have reported numerous examples of unsuccessful pregnancies, birth defects, and deaths among clones. The cause of many of these birth defects in cloned mammals is altered gene expression resulting from manipulation of the gametes and embryos. Dolly herself developed arthritis, although it is not known why.

Risks in Plants

Most of our plant crops were produced by selective breeding of wild plants. Weeds are often the wild relatives of crop plants. Some crops have been genetically engineered to resist herbicides, but there have been unforeseen problems. Many crop plants can cross-pollinate with their wild weed relatives. Cases have been reported of genetically engineered canola interbreeding with weeds, and the weeds' offspring becoming resistant to herbicide.

Accidental Changes to DNA

Sometimes DNA is inadvertently altered or damaged by environmental factors and personal choices. Usually, the damaged DNA is detected by the cell, in which case the DNA is repaired or the cell is destroyed. However, if the damage is not detected, normal cell function can be disrupted and diseases, such as cancer, can result.

Carcinogens

Carcinogens are chemicals or toxins that cause cancer. These chemicals can change a cell's DNA or change the way a cell reproduces, resulting in cells dividing uncontrollably and forming tumours. We sometimes come into contact with carcinogens unknowingly, but we often make choices to put ourselves at risk for cell damage. Smoking cigarettes is extremely dangerous because cigarettes contain thousands of chemicals, many of which are toxic carcinogens (Figure 2.36). Even people who do not smoke but who are exposed to second-hand smoke are at risk of damaging their cells' DNA.

Asbestos is another carcinogen. It was commonly used in buildings as insulation throughout Canada and the United States starting in the 1870s. It is able to resist fire, electrical, and chemical damage, so it seemed an excellent building material.

WARNING

CIGARETTES CAUSE LUNG CANCER

85% of lung cancers are caused by smoking. 80% of lung cancer victims die within 3 years.

lung cancer

Health Canada

Figure 2.36 Cigarette smoke contains many carcinogens. It is a health hazard not only for smokers but also for non-smokers close by.

It was not until almost one hundred years later that it became publicly known that asbestos would break down into tiny, invisible fibres (Figure 2.37). Inhaling the tiny fibres can cause irreparable damage to cells by physically breaking strands of DNA. This can lead to cancer in people who are exposed to asbestos on a regular basis. While the use of asbestos in building materials stopped in Canada in the 1970s, old buildings that contain asbestos must have it removed in order to eliminate the risk, but for many people, it is already too late.

Pesticides are chemicals that are sprayed onto crops to try to eliminate pests that cause damage to the crops. Some pesticides are carcinogens. Humans and other animals consume pesticides, often without knowing it, by drinking water that contains small amounts of pesticides, by eating food that has not been thoroughly cleaned to remove the chemicals, or by inhaling chemical particles from the air.

Figure 2.37 The tiny fibres of asbestos are extremely dangerous if inhaled.

Sun Exposure

It is now known that overexposure to the ultraviolet (UV) rays from sunlight and from tanning beds is a major cause of skin cancer. Moderate exposure to sunlight is important, as it allows our bodies to produce vitamin D. Overexposure, however, can cause sunburn and can damage DNA, which could result in cancer. Tanning beds are a more recent concern. Research shows that even a single use of a tanning bed can be extremely damaging and may greatly increase the chance of getting skin cancer. Skin cancer is one of the most common forms of cancer, and it is the most preventable. Limiting your sun exposure, using sunscreen, and avoiding tanning beds are easy ways to avoid overexposure to UV rays.

Genetic Conditions

Besides using the study of genetics and reproduction to improve the healthy organisms we already have, or to study diseases that result from altered or damaged DNA, science is able to shed light on the mysteries of genetic conditions. A genetic condition is a disease or disorder that is caused by damaged or faulty DNA. It is important to know how genetic conditions occur. In many cases, genetic conditions can be challenging for organisms to live with.

re*Search*

Overexposure to ultraviolet (UV) rays can cause skin discolorations such as moles. These moles can be an indication of skin cancer. Research the ABCD of moles to find out the guidelines for determining the difference between benign (harmless) and malignant (cancerous) moles. Present your findings in a skit, brochure, poster, or other format of your choice as a public health announcement.

Suggested Activity • • • • • • • • • • •
A19 Science, Technology, Society, and the Environment on page 72

You already learned that DNA is genetic material that is passed from parent organisms to their offspring. Sometimes, the combination of alleles can result in a genetic condition that can affect the life of the offspring. In most cases, genetic conditions are caused by recessive alleles. To inherit the condition, offspring would have to inherit a recessive allele from each parent. Remember that if a dominant allele is present, it masks the effect of the recessive trait. This is why genetic conditions are quite rare.

Genetic conditions can also occur as a result of an error in the copying of DNA during cell reproduction. Changes to a cell's DNA that cause genetic conditions are usually random, and result from small changes in the order of the chemicals in the DNA.

Male Infertility

Sometimes, males are unable to produce sperm that are viable or able to fertilize an egg. Approximately 10 % of all male infertility cases are recognized as a genetic condition. This type of infertility is a result of random mistakes, called mutations, in the DNA. The condition usually cannot be passed down, because the male is unable to reproduce, and so there is no child to inherit the condition. However, with the development of the assisted reproductive technology of intracytoplasmic sperm injection (ICSI) these defects may now be transmitted.

Breast Cancer

Research shows that some forms of breast cancer (about 10 percent of cases), are genetic. If there is a mutation in the genes that keep breast cells growing and reproducing at a normal rate, it can cause tumours (Figure 2.38). If a woman inherits or passes on the mutation, then there usually is a family history of breast cancer. However, most breast cancers are not hereditary. Sometimes, a random mutation can occur that causes breast cells to reproduce at a faster rate than normal, which also can cause cancer.

Sex-linked Genetic Conditions

Sex chromosomes, like all chromosomes, exist in pairs. In humans, they are the **X chromosome** and the **Y chromosome**. Females have two X chromosomes and males have one X chromosome and one Y chromosome. Females can only pass on X chromosomes to their offspring. Males can pass on either an X or a Y chromosome. Conversely, females receive X chromosomes from both the mother and the father. Males, however, receive an X chromosome from their mother and a Y chromosome from their father.

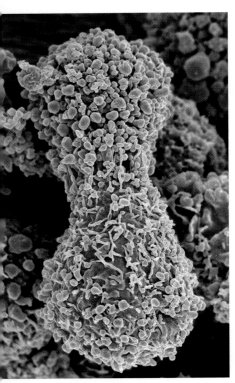

Figure 2.38 A breast cancer cell is able to divide at a much faster rate than healthy cells can.

©P

Some genes are located only on the Y chromosome, but many more genes are located exclusively on the X chromosome. For this reason, many traits are linked to the X chromosome (Figure 2.39). Genes that are located only on the X or the Y chromosome are said to be sex-linked genes.

Males are more likely to inherit sex-linked genetic disorders because they receive only one X chromosome. If a male inherits an affected X chromosome with a recessive allele, he will automatically display the recessive trait because the Y chromosome does not have the matching gene that could mask the effect of the recessive allele. In order for a female to display the recessive trait, she must inherit two affected X chromosomes. If she inherits a normal X chromosome from either parent, it would mask the recessive allele. However, she would be at risk of passing on the recessive allele to her offspring.

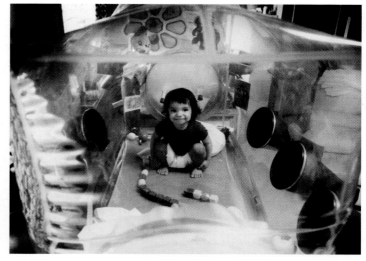

Figure 2.39 David Vetter, the "bubble boy," lived for 12 years inside a plastic bubble. He had Severe Combined Immune Deficiency (SCID), a genetic disorder that made his body incapable of fighting disease. The gene for SCID is found on the X chromosome.

Colour Blindness

Red-green colour blindness is one of the more common genetic disorders. The gene that controls the ability to distinguish between red and green is found on the X chromosome, and the allele for red-green colour blindness is recessive. People may be unable to distinguish between red and green, or they may view different versions of the colours. For example, green may appear to be almost blue, and red may appear pink. Tests for red-green colour blindness can be as simple as looking at Figure 2.40. Other forms of colour blindness are rare, and are not sex-linked.

Hemophilia

Another sex-linked genetic disorder is hemophilia. It is linked to the X chromosome. Hemophilia is a disorder in which the blood is unable to clot. Imagine getting a small cut and worrying that it might never stop bleeding. Hemophiliacs do not bleed at a faster rate than people who do not have hemophilia, but they do bleed for a longer time, so overall they lose a greater volume of blood than an unaffected person. Also, hemophiliacs may have spontaneous bleeding into the joints. This condition is very serious but also quite rare.

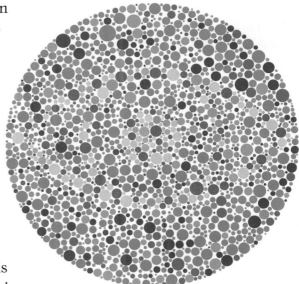

Figure 2.40 A simple test that is used to determine if someone has red green colour blindness. Can you see the image imbedded in the picture?

Other Genetic Conditions

Not all genetic conditions are the result of recessive alleles or sex chromosomes. Sometimes there are problems during meiosis, resulting in gametes with an abnormal number of chromosomes. If a gamete with an abnormal number of chromosomes is fertilized to form a zygote, the zygote will also have an abnormal number of chromosomes. Most zygotes with an abnormal number of chromosomes are not able to survive.

One example of a genetic condition caused by an abnormal number of chromosomes is trisomy 21, formerly known as Down Syndrome. In people with trisomy 21, there is an extra, or third, chromosome 21, instead of the usual pair. Instead of having a total of 46 chromosomes, there are 47 (Figure 2.41).

People with trisomy 21 often have smaller body frames and limbs, large tongues, and large, round eyes. They typically develop more slowly, both physically and mentally. Despite developmental delays, people with trisomy 21 can lead active, productive lives.

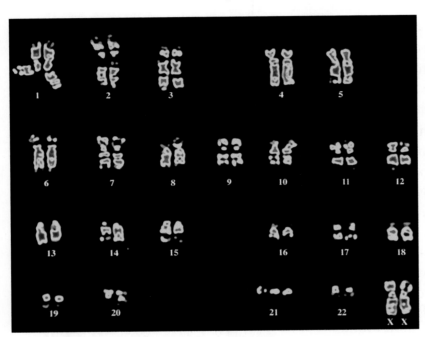

Figure 2.41 The extra chromosome 21 causes the symptoms associated with trisomy 21.

Genetic Conditions and First Nations and Métis Peoples

Genetic conditions are not viewed by First Nations and Métis peoples as disorders, diseases, or even conditions. In fact, the opposite is true. Dakota people view children born with special needs, such as children with Down syndrome, as children with sacred gifts. The Dakota believe that a reason exists why the children are born in this way. Perhaps those special, gifted, children are able to see that which other humans cannot, or perhaps they are able to perceive the spiritual world. These children are never labelled by the community as having a disorder or disease.

©P

Canadian and Saskatchewan Contributions to the Study of Genetics

New discoveries are always being made in all the areas of science, and genetics and reproduction are no exception. Scientists in Saskatchewan work with scientists in other provinces and countries to try to discover the causes for genetic conditions in order to try to prevent the conditions from occurring (Figure 2.42). Once a discovery is made, scientists and genetic counsellors can also use the information to test couples to see if they are at risk of having a baby with certain conditions.

Saskatchewan scientist Dr. Edmond Lemire and genetic counsellor Janet Lucas contributed to the study of a gene responsible for babies being born without any arms or legs. In the years since colleagues in Vancouver discovered the gene, support and testing have been offered to family members at risk of carrying the gene for this condition. Many years ago in 1962, Hans Renpenning a Saskatchewan medical student, discovered a gene responsible for causing significant learning disabilities in males. Renpenning went on to become an eye doctor, but his work is still being used to test families who may be at risk for passing the gene down to a son.

Dr. Irene Uchida and Dr. John Hamerton are Canadian geneticists who are internationally recognized for their work in finding out about the effects of radiation on human chromosomes. Dr. Murray Barr discovered an important cell structure that is now known as the Barr body, which is found only in cells from genetic females. This structure was used in the Olympics to determine the gender of athletes if there were concerns about athletes competing unfairly by entering competitions for the opposite gender. The gene responsible for causing cystic fibrosis was discovered by Toronto geneticist Dr. Lap-Chee Tsui and his associates in 1989.

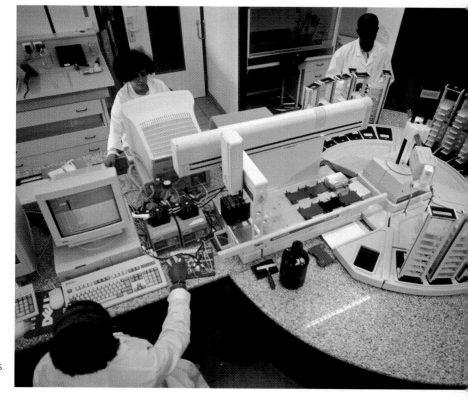

Figure 2.42 Research carried out in genetics laboratories involves many different techniques and technologies. Scientists carefully research the causes and effects of differences in genes in many species.

©P

2.3 Genetics, Technology, Society, and the Environment   **69**

Careers in Genetics and Reproduction

Suggested Activity • • • • • • • • • • • •
A20 Decision-Making Analysis
on page 72

re*Search*

Choose a career from the list on this page (or another career related to this unit) and prepare a poster that includes the following information:

- Education required
- Average salary
- Everyday duties
- Interesting facts

The study of genetics and how genes and chromosomes affect organisms can lead to some very interesting and rewarding careers. The study of reproduction and how it can be affected can also lead to many careers. The following is a list of some of the more common jobs related to reproduction and genetics

- Animal breeding
- Biology or science teacher or professor
- Biotech research
- Childbirth educator
- DNA forensics
- Family planning nurse
- Fertility specialist
- Gene therapy
- Genetic counselling
- Genetic modification of foods and seeds
- Genetics and paternity testing
- Military biological warfare protection
- Organ transplantation
- Pesticide development
- Pharmaceutical (medication) development

2.3 CHECK and REFLECT

1. Describe the concept of two-eyed seeing and explain how this idea can help foster respect for both holistic and analytical ways of understanding.

2. Describe two examples of technologies that humans use to select the traits of organisms.

3. Who were the earliest "plant technologists" in North America? What crop did they develop and how?

4. How have reproductive technologies benefited agricultural industries in Saskatchewan? Provide examples. What human needs do these technologies reflect?

5. Simplify an explanation of selective breeding so that a student in grade 4 could easily understand it.

6. What are some advantages of biotechnology? What are some disadvantages?

7. What are some intended and unintended consequences for the environment as a result of developments in biotechnology?

8. Predict potential impacts or issues that might be related to an increasing use of some types of biotechnology such as cloning and genetic engineering.

9. Brainstorm at least three ways to reduce your risk of cancer.

10. Identify three ways in which genetic conditions can arise. Provide examples of each.

Ask an Expert

Dr. Edmond Lemire: Genetics with a Twist

Dr. Edmond Lemire is one of the few medical geneticists in Saskatchewan. He acquired an interest in medical genetics while taking a biology course in college. His main interest lies in dysmorphology, which is the study of medical genetics that deals with birth defects.

Edmond works at the University of Saskatchewan and at the Royal University Hospital (RUH) in Saskatoon, Saskatchewan. Since the RUH is a teaching hospital, the job includes research into new genetic conditions and teaching medical students, in addition to seeing patients. The most interesting part of Edmond's work is the variety because there are so many genetic conditions and the study of genetics is always changing rapidly.

Edmond sees patients of all ages, from unborn children to adults, because of suspected or confirmed genetic disease. Sometimes patients are seen in his clinic, and other times, patients are seen after being admitted to the hospital. Edmond keeps track of the subtle physical findings in his patients, then searches through databases of information to try to match the physical findings with a genetic condition. Once a condition is diagnosed, genetic testing can be done to confirm the diagnosis. The family is informed of the results and of the chance of the condition occurring again. Often, other family members are also tested. Unlike other physicians who only deal with the patient, geneticists regularly deal with entire families (Figure 2.43).

Edmond is currently working on a project with two large families that involves a genetically inherited lung disease where affected individuals eventually need lung transplants. He is also working to try to identify the gene that is responsible for a serious birth defect in one First Nations community. A third research project involves hereditary breast cancer.

Adult patients usually go to see Edmond because of a personal or family history of cancer. Young patients are usually referred to Edmond because of developmental delays or learning problems. In our society, we are always curious about reasons why we are different from other people. Through the study of genetics, Edmond gets to answer those questions for his patients.

Figure 2.43 Couples with a family history of genetic diseases often consult a geneticist prior to having children.

Environmental Factors and Cancer

Purpose

To research common forms of cancer and to determine whether they can be caused by environmental factors (Figure 2.44)

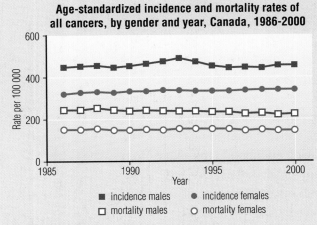

Age-standardized incidence and mortality rates of all cancers, by gender and year, Canada, 1986-2000

- ■ incidence males
- ● incidence females
- □ mortality males
- ○ mortality females

Figure 2.44 Although cancer rates have remained steady in Canada, some forms of cancer are more prevalent than others, and some forms are more preventable than others.

Source: "Progress Report on Cancer Control in Canada," Health Canada (2004). Reproduced with permission of the Minister of Public Works and Government Services Canada, 2010.

Procedure

1. Choose a form of cancer.

2. Use library or Internet resources to research its causes.

Questions

3. Can this form of cancer be passed down from generation to generation? Is it genetic?

4. Are there any environmental factors that can cause this form of cancer?

5. Is there anything we can do to try to prevent this type of cancer?

6. How common is this form of cancer in Canada? Whom does it mostly affect?

Pose New Questions

7. Suggest ways that a particular cancer-causing factor in the environment might be controlled.

A20 *Decision-Making Analysis*   Toolkits 4, 5

SKILLS YOU WILL USE
- Asking questions
- Summarizing information

Useful Genes?

What are the questions and issues raised by new technologies for recombining genetic material?

Initiating and Planning

New genetic technologies and research, such as the Human Genome Project (HGP), have allowed scientists to study the human genetic code further than ever before (Figure 2.45).

The goal of the HGP was to identify all of the genes that comprise the human genetic material (genome).

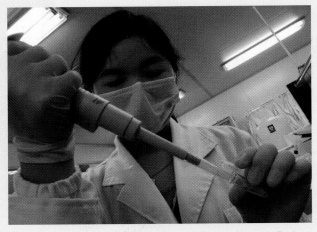

Figure 2.45 Collecting samples for the Human Genome Project

©P

In the course of their research, scientists discovered that the human genome consists of about 30 000 genes. This was surprising as scientists expected to find 100 000 genes. Scientists now suggest that the role of human genes is much more complex than originally thought.

Having such detailed information on human DNA has advanced research on a variety of genetic technologies, such as cloning, and on genetic disorders, such as cystic fibrosis, muscular dystrophy, and Huntington's disease. Such emerging technologies have led to a variety of questions and issues related to the development and application of both genetic research and the treatment of genetic disorders.

Select part A or part B and write a short report using the following questions as your guide. Use library and Internet resources that have been approved by your teacher. Be sure to evaluate your sources in terms of how recent they are and how reliable the information seems.

Performing and Recording

Part 1 — New Genetic Technologies to Treat Genetic Disorders

1. Select one of the genetic disorders mentioned on this page, in this section, or choose a disorder of your choice.

2. Research how the disorder is being treated today.

3. Describe how emerging genetic technologies may be used to treat this disorder in the future.

4. What potential questions or issues may arise from the use of this new treatment?

5. Do you agree with the use of this new treatment? Explain your position, using facts to support your opinion.

Part 2 — Emerging Recombinant Genetic Technologies

6. Select one of the genetic technologies from this section, or another genetic technology that interests you.

7. Research and describe how this technology works.

8. Describe possible applications for this technology.

9. What potential questions or issues may arise from the use of this new technology?

10. Do you agree with the use of this new technology? Explain your position, using facts to support your opinion.

Analyzing and Interpreting

11. After researching genetic technology and how it can be applied, do you think that continued advancement in this area of science is important? Explain your answer.

12. What do you think are some issues related to the use of this advanced genetic technology?

13. In your opinion, do the risks of using genetic technology outweigh the benefits, or do the benefits outweigh the risks? Explain.

Communication and Teamwork

14. Present your opinions, including your decision from part A or B, to the class. You may choose to create a poster, report, or pamphlet, or discuss your opinions as a debate or discussion.

15. Compare your opinions with those of your classmates. Do you all agree on the use of genetic technology?

16. What are some similarities in the opinions of your classmates?

17. What are some differences in the opinions of your classmates?

Key Concept Review

1. What is the difference between a characteristic and a trait?

2. Explain the difference between a heritable and a non-heritable characteristic. Give three examples of each.

3. In your own words, define DNA, chromosomes, genes, and alleles. Explain how they work together to pass on characteristics from parents to offspring.

4. Compare dominant and recessive traits using a Venn diagram.

5. What is discrete variation? What is continuous variation? Give an example of each.

6. Explain the difference between the terms "purebred" and "hybrid," using an example for each.

7. What biotechnology is commonly used in the cattle industry in Saskatchewan? Why is this technology useful?

Connect Your Understanding

8. A person with hitchhiker's thumb plays guitar with a local rock band. Explain how she displays both heritable and non-heritable characteristics. Include what you learned about First Nations and Métis perspectives on heredity.

Question 8 The ability to bend a thumb backward is called hitchhiker's thumb. It is a dominant trait.

9. A scientist wants to study continuous variation in a mouse population. List three mouse characteristics that he or she could investigate.

10. Explain how a chromosome may be involved in the inheritance of a genetic disorder, such as Severe Combined Immunodeficiency (SCID) syndrome or colour blindness.

11. Explain how two black dogs can breed to produce three black pups and one white pup.

12. Explain how selective breeding has affected the development of domesticated animals, such as dogs and racehorses.

13. Describe the application of genetic technology in the production of cloned animals such as Dolly the cloned sheep. How might this technology have a positive effect? How might it have a negative effect?

14. How does an understanding of heredity allow animal breeders to develop animals with desirable traits?

15. (a) List three ways in which crops have been improved through genetic engineering. In what other ways might crops be improved through genetic engineering?

    (b) Consider the First Nations and Métis perspectives on living holistically. How would a holistic understanding affect your answer to part (a)?

16. What types of observation and experimentation led us to a better understanding of how traits are expressed?

17. What are the benefits to understanding how genetic material functions?

18. Predict what the calf produced in a union between each of these parents might look like if the allele for white coat is recessive and the allele for brown coat is dominant. Explain your answers.

    (a) a purebred white cow and a purebred brown bull

    (b) a purebred brown cow and a purebred brown bull

    (c) a purebred white cow and a purebred white bull

    (d) a hybrid brown cow and a purebred white bull

19. Suppose that a woman who has normal colour vision, but whose father was colour-blind, marries a man with normal colour vision.

    (a) Is it possible that the couple might have colour-blind children? Explain your answer. Include a diagram.

    (b) If all the children of this family have normal vision, is it possible that colour blindness might recur in the next generation of this family? Explain your answer. Include a diagram.

20. In your opinion, what issues about the use of genetic engineering are important?

21. In terms of genetic manipulation, compare the scientific analytical way of thinking with holistic ways of thinking. How might the consideration of both types of thinking strengthen our understanding of genetics?

Reflection

22. What new understanding of DNA and chromosomes do you have?

23. In this chapter, you learned about carcinogens and other factors that can increase your risk of cancer. Does your lifestyle include choices that may increase your risk of cancer? Make a list of things that you can do or avoid to lower your risk of cancer.

24. You probably had heard about different biotechnologies such as genetic engineering or cloning before you started this chapter. What new understanding do you now have of biotechnology? Has your opinion changed on whether we should use biotechnology?

After Reading

Reflect and Evaluate

With a partner, share and summarize some of the questions you posed during this chapter. Compare any conclusions you drew. Write a three-sentence evaluation of the positive and negative effects of biotechnology on society. Share your evaluation with another pair of students.

Reflection on Essential Inquiry Questions

Contrast the genetic make-up of parents and offspring produced by (a) sexual reproduction and (b) cloning. **SI**

Model the number of cells involved in the processes of sexual reproduction in cattle, artificial insemination, in vitro fertilization, and cloning. How might these processes affect variability in a species? **TPS**

From the information included in this chapter, list positive and negative ways that technology and/or environmental factors can influence reproduction. **DM**

What did you learn from this chapter about cultural perspectives as applied to genetic conditions? **CP**

Unit Task

How have your ideas about your chosen Unit Task changed because of your new learning on the genetic code, inheritance of traits, and uses of biotechnology? Make notes on ways to relate the new information to your task.

The process of human reproduction can be affected by technology.

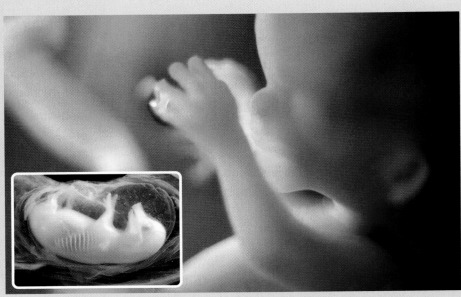

Outcomes

By the end of this chapter you will:

- examine the process and influences on the transfer of genetic information and the impact of that understanding on society past and present

- analyze the process of human reproduction, including the influence of reproductive and contraceptive technology

What you will learn:

- Human reproduction requires both male and female reproductive organs, which are dependent on hormones.

- A fertilized egg goes through many cell divisions and many changes in order to produce a human baby.

- The development of a baby can be affected by environmental factors during pregnancy.

- There are many new technologies that can be used to prevent pregnancy from occurring or can help a pregnancy to occur.

- First Nations and Métis cultures view human reproduction as sacred. Puberty and reproduction are part of the cycle of life, and involve the four aspects of a person.

All mammals appear essentially the same during the embryonic stage of development, but in the fetal stage they show the characteristics of their species. Mammals begin as a single, tiny, fertilized egg. The fertilized egg divides over and over to produce all the tissues, organs, and limbs that form a new individual. Compare the developing pig and the human fetus.

Key Terms

- blastocyst • contraception
- corpus luteum
- endometrium • estrogen
- fallopian tube • feedback
- fetus • follicle-stimulating hormone • gonads • hormones
- implantation • infertility
- menstrual cycle
- menstruation • ovaries
- ovulation • oxytocin • penis
- placenta • progesterone
- puberty • testes
- testosterone • urethra
- uterus • vagina
- vas deferens

Before Writing

Prepare to Select and Organize Information

When you are researching a topic, not all the information that you read will be useful to you. Get in the habit of deciding what is truly important and what is not essential. As you think about issues related to human reproduction and technology, skim the sections of Chapter 3 and decide which information could be truly useful and which is just nice to know.

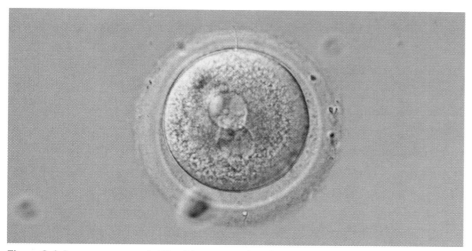

Figure 3.1 An ovum, or egg, fertilized by a sperm is called a zygote.

Puberty: The Beginning of Human Reproduction

From a biological point of view, human sexual reproduction exists to produce and then bring together the male and female gametes (Figure 3.1). Humans are usually born with the sex organs, or primary sex characteristics necessary for reproduction. These include the penis and testicles in males and the vagina, uterus, fallopian tubes, and ovaries in females. The physical appearance or physical genitalia, like many characteristics, show continuous variation. It is therefore biologically understandable, if uncommon, that some people are born with a combination of both male and female characteristics. An atypical combination of male and female physical features, including physical genitalia and chromosomes, is a condition known as an intersex state. Individuals with an intersex state are not necessarily hermaphrodites; they may not be able to produce both male and female gametes. An intersex state refers only to physical features and not to sexuality or gender. The topic of intersexuality is complex and for that reason, this chapter will discuss typical males and females.

Usually, we are born with the necessary male or female sex organs, but reproduction is impossible until our bodies receive instructions to start producing mature gametes. When are we physically able to reproduce? How do our bodies know that it is time to start producing mature gametes?

Here is a summary of what you will learn in this section:

- Humans are usually born with the necessary reproductive organs but are not yet able to reproduce.

- From a scientific perspective, puberty is the process of development and growth of the adult form, and sexual maturation, during which hormones direct the body to begin producing mature gametes.

- First Nations and Métis cultures view puberty as a transition from childhood to adolescence, which involves the physical, emotional, mental, and spiritual aspects of a person.

You have probably already heard the words that are used to answer these questions. From a scientific perspective, **puberty** is the period of growth and development of the final adult form and of sexual maturation. It is the time when hormones begin the changes that make our bodies produce mature gametes. Once our bodies are sexually mature, we are able to reproduce. **Hormones** are molecules that our bodies produce that give instructions to cells, "telling" them to respond in certain ways. You have probably all heard the words "puberty" and "hormones" before. Now you will learn how those words explain the changes in your body that allow you to mature into a reproductive adult.

In males, puberty usually begins between the ages of 13 and 16, whereas in females, puberty generally starts earlier. Menstruation, one of the last stages of puberty, usually begins about age 12–13. In both males and females, a very important hormone is called FSH, or **follicle-stimulating hormone**. FSH is produced in the brain and is circulated through the blood in the body. Its destination is the **gonads**, the reproductive organs that make gametes. In males, the gonads are the testes. In females, the gonads are the ovaries. Once FSH reaches the gonads, it signals the reproductive system to start performing its main job: producing sperm in males and producing mature eggs in females.

A21 *Quick Science*

What Do You Know About Puberty?

Purpose

To find out what you already know about puberty

Materials & Equipment
• recipe cards or thick paper   • markers

Procedure

1. On separate cards, write the terms "puberty," "hormones," and "human reproduction."

2. For each card, write down what you know in point form. Be sure to include what you know to be different in males and females.

3. With a partner, compare your cards and share what you know. Add any new information.

4. As you progress through the chapter, continue to add new information to each of the cards. You may wish to use additional cards for each category or create separate male and female categories.

Questions

5. Were you surprised by how much or how little you knew?

6. The ideas of puberty, hormones, and human reproduction are all connected. Give examples of each connection.

Pose New Questions

7. Suggest three questions about what you want to know about puberty or human reproduction.

©P

First Nations and Métis Perspectives on Puberty

The Elders from all First Nations and Métis peoples believe that the human body is sacred. Puberty, a normal part of human development, involves a careful balance of the physical, emotional, mental, and spiritual facets of a person.

In many First Nations and Métis cultures, girls learn from their mothers and grandmothers starting at a very early age. In some Plains Cree cultures, baby girls are often considered "little women" as they are born with the ability to give life. They are given adult names to reflect this belief. As a girl reaches adolescence, ceremonies such as the "walking out ceremony" of the Cree women welcome the girl to womanhood. Instruction is given through role modelling, stories, and direct talk. Elders and mothers teach their daughters to respect and honour themselves. The adolescent girl receives teachings on topics that are exclusive to a woman's life, such as menstruation and birth, from other women in the family and Elders in the community. Women Elders provide the adolescent girl with knowledge about her changing body. First Nations and Métis people who follow traditional values consider women "the life givers," not unlike Mother Earth.

The journey for boys into puberty often includes a ritual or a ceremony. It is a common belief among many First Nations and Métis peoples that a boy becomes a man later in life. Once the signs of puberty appear, such as a changing voice, boys undergo a ceremony. Among the Nakawē and the Cree, boys learn their roles and responsibilities through a Vision Quest ceremony that often lasts four days and four nights. During these ceremonies, boys suffer and survive hardships alone in the bush. At the end of the ceremony, boys become men and are given their name and given colours. From this time on, they are considered helpers and warriors.

Puberty, a transition from childhood to adulthood, can be expressed in southern and western quadrants of the sacred circle (Figure 3.2). During this time of change, Elders prepare young men and women for their roles and responsibilities.

During Writing

Making Notes

As you research, take notes in point form. Never copy word for word. Instead, choose key words, definitions, and any direct quotes that will support your writing purpose.

Suggested Activity • • • • • • • • • • •
A22 Quick Science on page 80

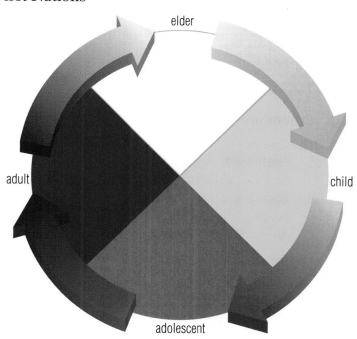

elder

adult

child

adolescent

Figure 3.2 The sacred circle called *Cankdeska wakan'* in Dakota is a visual way to represent the stages in life, seasons, and other patterns of Mother Earth.

1. What are primary sex characteristics?

2. Is an intersexed person the same as a hermaphrodite? Explain.

3. Give a brief explanation of what puberty is and the role of hormones in puberty.

4. What is follicle-stimulating hormone and where is it produced?

5. What are gonads? Name the male and female gonads.

6. Compare the scientific definition of puberty with the First Nations and Métis perspectives on puberty. What are some key differences?

7. In First Nations and Métis cultures, puberty is viewed differently for girls and boys. Identify some of the differences.

8. A holistic view of puberty includes more than just the physical aspect of maturation. How are the emotional, mental, and spiritual aspects of maturation important as people transition from childhood to adulthood?

A22 *Quick Science*

Puberty in Other Cultures

You have just learned about the changes that happen in boys' and girls' bodies as they enter the stage of their life known as puberty. In many cultures, the onset of puberty marks a special time in an adolescent's life. This special time is often celebrated with ceremonies, rituals, or traditions (Figure 3.3). Each culture has reasons for having girls and boys perform the rituals.

Purpose

To research puberty traditions in other cultures

Procedure

1. Choose a culture or religious group to research. Examples of cultures and groups that have traditions related to puberty include Africans, Brazilians, Jews, First Nations, Métis, and Inuit peoples, Muslims, Malaysians, Australian Aboriginals, and South Americans.

2. Decide whether you are researching the female rituals or the male rituals.

3. Use the Internet to find out what ceremonies, physical procedures, traditions, or rituals are performed in that culture.

4. Prepare a poster to summarize your findings. Present your findings to the class.

Questions

5. What traditions were most common among different cultures?

6. Were there any traditions or rituals that surprised you?

7. What is the purpose of having a cultural ritual for all adolescents?

Pose New Questions

8. Compare teenage society in Canada to the culture you researched. Are there any parallels to traditional rituals?

Figure 3.3 Bagisu youths perform a traditional song and dance during an initiation ceremony in Mbale, southeastern Uganda, August 6, 2010.

©P

Figure 3.4 Puberty is the period where young males begin to develop secondary male sex characteristics and appear more like adult males.

Puberty in Males

Once a male reaches puberty, the brain produces FSH, which travels to the gonads. In males, the gonads are the **testes** (singular: testis). Once FSH reaches the testes, the sperm-producing structures develop and other cells in the testes begin to produce another hormone called testosterone. **Testosterone** is the hormone that is responsible for developing the secondary male sex characteristics (Figure 3.4). Some secondary male sex characteristics are broader shoulders, a deeper voice, and growth of body hair such as facial, underarm, and pubic hair.

At puberty, males begin producing mature gametes, or sperm. Males can produce sperm throughout their life. Sperm have relatively short life spans. If sperm are not released, they die within a few days and are reabsorbed by the body. For this reason, new sperm are continuously produced. On average, a male can produce about 200 million sperm per day, even though only one sperm is needed to fertilize an egg.

What Do You Know About the Male Reproductive System? Part 1

Purpose

To create a matching game that can be used to help you remember the structures of the male reproductive system and their functions

Materials & Equipment

- recipe cards or thick paper
- markers

Procedure

1. Copy the name of each structure of the male reproductive system onto a separate card.

2. Copy the function of each structure of the male reproductive system onto a separate card.

3. Table 3.1 is incorrect. The structures and functions are scrambled. Without looking ahead in the text, do your best to match the structure and function of each part of the male reproductive system.

4. Copy down your answers with the heading "Matching: First Try." Keep these results to compare with your answers at the end of the unit.

Questions

5. How did you do in the matching game?

6. Were you surprised by how much or how little you knew?

Pose New Questions

7. Suggest a question about this game or about something you still want to know about the male reproductive system.

Table 3.1 A Mismatched Male Reproductive System

Structure	Function to Be Matched
Penis	Sac that protects the testes and helps to keep them cool
Urethra	A structure on top of the testis that stores sperm
Testis	Tubes where sperm travel from epididymis to the urethra
Scrotum	Tube to the outside of the body that expels urine and semen
Epididymis	Helps produce seminal fluid that combines with sperm to make semen
Vas deferens	Gland made up of seminiferous tubules and epididymis
Seminiferous tubules	Organ that delivers sperm during reproduction
Prostate gland	Tiny tubes that produce sperm

During Writing

Organizing for Writing

Once your research is complete, begin to organize your notes. Create headings for major subtopics, and gather your notes under each heading.

Male Reproductive Anatomy

Once sperm production begins during puberty, it usually continues throughout a male's entire life. Figure 3.5 shows the male reproductive system. Refer to Figure 3.5 as you read through this section to help you visualize the path of the sperm.

The testes are the sperm-producing glands. They are located in a sac called the **scrotum**. This sac is located outside of the body to keep the testes cool, which allows for better sperm production. The scrotum also protects the testes.

The testes are made up of **seminiferous tubules**. Cells within the seminiferous tubules divide by mitosis to produce diploid cells. These cells may divide over and over again by mitosis or they may progress into meiosis to produce haploid immature sperm. The sperm then move to a structure above each testis called the **epididymis** to finish maturing. In humans, it takes approximately 70 days for sperm to mature. The epididymis stores the sperm cells until it is time for them to leave the body.

The organ that delivers the sperm to the female during reproduction is the **penis**. How do the sperm travel from the epididymis to the penis?

From the epididymis, the sperm travel through the **vas deferens** up and around the bladder. Three accessory male glands—the seminal vesicle, the **prostate gland**, and the bulbourethral gland—produce a thick, milky fluid called seminal fluid. The seminal fluid combines with the sperm to make semen. One drop of semen can contain as many as 5 million sperm cells.

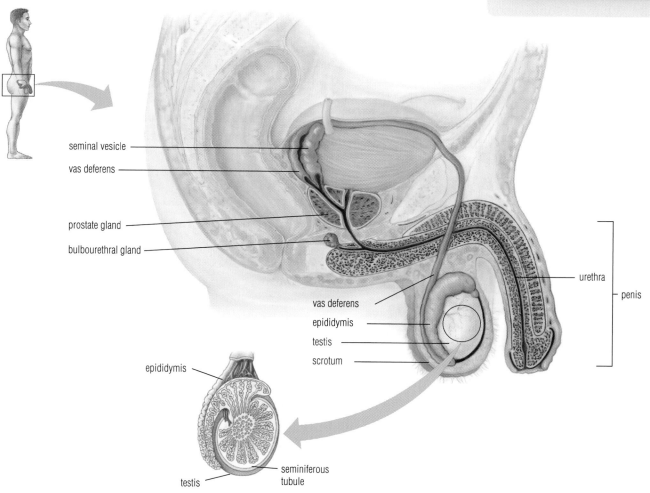

Figure 3.5 The male reproductive system

The vas deferens join with the **urethra**, which is the tube that carries urine from the bladder, through the penis, to the outside of the body. The urethra has two functions: to carry urine out of the body and to carry semen out of the body. A structure in the bladder functions as a valve to prevent urine and semen from being in the urethra at the same time.

The process by which semen leaves the body of the male is called ejaculation. During ejaculation, the sperm leave the epididymis and travel through the vas deferens to the urethra in the penis. Muscle contractions force the semen out of the penis.

Suggested Activity •··············
A24 Quick Science on page 84

3.2 CHECK and REFLECT

1. What is the main function of the male reproductive system?

2. How does puberty prepare males for reproduction?

3. What are some secondary male sex characteristics?

4. Using what you know about meiosis, describe the process of sperm production.

5. Briefly describe the path of sperm cells, from development to ejaculation.

6. Create a summary of all words in bold type in this section. Include definitions, locations in the body, descriptions of the structure, and explanations of the functions, wherever possible. You may wish to organize this information in a table or in a graphic organizer.

7. What are the advantages for both males and females to learn about the male reproductive system?

8. Explain how damage to the testicles might affect sperm production.

A24 Quick Science

What Do You Know About the Male Reproductive System? Part 2

Purpose

To review the structure and function of the male reproductive system

---
Materials & Equipment
- matching cards from A23 Quick Science

Procedure

1. Using the cards you made in Activity A23, match the structures with their functions.

2. Use the cards to play a game with a partner. You must correctly match a structure with a function in order to get a point.

Questions

3. Which structures of the male reproductive system were you familiar with?

4. Which structures of the male reproductive system were new to you?

Pose New Questions

5. Link the function of each structure in the male reproductive system to the production of healthy male gametes or to successful reproduction.

Here is a summary of what you will learn in this section:

- The main functions of the female reproductive system are to produce eggs for reproduction and to provide a safe place for fertilization and offspring development.
- Estrogen is an important hormone in the functioning of the female reproductive system.
- Each structure in the female reproductive system has an important function.
- The release of eggs occurs in a cycle.

Figure 3.6 Puberty is the period where young females begin to develop secondary sex characteristics that make them appear more like adult females.

Puberty in Human Females

Puberty in females begins the same way that it does in males: FSH, follicle-stimulating hormone, travels from the brain to the gonads. In females, the gonads are called **ovaries**, and they are located inside the body. The main function of the ovaries is to produce eggs. Ovaries also produce two main hormones called **estrogen** and **progesterone**.

Once hormones are released in their bodies, females begin to develop secondary female sex characteristics (Figure 3.6). Some secondary female sex characteristics are the growth of underarm and pubic hair, as well as the appearance of fat deposits in breasts and hips.

At puberty, females begin producing mature eggs. Before a female baby is born, her ovary cells begin meiosis, which will produce haploid cells. However, cell division is stopped midway and the immature eggs remain in a state of suspended meiosis. At the time of birth, a female has all her eggs; no new egg cells will be produced. A human female has approximately 1–2 million egg cells at birth, but most will die. Only about 400 000 eggs remain by the time a female reaches puberty.

What Do You Know About the Female Reproductive System? Part 1

Purpose

To create a matching game that can be used to help you remember the structures of the female reproductive system and their functions

Materials & Equipment

- recipe cards or thick paper
- markers

Procedure

1. Copy the name of each structure of the female reproductive system onto a separate card.

2. Copy the function of each structure of the female reproductive system onto a separate card.

3. Table 3.2 is incorrect. The structures and functions are scrambled. Without looking ahead in the text, do your best to match the structure and function of each part of the female reproductive system.

4. Copy down your answers with the heading "Matching: First Try." Keep these results to compare with your answers at the end of the unit.

Questions

5. How did you do in the matching game?

6. Were you surprised by how much or how little you knew?

Pose New Questions

7. Suggest a question about this game or about something you still want to know about the female reproductive system.

Table 3.2 A Mismatched Female Reproductive System

Structure	Function to Be Matched
Vagina	A muscular tube that acts as the birth canal
Urethra	A hollow, muscular organ where a fetus develops
Ovary	Fluid-filled sac in the ovary that stores egg cells held at second division of meiosis
Uterus	Tube to the outside of the body that expels urine
Fallopian tube (oviduct)	Gland that stores and releases eggs and produces estrogen and progesterone
Cervix	The structure that connects the vagina and the uterus
Follicle	Tube that guides an egg from the ovary to the uterus

Female Reproductive Anatomy

Once a female reaches puberty, the eggs resume meiosis and begin to mature. Each egg is surrounded by a special structure in the ovary called a follicle (Figure 3.7). The follicle nourishes, protects, and supports the development of the egg until it matures and is released in a process called **ovulation**. At ovulation, the follicle ruptures and the mature egg is released. Usually, one egg is released approximately every 28 days.

After an egg matures and is released from its follicle, the remaining, empty follicle then turns into the **corpus luteum**. The main function of the corpus luteum is to produce the hormone progesterone. You will learn more about the function of hormones later in this section.

Refer to Figure 3.7 as you read the following section to help you visualize the path of the egg. Once the egg is released, the finger-like projections at the end of the **fallopian tube** or oviduct sweep the egg up and into the tube. Once in the fallopian tube, the egg is kept moving toward the uterus by tiny hair-like structures within the tube. Unless an egg is fertilized by a sperm cell, the egg will die after 24 to 48 hours. If the egg is not fertilized and dies, it will disintegrate and eventually leave the body.

The **uterus** is a hollow, pear-shaped organ and has muscular walls to protect a developing baby. At the bottom of the uterus is the cervix. The **cervix** connects the uterus to the vagina. The **vagina** is a long, muscular tube that leads to the outside of the body. It is also called the birth canal, since the baby leaves the uterus through the vagina. The urethra carries urine from the bladder, which holds the urine. In females, the urethra has only this one job and it is not part of the reproductive system. The urethra does not meet up with any other tubes or ducts, so it has a separate exit from the body.

Suggested Activities •·········
A26 Quick Science on page 91
A27 Quick Science on page 91

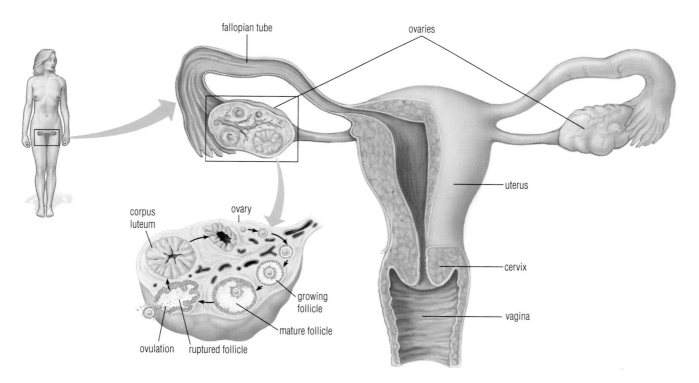

Figure 3.7 The female reproductive system. The ovary stores eggs that are at different stages of development.

The Menstrual Cycle

The release of an egg each month is only part of the monthly cycle called the **menstrual cycle**. Unlike in males, where gamete and hormone production are continuous, the production of gametes and hormones in females is a precisely timed sequence of events. The entire cycle takes about 28 days.

The menstrual cycle continues unless an egg has been fertilized. In the menstrual cycle, the hormones in the brain signal the ovaries, which in turn signal the uterus. Scientists call this type of communication within the body **feedback**. Positive feedback is communication in the body where the response to a change works in the direction of that change, whereas negative feedback is communication in the body where the response to a change works against that change and brings the body back to its previous state.

The menstrual cycle is a complicated process that involves four main hormones: follicle-stimulating hormone (FSH), luteinizing hormone (LH), estrogen, and progesterone. The following steps occur in the menstrual cycle:

- The brain releases FSH into the bloodstream.
- FSH reaches the ovary and signals it to begin developing the follicles. Many follicles begin growing, although only one will mature while the others disintegrate.
- The developing follicles produce estrogen and release it into the bloodstream.
- Estrogen reaches the uterus and the brain. The lining of the uterus begins to thicken. The lining is called the **endometrium**. The brain produces and releases LH into the bloodstream.
- LH reaches the ovary and causes the mature follicle to release an egg (ovulation).
- Once the egg is released, LH signals the empty follicle to develop into the corpus luteum.
- The corpus luteum produces progesterone and some estrogen and releases it into the bloodstream. The corpus luteum continues to produce progesterone and estrogen for about two weeks until it disintegrates.
- Progesterone reaches the uterus and the brain. The uterus continues to thicken the endometrium even more. The brain stops producing FSH and LH to prevent another egg from being released until the progesterone levels decrease again.

©P

Once the corpus luteum begins to disintegrate, the progesterone level in the body decreases. This signals the thick endometrium to break down and be shed from the body, along with the dead, unfertilized egg in a process called **menstruation**. Menstruation usually lasts four to seven days.

After menstruation, the progesterone level in the body reaches a certain low level, which "tells" the brain to begin releasing FSH again. Figure 3.8 shows the changes in the hormone levels, endometrium, egg, and corpus luteum during a menstrual cycle. Refer to Figure 3.7 for the stages of the egg and the corpus luteum within the ovary.

Suggested Activity •·············
A28 Inquiry Activity on page 92

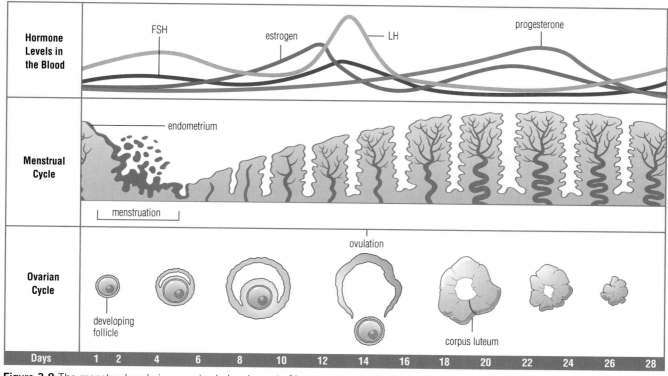

Figure 3.8 The menstrual cycle is a precise balancing act of hormones communicating with the body.

The four hormones, FSH, LH, estrogen, and progesterone, are involved in both positive and negative feedback in the female reproductive system (Figure 3.9). Follicle-stimulating hormone (FSH) and luteinizing hormone (LH) are both produced in the brain, and estrogen and progesterone are both produced in the ovaries.

The menstrual cycle starts during puberty, although often it takes years to establish a regular cycle. The cycle is interrupted if a pregnancy occurs and may not resume during lactation. Once the menstrual cycle resumes it continues until menopause. Menopause, which usually occurs between the ages of 45 and 54, involves a decrease in the production of estrogen by the ovaries, and the stoppage of the release of eggs by the ovaries.

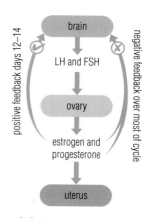

Figure 3.9 A summary of positive and negative feedback in the female reproductive system

During Writing

Analyzing and Evaluating Information

Once you have gathered facts, figures, and details necessary to help you make a judgement or express an opinion, analyze their importance, depth, and relevance to your topic. Organize the information from the most significant to the least, then figure out how everything fits together to help you evaluate or judge the impact of a situation.

First Nations and Métis cultures (in common with other cultures such as the Chinese, the ancient Egyptians, the Picts, and the Celts) call menstruation "moon time" or "moon cycle" because they have observed that a menstrual cycle, similar to a lunar cycle, occurs in 28 days. A woman's moon time is a very sacred and special time. Ceremonies exist where women Elders and grandmothers can address questions that young women might have. The Dené have a sacred ceremony, called the strawberry ceremony, for a young woman's first menstrual cycle. During this ceremony, female role models from the community, including Elders, are chosen by the mother of a young woman to sit together and share wisdom with the young woman.

Special protocols are followed during a woman's menstruation. Often, a woman refrains from certain ceremonies as her life-giving powers during her moon time can disrupt the balance of the ceremony. Also, different smudging ceremonies exist when women are menstruating.

3.3 CHECK and REFLECT

1. Name two functions of the ovaries.

2. Describe the functions of the follicle.

3. Describe what happens to an egg from the time it is released from the ovary to the time it leaves the body, if it has not been fertilized.

4. What is the difference between negative and positive feedback?

5. How are positive and negative feedback used in the menstrual cycle?

6. A friend says that the blood that appears during menstruation is blood that comes from your veins and arteries. Is your friend correct? Explain.

7. What is menopause and when does it occur? How does it affect a woman's ability to reproduce?

8. List, in order, the events that occur in the menstrual cycle. Be sure to include the hormones involved and explain what they do.

9. Why do First Nations and Métis peoples refer to menstruation as "moon time"?

10. Describe some of the First Nations and Métis traditions and practices surrounding menstruation.

11. Create a summary of all words in bold type in this section. Include definitions, locations in the body, descriptions of the structure, and explanations of the functions, wherever possible. You may wish to organize this information in a table or in a graphic organizer such as a concept map.

12. Why is it important for both males and females to learn about the female reproductive cycle?

©P

What Do You Know About the Female Reproductive System? Part 2

Purpose

To review the structure and function of the parts of the female reproductive system

Materials & Equipment

- matching cards from A25 Quick Science

Procedure

1. Using the cards you made in Activity A25, see if you can match the structures with their correct functions.

2. Set up the cards to play a game of memory with a partner. You must correctly match a structure with a function in order to get a point.

Questions

3. Which structures of the female reproductive system were you familiar with?

4. Which structures of the female reproductive system were new to you?

Pose New Questions

5. Link the function of each structure in the female reproductive system to the production of healthy female gametes or to successful reproduction.

How Many Eggs?

Females only release eggs once they reach puberty, and ovulation ends once they reach menopause.

Purpose

To calculate approximately how many eggs a female releases in her reproductive lifetime

Procedure

1. Assume a female begins to ovulate on her 13th birthday, and continues to ovulate every 28 days until her 52nd birthday.

2. Using 365 days per year, and 28 days per menstrual cycle, calculate the approximate number of eggs that will be released during this female's lifetime.

Questions

3. Were you surprised by the number of eggs released in a lifetime?

4. By the time a female reaches puberty, she has approximately 400 000 eggs. Using your answer from step 2, calculate the percentage of eggs that mature and are released.

5. Provide a possible explanation for the difference that exists between the number of available eggs and the number of released eggs.

Pose New Questions

6. Suggest a question about the female reproductive cycle that you would still like answered.

DI **Key Activity**

A28 *Inquiry Activity*

Toolkit 2

SKILLS YOU WILL USE
- Analyzing patterns
- Drawing conclusions

Female Reproductive Hormone Cycles

Initiating and Planning

How do hormone levels control the processes of ovulation and menstruation?

Read through the activity very carefully. Predict how each of the hormones affects the processes of ovulation and menstruation. Construct a hypothesis that explains your predictions.

Performing and Recording

1. Examine Figure 3.10, which shows the changing levels of FSH, LH, estrogen, and progesterone in a typical menstrual cycle. Predict when ovulation occurs, in relation to hormone levels.

2. Predict when menstruation begins, in relation to hormone levels.

3. Construct a data table to show the relative concentration of each hormone on each day of the cycle. Use the numbers from 0–60 on the left-hand side of the graph.

4. Use the data to locate the largest increase and decrease of each hormone within the cycle.

Analyzing and Interpreting

5. What is the largest increase of LH? When does this increase occur?

6. Based on this large increase of LH, when would you expect ovulation to occur? Does the data in your table support or contradict the prediction you made in step 1?

7. What are the largest decreases of estrogen and progesterone? When do they occur?

8. Based on the decrease of estrogen and progesterone, when would you expect menstruation to begin? Does the data in your table support or contradict the prediction you made in step 2?

Communication and Teamwork

9. Write a conclusion about the four hormones discussed in this activity and how they relate to ovulation and menstruation.

10. Did you work with a partner in this activity? If so, how did discussing the graph help you? If not, what were the positive and negative aspects to working alone in this activity?

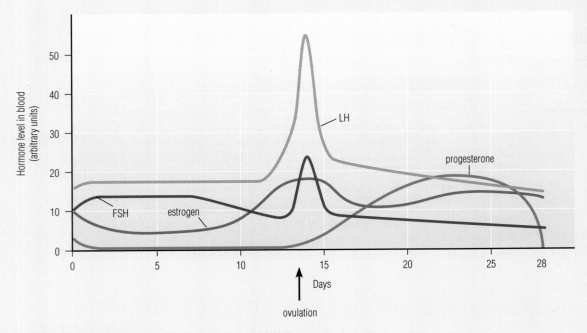

Figure 3.10 Varying levels of different hormones during the menstrual cycle

©P

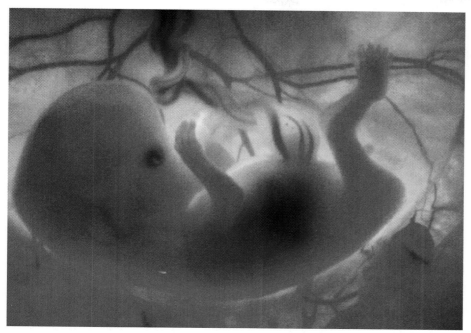

Figure 3.11 Human development, seen here at the 11-weeks stage of pregnancy, begins in a tiny human egg cell.

Fertilization of the Egg

In the last section, you learned what happens to an egg if it is not fertilized. What happens if it is fertilized? How does the body know when an egg has been fertilized? Menstruation does not proceed as usual, but hormones continue to play a major role in regulating the processes in a female's body, even when an egg becomes fertilized.

For an egg to be fertilized by sperm, sperm from a male has to be deposited into the vagina of a female during sexual intercourse. Once sperm cells enter a woman's body, they are propelled by their flagella, or tails, and by the contractions of the female reproductive organs. From the vagina, sperm move through the cervix, into the uterus, and then into the fallopian tubes, attracted by compounds released by the egg. Although hundreds of millions of sperm are released into the vagina, most will die while searching for the egg.

Fertilization begins when a haploid egg is joined by a haploid sperm to become a diploid zygote, just as you learned in Chapter 1. The structure of the egg helps to develop the baby (Figure 3.11). Although human egg cells are about the size of the tip of a pin, they contain many of the necessary structures that allow for healthy human development.

Here is a summary of what you will learn in this section:

- The development of an individual human being begins when an egg cell is fertilized by a sperm cell.

- Females show physical signs of pregnancy once an egg has been fertilized.

- A human baby requires approximately nine months or forty weeks in the mother's uterus in order to develop fully.

---

*info***BIT**

Twinning and Multiple Embryos

Multiple embryos are a normal, if unusual, happening in human development.

If a zygote divides by mitosis but the cells separate completely at cytokinesis, each cell may go on to develop into an embryo. These two embryos would be monozygotic twins, having identical genetic material. If complete cell separation occurs a second time, triplets or even quadruplets may be the result.

If more than one follicle matures at any time, more than one egg may be released at ovulation. If two eggs are released and fertilized, the result will be fraternal twins.

Egg Structure

Purpose

To examine the structure of a chicken egg in order to compare it with the structure of a human egg

Materials & Equipment

- one raw chicken egg
- bowl or shallow dish
- water
- tweezers or dissecting probe

Procedure

1. Examine the shell of the egg. Record your observations and predict the function of the shell.

2. Fill the bowl or dish with water approximately halfway.

3. Carefully crack the egg into the bowl or dish. Try to keep the shell intact as much as possible. Try not to break the yolk. Touch as little of the inside of the egg as possible.

4. Using Figure 3.12 as a guide, locate all of the named structures on the egg in the bowl.

5. Create a table to keep track of the functions of each of the structures of the egg.

6. With a partner, make predictions about what the function of each structure might be.

7. Use library or Internet resources to research whether your predictions were correct. Make sure to include any corrections in your table.

Questions

8. How close were your predictions to the actual functions of each of the egg structures?

9. Compare the yolk to a human egg cell. How are they similar? How are they different?

Pose New Questions

10. Attempt to relate the differences between chicken eggs and human eggs to the differences between chicken and human development.

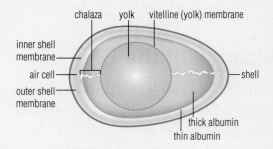

Figure 3.12 The structure of a chicken egg

After Fertilization

Scientists define fertilization or conception as the moment the ovum and the sperm join together. When a human life begins is a subject for debate. While different people may have differing views about the start of human life, for traditional knowledge keepers and Elders of various First Nations and Métis peoples, life begins at conception. This view is based on several key values. The first guiding value is that Creator gave Spirit to all living things and thus all life is sacred. Life, a gift from Creator, therefore deserves respect.

From a scientific perspective, fertilization or conception occurs when a sperm cell reaches an egg cell in the fallopian tube and penetrates the outer egg membrane (Figure 3.13). At this moment, fertilization or conception will have taken place. Once this happens, the surface of the egg becomes impermeable to any other sperm cells.

Once the egg has been fertilized, it continues through the fallopian tube toward the uterus (Figure 3.14). Approximately 24 hours after fertilization, the zygote begins the process of cleavage, a special form of mitotic cell division. Once the developing embryo reaches the uterus, it will have undergone numerous cleavages to form a hollow ball of cells called a **blastocyst**.

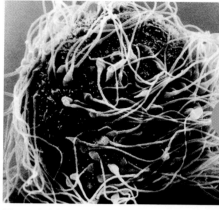

Figure 3.13 The human egg may be surrounded by hundreds of sperm, but only one will fertilize the egg.

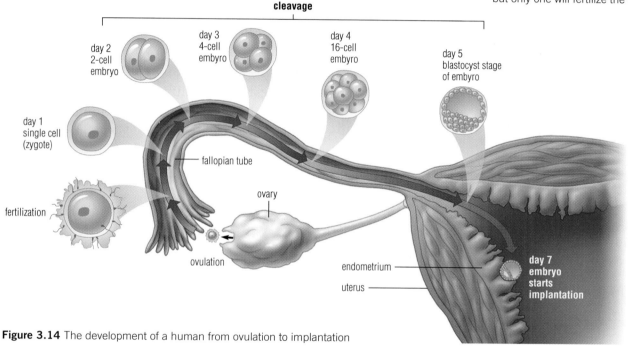

Figure 3.14 The development of a human from ovulation to implantation

The blastocyst stage of the embryo contains an inner mass of cells that give rise to the embyro proper, or early form of the baby. The cells of the outer layer of the blastocyst divide to form two different tissues: the amnion and the chorion. The amnion forms the amniotic sac, which is a fluid-filled sac that protects and cushions the developing embryo. It allows the embryo to move freely without being constricted by the uterus. The chorion helps form the placenta (Figure 3.15).

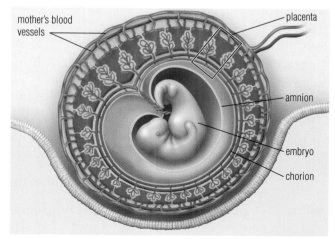

Figure 3.15 The embryo is suspended in the amnion. The chorion and the endometrium form the placenta.

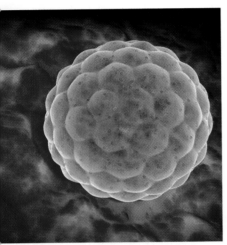

Figure 3.16 A blastocyst implanting itself into the endometrium

The **placenta** is the organ that connects the developing embryo to the wall of the uterus. It allows the exchange of nutrients, oxygen, and carbon dioxide between the mother and the embryo. The placenta contains blood vessels from both the mother and the developing embryo. The embryo is connected to the placenta by the umbilical cord. The blood of the mother and the embryo do not mix freely, because the placenta does the job of taking in nutrients, eliminating wastes, and exchanging gases between them.

Implantation

Once the blastocyst reaches the uterus, it attaches itself into the endometrium that lines the uterus in a process called **implantation** (Figure 3.16). Once implantation has taken place, hormonal changes prevent the corpus luteum from breaking down in the ovary. Because the corpus luteum does not break down until approximately 16 weeks of pregnancy, progesterone continues to be produced and the endometrium is not shed. The vastly altered endometrium remains in the uterus, providing nutrients to the developing embryo and helping to form the placenta. At 10–12 weeks, the placenta begins to take over the role of maintaining the pregnancy.

Signs of Pregnancy

Once the hormonal changes begin to occur at the start of pregnancy, there are many signs and symptoms that a female might notice as her body prepares for major changes. Some of the signs and symptoms are

- a missed menstrual period
- nausea or vomiting
- breast soreness or tenderness
- breast enlargement
- a feeling of being more tired than normal
- craving different foods or disliking foods that once were enjoyed
- a metal-like taste in the mouth
- mood swings or irritability

Every pregnancy is different and not all symptoms may be present, or there may be different symptoms. Often, a diagnosis from a medical professional is necessary to confirm pregnancy.

The Fetus

Once the developing embryo has been implanted for approximately eight or nine weeks, it is referred to as a **fetus**. Remember that the developing fetus started with the fusion of two cells, an egg and a sperm, and will eventually undergo enough mitotic divisions to produce a baby that is sufficiently developed to leave the body of the mother and enter the world. The time it takes for the zygote to become an embryo, then a fetus, and finally, a fully developed baby is approximately nine months. Many cell divisions take place in that nine-month period, and the fetus grows quite quickly (Figure 3.17).

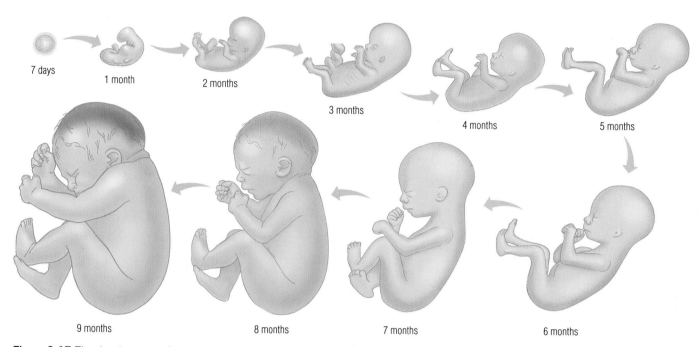

Figure 3.17 The development of the organs and tissues of the growing baby occur at distinct time periods during pregnancy.

Birth

Once the fetus has developed for nine months, it is ready to leave the support and safety of the mother's uterus and enter the outside world.

It is not known precisely what begins the process of birth. The release of a hormone called **oxytocin** makes the uterus contract rhythmically. These contractions may cause the amniotic sac to burst or the sac may burst before contractions begin. The amniotic fluid is released from the body. This is commonly known as the water breaking.

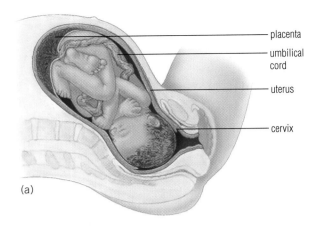

(a)

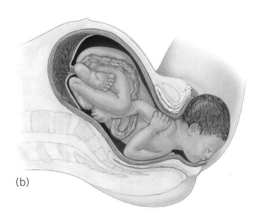

(b)

placenta
umbilical cord
uterus
cervix

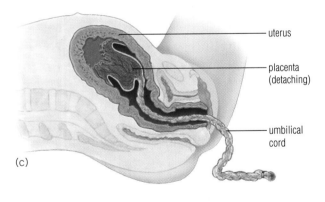

(c)

uterus
placenta (detaching)
umbilical cord

Figure 3.18 The three stages of birth include (a) the dilation of the cervix, (b) the delivery of the baby, and (c) the delivery of the placenta.

Suggested Activity • • • • • • • • • • •
A30 Quick Science on page 99

In a typical birth, commonly called labour, the cervix widens or dilates to approximately 10 cm over the course of several hours (Figure 3.18(a)). This dilation allows the baby to move from the uterus, through the cervix, and into the birth canal, or vagina (Figure 3.18(b)). Once the baby is able to pass through the cervix, it comes out of the vagina. The head is born first, usually face down. After the head is born, the baby rotates so that he or she is facing sideways. This allows the shoulders to be born more easily. As soon as the shoulders are free, the rest of the body is born quite quickly. At birth, the baby is able to breathe and function on its own, so the umbilical cord can be cut, thus severing the baby's connection to the placenta and the mother. Approximately 15 minutes after the birth of the baby, the placenta detaches itself from the wall of the uterus and passes out of the body through the vagina (Figure 3.18(c)).

Complications that prevent a vaginal birth can mean that the baby must be delivered by Caesarean section, or C-section. In a C-section, the baby must be taken out of the mother's body by cutting open the abdominal wall and removing the baby from the uterus. For example, the baby usually positions itself upside down in the uterus by the time of birth so that it can leave head first through the cervix and vagina. When the baby does not turn itself upside down, the baby is said to be in breech position, meaning that it is positioned to come out buttocks or feet first. Some babies in breech position or other babies in life-threatening situations have to be delivered by Caesarean section.

First Nations and Métis Perspectives on Birth

First Nations and Métis people have different beliefs around reproduction and birth. In traditional times, women were the centre of communities because they were considered the life givers and teachers of culture and languages.

Elders often teach that all people, regardless of cultural heritage, hear the first drumbeat deep within the woman's being, which lays the foundation of how we are to live out our lives in rhythm with the natural world. There are different methods of birthing depending on the culture and there are also traditional midwives who have vast knowledge of women's physiology, including which plants and herbs to use to help ease the pain associated with birth. In the past, First Nations and Métis women gave birth standing up. This type of birthing was considered more natural and easier for both the woman and the child.

Different ceremonies are performed before and after the birth. Naming ceremonies, for example, are common with terms, words, phrases, and analogies linked to the natural world.

During Writing

Expressing an Opinion

When you have researched and carefully chosen your information for writing, you will be ready to express an informed opinion. Think about the topic and the direction that your research has indicated. Form a statement by combining the topic with your informed point of view. Organize your evidence to support your statement.

3.4 CHECK and REFLECT

1. What is fertilization? Where in the body does fertilization occur?

2. The functions of the structures of the chicken egg are closely related to those involved in human pregnancy. What structure in the chicken egg has the same function as the amniotic fluid during pregnancy?

3. What structures form the placenta? What is the function of the placenta?

4. At what point does pregnancy begin?

5. What happens during implantation?

6. Why is a missed menstrual period a common sign of pregnancy?

7. Explain the difference between an embryo and a fetus.

8. Describe what happens during birth. How does it begin? How does it end?

9. How do your ideas about birth compare with the traditional ideas of some First Nations and Métis people described in this section?

A30 Quick Science

Promoting Healthy Pregnancies

There are many things that a pregnant female can do to ensure the healthy growth and development of her baby.

Purpose

To create a poster or brochure that provides information about how to have a healthy pregnancy

Procedure

1. Research guidelines for women to follow while pregnant. Make sure to include reasons for ensuring each guideline is followed.

2. Prepare a poster or brochure that conveys all of the information you found.

Question

3. Which of the guidelines for healthy pregnancies did you already know about before beginning your research? Which were new to you?

Pose New Questions

4. Suggest a new way to make information about the importance of a healthy pregnancy available to young people in Canadian society.

Dawn McGowan: Neonatal Nurse

Dawn McGowan, a Métis woman of Saulteaux (Nakawē) and Swedish descent, is a nurse who practises neonatal medicine in the city of North Battleford. Dawn has been a nurse for 31 years. For the first 20 years of her career, she worked as a licensed practical nurse in the field of maternity in Whitehorse, Yukon Territory. Then, after four years of additional training in the Nursing program at the University of Saskatchewan, she earned her nursing degree, graduating with Distinction. She worked at the Royal University Hospital in Saskatoon in Neonatal Intensive Care. Dawn now works as a registered nurse in the neonatal unit at the Women's Health unit, which includes newborns, at Battleford's Union Hospital.

As a neonatal nurse, Dawn assists with the delivery of premature babies and cares for them in the early weeks of life. These premature babies, often born at only 24 weeks, have many complications such as infections. They may require intubation to breathe and extensive attention until they are old enough and strong enough to leave the hospital at 40 weeks. "The smallest baby I ever cared for weighed no more than one pound," Dawn said proudly. "Life, no matter how small, has meaning." (Figure 3.19)

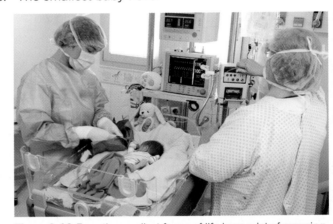

In addition to her duties as a neonatal nurse, Dawn serves on a medical team that performs emergency transport of sick babies, either by plane or by ambulance. She is the person responsible for resuscitation procedures and life support, if needed by the patient. The range of this specialized team extends from as far north as La Ronge down to the southwestern corner of Saskatchewan near Swift Current.

Figure 3.19 Even the smallest forms of life have a lot of meaning.

Q: Who inspired you to become a nurse?

A: I don't remember wanting to be anything but a nurse. My mother had a drive to care for other people. Her caring ways inspired me.

Q: What challenges do you face as a neonatal nurse?

A: Sometimes, rarely, we lose a baby, but you have to see the positive side even in tragedy. The resilience we need must outweigh the grief we feel. To be a nurse means that you have to have a different kind of belief system, a kind of strength and caring that allows you to continue to advocate and to care for people despite the tragedies.

Figure 3.20 Technology has drastically changed the way we live.

Here is a summary of what you will learn in this section:

- There are many methods of contraception that prevent pregnancy from occurring.
- Infertility can sometimes be treated using science and technological advances.
- In various different ways, society affects how science and technology proceed.
- Scientific and technological advances can be controversial because of the different social and cultural beliefs that exist in society.

Technology and Reproduction

It is often said that in today's society, people want what they cannot have. Tall people want to be short, short people want to be tall, people with curly hair would rather have straight hair, and rarely are people happy with their bodies. Another way that society has changed is that we want everything as fast as possible. Have you ever had to deal with a slow Internet connection or a long lineup at a store? Many people become extremely frustrated with having to wait for anything. Science and technology work together to alleviate some of these problems. Through science, we develop knowledge that helps us understand and explain why these problems occur. Technology is the development of solutions to these problems.

Imagine a time without cellphones, or Internet, or even television (Figure 3.20). How long do you think it took for information to get where it needed to go? What would you do without those three major technological advances? How would your life be different?

Science and technology also work to help overcome health problems. For example, we have medications to relieve pain and cure illnesses, and we have procedures that can be done to improve a bodily ailment. The same is true for reproduction. Science and technology have really affected what is possible in this area.

Am I Affected by Technology?

Science and technology are linked, but what is the difference between them? Science has been defined as the development of knowledge. Science helps us to explain and interpret the world around us. Technology has been defined as the application of knowledge. Technology strives to solve problems and achieve a goal. Science and technology are unquestionably related.

Purpose

To begin to understand what technology is and how it is used in our society

Procedure

1. Classify each item in the list below as either "Science" or "Technology."
   - airplane
   - theory of evolution
   - MP3 player
   - study of movement of snakes
   - vaccines
   - DNA paternity testing
   - discovery of a new species of insect
   - exploration of the Moon
   - automated bank machines

2. Brainstorm a list of different technologies used in the home, a list of technologies used at school, and a list of technologies used in the health-care field.

3. Even though technology has many benefits, including making our lives easier in some ways, there are often drawbacks or issues that arise with the use of new technology. Choose one of the examples of technology that you brainstormed in step 2. For the example you have chosen, make a list of the benefits of this technology, a list of negative aspects or issues regarding this technology, and a list of possible solutions to the negative aspects or issues involved with this technology.

Questions

4. How is your life directly affected by technology?

5. How does technology affect science?

Pose New Questions

6. Research an example in which a technology developed from a scientific discovery and another where the technology developed ahead of the scientific theory.

Social and Cultural Perspectives

Many First Nations and Métis peoples view the topic of human reproduction from a holistic perspective. Just as good health is seen as a balance among the physical, mental, emotional, and spiritual dimensions of a person, many First Nations and Métis people understand procreation as having physical, mental, emotional, and spiritual dimensions. The physical dimension, for example, includes the strength and health of the parents to care for the family. The spiritual dimension is the sacredness of life at the time of conception. A balance among the four dimensions of procreation is achieved by commitment and obligation to the baby, the sacred gift of Creator, and to the family and community.

An analytical perspective focuses only on certain aspects of the physical dimension. The analytical view does not consider commitment and obligation, but searches for technological ways to control or manipulate the process of reproduction. A holistic understanding searches for ways to live harmoniously with the natural consequences of procreation, rather than interfere with the sacredness of procreation by using reproductive technologies.

Many issues surround the use of contraceptive and reproductive technologies. On the issue of contraception, most traditional First Nations and Métis Elders are opposed. Among the Dakota people, for example, it is believed that one should never prevent pregnancy or end it, because all life is sacred. There is a strong cultural belief that the prevention of a pregnancy would bring a harsh consequence.

All cultures and religions have moral and ethical beliefs surrounding reproduction and contraception. There are also different beliefs about when exactly a fertilized egg is considered to be a person (Figure 3.21). For this reason, some methods of contraception are considered to be the ending of a human life. There are also very strong opinions and beliefs about what is considered to be acceptable in terms of reproductive technology. It is important to know that just because contraception and reproductive technologies are available, they are not intended to infringe upon the rights of all members of society. People can make their own decisions about what is acceptable and what is not, based upon their cultural and moral beliefs.

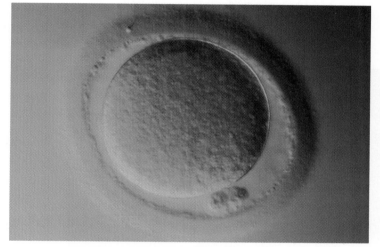

Figure 3.21 Is a fertilized egg considered to be a person? Many moral and ethical issues surround contraceptive and reproductive technologies.

Suggested Activity •············
A32 Science, Technology, Society, and the Environment on page 109

Contraception

For many different reasons, some couples intentionally try to prevent pregnancy. This is known as **contraception** or birth control. There are many forms of contraception, and each form is an example of how technology works with science to change the outcome of an event. Without contraception, the chance of pregnancy is usually quite high. Different forms of contraception have different rates of efficiency. No form of contraception can guarantee to prevent pregnancy. Abstinence, or not having sex, is the only 100 percent effective way to avoid pregnancy.

Condoms

There are two main types of condoms, one worn by males, and one worn by females (Figure 3.22). The most common type of condom is the male condom. It is made of latex and it fits over the penis to catch any secretions, including semen. This prevents any semen from entering the vagina of the female, and therefore prevents sperm cells from reaching an egg cell. The female condom works in much the same way. It is a bag-shaped device made of a soft plastic that fits inside the vagina to catch any semen that is ejaculated from the male. Another barrier-type contraceptive is the diaphragm, which is inserted into the vagina and fits over the cervix.

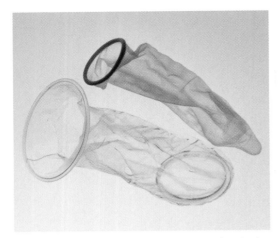

Figure 3.22 The male and the female condom both work by preventing semen from entering the vagina and reaching an egg cell.

Oral Contraceptive Pill

The oral contraceptive pill is commonly referred to as the birth control pill (Figure 3.23). The pill contains a combination of estrogen and progesterone, which works to suppress the normal ovarian production of these hormones and so prevents ovulation and keeps the endometrium from thickening. One oral contraceptive pill a day provides enough hormones to trick the body into not releasing an egg. The pill is taken for 21 consecutive days each month. Menstruation occurs during the remaining seven days of the cycle.

In addition to preventing ovulation, oral contraceptive pills may be taken to regulate menstruation and hormone levels.

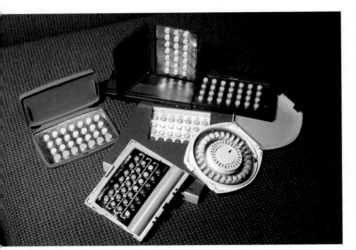

Figure 3.23 There are numerous different brands of oral contraceptives, each with different combinations of estrogen and progesterone.

Contraceptive Injections

Contraceptive injections contain a form of progesterone called progestin, that is injected into a muscle (Figure 3.24). In a way similar to oral contraceptive pills, the hormone injection prevents ovulation. It also thins the endometrium, which prevents implantation if, for some reason, an egg were accidentally released and fertilized.

Depending on the type of contraceptive injection, it may need to be administered every one, two, or three months in order to remain effective.

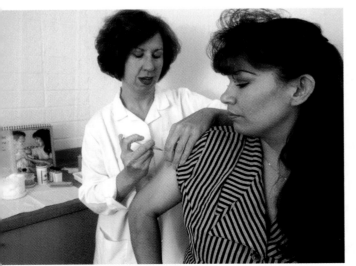

Figure 3.24 Contraceptive injections are given every one, two, or three months.

©P

Intrauterine Device

There are two types of intrauterine devices, also called IUDs (Figure 3.25). IUDs are inserted into the uterus to help prevent pregnancy (Figure 3.26). One type contains a hormone that is slowly released into the uterus to thin the endometrium and to thicken the mucous that is present in the cervix. The thicker mucous helps to prevent sperm from entering the uterus and therefore the fallopian tubes. The second type of intrauterine device is made of copper, which changes the internal chemistry of the uterus, making it impossible for sperm to survive.

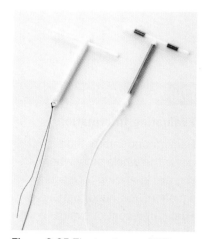

Figure 3.25 The two types of IUD are hormone and copper.

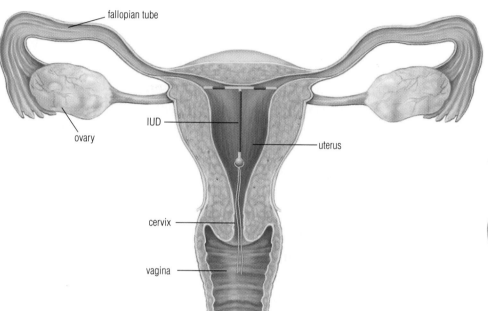

fallopian tube

ovary

IUD

uterus

cervix

vagina

Figure 3.26 The intrauterine device is inserted into the uterus to prevent conception.

Figure 3.27 A tubal ligation disconnects the fallopian tubes.

Sterilization

Sterilization is a permanent form of birth control. Both men and women can choose to undergo sterilization. The procedure for women is called tubal ligation (Figure 3.27). In this process, the fallopian tubes are surgically disconnected from the uterus, which prevents the egg from ever meeting sperm. The male procedure is called a vasectomy (Figure 3.28). In this process, the vas deferens is surgically disconnected, preventing sperm from ever reaching the glands that produce semen. The amount of semen that is ejaculated remains the same, but there are no sperm cells in the fluid.

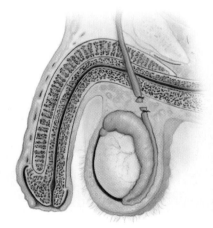

Figure 3.28 A vasectomy disconnects the vas deferens.

Reproductive Technologies

Approximately 10 percent of couples who are trying to have a baby encounter difficulty conceiving. From a scientific viewpoint, **infertility** is defined as problems producing suitable gametes, difficulty conceiving, or problems with implantation. In women, infertility can be caused by a blockage in one or both of the fallopian tubes, which prevents sperm from entering or an egg from leaving. Other causes are irregular ovulation or non-ovulation, or problems with the ovaries not producing mature eggs. In men, most cases of infertility are due to a low sperm count, meaning very few sperm cells are produced in the testes and deposited into the vagina. Technology has advanced in such a way that many causes of infertility can be treated.

One common reproductive technology is the use of fertility drugs. Depending on the cause of infertility, fertility drugs can increase hormone levels, correct hormone imbalances, or enhance or inhibit the actions of hormones. The goal of fertility drugs is to stimulate the follicles to produce mature eggs. Other common assisted reproductive technology (ART) procedures used to treat infertility are artificial insemination and in vitro fertilization.

During Writing

Evaluating Information

Background information is never the whole story when you are analyzing an issue or situation. You need to make a final judgement or evaluation of the situation by telling your readers what is most important and why they should care about the topic. Make recommendations about what should be done.

Artificial Insemination

The process of artificial insemination (AI) is commonly used when the sperm are having trouble reaching the egg or when the male is not producing enough sperm. In some cases, the sperm are unable to swim or survive in the vagina. In other cases, where not enough sperm is produced, the chances of a sperm reaching the egg are drastically reduced. Semen is inserted directly onto the cervix or into the uterus in an attempt to get the sperm closer to the egg.

Sometimes the intended father is either unable to produce sperm or the sperm that are produced are unable to swim. In that situation, sperm from another male can be used for artificial insemination. In this case, the person who provided the sperm is the biological father of the baby.

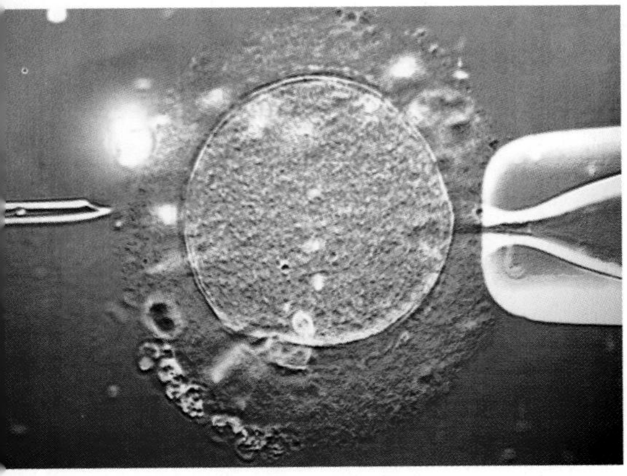

Figure 3.29 During one type of in vitro fertilization, a technique called Intra-Cytoplasmic Sperm Injection (ICSI), sperm is inserted directly into the egg.

In Vitro Fertilization

The term *in vitro* means "in glass." In vitro fertilization (IVF) is just that: fertilization of the egg in a glass test tube or dish. The process of in vitro fertilization involves powerful fertility drugs that stimulate the ovaries to develop more than one mature egg. The mature eggs and sperm are collected and put in a dish where fertilization takes place.

The eggs and sperm used for IVF can come from the intended parents or from other people who act as gamete donors. If the intended mother is unable to produce usable eggs, another female's eggs can be used. Similarly, the sperm used to fertilize the egg can come from either the intended father or another male.

In most cases, the egg and the sperm are prepared for fertilization and incubated together for about 18 hours. In other cases, the sperm is actually inserted right into the egg (Figure 3.29). If the eggs are successfully fertilized and are beginning to show signs of cell division, they are inserted into the uterus of the female.

Once inserted, the embryos may implant in the endometrium and the pregnancy will proceed as normal. In most cases, more than one embryo is inserted into the uterus in the hope that at least one will be able to implant. For this reason, in vitro fertilization can often result in multiple births, though it does not always happen. There is a worldwide movement toward single embyro transfer. Sometimes, the cervix or uterus of the intended mother is unable to support the developing embryo. In this case, embyros are transferred to the uterus of another female, or surrogate mother, where the pregnancy can proceed as normal. The baby will still retain the genetic information of the biological parents, but it grows and develops in the body of another female.

Suggested Activity •··········
A33 Science, Technology, Society, and the Environment on page 109

reSearch

In this section, you learned about different contraceptive technologies. However, as with all technologies, each has unique risks and benefits. Select one of the technologies. Use library or Internet resources to research the pros and cons. Summarize your findings in a pamphlet, poster, or brochure that explains the risks and benefits.

3.5 CHECK and REFLECT

1. What is one important difference between science and technology? How do you think they affect one another?

2. Define contraception in your own words. List some possible reasons why a person might want to use contraception.

3. List the hormonal forms of birth control presented in this section and explain how they prevent pregnancy.

4. Condoms and sterilization are two forms of birth control. How are they similar? How are they different?

5. Explain the process of in vitro fertilization.

6. List two possible causes of infertility in both males and females. For each cause, name a form of reproductive technology and explain how it can overcome the problem.

7. What is a surrogate mother? Why might someone choose to employ a surrogate mother?

8. Consider the First Nations and Métis perspective, as well as your own beliefs, on contraceptive and reproductive technology. What might be some social and cultural concerns about using or developing these technologies?

Ask an Elder

Ann Marie Lemaigre: Niotlsini's gift

For Saskatchewan's Dené people, as for all First Nations and Métis peoples, all life is sacred. Ann Marie Lemaigre, an Elder from the Clearwater River Dené Nation, describes her people's views on the sacredness of life. Further teachings and contributions were provided by Elder Mary Ruelling, also from the Clearwater River Dené Nation. This profile was written through the help of Jeannie Auramenko, a teacher and Dené interpreter.

According to Elder Ann Marie, "It is from the Creator that all created things come." From that perspective, all life is sacred. She sums up the Dené belief by saying, "Niotlsini (Creator) is responsible for creating all things, including human beings. He is deemed as the absolute force of everything. The sacredness of life stems from Niotlsini. He is the giver and the preserver of all life. Through our Dené prayers, we acknowledge Niotlsini (Creator/God) for thanksgiving, for our way of life, the life given to each one of us, living in harmony with all living things, and respect for all."

The Dené believe that all living things are interconnected and interdependent. The Dené people who practise the traditional ways show respect for the land through traditional land management. They hunt and harvest only what they need. Some of the Dené still travel along the traplines, snaring animals for their furs to earn a living (Figure 3.30). Trappers carefully monitor and observe that their way of life is in harmony with the land.

"Human beings are dependent upon all growing matter. We are a part of the puzzle. However, we are the most needy of all living things. We cannot survive without our natural brothers and sisters. These include the plants, animals, birds, and fish. The Dené make offerings to the natural brothers and sisters. The offering will consist of what they have as their sustenance.

This is followed by a prayer. For example, when travelling by boat or canoe, before you enter the water, you say a prayer to the water spirit asking for protection, thanksgiving, and safe travel. Some will touch the water and recite a prayer. The land is here to look after us, as well as the water," says Elder Ann Marie Lemaigre.

Elder Lemaigre's words illustrate a holistic way of thinking.

Figure 3.30 The Dené people who practise the traditional ways, show respect for the land through traditional land management.

©P

What Do You Think Is Right?

Each culture has its own traditions and beliefs. What are some different cultural beliefs about contraceptive and reproductive technology?

Purpose

To research a culture or religion and find out beliefs surrounding contraceptive and reproductive technology

Procedure

1. Choose a culture or religion. (Do not overlook your own culture.)

2. As you conduct your research, be sure to analyze your findings for reliability and bias.

3. Answer the following questions from the point of view of the culture or religion you are researching:

- At what point does human life begin?
- What form(s) of contraception are considered acceptable? Are there any exceptions based on certain situations?
- In what situation(s) is the use of reproductive technology considered acceptable?

Questions

4. Which cultural rules or guidelines do you agree with? Explain.

5. Which cultural rules or guidelines do you disagree with? Explain.

Pose New Questions

6. Suggest a question about religions or cultures and contraceptive or reproductive technology.

Treating Infertility

Purpose

To find out more about reproductive technologies available to treat infertility

Procedure

1. Choose one of the types of reproductive technology discussed in this section, or another type of your choice, to research.

2. Present your findings in a format of your choice, such as a newscast, skit, poster, or public service pamphlet. Be sure to include your answers from the questions below.

Questions

3. How did your research findings define successful treatment of infertility?

4. What is the success rate of the method you chose?

5. What are some of the risks associated with this method?

6. Who is eligible to try this procedure?

7. What are the costs of having this procedure? Who is responsible for paying for them?

8. What are some of the arguments in favour of using this procedure?

9. What are some of the arguments against using this procedure?

Pose New Questions

10. What are some questions you still have about reproductive technology?

Key Concept Review

1. Briefly define puberty, from a scientific viewpoint and then from First Nations and Métis perspectives.

2. Create a table with the headings Male, Female, and Both. Classify each of the following terms under the most appropriate heading.

   - FSH
   - testosterone
   - estrogen
   - progesterone
   - LH
   - scrotum
   - follicles
   - oviduct
   - vas deferens
   - seminiferous tubule
   - gonads
   - hormones
   - secondary sexual characteristics
   - epididymis
   - cervix

3. List as many differences between egg cells and sperm cells as you can.

4. List as many similarities between egg cells and sperm cells as you can.

5. What are hormones? What is their function? Give an example of a hormone and describe what it does.

6. Describe the process of sperm formation, including the hormones involved.

7. Describe the process of egg formation, including the hormones involved.

8. Explain how hormones regulate the beginning of puberty.

9. Sperm are stored in the epididymis in the scrotum. Explain the advantage of having the sperm stored in the scrotum.

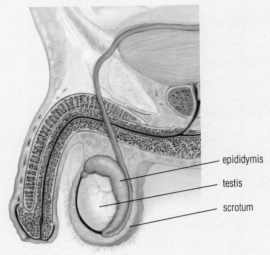

epididymis

testis

scrotum

Question 9

10. Describe the process of menstruation, including the hormones involved.

11. What is the difference between negative and positive feedback? Give an example of each.

12. Explain the difference between fertilization and implantation.

13. What changes take place in the woman's body in order for pregnancy to occur?

14. How is the process of mitosis similar to what happens to a fertilized egg?

15. What is the difference between an embryo and a fetus?

16. How does a developing embryo obtain nutrients from the mother?

17. Explain the process of birth, including the hormones involved.

18. What causes the endometrium to thicken and then to be shed during the menstrual cycle?

19. What is the placenta and how is it formed? Describe its function.

©P

20. Name three methods of contraception described in this chapter. Explain which stage of the reproductive process they inhibit.

21. Briefly explain the position of First Nations and Métis cultures on the issue of contraceptive and reproductive technology.

Connect Your Understanding

22. If a male reaches puberty at age 13 and continues to produce sperm until age 80, estimate the number of sperm cells he will produce in his lifetime.

23. Explain why there are so many more sperm produced than eggs.

24. A low sperm cell count is one cause of male infertility. Explain how reproductive technology might solve this problem.

25. A thermostat on a refrigerator works by a feedback system. Explain how this works, and identify whether this is an example of positive or negative feedback.

26. Explain how a developing fetus might be affected by the actions of the mother.

27. Sometimes a fertilized egg does not move into the uterus, but remains in the fallopian tube. Explain why this might be a dangerous situation for the mother.

28. Create a flow chart that explains how male and female gametes form a zygote. Use at least 10 terms from this chapter.

29. Some people choose to give birth with the help of a midwife instead of a doctor. Research the role of a midwife and how it differs from the role of a doctor. Present your findings in a report.

30. This chapter discusses physical methods of birth control, including barrier methods such as condoms, and hormonal forms of birth control. Research at least two behavioural methods of birth control and present your findings in a paragraph, skit, or other format of your choice.

Reflection

31. Pose three questions you still have about any of the topics in this chapter.

32. What is your opinion on the moral and ethical issues involved with the use of contraceptive and reproductive technology?

After Writing

Reflect and Evaluate

Share your summary of information about a reproductive technology with a classmate who wrote about a different technology. Listen to a reading of your classmate's article. What was the most important information you heard? What was nice to know but not entirely necessary? Reconsider your own summary with the same questions. Write a statement to express what you have learned about researching and taking notes.

Reflection on Essential Inquiry Questions

Compare ways that different forms of contraception prevent the transfer of genetic information in humans. **SI**

Your life started when two haploid cells joined together to form a single diploid cell. Now your body is made up of trillions of cells. Compare models of cell division with models of reproduction of an entire organism. **TPS**

Which reproductive technologies are designed to improve fertility in humans? Are there any ethical concerns about these technologies? **DM**

Suggest ways that two-eyed seeing may be useful to the formation of a view of human reproduction that combines analytical and holistic perspectives. **CP**

Unit Task

This chapter detailed human reproduction and technological methods to promote or prevent pregnancy. How can you apply your learning to the social and ethical issues highlighted by the Unit Tasks? Add to your notes on your chosen task.

UNIT A Summary

KEY CONCEPTS	CHAPTER SUMMARY

1 Cell division occurs in both asexual and sexual reproduction.

- Cell cycle
- Mitosis
- Meiosis
- Diploid
- Haploid
- Asexual reproduction
- Sexual reproduction

- The cell cycle is important for the growth, repair, and reproduction of all organisms. (1.1)
- Mitosis is the division of the nucleus and cytokinesis is the division of the cytoplasm. (1.1)
- There are many forms of asexual reproduction, all of which only require one parent. (1.2)
- Advantages of asexual reproduction include the production of many identical offspring. (1.2)
- Sexual reproduction in animals is achieved by the union of male and female gametes. (1.3)
- Advantages of sexual reproduction include the production of offspring with variation in characteristics. (1.3)

2 Genetic information is passed from parent to offspring.

- Dominant traits
- Recessive traits
- Heritable traits
- Non-heritable traits
- Genetic disorders
- Environmental factors
- Two-eyed seeing

- Heritable traits are the characteristics of an organism that are inherited from the organism's parents. (2.1)
- The nucleus of the cell contains DNA, which is responsible for heredity. (2.2)
- Genes are segments of DNA that contain instructions for characteristics. Alleles are variations of genes. (2.2)
- Traits can be dominant or recessive, and the combination of genes from the parents determines which traits the offspring will display. (2.2)
- Some personal choices and environmental factors can alter a cell's DNA. (2.3)
- Food and crop production, population size, the spread of disease, and the environment are all affected by the study of genetics. (2.3)

3 The process of human reproduction can be affected by technology.

- Gamete production
- Male reproductive system
- Female reproductive system
- Human development
- Contraceptive and reproductive technology

- Puberty is when males and females begin to produce mature gametes. (3.1)
- The male and female reproductive systems produce gametes and are regulated by hormones. (3.2, 3.3)
- Fertilization occurs when the nucleus of an ovum fuses with the nucleus of a sperm. (3.4)
- It takes approximately nine months for a human to develop from conception to birth. (3.4)
- Contraceptive and reproductive technologies can affect reproduction. (3.5)
- Scientists usually investigate things by thinking analytically; Elders usually know things by thinking holistically. (3.5)

VOCABULARY

KEY VISUALS

- analytical (p. 7)
- asexual reproduction (p. 18)
- binary fission (p. 20)
- budding (p. 20)
- cancer (p. 12)
- carcinogens (p. 12)
- cell cycle (p. 8)
- chromosome (p. 9)
- cleavage (p. 29)
- clones (p. 18)
- cross-pollination (p. 31)
- cytokinesis (p. 9)

- diploid (p. 10)
- DNA (p. 9)
- eggs (p. 27)
- embryo (p. 29)
- fertilization (p. 27)
- fragmentation (p. 22)
- gametes (p. 27)
- grafting (p. 22)
- haploid (p. 11)
- hermaphrodites (p. 30)
- holistic (p. 7)
- interphase (p. 9)
- meiosis (p. 29)

- mitosis (p. 9)
- ovules (p. 31)
- parthenogenesis (p. 20)
- pollen (p. 31)
- self-pollination (p. 31)
- sexual reproduction (p. 27)
- sperm (p. 27)
- spores (p. 21)
- tumour (p. 12)
- vegetative reproduction (p. 21)
- zygote (p. 29)

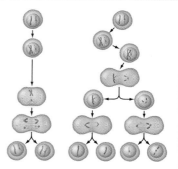

Mitosis and meiosis

- allele (p. 51)
- artificial insemination (p. 62)
- artificial reproductive technology (p. 62)
- characteristic (p. 40)
- continuous variation (p. 44)
- discrete variation (p. 44)
- dominant allele (p. 53)

- dominant trait (p. 53)
- gene (p. 50)
- genetic code (p. 49)
- genetic engineering (p. 62)
- heredity (p. 43)
- heritable characteristics (p. 43)
- hybrid (p. 52)
- in vitro fertilization (p. 62)

- non-heritable characteristics (p. 43)
- Punnett square (p. 54)
- recessive allele (p. 54)
- recessive trait (p. 54)
- selective breeding (p. 61)
- trait (p. 40)
- two-eyed seeing (p. 60)
- X chromosome (p. 66)
- Y chromosome (p. 66)

Heritable traits

- blastocyst (p. 95)
- cervix (p. 87)
- contraception (p. 103)
- corpus luteum (p. 87)
- endometrium (p. 88)
- epididymis (p. 83)
- estrogen (p. 85)
- fallopian tube (p. 87)
- feedback (p. 88)
- fetus (p. 97)
- follicle-stimulating hormone (p. 78)

- gonads (p. 78)
- hormones (p. 78)
- implantation (p. 96)
- infertility (p. 103)
- menstrual cycle (p. 88)
- menstruation (p. 89)
- ovaries (p. 85)
- ovulation (p. 86)
- oxytocin (p. 97)
- penis (p. 83)
- placenta (p. 96)

- progesterone (p. 85)
- prostate gland (p. 83)
- puberty (p. 78)
- scrotum (p. 82)
- seminiferous tubules (p. 83)
- testes (p. 81)
- testosterone (p. 81)
- urethra (p. 84)
- uterus (p. 87)
- vagina (p. 87)
- vas deferens (p. 83)

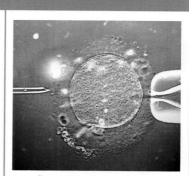

Reproductive technology

A34 Should Research Have Limits?

Toolkits 4, 5

SKILLS YOU WILL USE
- Determining bias
- Stating a conclusion

Question

Should there be any limits placed on research into making changes to the genetic information contained within an organism's cells?

Task Overview

There are advantages and disadvantages to the results of genetic research and many different opinions about what is right and how far research should go. Decisions need to be made. As part of a team, you will draft a set of laws to guide the future of research into genetic and reproductive technology.

Members of society have different opinions because of their jobs, their cultural beliefs, and their morals. All of these aspects must be considered. Your team's job is to analyze the opinions of all members of society and come to a conclusion that satisfies as many of society's needs and wants as possible (Figure 3.31).

Figure 3.31 Making decisions for a large group of people requires respect, patience, and an open mind.

A35 Double the Money

Toolkits 4, 7

SKILLS YOU WILL USE
- Organizing information
- Evaluating research procedures

Question

Will a doubling of funds for a biomedical genetics research project lead to a doubling of results useful to society?

Task Overview

A local university has requested a doubling of funds from the Canadian government to expand the department's research project on reproductive technology.

The information generated by the research will advance understanding and treatment of human diseases.

As members of a four-person expert panel, you are to investigate the issue from multiple social stances including the ethical, legal, and social implications. You will decide whether the funding is to be increased and, if so, by how much. You will announce your decision to the public in an appropriate presentation.

A36 Talk the Talk, Walk the Walk

Toolkits 4, 7

SKILLS YOU WILL USE
- Asking questions
- Reporting results

Question

How can a particular ethical scenario force people to analyze their opinions?

Task Overview

In this task, you will choose an issue in the area of genetics and reproduction.

You will write a scenario on the issue that provides three choices for the reader. Present the scenario to as many people as possible. Analyze the results of the survey, suggest readers' reasons for their choice, and report your findings.

UNIT A Review

Using Key Terms

1. Create a concept map that illustrates your understanding of the following terms and how they relate to reproduction.
   - mitosis
   - meiosis
   - gametes
   - eggs
   - sperm
   - asexual reproduction
   - sexual reproduction
   - heredity
   - characteristics
   - traits
   - DNA
   - genes
   - alleles

Reviewing the Big Ideas

2. What is the function of cell division?

3. Explain the difference between a haploid cell and a diploid cell.

4. Describe the reason gametes contain only half the DNA of body cells.

5. List three environmental factors that can cause changes in a cell's DNA that may lead to cancer.

6. What is the difference between mitosis and cytokinesis?

7. Describe how a hybrid black cat differs from a purebred black cat.

8. What is a zygote? How is it formed?

9. Outline the path of development in animals from gamete to embryo.

10. Sketch the parts of a flower that are involved in reproduction. Describe how each part functions in cross-fertilization.

11. Summarize how bacteria cells divide by binary fission.

12. Explain the difference between asexual and sexual reproduction and the advantages and disadvantages of each.

13. How does binary fission differ from meiosis?

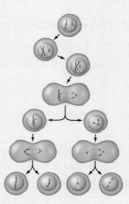

Question 13

14. Briefly list the costs and benefits of asexual and sexual reproduction in terms of diversity.

15. What is similar about egg and sperm cells? What is different?

16. Differentiate between heritable and non-heritable characteristics. Provide two examples of each type.

17. Use a diagram to compare the inheritance of dominant and recessive traits.

18. What is meant by the term "genetic code"?

19. What is the general structure of the DNA molecule?

20. Explain the relationship among DNA, chromosomes, genes, and alleles.

21. Sketch a simple diagram of a human cell and include information about the roles of chromosomes, genes, and DNA.

22. Explain the effect that technology such as artificial insemination, that is used in the livestock industry, has on the genetic variation of domesticated animals such as cattle and sheep.

23. Compare and contrast genetic engineering with other types of reproductive technology. List possible advantages and disadvantages of each.

24. Describe three examples of genetic engineering.

25. Compare and contrast gamete formation in male and female humans.

26. What is the main function of the male and female reproductive systems in humans?

27. Write out the path that mature sperm cells take from the testes to the outside of the body.

28. Describe the function of the follicles in the production of egg cells.

29. Compare the roles of LH and FSH in regulating the female reproductive cycle.

30. Name and state the function of the four hormones discussed in Chapter 3.

31. Describe positive and negative feedback using two hormones in the female reproductive system.

32. Write out the path that a mature egg cell takes from the ovary to the outside of the body.

33. Where in the body is an egg usually fertilized by sperm?

34. What is the difference between fertilization and implantation?

35. Explain cleavage in terms of zygote development.

36. What is the placenta and what is its function?

37. Explain the relationship between technology and reproductive technologies.

38. Describe how four of the methods of contraception discussed prevent pregnancy from occurring. Be sure to explain what part of the regular reproductive process is interrupted.

39. Describe a situation where in vitro fertilization might be used and explain what in vitro fertilization is.

40. Elder Lemaigre understands that human reproduction is sacred. In what way, if any, does a scientific understanding of human reproduction involve the idea of sacredness?

Connecting the Big Ideas

41. Explain how the three Big Ideas are related. You can write a description, use a concept map, or draw an illustration to show the relationships.

42. Which type of reproduction, sexual or asexual, is responsible for an increased amount of genetic variation in plants and animals? Support your answer with examples.

43. What impact does the cloning of domesticated animals have on genetic diversity? Would cloning of wild animals ever be a possibility? Explain your answer.

44. Describe the similarities and differences between cell division and human reproduction. How are these connected?

Using the Big Ideas

45. Imagine that your gonads were exposed to a high dose of radiation. Explain some of the possible consequences, including any impact on future generations.

46. Explain how you would create a new breed of dog.

47. List reasons you would or would not be concerned about drinking milk from cows treated with a growth hormone.

48. Describe how you would conduct research to identify issues arising from the development of new reproductive technologies.

49. Suppose someone is making a personal choice on an issue related to human reproduction. Suggest an advantage to them of using two-eyed seeing.

50. A student states that genetic engineering is "perfectly safe." What safety and ethical issues do you think might arise over the use of genetic engineering?

51. As a society, how should we make decisions about the uses of technology such as genetic engineering and cloning?

Reflection

52. Describe three things about reproduction that you did not know before you started working on this unit.

53. List questions for further study that you have about the transmission of genetic material in sexual reproduction or asexual reproduction.

54. Based on your unit work, describe three ways in which technology has been developed to meet human needs and wants.

55. Write a paragraph about the balance among the physical, emotional, mental, and spiritual dimensions when two people have a baby.

56. Describe at least one career choice that would be related to what you have learned in this unit. Research the education required, average salary, and average job duties of this career.

57. Describe a human being from two points of view as studied in this unit: (a) a scientific way of understanding, and (b) a holistic way of understanding.

Reflection on Essential Inquiry Questions

How is genetic information transferred through different methods of reproduction? **SI**

How do models of cell division compare with models of reproduction of an entire organism? **TPS**

How can technologies, environmental factors, and personal choices influence reproduction? **DM**

How do cultural perspectives contribute to analytical and holistic understandings of human reproduction? **CP**

Atoms and Elements

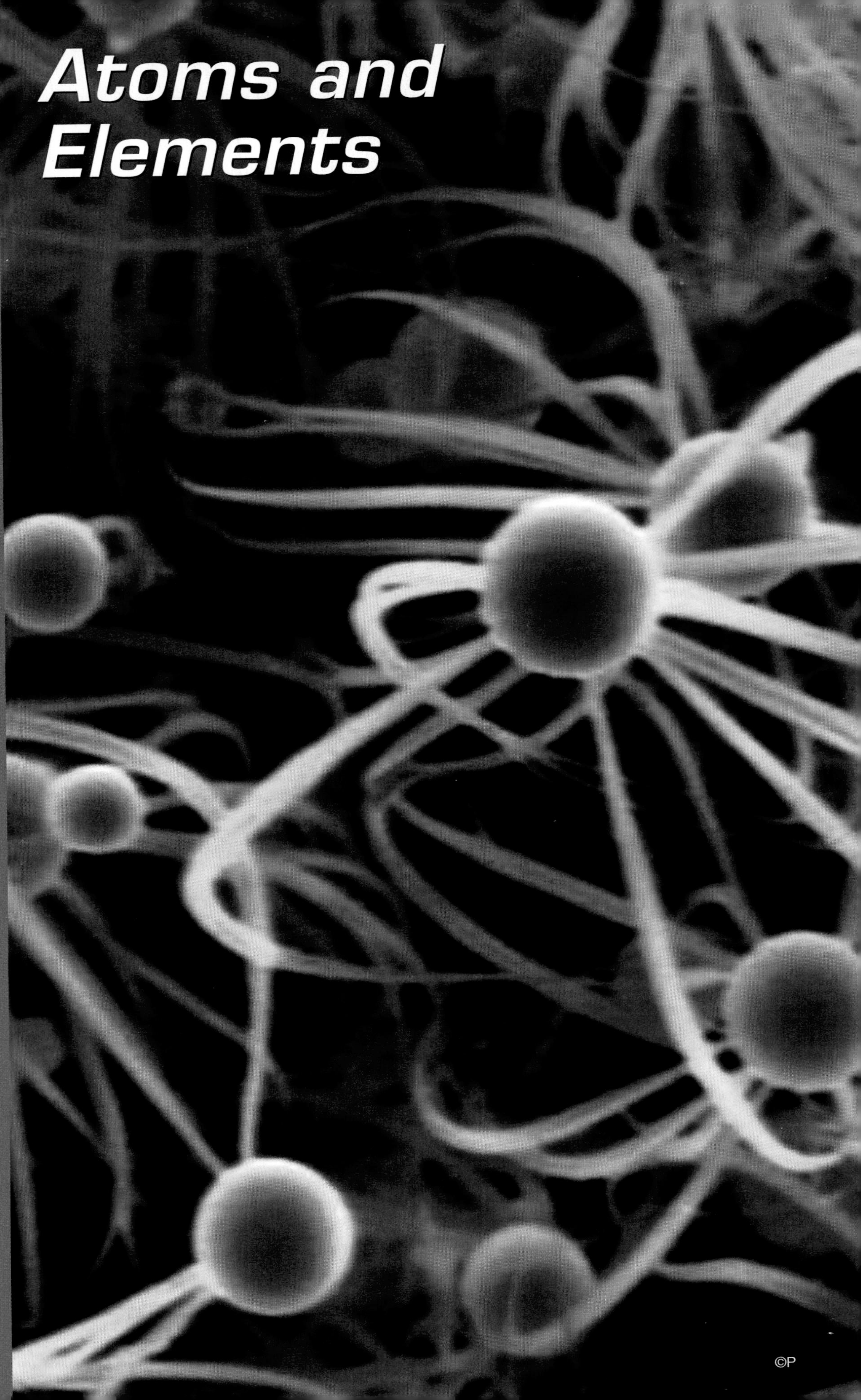

Each of these octopus-like structures has a tiny metal head and "nanowire" arms made of a substance scientists call silica. Silica is a useful material because of its properties. It is a major part of common substances such as sand and glass. Silica nanowires, shown here magnified about 20 000 times, have characteristics that allow for their potential use in communications devices.

©P

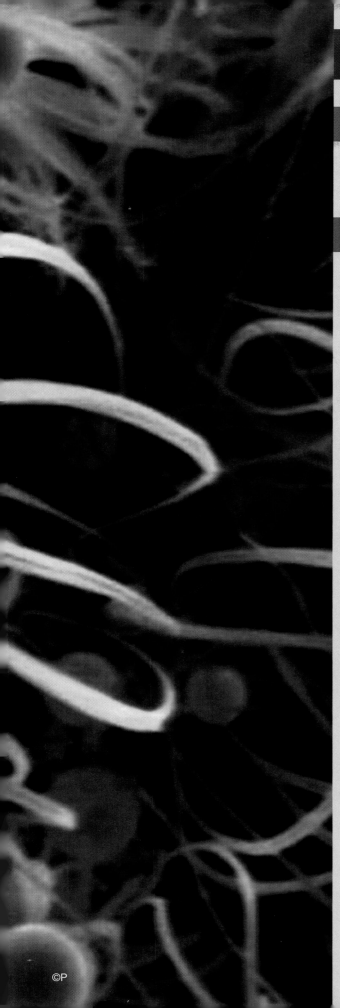

Big Ideas

4 People of all cultures investigate matter according to various properties.

- **4.1** Investigating Matter
- **4.2** Physical and Chemical Properties **DI**

5 The periodic table is a tool for organizing scientific understanding of elements.

- **5.1** Developing Models of Matter **DI**
- **5.2** The Elements
- **5.3** Combining Elements to Form Compounds
- **5.4** The Periodic Table

Essential Inquiry Questions

How do properties of matter enable us to differentiate between various substances? **SI**

How have scientists advanced their understanding of the atomic theory? **TPS**

What are the impacts of using various materials to create household, commercial, industrial, and agricultural products? **DM**

How do people from different cultures think about the structure and composition of materials in the physical world? **CP**

Unit Task

Every substance has special properties that may make it useful or hazardous or both. In this unit, you will learn about the scientific components that make up different substances and explain their unique properties. At the end of this unit, you will address some or all of the Essential Inquiry Questions by completing a Unit Task. Your Unit Task will be designing and testing a homemade toothpaste by investigating the properties of the ingredients in commercial toothpastes.

©P

People of all cultures investigate matter according to various properties.

Outcomes

By the end of this chapter, you will:

- distinguish between physical and chemical properties of common substances, including those found in household, commercial, industrial, and agricultural applications

What you will learn:

- Investigate and identify physical and chemical properties of substances.
- Describe physical and chemical properties of common substances based on observable evidence.
- Plan and safely conduct an inquiry into the properties of common substances using appropriate equipment.
- Distinguish between "generalizable" ideas produced by scientists and "place-based" ideas used by First Nations and Métis cultures.
- Understand the properties of matter that help us work safely with different substances and provide society's needs for new products.

The same properties of water that cause it to form beads on the surface of a leaf allow water to form a column in the xylem of a plant's stem. The column of water stretches from the roots to the top of even the tallest trees.

Key Terms

- adhesion • chemical change
- chemical property
- chemical reaction • cohesion
- combustibility • compound
- element • mass • matter
- mechanical mixture
- Medicine Wheel
- physical property • property
- pure substance • solution
- suspension • volume

Before Reading

The Language of Chemistry

Make a "Language of Chemistry" table for the key terms listed in the margin. Your table should have three columns: Key Term, Before Reading, and During Reading. Under Key Term, write each term on one row. Record what you think each term means in the same row under Before Reading. This could be a statement or a labelled diagram. As you read through the chapter, make notes for yourself under During Reading to clarify your ideas about each term.

Figure 4.1
Fireworks displays, such as this one seen at the Fireworks Festival in Saskatoon on Labour Day, combine art and chemistry.

Here is a summary of what you will learn in this section:

- Three models of understanding matter include: Indigenous, ancient Greek, and scientific.

- Matter is composed of particles. The type of particles and their arrangement in a substance determine its properties.

- Scientists classify matter as a pure substance or a mixture.

- Scientists further classify mixtures as mechanical mixtures, suspensions, or solutions.

The Chemistry of Fireworks

On Canada Day, when darkness falls, the skies of many towns and cities across the country come alive with colours and sounds. Flares of red, blue, green, and white are joined by cracks and bangs as fireworks displays mark Canada's national day of celebration (Figure 4.1). Fireworks are an ancient technology, first invented in China over 2000 years ago. Today, fireworks can be seen around the world and their creation is an art form called pyrotechnics. Pyrotechnics is a branch of chemistry, the science that involves understanding and changing matter.

The spectacular sights, sounds, and smells of fireworks come from the fusion of chemistry and art. Designers of fireworks use the knowledge that some substances burn with brilliant colours when heated (Figure 4.2). Aluminum metal is used in the kitchen as cooking foil. However, when aluminum is heated by an explosion, the metal burns with a bright white flame. The types of fireworks that light up the night sky or leave a thick glowing trail of light often contain aluminum.

Many substances change colour when heated. The green colours in fireworks usually come from heated substances containing copper. The bright yellow-orange colours are based on sodium, a substance present in table salt. The cracks and bangs of fireworks are produced when certain substances heat up and expand rapidly. The rapid expansion makes the sound. The explosions are often so powerful that they can be felt as well as heard.

Figure 4.2 Fireworks are lit with a flame.

Observing Changes in Matter

When substances are mixed, they may change in state (solid, liquid, or gas) or they may change into different substances with different characteristics. Watch for changes in colour, volume, and state as you complete this activity.

Purpose

To observe changes in matter

Materials & Equipment

- 50-mL graduated cylinder
- bromothymol blue indicator solution (a chemical indicator that changes from blue to blue-green to yellow as the solution becomes acidic)
- three resealable plastic bags
- two scoopulas
- sodium hydrogen carbonate powder (baking soda)
- calcium chloride powder

Procedure

1. Use the graduated cylinder to measure 30 mL of bromothymol blue.

2. Hold open a resealable plastic bag. Place one scoop of sodium hydrogen carbonate powder into a corner of the bag.

3. Pour the bromothymol blue into the bag. Squeeze out the air, and quickly seal the bag.

4. Mix the contents by squeezing the bag for about 20 seconds. Use your hands to detect any temperature change of the bag over the mixing time.

5. Observe and record as many changes to the substances in the bag as you can.

6. Use a second resealable plastic bag. Repeat steps 1 to 5 but use one scoop of calcium chloride powder for step 2 instead of the sodium hydrogen carbonate powder.

7. Use a third resealable plastic bag. Repeat steps 1 to 5 but, this time, place one scoop of sodium hydrogen carbonate powder in one corner of the bag and one scoop of calcium chloride powder in the other corner for step 2.

8. Clean up your work area. Follow your teacher's instructions to safely dispose of all materials used.

9. Wash your hands thoroughly.

Questions

10. Describe what you observed when you mixed the bromothymol blue with
    (a) sodium hydrogen carbonate powder
    (b) calcium chloride powder
    (c) both powders

11. Were there any changes to the substances in this activity? How do you know? State the evidence to support your answer.

Pose New Questions

12. What evidence might confirm that a new substance was formed?

13. What evidence might be different if the quantity of one substance were doubled? tripled?

Understanding Matter

Every culture worldwide has its own ways of understanding the physical world. Some First Nations and Métis peoples use a circle—a sacred **Medicine Wheel** (or sacred circle)—to help them understand. A Medicine Wheel connects everything in the universe together into one whole. As explained in the previous unit, this holistic way of understanding is common sense to First Nations and Métis peoples. The Medicine Wheel is organized into a pattern of four. For example, there are four directions: east, south, west, and north. There are four seasons: spring, summer, fall, and winter, although in some First Nations cultures, six seasons exist. There are four colours: yellow, red, blue (or black), and white. Details vary depending on the Indigenous nation or community (Figure 4.3).

Many First Nations communities understand the composition of the physical world in terms of four elements. Saskatchewan First Nations, such as the Nakawē, and the Métis people recognize fire, water, air or wind, and rock as the four elements. For these cultures, the four elements are more than non-living constituents that make matter. Fire, water, wind, and rock are Spirits that give and take life.

In the Nakawē creation story, the four elements arose as the Woman or Mother's Spirit that gave birth to the physical universe. The fire is the initial Spirit of Mother Earth and is the power of woman Spirit that creates the physical world. Fire helped form the rocks, the second element, and is responsible for the shaping and creation of Mother Earth. Air or wind, the next element, came from the life forces in the rock. As the rock cooled, fog condensed and formed the last element, water.

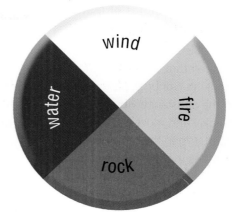

Figure 4.3 This Medicine Wheel shows how some Saskatchewan Cree communities understand what the physical world is made of. First Nations and Métis peoples believe that Spirit flows through these four elements.

Other Views on Nature of Matter

Many ancient cultures, including East Indian and Islamic, also developed elaborate explanations of the nature of matter. Greek philosophers believed that matter is made from combinations of four simple forms of matter: earth, fire, water, and air, which Greeks called "elements." About 440 BCE, the Greek philosopher Democritus argued that breaking down rock into powder and then grinding the powder further would reduce it to tiny bits of matter that could not be broken down any more. His philosophical idea was not popular because it contradicted philosophical authorities at the time.

infoBIT

Origin of "Atom"

The modern term "atom" is derived from the Greek *atomos*, meaning indivisible.

infoBIT

Changes of States of Matter

For a given substance, the state it is in is related to its temperature. As a substance gains heat energy, particles in the substance vibrate more quickly and move farther apart. When the temperature reaches the melting point, a solid will change into a liquid, and at the boiling point, a liquid will change into a gas. At very high temperatures, the particles in a gas have been found to change into another form. Since the particles are no longer the same as those in the gas state, this state of matter is given another name—plasma.

Suggested Activities • · · · · · · · ·
B2 Inquiry Activity on page 128
B3 Quick Science on page 130

Figure 4.4 Aluminum foam is a combination of two different materials in different states, a solid and a gas.

A scientific model about the structure of matter did not take shape until the early 1800s. Scientists began having confidence in a model postulated by John Dalton in England, which assumed that the smallest bit of matter was an "atom." Each different kind of matter is composed of a different kind of atom. This generalized idea about what makes up the physical world took almost 100 years before it became a common-sense idea for all scientists. Different models describing atoms have evolved over time to explain the structure of matter, and these will be analyzed in Chapter 5.

Forms of Matter

Matter is a general term used to describe all objects in the universe. Scientists define **matter** as anything that has mass and takes up space. **Mass** is a measure of the amount of substance in an object. For example, a brick has more mass than an equal-sized chunk of Styrofoam™. Mass is usually measured in kilograms (kg) or in grams (g). **Volume** is a measure of how much space an object occupies. For example, a volleyball has a volume larger than that of a baseball. Volume is often measured in litres (L) or in millilitres (mL). It is also measured in cubic centimetres (cm^3), especially for solid objects. All matter has some volume, even if that volume is very small.

Scientists believe that matter in the universe commonly exists in four states: solid, liquid, gas, and plasma. Substances may be solid, liquid, gas, or plasma, or a combination of materials in one or more states. For example, foam is a mixture of a liquid and a gas, or a solid and a gas. Bubbles in a foamy bubble bath are liquid films of soap with air trapped inside them. Styrofoam™ is a solid plastic containing trapped air. Lightweight aluminum foam can be made by trapping gas inside melted aluminum and then letting the metal harden (Figure 4.4).

Learning Checkpoint

1. What are two features that are common to all forms of matter?

2. Why do you think people from all cultures want to explain the nature of matter?

3. How does a Medicine Wheel help Indigenous people organize their understanding of the physical world?

Classifying Matter

All matter is made up of different types or combinations of particles. For example, gold and iron are both metals, but they have very different characteristics. Pure gold is yellow and is so soft that a fingernail can put a mark on it, whereas iron is grey and much too hard to scratch with a fingernail. These two metals have different characteristics because the particles that make up each metal are different. That is, all particles of gold are identical, and all particles of iron are identical, but particles of gold are different from particles of iron.

Different types and combinations of particles give every type of matter particular characteristics, or properties. A **property** is a characteristic that describes a substance. Scientists classify matter as pure substances or mixtures, depending on how their particles are arranged.

During Reading

Examples Help Give a Word Meaning

Authors use examples to help readers really see the meaning of a word in their minds. If you can picture the example, you can usually understand the concept or idea. Watch for examples as you read. They will help you understand new terms.

Pure Substances

A **pure substance** is made up of only one kind of particle. It has a unique set of properties, such as colour, hardness, boiling point, and melting point. Scientists further classify pure substances as elements or compounds, depending on their composition.

- An **element** is a pure substance made up of one type of particle that cannot be broken down into any simpler substance by chemical means. For example, gold is a pure substance that is an element (Figure 4.5). Later in this unit, you will learn how elements are organized into a periodic table according to their properties.

- A **compound** is a pure substance that is made from two or more elements that are chemically combined. For example, sugar is a pure substance that is a compound (Figure 4.6). Water is also a compound containing the elements hydrogen and oxygen.

Figure 4.5 An ancient gold mask from Peru in South America. Gold is an element and a pure substance.

Figure 4.6 White sugar is a compound and a pure substance. All sugar particles are like all other sugar particles. It is a compound because sugar particles are made from more than one element (carbon, hydrogen, and oxygen).

Mixtures

A mixture is a combination of pure substances. However, the substances in a mixture do not combine chemically as happens when a compound forms. Each substance remains in its original form, although each is not always easy to see distinctly in the mixture. There are three main types of mixtures: mechanical mixtures, suspensions, and solutions.

Figure 4.7 A chocolate chip cookie is a mechanical mixture.

Figure 4.8 A salad vinaigrette is a mixture of oil, vinegar, and spices.

Figure 4.9 Tea is a solution of water and the extract of tea leaves that dissolve in the water.

- In a **mechanical mixture**, the different substances that make up the mixture are visible (Figure 4.7). Soil is an example of a mechanical mixture. So is a mixture of salt and pepper. A mixture in which the different parts are visible is called heterogeneous. The prefix "hetero-" means different.

- In a **suspension**, the tiny particles of one substance are held within another to create a cloudy mixture (Figure 4.8). Tomato juice is an example of a suspension. These particles can be separated out when the mixture is poured through filter paper. A suspension is also a heterogeneous mixture.

- In a **solution**, the different substances that make it up are not individually visible (Figure 4.9). One substance is dissolved in another, creating a homogeneous mixture. The prefix "homo-" means same, and all parts of a homogeneous mixture look the same. Examples of solutions are sugar dissolved in hot coffee, and acetic acid dissolved in water to make vinegar.

A Summary of Matter Classification

Scientists classify matter as pure substances or mixtures. Mixtures may be further classified as either heterogeneous or homogeneous, depending on their appearance. This is summarized in Figure 4.10.

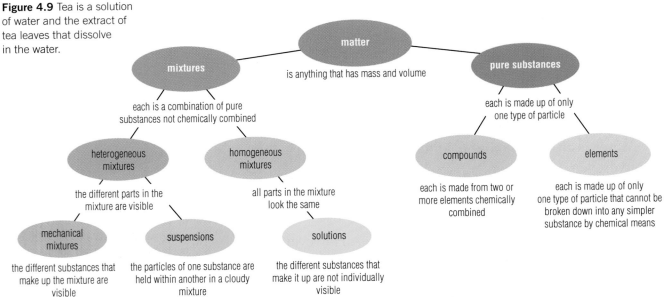

Figure 4.10 A scientific classification of matter

©P

A Practical Use for Mixtures in Saskatchewan

Solution mining for potash in Saskatchewan (Figure 4.11) has been taking place for almost fifty years. The term potash refers to potassium-bearing materials, mainly potassium chloride (KCl). The world's first potash solution mine was established in 1964 at Belle Plaine, near Regina. This type of mining involves the use of water or hot water to dissolve desired minerals from a geological ore zone. Boreholes are drilled vertically or at an angle into the ore to allow water (or other leaching agents) to enter the deposit. The solution that then forms underground is brought to the surface through a second borehole and is processed by evaporation, crystallization, and drying. Although conventional mining of potash occurs in Saskatchewan, there are a number of benefits of using solution mining. Some of these benefits include a shorter time to production, lower technical risk, and lower environmental impact. Knowing the properties of the minerals allows mining companies to develop new mining techniques.

Figure 4.11 Mosaic power area supervisor talks about the solution mining process at the potash mine site in Belle Plaine.

4.1 CHECK and REFLECT

1. Name the four elements believed by the Nakawē people to make up the physical world. Which element is responsible for the shaping and creation of Mother Earth?

2. How do scientists define compounds and elements? Give an example of each.

3. How is a mechanical mixture different from a solution according to the common scientific classification system?

4. Is a compound, such as water, a pure substance or a mixture? Explain.

5. What are the four common states of matter that scientists use to describe matter in the universe?

6. Can a sample of matter exist in two states at one time? Use an example to explain your answer.

7. Classify each of the following as a homogeneous mixture, a heterogeneous mixture, or a pure substance. Justify your answer in each case.

(a)   (b)

Question 7

8. What are two benefits of solution mining for potash (material containing mainly potassium chloride) over conventional mining of potash in Saskatchewan?

9. Describe three things about forms of matter that you learned about in this section.

SKILLS YOU WILL USE
- Using appropriate equipment and tools
- Recording and organizing data

B2 *Inquiry Activity*

Toolkit 1

Identifying Gases

Changes to matter can result in the formation of gases. There are many different kinds of gas, and we can use their properties to help identify them. Three common gases are oxygen, carbon dioxide, and hydrogen.

Initiating and Planning

What are the gas tests that can be used to identify oxygen gas, carbon dioxide gas, and hydrogen gas?

Materials & Equipment

- three medicine droppers
- three medium test tubes
- test-tube rack
- 3% hydrogen peroxide solution
- dish soap
- two scoopulas
- potassium iodide powder
- matches
- wooden splints
- 0.1 M acetic acid solution (vinegar)
- sodium hydrogen carbonate powder (baking soda)
- 2 M hydrochloric acid solution
- forceps
- mossy zinc chunks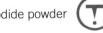
- large test tube
- test-tube holder

CAUTION: Hydrogen peroxide may sting your skin. Potassium iodide will stain skin and clothing. Keep your hair tied back when working near open flames.

Performing and Recording

Part 1 — Preparation of Oxygen

1. Using a medicine dropper, add 1 mL (about 20 drops) of hydrogen peroxide solution to a clean test tube.

2. Add two drops of dish soap.

3. Use a scoopula to add a small amount (less than the size of a pea) of potassium iodide powder to the test tube.

4. Use matches to light a wooden splint.

5. Blow out the flame to make a glowing splint. Insert the glowing splint into the mouth of the test tube (Figure 4.12). Observe and record what happens to the glowing splint.

Figure 4.12 A glowing splint will reignite in the presence of oxygen.

6. Clean up as directed by your teacher.

Part 2 — Preparation of Carbon Dioxide

7. Using a medicine dropper, add 1 mL (about 20 drops) of acetic acid to the second clean test tube.

8. Use the second scoopula to add a small amount (less than the size of a pea) of sodium hydrogen carbonate powder to the test tube.

9. Use matches to light a wooden splint.

©P

10. Insert the flaming splint into the test tube (Figure 4.13). Observe and record what happens to the splint.

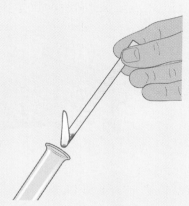

Figure 4.13 A flaming splint will be extinguished in the presence of carbon dioxide.

11. Clean up as directed by your teacher.

Part 3 — Preparation of Hydrogen

12. Using a medicine dropper, add about 2 mL of hydrochloric acid to the third clean test tube.

13. Use forceps to add a small piece of mossy zinc to the third test tube. Use a test-tube holder to place a large test tube upside down and over the smaller test tube in order to trap any gas (Figure 4.14).

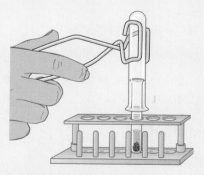

Figure 4.14 Trapping hydrogen gas

14. Keep holding the large test tube upside down as you lift it off the small test tube. Use matches to light a wooden splint.

15. Insert the flaming splint into the large test tube. Observe and record what happens to the splint.

16. Clean up your work area. Follow your teacher's instructions to safely dispose of all materials used. Wash your hands thoroughly.

Analyzing and Interpreting

17. Describe what happens in a positive test for oxygen gas.

18. Describe what happens in a positive test for carbon dioxide gas.

19. Describe what happens in a positive test for hydrogen gas.

20. Write a procedure for distinguishing between oxygen gas and carbon dioxide gas.

Communication and Teamwork

21. Explain why the three parts of this activity can be used to distinguish among oxygen, hydrogen, and carbon dioxide gas but not to determine whether an unknown gas is one of these three.

Foam in a Cup

You can manipulate matter to change its properties. In this activity, you will mix together different liquids and a solid to produce a completely different substance: a foam.

Purpose

To produce a new substance, such as a foam, and observe its characteristics

Materials & Equipment

- corn syrup
- two 250-mL beakers
- two colours of food colouring
- stirring rod
- teaspoon
- sodium hydrogen carbonate powder (baking soda)
- water
- 50-mL graduated cylinder
- vegetable oil
- white vinegar
- medicine dropper

Procedure

1. Pour about 30 mL of corn syrup into a beaker. Stir in three drops of one food colouring. Use a teaspoon to sprinkle a heaping spoonful (about 20 g) of sodium hydrogen carbonate powder on the corn syrup.

2. Pour 30 mL of water into a graduated cylinder. Hold the beaker at a slight angle, and carefully pour the water in down one side. Add 30 mL of vegetable oil to the beaker in the same way.

3. Into a separate beaker, pour 20 mL of vinegar. Add three drops of the other food colouring. Record your observations.

4. Fill the medicine dropper with coloured vinegar from the second beaker.

5. Position the tip of the medicine dropper at the very bottom of the first beaker, then squeeze the bulb in order to release all the vinegar (Figure 4.15). Record your observations.

Figure 4.15 Adding coloured vinegar to the first beaker

6. Clean up your work area. Follow your teacher's instructions to safely dispose of all materials used. Wash your hands thoroughly.

Questions

7. Write a statement to describe your observations in step 3.

8. Write a statement to describe your observations in step 5.

9. What types of changes did you observe?

10. Describe a characteristic of foam that you observed.

11. Describe the state or states of matter of the foam produced in step 5.

Pose New Questions

12. Why did you have to position the tip of the medicine dropper containing coloured vinegar at the very bottom of the first beaker?

13. What effect do you think simply pouring the coloured vinegar into the first beaker would have?

Figure 4.16 A fire produces many changes in matter.

The Chemistry of a Campfire

A fire can be fascinating to watch (Figure 4.16). Although all the flames may look similar, each particular spark or flicker is unique—never repeating in exactly the same way.

From an Elder's point of view, the gathering of wood is an important first step in building a campfire. Historically, wood was not readily available on the Saskatchewan plains. First Nations people burned buffalo dung to make fire. To start a fire, a bow drill was used. It is a horizontally positioned bow with its drawstring wrapped about a thick stick that rubs against smaller pieces of wood, called kindling. The sawing motion of the bow creates friction on the kindling, which ignites it.

From a scientist's point of view, investigations on lighting a fire demonstrate some clear patterns. Every fire needs the same three components to get started: fuel, oxygen gas, and heat. Scientists work toward developing generalized explanations of phenomena. In a scientific explanation of a campfire, the fuel is typically wood, a complex natural material that is rich in carbon. Carbon reacts with oxygen in the air, but only if the air can reach the carbon in the wood. The first step in building a campfire is usually to split a log into kindling. By chopping a thick log into smaller pieces, much more carbon in the wood is exposed to the air. Oxygen gas has easy access to the carbon at the surface of the wood and so can react with it.

Here is a summary of what you will learn in this section:

- Physical properties describe the characteristics of a substance that can be observed or measured.

- Chemical properties describe the chemical reactivity of a substance and ways in which it forms new substances.

- Physical properties include smell, colour, melting point, boiling point, density, solubility, conductivity, hardness, lustre, texture, and malleability.

- Chemical properties include combustibility and reaction with water or acid.

info**BIT**

More on an Elder's View of a Fire

First Nations people might show respect to Mother Earth by sprinkling some tobacco on the ground where the wood for a fire is found, in thanks for the gift of fire that the wood will bring. They understand that Fire is a Spirit. When one blows on a fire, one prevents Fire Spirit from doing its work and is a sign of disrespect. As a result, Elders, Knowledge Keepers, and helpers will never blow on a fire. During traditional ceremonies, whenever a fire is lit, or when matches are used, they allow a fire to burn out on its own.

The components of a fire must be in just the right balance. When lighting a fire, extra oxygen is sometimes needed. Gentle blowing on the first embers of the fire can help. There is enough oxygen in the breath to provide an extra boost. It is important not to blow the heat energy of the first sparks away from the fuel, as this will blow out the fire. Since combustion releases heat energy, there is no need to keep relighting the flame.

B4 *Quick Science*

Observing a Physical Change

Soda pop contains carbon dioxide. In the air, carbon dioxide exists as a gas. However, when carbon dioxide dissolves in water, this is not the case. The particles of water and carbon dioxide are attracted to each other, so they intermix, forming a solution. Disrupting these attractions produces a change that you will observe.

When a substance undergoes a physical change, such as melting, its appearance or state may change, but its composition stays the same. For example, melted chocolate ice cream has the same composition as frozen chocolate ice cream. In contrast, a chemical change results in the formation of a new substance or substances with different properties.

Purpose

To investigate a change in matter

Materials & Equipment
• two drinking glasses
• soda pop
• chewy mint candy

CAUTION: Do not eat or drink anything in the lab, including the soda pop and candy.

Procedure

1. Fill each of the two glasses about two-thirds full with soda pop.

2. Into one glass, drop a piece of mint candy. Observe what happens in both glasses, and record your observations.

Questions

3. Adding candy to the soda pop caused a mainly physical change that disrupted the attraction between particles of liquid. How did you recognize this physical change?

4. Can you tell whether the composition of the candy changed after it was added to the soda pop? Why or why not?

5. Consider the change that took place. Suggest one reason that you would describe it as a physical change. Suggest one reason that you might also describe it as a chemical change.

6. In the procedure, you were instructed to fill two glasses with soda pop in step 1 but to add candy to only one glass. What is the reason for this?

7. Suggest ways to modify the procedure to produce an interesting effect or display involving the change in properties. Check with your teacher before trying it out.

Pose New Questions

8. How many changes, both physical and chemical, are involved in this activity? What are they and what vocabulary would you use to describe the changes?

Physical Properties of Water

All life on Earth depends on water. As depicted by the Nakawē story of creation, water was one of the four elements that arose from the Woman's Spirit heart. Among all First Nations and Métis peoples, water is sacred and is treated with great respect.

Our bodies are about 70 percent water. Some plants are 95 percent water. A characteristic of water is that it sticks to itself, a property scientists call **cohesion**. Due to cohesion, water forms beads on non-absorbent surfaces, such as glass. Water also sticks to other substances, a property scientists call **adhesion** (Figure 4.17). A towel is able to mop up water by using this property of water.

A **physical property** describes a characteristic of a substance that can be observed or measured without changing its composition. Water has many interesting physical properties that make it very useful to organisms. One example is being a liquid at room temperature. Also, the properties of adhesion and cohesion help move water up through the stems of plants, including tall trees.

Most materials shrink when they freeze. Water does not. Because of the special arrangement of water particles during freezing, water actually expands. This makes ice less dense than liquid water. As a result, ice floats on water. Why is this important? In winter, the ice on a body of water shelters the fish below. Floating ice can also make a useful temporary roadway or platform for ice fishing (Figure 4.18). However, the same properties that make water useful can also cause problems. As ice forms, it widens cracks in roads. In addition, snow and ice on the roofs of houses can cause damage due to melting and refreezing. Not only is the ice heavy, it can block gutters and downspouts that are meant to keep water flowing off the roof and away from the sides of a building.

Observing Physical Properties

Figure 4.19 shows a dull, red, clouded piece of beach glass. Three physical properties of the glass include its lustre (shiny or dull), its colour, and its transparency (how much light it allows through). Other physical properties can be observed using appropriate tools or measuring devices. For example, in grade 8, you measured the mass and the volume of objects and fluids to determine their densities. Table 4.1 on the next page lists a number of other physical properties.

Figure 4.17 Water sticks to itself, forming droplets (cohesion), and to the spider web (adhesion).

Figure 4.18 In winter, fish are protected from freezing temperatures by the ice at the surface of the water. People can use this same ice as a platform when fishing.

Figure 4.19 The pieces of beach glass show a variety of physical properties.

Table 4.1 Physical Properties of Matter

Property	Description	Examples	What It Looks Like
Colour and lustre	Colour is the first appearance of a substance. Lustre (shine) is the way the surface of a substance looks in the light.	The names for some substances, such as gold, are also the names of colours. Gold has lustre; concrete is dull.	Gold and silver coins are very lustrous.
Melting point	Melting point is the temperature at which a solid changes into a liquid. It is the same temperature as the freezing point of the same substance from a liquid to a solid. Melting point is affected by atmospheric pressure.	The melting point of ice at average sea-level atmospheric pressure is 0°C. Water freezes at 0°C.	Solid water melts at 0°C.
Boiling point	Boiling point is the temperature at which a liquid changes into a gas. It is the same temperature as the condensation point of the same substance from a gas to a liquid. Boiling point, like melting point, is affected by atmospheric pressure.	The boiling point of water at average sea-level atmospheric pressure is 100°C.	Water boils at 100°C.
Density	Density is the amount of mass in a given volume of a substance. Density is affected by temperature.	At 25°C, the density of pure water is 1 g/mL. The density of gold is 19 g/mL. Water is denser than oil, but gold is denser than water.	Fluids and solids with different densities
Solubility	Solubility is the maximum amount of substance that can dissolve in water. The solubility of a substance is affected by the temperature of water.	The solubility of pure salt (sodium chloride) is 35 g/100 mL of water at 0°C.	Chocolate powder dissolves fast in hot water.
Ductility	Any solid that can be stretched into a long wire is said to be ductile.	Copper is a common example of a ductile material.	The ductility of copper allows it to become thin wire.

Property	Description	Examples	What It Looks Like
Crystal shape	When particles in a substance line up in a regular pattern, smooth surfaces and sharp edges are created to give the crystal shape of the substance.	The rock mineral quartz forms long, six-sided crystals and halite (rock salt) forms cubes.	A quartz crystal showing smooth surfaces and sharp edges
Conductivity	Conductivity is the ability of a substance to conduct electricity or heat energy. A substance that conducts electricity or heat energy is called a conductor. A substance with little or no conductivity is an insulator.	Most metals are good conductors. Copper is a very good conductor of electricity and so is used to make electric wires. Styrofoam™ and glass are insulators.	Electric circuit with copper wires to conduct electricity
Hardness	Hardness is a substance's ability to resist being scratched. Hardness is usually measured on the Mohs hardness scale from 1 to 10.	The mineral talc is the softest substance on the Mohs hardness scale (1). Emerald is quite hard (7.5). Diamond is the hardest (10).	An emerald gemstone is fairly scratch resistant.
Texture	Texture is described as the feel of the surface of a substance.	The surface of a raw gemstone usually feels rough when it is mined. The surface can become smooth after having been cut and polished.	Raw diamond has a rough surface until it has been cut and polished.
Malleability	A substance that can be pounded or rolled into sheets is said to be malleable.	Aluminum foil is an example of a malleable substance. Metals such as gold and tin are also malleable.	Aluminum foil is easily shaped and moulded since it is highly malleable.

Observing Chemical Properties

Suggested Activities •·········
B6 Inquiry Activity on page 142
B7 Inquire on Your Own on page 144

A **chemical property** is a characteristic of a substance that describes how it reacts when it changes into a new substance or substances. The change may occur when the substance interacts with other substances, such as acids, or when the substance is exposed to heat energy or light. A **chemical change** always results in the formation of a new substance or substances with different properties. For example, when zinc metal and hydrochloric acid are mixed, they undergo a chemical change that produces two new substances: hydrogen gas and a compound called zinc chloride. A **chemical reaction** is a process in which a chemical change occurs.

Chemical properties can be observed only when a chemical change occurs. If you mix baking soda and vinegar, as in Inquiry Activity B2 on page 128 and Quick Science B3 on page 130, you will produce a chemical change that involves the formation of gas bubbles. In general, evidence of chemical change can include colour change, odour, temperature change, the production of light, the formation of a new solid inside a liquid, or the production of a new gas (Figures 4.20 and 4.21). However, observing any or all of these properties does not guarantee that a chemical reaction has occurred. Table 4.2 lists various chemical properties.

Figure 4.20 Chemical changes made this banana ripe—and then rotten.

Table 4.2 Examples of Chemical Properties

Chemical Properties
Absorbs heat during reaction
Combustible
Forms gas when heated
Reacts with acid
Reacts with water
Emits heat energy during reaction
Emits light during reaction
Forms a precipitate (solid) in a solution

Figure 4.21 Fireflies contain a chemical called luciferin. When luciferin reacts with oxygen, light is emitted.

Heat and Chemical Change

Heating a substance can result in chemical changes. For example, when baking soda is heated, it undergoes a chemical change that results in the production of carbon dioxide gas. This is very useful in cooking. It is this chemical reaction of baking soda in some baked foods that produces the gas needed to lift the cake and make it light and fluffy (Figure 4.22). If you forget to add baking soda to a cake batter, the cake will be flat and dense.

Heating causes many different kinds of substances to react. Burning is an example of this kind of chemical change. Paper is combustible. When a flame or spark is applied, the heat energy starts the reaction of paper with oxygen to produce heat energy, light, carbon dioxide, and water. Once the reaction has started, it gives off enough heat energy to keep the paper burning. **Combustibility** is the ability of a substance to react quickly with oxygen to produce heat energy and light.

When some substances are mixed, their reaction absorbs heat energy from the surroundings. A chemical cold pack, for example, depends on a reaction that absorbs heat energy (Figure 4.23). Typically, a chemical cold pack is filled with water but also has an inner bag or tube full of chemicals. The inner compartment keeps its contents separated from the water until it is time to use the cold pack. When the inner bag is popped open, the chemicals within mix with the water in the cold pack. The reaction absorbs heat energy from the surroundings, and so the pack feels cold to the touch.

Figure 4.22 When baking soda in a cake batter is heated, it produces a new substance: a gas.

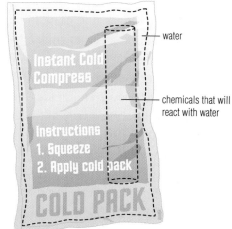

water

chemicals that will react with water

Figure 4.23 A chemical cold pack has an inner compartment containing reactive chemicals and an outer compartment containing water.

Learning Checkpoint

1. Describe the first step in building a campfire from an Elder's point of view and from a scientist's point of view.

2. What is a physical property? List three physical properties of water.

3. What is a chemical property? List three examples of chemical properties.

4. How does a physical change differ from a chemical change?

5. What kind of ideas do scientists usually develop? Give an example.

Ask an Elder

Julie Pitzel:
Birch Syrup, a Traditional Use of the Land

Elder Julie Pitzel is a Métis Elder of Dené, Cree, Scottish, and French descent. She is a retired principal who lives and works as a counsellor for a healing lodge. She teaches life skills from a traditional perspective at the Métis Addictions Council of Saskatchewan in the city of Prince Albert. Growing up in the community of Buffalo Narrows in northern Saskatchewan, Elder Julie learned the traditional ways of her family on the traplines where they caught muskrat, beaver, wolf, otter, weasel, and fish.

Elder Julie came to know many important teachings and skills on the traplines. By her grandmother's and grandfather's side, she learned to make lye soap, to smoke fish, to tan hides, and to produce birch syrup. All are gifts from the land.

When we think of syrup, often maple trees come to mind. However, in Elder Julie's community, where birch trees are abundant, syrup was made from their sap. To make birch syrup requires a lot of patience, she explains. After a grove of suitable trees is found, the trunks are tapped using a sharp nail, knife, or stick, and the sap is allowed to flow freely (Figure 4.24). A pail hanging by a branch catches the sap. In earlier times, Elder Julie explains, her people used a birch bark basket instead of a pail. This sap must be made into syrup. A shallow hole with a small circumference is dug into the earth and fire is made inside it. Sticks of 20 cm in length are placed above the fire, far enough so that they do not burn too quickly. An iron pot filled with sap is placed on the sticks over the fire and boiled until thick rich syrup is made. To decide on the quality of the syrup's consistency, a soup ladle of syrup is slowly poured back into the pot to see what the syrup looks like.

Before iron pots were available, Elder Julie's people heated stones over the fire and these were placed into the syrup in the birch bark baskets. The gooey solution took a long time to make because as these heated stones cooled, they needed to be replaced with hot ones.

Not all Indigenous communities make birch syrup the same way. Elder Julie describes a method that works well with birch trees in the Buffalo Narrows area, but environmental conditions could be quite different in other communities. The method she describes works well in one place, but not necessarily in all places. This type of understanding is called "place-based knowledge." We learn place-based knowledge from Elders. From generations of experience, place-based knowledge is perfected. Scientists, however, try to produce ideas that work in all places. For example, they use the idea that matter is made of particles to explain the physical and chemical properties of matter. Scientists work toward developing "generalizable knowledge." To do this, scientists must sometimes ignore unique features of one particular place.

Traditional life required much understanding, patience, and hard work. Knowledge about the land and its gifts allowed First Nations and Métis peoples to survive the harsh Saskatchewan climate.

Figure 4.24 A deep cut is made in this birch trunk and a V-shaped tab of bark is pulled out to collect the sap.

©P

Controlling Changes to Matter

In our daily lives, there are many examples of how understanding and controlling changes in matter help us meet our basic needs. Being able to change materials from one form to another allows us to make products that are not only useful but that also support a sustainable environment. For example, chemicals made from corn can be used to make juice bottles, remove paint or nail polish, and fuel some cars. Corn is put through a chemical change called fermentation. Once this chemical process is complete, the new substances are recovered, purified, and made into solvents (Figure 4.25), biodegradable plastics, and automobile fuel.

An advantage of corn-based biodegradable plastics is that they can be broken down by bacteria. However, making and using corn-based products also has its drawbacks. People sometimes cut down rainforests to make way for cornfields. Corn that would otherwise be used for food is sometimes diverted to make disposable products.

Figure 4.25 The inks used here contain solvents made from corn.

Suggested Activity • • • • • • • • • • •
B5 Science, Technology, Society, and the Environment on page 141

reSearch

Many of the items you used today are made from polyethylene. Research to find out what these polyethylene plastics are. Adding cornstarch to plastic is one way to make the plastic biodegradable. Find out about other "green" products by doing research using the Internet.

Traditional Uses of Substances

First Nations people understood details about properties of matter without knowing the scientific ideas of physical and chemical changes. Their ideas about the physical world served them very well. Their way of knowing and the scientific way do not contradict each other. Both add to humanity's understanding.

Preservation of Fish

Understanding matter and its many transformations allowed First Nations people to prevent spoilage and allowed them to store meat which would otherwise quickly rot in the heat of summer. Dehydrating meats was a means to slow down bacterial decomposition. An example of this important process is the preservation of fish (Figure 4.26). According to the Elders, whitefish, jackfish, and occasional red sucker fish made up a large part of their diet. To preserve these fish, they are smoked.

Figure 4.26 The skills of preserving fish allowed First Nations people to store their catch in the summer for eating in the winter.

infoBIT

An Ancient Skill

Rock paintings created by First Nations people along the Churchill River in northern Saskatchewan are believed to be hundreds of years old. They used ochre, a reddish-brown mineral, to give colour to their paint. Ingeniously, these people also knew how to stop their paintings from fading over time due to exposure from water and the Sun. They made a gelatin-like substance, called "isinglass," from dried swim bladders of freshwater fish and mixed it with ochre to add to the paint.

Figure 4.27 The roots of bunchberries have been used by some First Nations peoples as a cold remedy and the bark has been used as a laxative.

First, the scales are removed and the fish prepared. With a sharp knife, a cut is made from the head, along the length of the back toward the tail. The tail is kept intact. After the fish is split open (still in one large filet), the organs and bones are removed. Lengthwise and widthwise cuts are made into the flesh to form small squares.

A lean-to, shaped like a tripod, is fashioned out of wood and lashed together. A shelf of sticks is built near the top where the poles of the lean-to meet. A fire is lit under the lean-to beneath the shelf. Old dried poplar wood produces the best smoke. Often it takes two days for the fish to be completely smoked and ready to eat. Smoking fish ensured that the First Nations people could preserve their catch for a few days in the summer or for eating during the winter.

Medicine

The healing tradition of the First Nations and Métis peoples is a holistic process that includes physical, mental, emotional, and spiritual healing. Herbal medicines in combination with prayer and ceremony have been used by First Nations and Métis peoples of Saskatchewan for many generations. The herbs used could be a plant or part of a plant or a substance extracted from a plant such as a sap or an oil (Figure 4.27). A herbal medicine may contain more than one type of herb. These herbs, which contain a mixture of naturally occurring substances, contrast with modern pharmaceutical drugs containing pure compounds.

In the past, it was not uncommon for healers to be women since knowledge about plants and herbs were women's teachings. These medicine women possessed knowledge about plants, herbs, and roots used in remedies such as teas. It is well documented that a substance in willow bark, originally employed by First Nations healers, is now known by its chemical name, *acetylsalicylic acid*, a chemical compound commonly known as Aspirin®.

According to many Elders, the derivation of traditional medicines did not occur by accident or through trial and error. Some medicine women would go on a fast for several days during which time they would meditate on the medicines and plants they would mix to create the desired effects. Certain families have spiritual understanding to mix medicines for heart disease, diabetes, hepatitis, and other illnesses. Today Elders are concerned about the way traditional medicines might be exploited by some pharmaceutical companies.

1. For each of the following substances, list four physical properties.

   (a) water

   (b) iron metal

   (c) baking soda (sodium hydrogen carbonate)

2. What does a chemical property describe about a substance?

3. Identify each of the following observations as evidence of either a physical change or a chemical change.

   (a) A piece of copper is heated until it melts.

   (b) A silver spoon darkens when left in the air.

   (c) Paper burns in a candle flame.

   (d) A piece of plastic is stretched until it breaks.

   (e) Table salt melts at 801°C.

4. From the following list, indicate which items would make good conductors.

   (a) copper   (b) Styrofoam™

   (c) iron   (d) woollen mitten

5. Identify each of the following as a statement that describes either a physical property or a physical change.

   (a) Ice melts.

   (b) Hydrogen is a colourless gas.

   (c) You chop a carrot.

   (d) Copper wires bend easily.

   (e) The ruby slippers are red.

6. What is an advantage and a disadvantage to the environment of making corn-based products?

7. Compare traditional medicine used by First Nations and Métis peoples and modern pharmaceutical drugs.

B5 Science, Technology, Society, and the Environment

Polyethylene Plastic

Polyethylene plastic is flexible, heat resistant, and strong. Children play with polyethylene toys, athletes drink from polyethylene bottles, and police officers wear polyethylene vests. Unlike some other types of plastic, polyethylene is considered safe to use in food containers.

What happens to polyethylene products when we no longer need them? If they cannot be re-used, another option is to recycle them. Some types of polyethylene plastics break down more easily when exposed to sunlight. These types of plastics are considered photodegradable. However, the process takes a long time and releases tiny pieces of polyethylene as solid waste.

1. Make a list of items you used today that are made from polyethylene. Identify which items you could live without and which are necessities.

2. Describe two ways you could help decrease the amount of polyethylene that goes into landfills.

3. Is the process of photodegradable plastic decay a physical or chemical change? Support your response.

4. What are some possible benefits of using photodegradable polyethylene to make disposable food containers or shopping bags? What are some possible problems with this type of plastic?

Investigating Physical and Chemical Changes

You can use a chemical reaction to change one substance into another substance that has different physical and chemical properties. You can also use heat energy to change the properties of substances.

Initiating and Planning

What are some characteristics of physical changes and chemical changes?

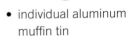

Materials & Equipment

- three scoopulas
- sodium carbonate powder
- 250-mL beaker
- medicine dropper
- 0.5 M hydrochloric acid
- individual aluminum muffin tin
- white table sugar
- candle
- candle holder
- matches
- tongs or wooden clothespin

- three test tubes
- 0.5 M solution of copper(II) sulphate
- 0.5 M solution of sodium carbonate
- two 5-mL measuring spoons
- test-tube rack
- copper(II) sulphate (solid)
- water
- stirring rod

CAUTION: Copper(II) sulphate is poisonous and can stain your clothes and skin. Keep your hair tied back when working near open flames.

Performing and Recording

1. Copy Table 4.3 into your notebook. Be sure to leave a row for each test.

Test 1 — Sodium carbonate and hydrochloric acid

2. Using a scoopula, add a small amount (the size of a pea) of sodium carbonate powder to a beaker. In your observation table, describe the appearance of the sodium carbonate powder.

3. Observe the hydrochloric acid, and record what you see in your observation table.

4. Write a statement about the kinds of evidence for physical or chemical change that you will look for when you add the hydrochloric acid to the sodium carbonate powder.

5. Using a clean medicine dropper, add five to eight drops of hydrochloric acid to the sodium carbonate powder. Record your observations.

Test 2 — Sugar and heat

6. Obtain an aluminum muffin tin. Use a clean scoopula to put a small amount of sugar (the size of a pea) in the centre of the aluminum muffin tin. Record your observations of the sugar.

7. Suggest possible ways that the sugar might change with heating.

8. Place the candle securely in a candle holder, and then light the candle.

9. Using tongs or a wooden clothespin, hold the aluminum muffin tin over the candle's flame. Slowly move the muffin tin back and forth over the flame to heat the sugar. Record your observations.

10. Place the aluminum muffin tin in a safe place to cool.

Table 4.3 Observations of Physical and Chemical Changes

Test	Observations		
	Before Change	**During Change**	**After Change**
Sodium carbonate and hydrochloric acid			

Test 3 — Copper(II) sulphate and sodium carbonate

11. Using a measuring spoon, add 5 mL of copper(II) sulphate solution to a clean test tube. Using a different measuring spoon, add 5 mL of sodium carbonate solution to another test tube. In your observation table, describe the appearance of each solution.

12. Write a suggestion about what you think will happen when the solutions are combined.

13. Combine the solutions, and record your observations.

14. Dispose of the solutions as directed by your teacher.

Test 4 — Copper(II) sulphate and water

15. Using a scoopula, add a small amount (the size of a pea) of solid copper(II) sulphate to a clean test tube. In your observation table, describe the appearance of the substance.

16. Write a suggestion about what you think will happen when you add water to the copper(II) sulphate.

17. Fill the test tube two-thirds full of water and record your observations (Figure 4.28). Use a stirring rod to mix the water and copper(II) sulphate, and record any additional observations.

18. Clean up your work area. Follow your teacher's instructions to safely dispose of all materials used. Wash your hands thoroughly.

Analyzing and Interpreting

19. Which of the changes that you observed appeared to be
    (a) physical?
    (b) chemical?

20. What evidence supports each of your answers above?

21. Identify two physical and two chemical properties for each of the following substances:
    (a) sodium carbonate
    (b) white table sugar
    (c) copper(II) sulphate

Communication and Teamwork

22. Create a flow chart that a classmate could follow in order to identify physical and chemical changes.

Figure 4.28 Adding water to copper(II) sulphate

Properties of Common Substances

Elements, compounds, and mixtures are part of everyday life. From the kitchen to the chemistry lab, we make use of different substances for their different properties.

Question

How can you use chemical and physical properties to distinguish among common substances (Figure 4.29)?

Figure 4.29 Common substances

Figure 4.30 Possible materials and equipment

> **CAUTION:** Keep your hair tied back when working near open flames. Take note of safety precautions for the substances you will be working with.

Design and Conduct Your Investigation

1. Choose at least three substances to investigate. They may be substances from your chemistry lab or from home.

2. Decide which properties you will investigate. Select some from the list below, or add others.
   - colour and lustre
   - combustibility
   - conductivity
   - density
   - hardness
   - melting point
   - solubility
   - texture
   - reaction with acid
   - reaction with water

3. Have your teacher approve your list of test substances and the properties you wish to investigate.

4. Think about these questions as you plan your procedure:
   - (a) How will you observe different properties, and what materials and equipment will you need to make these observations (Figure 4.30)?
   - (b) How will you record your results?
   - (c) How will you organize and present your results?

5. Write up your procedure. Show it to your teacher for approval before carrying it out.

6. Carry out your procedure, and collect your observations.

7. Present your results in a poster or in another format suggested by your teacher.

Ask an Expert

Fadiah Parsons: Fine Baking Designer

Meet Fadiah Parsons, a fine baking designer from Torquay, Saskatchewan. She has been baking specialty cakes, cookies, and desserts for 15 years and has gained wide acclaim for her work. Some of Fadiah's work has been featured in magazines. Many people have described her baked goods as "edible works of art" because of their striking appearance (Figure 4.31). But there is more to a great cake than simply appearance. Can you imagine constructing a cake standing nearly 1 m tall? And even if you could do that, how long do you think it would stand before falling over? "It is all in the ingredients," Fadiah says.

Most people are familiar with the common angel food cake and its light, fluffy texture. But one must consider the facts that it is usually only about 10 cm tall and lasts for only a day or two. Most of these cakes use only the egg whites, which is why they are light and fluffy. Angel food cakes, however, could never stand up to 1 m tall because the same properties that make them light and fluffy also make them unstable in structure. The cakes constructed by Fadiah use plenty of whole eggs, whole milk, and a lot of sugar. "Sugar gives body and is also a preservative. Without it, the cakes would be soggier, denser, and would not last as long," states Mrs. Parsons.

The cakes themselves are tasty, but it is the fondant icing that makes them special. The skill is in adding the liquids (glucose, glycerine, gelatin, shortening, and water) to the icing sugar when mixing the fondant icing, and then adding just enough icing sugar to adjust the stiffness without making it too sticky. Fondant icing is kneaded, unlike a poured icing that is heated into a liquid and then poured. A poured icing would be fine for small, light cakes and petit fours, but would never work on tall cakes since it would simply flow to the bottom of the cake before it hardened. The fondant icing makes the cake firm in structure and also allows Fadiah to become an artist.

Figure 4.31 Fadiah Parsons' "edible works of art"

Key Concept Review

1. Explain how First Nations and Métis peoples traditionally described matter.

2. Describe a Nakawē belief in how the elements were formed.

3. What is the main difference between a pure substance and a mixture? Name an example of each.

4. What is a chemical change?

5. Identify and describe two different cultural types of ideas about the physical world.

6. Describe the difference between cohesion and adhesion, using an example.

7. What are two physical changes that cooling a hot substance may result in?

8. For each example, identify whether the property described is chemical or physical. Justify your answer in each case.

   (a) Bronze metal has a shiny lustre.

   (b) When silver nitrate is added to calcium chloride, a cloudy solid (precipitate) appears.

   (c) Mercury is a liquid at room temperature.

Connect Your Understanding

9. Identify each of the following observations as potential evidence of either a physical change or a chemical change. Justify your answer in each case.

   (a) Oak leaves turn red in autumn.

   (b) When a salt solution is left to dry, a white powder remains in the container.

   (c) A gas comes off a boiling kettle.

10. Describe a practice by Indigenous people that illustrates the use of place-based knowledge. Make sure to mention the place-based idea or property of matter involved.

11. Identify one advantage, and one limitation, to understanding nature based on generalizable knowledge.

12. Why will water form droplets on a smooth surface, such as a countertop?

13. Classify and compare the following mixtures.

    (a) a drink made by dissolving drink crystals in water

    (b) a cup of tea with tea leaves in it

    (c) orange juice with pulp

(a)   (b)

(c)   **Question 13**

14. How can the application of heat energy result in a chemical change? Explain, using an example.

15. Metal foams are 75 to 95 percent air. What effect does this have on the density of metal foam compared to solid metal?

16. If water freezes inside of a building's water pipes, the pipes may burst. Explain why this happens, in terms of a physical change or a chemical change.

Question 16

17. (a) What properties of polyethylene plastic make it useful?

    (b) What are some concerns associated with the use of polyethylene?

18. Winter car tires are made from a soft type of rubber that remains flexible, even in icy temperatures. Winter tires also have deeper grooves than all-season tires. Do you think people should be required by law to have winter tires for their vehicles? Why or why not? Support your response with a discussion of the properties of rubber tires.

19. List five items you have used today. Try to identify one substance that each item is made from and the property or properties that make that substance useful. For example: cellphone—plastic—lightweight and hard

20. To make birch syrup, a place-based method described by Elder Julie is to have the sap collected and then boiled over a fire until thick rich syrup is made. A scientific explanation of the process is that boiling off the water increases the sugar concentration of the syrup and makes the syrup more viscous. Describe what is happening to the particles in the syrup at each stage in the process.

21. Consider a homogeneous mixture, such as a salt solution, and a heterogeneous mixture, such as rice and pebbles. Suggest and compare how you could separate the substances within each type of mixture.

22. Use the Internet or your library to find out more about conventional potash mining versus solution mining of potash. Make two lists: Comparisons and Contrasts.

Reflection

23. How has your opinion on the prevalence of chemical substances in our society changed since completing this chapter?

After Reading

Reflect and Evaluate

Review the "Language of Chemistry" table you made at the beginning of the chapter and think about the strategies you used to find word meanings. How did the strategies help you add definitions and explanations of new terms in the "During Reading" section of the table? Compare your table and use of strategies with a partner, and discuss how each strategy helped you get a clear picture of new vocabulary.

Reflection on Essential Inquiry Questions

What properties of matter did you learn that enable us to differentiate between various substances? **SI**

What methods did you learn that could be used to investigate the properties of matter? **TPS**

What are some impacts on the environment due to creating materials or altering matter to meet our needs that you became aware of after studying this chapter? **DM**

What do you know about how people from different cultures understand the nature of matter? **CP**

Unit Task

What steps should you take before investigating the properties of different substances? List some of the physical and chemical properties that you could investigate in the Unit Task, which involves the design of a homemade toothpaste. Make a list of safety precautions that you and your lab partners will need to follow.

The periodic table is a tool for organizing scientific understanding of elements.

Key Terms

- alkali metals • alloy • atom
- atomic mass • atomic mass unit • atomic number
- atomic theory • bond
- chemical formula
- covalent bond • diatomic molecule • electron • group (chemical family) • halogens
- ion • ion charge • ionic bond
- ionic compound • isotope
- lattice • law • mass number
- metalloids • metals
- molecular compound
- molecule • neutral
- neutron • noble gases
- non-metals • nucleus
- period • periodic law
- periodic table
- polyatomic ion
- proton • relative mass
- subatomic particle
- theory • transition metals

What you will learn:

- Explain how scientific models of the atom and descriptions of the characteristics of subatomic particles are based on experimental evidence.

- Conduct investigations and inquiries into the physical and chemical properties of elements and compounds.

- Compare physical properties of elements within a group and between groups in the periodic table.

- Explain the relationship between atomic structure and the arrangement of elements in the periodic table.

- Assess social, environmental, and economic impacts of the use of elements and compounds to make decisions.

At night, signs created from tubes of neon gas light up the streets. One of the properties of the element neon is that it is a gas at room temperature. Another property of neon gas is that it glows when an electric current passes through it.

Before Writing

What's My Topic?

Good writers let their readers know very quickly the topic of their writing. Check the opening sentences of the paragraphs in section 5.1. How many of them state the topic clearly and up front?

©P

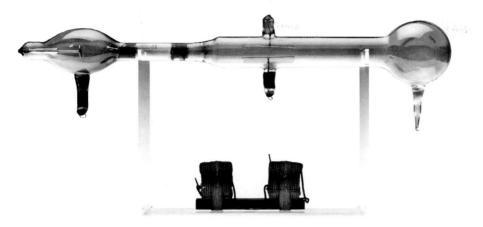

Figure 5.1 A cathode ray tube like this one was used by J.J. Thomson, an English physicist, to research the structure of the atom.

Models, Theories, and Laws in Science

To understand the nature of matter or the physical world, scientists construct models to represent and explain observed phenomena (Figure 5.1). These models are tested or the explanations are verified multiple times to establish theories that are generally accepted by the science community. A **theory** is a generalized explanation of a set of related observations or events supported by research and good arguments. The explanation may be a statement, an equation, a model, or a combination of them. Scientists use theories to predict further observations. For new evidence that an existing theory cannot explain, the theory is replaced or modified to explain the new evidence.

Scientists have developed different models of the atom to explain the structure and properties of matter. As new evidence evolved, many of these models were modified. The most advanced one used today by physicists and chemists is the quantum mechanical model. See Table 5.1 on page 152.

In contrast to a theory, a scientific law does not often change. A **law** is a generalized description of some aspect of the physical world under certain conditions. It is supported by many observations or tests in which scientists have confidence. So, a scientific law has become accepted as a fact. Theories do not become laws. They are used to explain laws. Later, in section 5.4, you will see how the periodic law helps extend your knowledge of the nature of the periodic table.

Here is a summary of what you will learn in this section:

- An element is a pure substance made up of one type of particle, or atom, that cannot be broken down into other substances by chemical reactions.

- Scientists have changed their model of the atom over time based on new experimental evidence.

- The current scientific model of the atom includes three subatomic particles: electrons, which have a negative charge, protons, which have a positive charge, and neutrons, which have no electric charge.

Calcium Metal in Water

Like copper and iron, the element calcium is a metal. However, calcium is easy to tell apart from metals like copper and iron.

Purpose

To observe how calcium metal reacts with water

Materials & Equipment

- two 400-mL beakers
- two medium test tubes
- two rubber stoppers
- water
- pieces of calcium metal
- paper towel
- forceps
- candle and matches or lighter
- wooden splints
- test-tube clamp or tongs
- phenolphthalein (a chemical indicator that changes from colourless to pink as the solution becomes "basic"—the opposite of "acidic" in the language of science)
- medicine dropper

CAUTION: Keep your hair tied back when working near open flames. Do not touch calcium metal with your bare hands as the metal will react with moisture in your skin.

Procedure

1. Fill a beaker with about 300 mL of water. Completely fill a test tube with water. Place a rubber stopper over the opening of the test tube, and then place the test tube upside down in the beaker. Reach into the water, and remove the rubber stopper. Try not to let any air into the test tube.

2. Dry your hands well. Your teacher will give you a few pieces of calcium metal on a paper towel. Use forceps to drop a piece of calcium metal into the water. Adjust the position of the test tube so that the mouth of the test tube covers the calcium metal. Observe what happens.

3. Light a wooden splint.

4. Use clamps or tongs to lift the test tube out of the water without turning it upright. Place the flaming splint under the mouth of the test tube, and observe what happens.

5. Repeat step 1 with a clean beaker. Add five drops of phenolphthalein to the water in the beaker, and then repeat steps 2 to 4.

6. Clean up your work area. Follow your teacher's instructions to safely dispose of all materials used. Wash your hands thoroughly.

Questions

7. Why is it important to keep the test tube upside down after removing it from over the piece of calcium metal?

8. The burning splint test in step 4 allowed you to identify the type of gas produced in this experiment. What was the gas? What evidence supports your answer?

9. How does the phenolphthalein indicator solution respond when calcium reacts with water?

Pose New Questions

10. Do all metals react this way?

11. Might this process have any use in solving technological problems?

Models of the Atom

An **atom** is considered by scientists to be the smallest part of an element that has all the element's properties. For example, copper metal is made up of atoms of copper, which are all very similar. But they are very different from atoms of iron (Figure 5.2). This is why a piece of copper metal has properties different from those of a piece of iron metal.

Atomic theory is a theory that explains the nature of matter by stating that matter is composed of discrete units called atoms. Atomic theory helps us understand why there are different kinds of atoms. It explains how atoms of the over 100 known elements exist in nature, and how they combine to form all other forms of matter, including compounds and mixtures.

Different models of the atom have evolved over time. Table 5.1 on the next page is a timeline of the major scientific atomic models in the order they were proposed. The contributing individuals and their ideas are included as well as their methods, so you can understand how technology has influenced scientific understanding of the atom.

Figure 5.2 Copper and iron are both made up of atoms. However, copper has properties very different from those of iron.

Different Ways of Understanding

The constantly changing model of an atom tells us something important about science. In a scientific way of understanding, it is common sense to break apart (analyze) things into their smaller parts, and then study the parts separately and in great detail. This analytical way of thinking is almost the opposite of the holistic way of thinking, which is common sense in Indigenous cultures. In holistic thinking, a part of something only has meaning in terms of its relationship to the whole thing. For example, the meaning of a person is determined by a person's relationships with the community, the physical surroundings, and Mother Earth. In analytical thinking, the meaning of a person is found by understanding the different parts of the person—the body systems, the organs, the cells, the molecules, etc.

Both ways of thinking—holistic and analytical—help us better understand what makes up the physical world. There are specific reasons for choosing to view the physical world through one of these approaches. Scientists aim at developing broad generalizations about the workings of nature, whereas Indigenous Elders focus on methods that help solve practical, local problems.

Atomic Model Timeline

Table 5.1 Development of Atomic Models

Who	John Dalton	J.J. Thomson
Where	England	England
When	Early 1800s	1897
Key Parts of Model	• All matter is made of small, indivisible particles called atoms. • All the atoms of an element are identical in properties such as size and mass. • Atoms of different elements have different properties. • Atoms of different elements can combine to form new substances. 	• Each atom is composed of smaller particles. • The atom is a positively charged sphere with electrons scattered throughout it.
Evidence Supporting Model	Dalton reconsidered the ancient idea that each different kind of element is composed of a different kind of atom. His work and experiments led him to imagine that all atoms were like small spheres but that they could have different properties.	Thomson experimented with electric currents in glass tubes called cathode ray tubes. He was able to cause atoms of all the elements he tested to produce streams of negatively charged particles, later called **electrons**. Since atoms have no overall electric charge, they must also contain positive charges, now called **protons**.

©P

Who	Ernest Rutherford	Niels Bohr	Modern Quantum Mechanical Model
Where	England	Denmark	
When	1911	1913	
Key Parts of Model	• All of the atom's positive charge and most of the atom's mass is concentrated at a tiny point in the centre, called the **nucleus**. • Electrons surround the nucleus and occupy most of the atom's volume, but contain only a small fraction of its mass. 	• Electrons are arranged in specific energy levels around the nucleus of an atom. • The maximum number of electrons in each of the first three levels is two, eight, and eight. • German physicist Friedrich Hund was the first to determine how electron pairing occurs (shown in the Bohr diagrams below for hydrogen and magnesium). hydrogen atom energy levels magnesium atom	• Electrons do not exist as tiny points inside the atom. • Electrons exist in specific energy levels, but they surround the nucleus in the form of an "electron cloud." cloud of electrons nucleus
Evidence Supporting Model	Rutherford shot positively charged particles at a very thin foil of gold. Most of the positively charged particles went right through the foil, but about 1 in 10 000 of the charges bounced back from the foil as if it had been deflected by something very massive and positively charged—the nucleus. nucleus atom In 1932, James Chadwick, Rutherford's student, proposed that in addition to protons, the nucleus also contains neutral particles called **neutrons**. Each neutron in an atom has about the same mass as each proton in the same atom.	Bohr concluded from his experiments that electrons jump between specific energy levels around the nucleus by gaining or losing energy. Each level can contain only a specific number of electrons.	Based on scientific arguments and evidence, many scientists concluded that electrons could exist at various distances from the nucleus, rather than at specific energy levels as Bohr originally stated. The chance of finding electrons at particular distances can be calculated. This probable distance changes depending on the different energy levels Bohr had identified.

©P

5.1 Developing Models of Matter   **153**

1. Describe basic differences between an Indigenous approach to understanding the physical world and a scientific approach.

2. Explain why scientists want to develop models of the atom.

3. What are the key points of Dalton's atomic model?

4. What evidence led J.J. Thomson to believe that atoms of all elements contain electrons?

reSearch

Modern understanding of the properties of matter is built on the inquiries of many different people from around the world working over the ages. The alchemists, for example, were people who tried to use magic and chemical changes to turn various substances into gold. In 1597, the German alchemist Andreas Libau published *Alchemia*, a book describing the achievements of alchemists. In it, Libau explained how to prepare chemicals such as hydrochloric acid. Use reliable sources from the Internet to find out what else the alchemists discovered.

Suggested Activity •⋯⋯⋯⋯
B9 Quick Science on page 156

A Summary of the Modern Model of the Atom

All elements and compounds are composed of atoms, and one atom is the smallest unit of any element. Although there are more than 100 different elements, each with its own kind of atoms, the atoms themselves are made of different kinds of smaller particles, called **subatomic particles**. Three subatomic particles that relate closely to the property and reactivity of atoms are protons, neutrons, and electrons, and these particles have different properties.

One such property is relative mass. **Relative mass** compares the mass of an object to the mass of another object. An electron is the smallest of the above three subatomic particles, so scientists chose to assign it a relative mass of 1. Compared to it, a proton has a relative mass of 1836, meaning that it is 1836 times heavier than an electron. A neutron is 1837 times heavier than an electron. This property of the particles is summarized in Table 5.2, along with electric charge and location within the atom.

Table 5.2 Properties of Subatomic Particles

Name	Symbol	Relative Mass	Electric Charge	Location
Proton	p	1836	1+	nucleus
Neutron	n	1837	0	nucleus
Electron	e	1	1−	in energy levels surrounding the nucleus in the electron cloud

1. How does J.J. Thomson's atomic model differ from the model depicted by a Bohr diagram?

2. Atoms contain electrons, which are negatively charged. Why are atoms electrically neutral?

3. Explain how J.J. Thomson's conclusion about electrons was an important step in the development of the atomic theory.

4. A statement is missing from the atomic theory below. What is missing?
   • Atoms of different elements have different properties.
   • All matter is made of small, individual particles called atoms.
   • Atoms of different elements can combine to form new substances.

5. (a) Why do you think it took so long for people to accept the concept of atoms?
   (b) Describe a discovery or experiment that might have made it easier for people to believe in atoms.

6. Describe three ways in which protons are different from electrons.

7. Describe the evidence that led Rutherford to his conclusion about the atomic nucleus.

8. Describe how the relative mass of a subatomic particle is defined.

9. Which two subatomic particles contribute to the majority of the mass of an atom?

10. Write the electric charge for each of the following subatomic particles.
    (a) neutron
    (b) proton
    (c) electron

11. What are three features of a Bohr diagram that you observe from the Bohr diagrams for hydrogen and magnesium in Table 5.1 on page 152?

12. The most advanced model of the atom used today by scientists is the quantum mechanical model. How is this model different from the historic atomic models developed by Dalton, Thomson, Rutherford, and Bohr?

13. Use the following Bohr diagram of a fluorine atom to complete this question.

Question 13

(a) How many electrons does a fluorine atom have?
(b) How many protons does a fluorine atom have?

14. Consider a scientific element that is important in your life—for example, an element that makes up your watch or ring. How have your ideas about the composition of this element changed since completing this section?

Developing the Atomic Theory

It takes many scientists exploring different possibilities to refine a theory. The modern atomic theory took shape only after many debates, novel ideas, and experiments. Even today, scientists are making discoveries that will add to our understanding of the atom.

Purpose

To learn about the contribution of particular scientists to atomic theory

Procedure

1. Choose a scientist to research from the timeline shown in Figure 5.3 or one that is approved by your teacher.

2. Find information from two sources on the scientist that you have decided to research.

   • Focus on one way that the scientist's work has shaped our understanding of the atom.

   • Find out about at least one challenge that the scientist had to overcome.

Questions

3. How did your scientist's contributions alter the previous model of the atom?

4. How were your scientist's ideas revised once further research was done?

5. Do you think today's atomic model will be changed in the future? Why or why not?

6. Why are collaboration and communication between scientists necessary?

Pose New Questions

7. Ultimately, who do you think made the most significant contribution to current atomic theory? Justify your response.

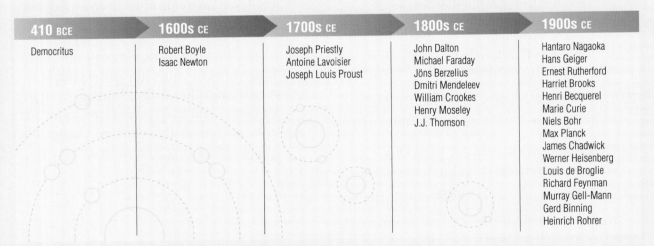

410 BCE	1600s CE	1700s CE	1800s CE	1900s CE
Democritus	Robert Boyle Isaac Newton	Joseph Priestly Antoine Lavoisier Joseph Louis Proust	John Dalton Michael Faraday Jöns Berzelius Dmitri Mendeleev William Crookes Henry Moseley J.J. Thomson	Hantaro Nagaoka Hans Geiger Ernest Rutherford Harriet Brooks Henri Becquerel Marie Curie Niels Bohr Max Planck James Chadwick Werner Heisenberg Louis de Broglie Richard Feynman Murray Gell-Mann Gerd Binning Heinrich Rohrer

Figure 5.3 Timeline of contributors to the atomic theory

Figure 5.4 Many elements have properties that make them well-suited for use in jewellery.

The Elements We Wear

Jewellery is very personal. Some people never wear it. Others wear it all the time. Sometimes, as in Figure 5.4, people wear it for special occasions. The element gold is used in making jewellery because of its attractive colour and its resistance to corrosion. Gold is also one of the least reactive metals so it does not usually irritate human tissues and can be worn for long periods without causing discomfort. These properties of gold make it a precious metal.

A powwow is a traditional gathering of First Nations people for special ceremonies and celebrations. During a jingle dance for healing, the women dancers wear a dress decorated with jingles, which are tiny cone-shaped bells made from tin or sheet metal (Figure 5.5). The noise that the bells make at the dance represents the sound of water. Water, as you learned in section 4.1, is a sacred part of the physical world for many Indigenous people. The sound of water during the dance is intended to bring healing. Tin and other metals are hard enough to last longer than the traditional jingles made from shells or hooves from deer or moose, and the metals produce a good sound necessary for the dance.

Figure 5.5 As the dancer moves, the jingles on the dancer's dress make noise that represents the sound of water.

Meet the Elements

Like the early chemists, you will examine various elements and observe their different properties (Figure 5.6). You will then look for patterns that you can use to group these elements.

Purpose

To compare the properties of familiar elements

Materials & Equipment

- samples of elements (such as aluminum, carbon, copper,

  iodine, (T) (🖐)

  magnesium, (🔥)

  silver, sulphur, (🔥)

  or zinc (🔥))
- magnet
- low-voltage conductivity tester
- hand magnifying lens

CAUTION: Follow your teacher's directions about handling each element. Some are too reactive or toxic to touch. If a container is sealed, do not open it.

Figure 5.6 Pure iodine is a solid, shiny, deep purple coloured crystal.

Procedure

1. Create an observation table in your notebook with the following column headings: Element, Symbol, State, Appearance, Hardness, Magnetism, Electrical Conductivity. Give your table a title.

2. Your teacher will tell you how many element samples to observe. They may be examined in any order. Each time you examine an element, record its name and symbol in your table.

3. Examine each element, and record your observations of its properties in your table. Use the following guidelines to help you:

   State: Is it a solid, a liquid, or a gas at room temperature?

   Appearance: Describe its colour, lustre, opacity, and texture.

   Hardness: Is it easily scratched?

   Magnetism: Is it magnetic?

   Electrical Conductivity: Does it conduct an electric current?

Questions

4. What similarities are there among most of the elements that conduct electricity? Do any of these elements have different properties from the other conductive elements? Explain.

5. Are all conductive elements that you observed also magnetic?

6. Given that copper is a metallic element, classify each of the elements that you observed as either metallic or non-metallic.

Pose New Questions

7. How many magnetic elements did you find? How might these elements be useful?

8. What other questions could you ask about the properties of the elements used in this activity?

Elements and Their Symbols

Scientists have discovered approximately 90 elements that occur naturally on Earth. In recent years, scientists have made more than 25 new elements artificially in laboratories. Some only last for a few seconds. Based on the properties of elements, all can be sorted into three classes: metals, non-metals, and metalloids.

Metals and Their Properties

Most elements are **metals**. Of the metals, most are shiny and silver or grey in colour. They are all excellent conductors of electricity and heat. They are also malleable and ductile. As described in Chapter 4, a malleable substance can be beaten into sheets, and a ductile substance can be stretched into long wires.

Silver is a metal (Figure 5.7). Pure, polished silver has an attractive, almost white appearance. It can be moulded and shaped easily and is often used to make jewellery or special table cutlery. It is also one of the best conductors of electricity.

Some metals, such as sodium, react explosively with water. Others, such as platinum, will not react even if mixed with strong acids. Almost every metal is a solid at room temperature, but mercury metal is unique in that it is a liquid at room temperature.

Figure 5.7 Silver metal is used in jewellery, coins, and table cutlery, which is sometimes called silverware.

Suggested Activity • • • • • • • • • • • •
B11 Quick Science on page 166

Combining Metals

Both tin and gold have a low melting point. This means they can be poured into a mould and made into a wide variety of shapes. However, they are too weak to be used alone for some purposes. Tin is used to coat other metals to form tin cans because it is non-toxic. To make gold jewellery stronger, melted gold is mixed with other melted metal elements. The mixture is cooled to become a solid solution (Figure 5.8).

A solution of two or more metals is called an **alloy**. An alloy of gold and a white metal, such as nickel or manganese, is sometimes called white gold because it has a lighter colour than pure gold. White gold is often used in engagement rings and wedding bands to give them strength and durability. An understanding of the metal elements and how they combine has led to the invention and mass production of a wide range of alloys. Alloys are also used in magnets, sports equipment, vehicles, and many household items.

Figure 5.8 These pieces of jewellery are made from pure gold and a mixture of gold and other metals.

Non-Metals and Their Properties

Only 17 of the known elements are classified by scientists as **non-metals**. These elements are grouped together not because they have similarities, but because they simply do not resemble metals. For example, 11 of the non-metals are gases at room temperature, five are solids, and one, bromine, is a red-brown liquid (Figure 5.9). Solid non-metals generally do not conduct heat or electricity well, are brittle and not malleable, and have little or no metallic lustre. Sulphur is an example of a solid non-metal (Figure 5.10). It is brittle and will crumble if struck. It is yellow, does not conduct electricity, and is not shiny. It is reactive and will burn in air to produce a poisonous gas. With a little heating, it will melt into a liquid.

Figure 5.9 The element bromine is a red-brown liquid at room temperature. Pure bromine is very reactive and toxic.

Figure 5.10 The element sulphur is a yellow solid.

Metalloids and Their Properties

The remaining elements are called metalloids. The **metalloids** are elements with metallic and non-metallic properties. Metalloids conduct electricity but not very well, and so they are called semiconductors. It is easier to control the flow of electricity through semiconductors than through conductors. For this reason, metalloids are often used in electronic devices, such as computers.

Silicon is the most common metalloid. Pure silicon is shiny and grey, but unlike a metal, it is brittle (Figure 5.11). Although pure silicon is rare in nature, in combination with other elements it makes up sand and many other compounds. The microscopic structures shown in Figure 5.12 are made from a silicon compound. About 40 percent of the mass of almost any rock comes from silicon. It is also a major component of glass.

Figure 5.11 Pure silicon is shiny but brittle.

Figure 5.12 These microscopic structures, called "silicon nanoflowers," contain wires that could be used in tiny electronic devices. Each flower is about 0.005 mm long.

Element Symbols

Many languages spoken worldwide have their own name for each of the elements. To make communicating easier, chemists have agreed to use the same set of symbols for the elements. For example, the symbol for the element hydrogen is H. An element symbol also represents one atom of the element in chemical formulas and chemical equations that describe chemical reactions. Many of the names for elements that have been known for a long time are based on their Latin names.

©P

The names of the elements silicon and silver, like sulphur, begin with the letter "s." In fact, they both begin with "si." To tell them apart, silicon was given the symbol Si. Silver, which has the Latin name *argentum*, was given the symbol Ag. Table 5.3 lists some of the elements' names and symbols.

Table 5.3 Selected Element Names and Symbols

English Name	Symbol	Non-English Name and Meaning
Non-Metals		
hydrogen	H	*Hydro genes*—water generating
helium	He	*Helios*—the Sun
neon	Ne	*Neos*—new
argon	Ar	*Argos*—inactive or idle
fluorine	F	*Fluere*—flowing
chlorine	Cl	*Chloros*—yellow-green
bromine	Br	*Bromos*—pungent odour
iodine	I	*Iodes*—violet
oxygen	O	*Oxy genes*—acid forming
phosphorus	P	*Phosphoros*—light bringer
carbon	C	*Carbo*—charcoal
Metalloids		
silicon	Si	*Silex*—flint
germanium	Ge	*Germania*—Germany
Metals		
lithium	Li	*Lithos*—stone
sodium	Na	*Natrium*—Latin name for soda ash
potassium	K	*Kalium*—Latin name for potash
rubidium	Rb	*Rubidius*—ruby-red
magnesium	Mg	*Magnesia*—a location in Greece
calcium	Ca	*Calx*—limestone
chromium	Cr	*Chroma*—colour
iron	Fe	*Ferrum*—ancient Latin name
nickel	Ni	*Kupfernickel*—devil's copper
copper	Cu	*Cuprum*—Cyprus
silver	Ag	*Argentum*—ancient Latin name
gold	Au	*Aurum*—glow of sunrise
mercury	Hg	*Hydragyrum*—liquid silver
lead	Pb	*Plumbum*—ancient Latin name

An element symbol consists of one or two letters. The first letter is always capitalized. If there is a second letter, it is not capitalized. The symbols in the middle column of Table 5.3 show how these rules are followed. These rules about capitalization are very important. For example, the symbol Co stands for the metal element cobalt, while CO represents carbon monoxide, a poisonous compound produced in car exhaust that is made up of the elements carbon (C) and oxygen (O).

Learning Checkpoint

1. What makes mercury different from other metal elements?
2. (a) Compare and contrast the properties of silver, sulphur, and silicon.
   (b) How are these elements classified?
3. Give the symbols for the elements nitrogen, nickel, and lead.
4. How is the Latin name for gold related to its element symbol?

Some Common Elements

Human history has long been influenced by the availability of certain elements. The Iron Age began several thousand years ago, when technologies to obtain iron from iron ore became widespread. When another element, carbon, was added to iron, steel was formed.

Two other elements, hydrogen and oxygen, can combine to make water, a pure substance vital to living organisms. Another two elements, sodium and chlorine, can combine to form another pure substance that rivals water in importance: table salt. Without either water or salt, life as we know it could not survive.

Iron (Fe)

Like most metals, iron is silver-grey and can be moulded and shaped when heated. Iron is very strong, and when combined with carbon to make steel, it is even stronger (Figure 5.13). It is hard enough to keep a sharp edge, a property that people have used for centuries in order to make tools and household items.

Carbon (C)

Pure carbon exists in several forms, including graphite and diamond. Both diamonds and graphite form underground as the remains of organisms become compressed. Coal is a black solid composed mostly of carbon in the form of graphite. Around the world, coal is mined and burned to produce heat energy, mainly for generating electricity. Burning coal produces air pollution and is a major contributor of greenhouse gases to the atmosphere. These gases can affect our climate.

In diamond, the carbon atoms are connected differently than they are in graphite. Diamond is the hardest natural substance known, yet light can easily pass through it. These properties make it a prized gemstone (Figure 5.14).

Carbon is also one of the main building blocks of life. Your body and the food you eat contain many different carbon compounds.

Figure 5.13 Iron is very strong and somewhat flexible. These properties make it useful for building bridges and other structures.

Figure 5.14 Diamonds are found in a rock called kimberlite. Extremely high temperatures and pressures are needed for diamonds to form.

Hydrogen (H)

Hydrogen is the most common element in the universe. It makes up most of the atoms in the stars as well as large planets like Jupiter and Saturn. Hydrogen atoms are the simplest and lightest of all atoms. At the centre of stars, including our own Sun, hydrogen nuclei combine in a nuclear fusion reaction (forced together by high pressure) to form atoms of other elements.

On Earth, almost all of the hydrogen atoms that are present are in water. Pure hydrogen occurs in nature as a gas in the form of two hydrogen atoms connected together (H_2). The gas is colourless, odourless, and lighter than air. Its low density means it can be used in weather balloons (Figure 5.15). It is also extremely flammable, which is a good reason for not using it in balloons that carry people.

Figure 5.15 A hydrogen-filled weather balloon

Oxygen (O)

Pure oxygen is a gas at room temperature. It makes up about 21 percent of the air we breathe, and our bodies need a constant supply of oxygen to survive (Figure 5.16). Just as pure carbon can exist in more than one form, so can pure oxygen. The oxygen gas that we breathe is in the form of two oxygen atoms connected together (O_2). This form is simply called oxygen gas. Most of the oxygen gas in Earth's atmosphere comes from plants and algae, which produce oxygen while using sunlight to make sugar.

Figure 5.16 This person is using an oxygen tank to help her breathe more easily.

Ozone is a form of pure oxygen in which three oxygen atoms are connected together (O_3). Ozone is toxic for living organisms to breathe, and when it occurs close to the ground it is a pollutant (Figure 5.17). However, in the upper atmosphere, ozone forms a layer that absorbs harmful ultraviolet light. Without the ozone layer, ultraviolet light would kill much of life on Earth.

Oxygen is the most common element on Earth's surface. Oxygen makes up more than 50 percent of the mass of most rocks, in which it is combined with other elements such as silicon or aluminum. When certain kinds of rocks are ground up, they become sand, which can be melted and rehardened to form glass. Most of the atoms in glass are oxygen atoms.

Figure 5.17 A leaf damaged by ground-level ozone

Sodium (Na)

Sodium is a metal, and so it shares many properties with iron. Both conduct electricity and are shiny, silver-grey, malleable, and ductile. However, they also have distinct differences. Iron reacts slowly with oxygen and moisture to form rust. In contrast, sodium metal reacts immediately and violently if it contacts either air or water (Figure 5.18). Pure sodium metal is usually stored in oil, where it can remain without reacting for a long time.

Sodium metal is so soft that a knife easily cuts right through it. Sodium also melts quite easily as it has a melting point of 98°C. Because it is so reactive, pure sodium does not exist on Earth, so these properties may seem unfamiliar to us. We are more familiar with sodium in compounds such as table salt (NaCl), which it forms with the element chlorine (Cl).

Figure 5.18 Sodium metal burns in air.

Chlorine (Cl)

Chlorine, a non-metal, is a yellow-green gas at room temperature (Figure 5.19). It occurs in nature in the form of two chlorine atoms connected together (Cl_2). High concentrations of chlorine gas are toxic to living organisms and will quickly destroy lung tissue. At lower concentrations, chlorine is extremely useful as a disinfectant. It is added to swimming pools and community water supplies in order to kill bacteria and other organisms that spread disease.

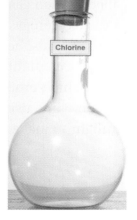

Figure 5.19 Used in the correct concentrations, chlorine will purify community water supplies.

During Writing

Adding Details

To add details to your writing, explain what something is and provide one or more examples or even describe real-life situations to give a good picture of the topic. Note the ways that the paragraph on chlorine uses some of these methods for adding details.

©P

1. (a) Give the names and symbols of the two elements that are liquids at room temperature.

   (b) Classify each of the elements you named in (a) as a metal, a metalloid, or a non-metal.

2. Using Table 5.3 on page 161, identify what element was named after each meaning below, then write the symbol for that element.

   (a) ruby-red

   (b) the Sun

   (c) water generating

   (d) acid forming

   (e) charcoal

   (f) colour

3. Using Table 5.3 on page 161, find the common name and symbol of each element from the ancient Latin name provided below.

   (a) natrium

   (b) ferrum

   (c) argentum

   (d) plumbum

4. List the following elements in order of their ability to conduct electricity, starting with the least conductive: Si, Ag, S.

5. List two elements present in each of the following.

   (a) steel

   (b) water

   (c) table salt

6. The metal element shown in the photograph reacts violently with water. Suggest the identity of the element shown. Justify your response.

Question 6

7. Identify the element that has each of the following properties.

   (a) It is the lightest element.

   (b) It is the most common element on Earth's surface.

   (c) It is the major component of steel because of its strength.

   (d) It is a metalloid that is a major component of glass.

   (e) It exists in several forms, one of which is the hardest natural substance known.

   (f) It is a yellow-green gas used to kill bacteria and other organisms in swimming pools.

8. (a) What is ozone?

   (b) Explain how ozone can be both harmful and beneficial to life.

9. Briefly describe three environmental issues related to pure elements that you learned about in this section.

Growing Silver

A crystal is a solid with atoms that are arranged in a very regular way. Some crystals, such as salt crystals, contain two or more types of elements. Other crystals, such as silver crystals, contain atoms of only one type of element (Figure 5.20). To produce a sample of silver, you can grow a crystal from its atoms.

Purpose

To grow a silver crystal

Materials & Equipment

- microscope slide
- dissecting microscope
- 2 cm of copper ribbon
- 0.1 M silver nitrate solution in a dropper bottle

CAUTION: Do not get silver nitrate on your skin. Wear gloves for this activity.

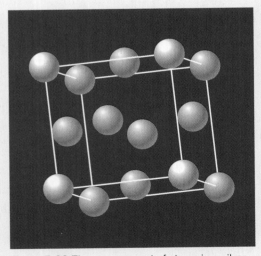

Figure 5.20 The arrangement of atoms in a silver crystal is very regular.

Procedure

1. Place a piece of copper ribbon on the microscope slide.

2. Place the slide on the microscope stage, and focus on one edge of the piece of copper ribbon. Record your observations of the copper ribbon.

3. Squeeze a drop of silver nitrate solution onto the copper ribbon.

4. Look through the microscope to observe changes to the copper ribbon. Look for silver crystals forming on the edges of the copper. Record your observations.

5. Wash your hands after putting the materials and equipment away.

Questions

6. Based on your observations, describe some of the properties of copper and silver.

7. What evidence suggests that the crystals that formed were silver crystals and not copper?

8. Do you think the changes you observed were physical or chemical? Explain.

Pose New Questions

9. Silver is a highly valued element. Why could we not "grow" silver on a massive scale instead of mining it?

10. Compose a question about the production of silver that you would like to know more about.

©P

Figure 5.21 Hydrogen peroxide is a chemical compound that may be used to create highlights in hair.

Here is a summary of what you will learn in this section:

- Compounds are pure substances composed of two or more elements that combine chemically in a specific ratio.

- Ionic compounds form when metallic and non-metallic elements combine chemically.

- Molecular compounds form when non-metallic elements combine chemically.

Elements and Compounds Everywhere

We live in a chemical world. Every kind of substance that you can think of is made of elements or compounds. Water, air, the ink in your pen, hair dyes and bleaches, the lead-lined cover that protects you during a dental X-ray, and lifesaving medicines are all made of elements and compounds (Figure 5.21).

A quick look around your home will reveal an amazing variety of chemicals in your cupboards and on your shelves. In the bathroom, you will find water, soap, shampoo, deodorant, and toothpaste—all elements or compounds. In the storage area, you might find cleaning products, such as ammonia and bleach, and perhaps painting and gardening products. In your kitchen, you might find table salt, baking soda, and baking powder. Each of these products contains one or more compounds.

Compounds

Recall that a compound is a pure substance made up of two or more elements that are chemically combined. For example, water is a compound consisting of the elements hydrogen and oxygen. Hydrogen peroxide is also a compound of the elements hydrogen and oxygen but with completely different properties than water (Figure 5.22).

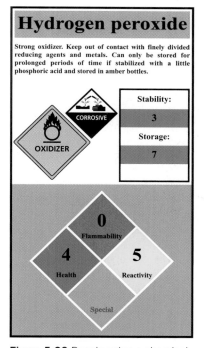

Figure 5.22 People using a chemical such as hydrogen peroxide in their workplace must, by law, be trained in the meaning of all the safety symbols on the label.

Table 5.4 Properties of Water and Hydrogen Peroxide

Water (H_2O)
• colourless liquid • boils at 100°C • stable in strong sunlight • dissolves the chemical potassium iodide • does not bleach pigments

Hydrogen peroxide (H_2O_2)
• blue liquid • boils at 150.2°C • breaks down in light • reacts with the chemical potassium iodide • strong bleaching agent

Some of the differences between water and hydrogen peroxide are listed in Table 5.4. Pure hydrogen peroxide is a blue liquid that can dissolve in water to form a solution, which is commonly available in pharmacies. In certain concentrations, it can be used on skin to kill bacteria or in hair as a bleaching agent.

All compounds have properties that make them potentially useful as well as hazardous. If a highly concentrated solution of hydrogen peroxide gets on the skin, it will cause a burn. Even water, if consumed in huge volumes, can make a person sick. Understanding the properties of compounds gives us the knowledge to make use of compounds safely and responsibly.

B12 *Quick Science*

Water and Hydrogen Peroxide (Teacher Demonstration)

Purpose

To observe properties of water and hydrogen peroxide

Materials & Equipment

- blue litmus paper (a chemical indicator that turns pink in an acidic solution)
- two 400-mL beakers
- water
- hydrogen peroxide solution

- cobalt chloride paper (a chemical indicator that is blue when dry and is pink in the presence of water)

- scoopula
- stirring rod
- potassium iodide crystals
- 250-mL graduated cylinder
- basin
- dish soap
- matches
- wooden splint

CAUTION: Hydrogen peroxide is corrosive to skin. Potassium iodide will stain skin and clothing.

Procedure

1. Your teacher will dip one piece of blue litmus paper into water and another into hydrogen peroxide solution. Observe the litmus paper.

2. Your teacher will dip one piece of cobalt chloride paper into water and another into hydrogen peroxide solution. Observe the cobalt chloride paper.

3. Observe as your teacher pours water into a beaker and then stirs in some potassium iodide crystals.

4. Your teacher will place the graduated cylinder in the basin and then pour 20 mL of hydrogen peroxide solution and three drops of dish soap into the graduated cylinder. Observe as your teacher adds a small scoop of potassium iodide crystals.

5. Step 4 will produce bubbles of gas. Observe as your teacher places a glowing splint into the gas.

Question

6. Describe three differences in the properties of water and hydrogen peroxide that you observed.

Pose New Questions

7. What questions could you ask about two substances you learned in this chapter that contain the same element but have very different properties?

©P

Two Types of Compounds

A small change in the way the atoms combine can make a big difference in the chemical and physical properties of compounds. Although millions of compounds are known to scientists, they classify almost all of them as one of two types: ionic or molecular.

Ionic Compounds

Common table salt is familiar to most people as a white substance composed of tiny crystals. As described in section 5.2, table salt forms when a very reactive metal—sodium—combines with a poisonous, yellow-green non-metal—chlorine gas. When sodium metal is placed in a container of chlorine gas (Figure 5.23), the metal explodes in a bright orange flame. As the sodium burns, a white, coarse-grained powder is produced. This new substance is table salt, or sodium chloride (NaCl). Sodium chloride is a typical ionic compound and has properties very different from the properties of the elements sodium and chlorine.

During Writing

Keep Your Emotions in Check

Scientists try to be objective rather than emotional. They base their arguments on research—their conclusions are drawn from observations and experiments. As you prepare arguments for a debate, remember to keep emotions in check and to base your points on scientific research.

Suggested Activity •·········
B13 Quick Science on page 174

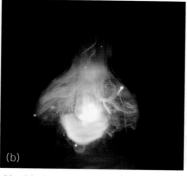

Figure 5.23 Sodium (a) is a metal. Sodium combines with chlorine gas in a violent reaction (b). The compound that forms is sodium chloride, NaCl (c).

Ionic compounds are pure substances usually consisting of at least one metal and one non-metal. Most ionic compounds share the following properties:

- have high melting points
- form crystals, which are very regular three-dimensional arrangements of particles
- dissolve in water to form solutions that conduct electricity
- are solids at room temperature

Table salt will not melt until it is heated to 800°C. When sodium chloride is dissolved in water or melted, it will conduct electricity. Investigations of this property led to the study of electrochemical cells, which can convert chemical energy into electricity.

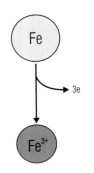

infoBIT

Meaning of "Ion"

The word "ion" comes from a Greek word meaning to go or to wander.

Forming Ionic Compounds

When elements combine to form an ionic compound, an atom or a group of atoms loses or gains electrons to form an **ion** with an electric charge. Metal atoms generally tend to lose electrons. Since electrons have a negative charge, a metal atom that loses electrons becomes a positive ion. Many non-metal atoms can gain electrons and so become negative ions. When sodium combines with chlorine, an electron from the highest energy level of a sodium atom moves over to a chlorine atom. This produces a positive sodium ion and a negative chloride ion. The process is shown in Figure 5.24. The ionic compound formed, sodium chloride, is **neutral**—there is no overall electric charge—the positive and negative charges are equal.

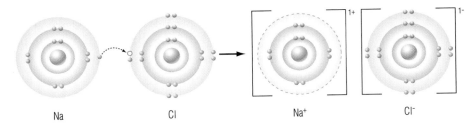

Figure 5.24 A sodium atom becomes a positive ion when it loses an electron to chlorine. By gaining an electron, chlorine becomes a negative chloride ion. Together, they form a neutral ionic compound.

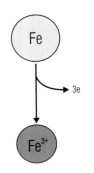

Figure 5.25 When an iron atom loses electrons, it becomes a positive ion.

Some metals can form more than one type of ion. For example, an iron atom can lose two electrons to become an ion with a 2+ charge or it can lose three electrons to become an ion with a 3+ charge (Figure 5.25). Sometimes, a group of atoms of different elements with an overall electric charge acts as a single ion. This type of ion is called a **polyatomic ion**. For example, baking soda, or sodium hydrogen carbonate ($NaHCO_3$), is an ionic compound composed of positive sodium ions (Na^+) and negative hydrogen carbonate ions (HCO_3^-).

Positive and negative ions attract each other. Scientists call the attraction between atoms or ions a **bond**. The attraction between two ions of opposite charges is called an **ionic bond**. Ionic bonding is not a one-direction attraction—it can extend in all directions. In an ionic compound, ions are arranged in a crystal **lattice**, which is a regular, patterned three-dimensional structure (Figure 5.26). Each ion is attracted by more than one oppositely charged ion in its neighbourhood. Since the ions are held strongly in the crystal lattice, it is not easy to break them apart. This explains why most ionic compounds are hard solids with high melting points.

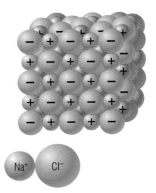

Figure 5.26 The positive and negative ions in this table salt are held together by ionic bonds.

©P

1. What is the main difference between a compound and an element?

2. What two kinds of elements usually join together to form an ionic compound?

3. How must atoms change so that they can join to form an ionic compound?

4. What physical property or properties could you use to identify an ionic compound?

Molecular Compounds

Table sugar, water, and hydrogen peroxide are common molecular compounds. **Molecular compounds** are pure substances usually formed when non-metal elements combine. In a molecular compound, atoms join together by sharing electrons in their highest energy level to form small groups, called **molecules**. A molecule is the smallest possible amount of a pure substance that can exist. Most molecular compounds share the following properties:

- can be solids, liquids, or gases at room temperature

- are usually good insulators, or poor conductors, of electricity

- have relatively low boiling points

Scientists call the sharing of a pair of electrons between atoms a **covalent bond**. A molecule is a neutral group of atoms held together by covalent bonds. There are a number of ways to represent the bonding in a molecule. In every representation of water in Figure 5.27, two hydrogen atoms are bonded to an oxygen atom in the middle. The Bohr diagram of water shows that each hydrogen atom forms a covalent bond with the oxygen atom (Figure 5.27 (a)). In the ball-and-stick model, each stick represents a bond between atoms (Figure 5.27 (b)). In the third diagram, the areas in which the atoms overlap represent the bonds that hold the atoms together (Figure 5.27 (c)).

Suggested Activities •·········
B14 Skill Builder on page 174
B15 Quick Science on page 175

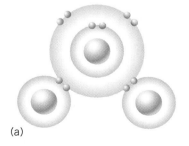
(a)

(b)

(c)

Figure 5.27 Representations of a water molecule: (a) a Bohr diagram; (b) a ball-and-stick model, in which the sticks represent the bonds between atoms; (c) a diagram with overlap between atoms to show how they are bonded

Figure 5.28 A ball-and-stick model of a hydrogen peroxide molecule: the stick between the two oxygen atoms in the middle represents the bond between the atoms.

A hydrogen peroxide molecule is made from joining two hydrogen atoms to two oxygen atoms as shown by the ball-and-stick model in Figure 5.28. How can the same two elements (hydrogen and oxygen) combine to form molecular compounds as different as water and hydrogen peroxide? Compared to a water molecule, the structurally different hydrogen peroxide molecule is larger and the atoms are held together by different bonds. This explains why the two compounds have very different physical and chemical properties.

For some elements, each atom of the element shares electrons with another atom of the same element to form a more stable molecule to exist in nature. Since each of their molecules contains two atoms of the same element, these elements are said to occur in nature as **diatomic molecules**.

Chemical Names and Formulas

Every compound has a chemical name and formula. The **chemical formula** identifies which elements, and how many atoms or ions of each, are in the compound. For example, sodium chloride's formula is NaCl. NaCl contains one sodium ion and one chloride ion. Baking soda's chemical name is sodium hydrogen carbonate, and its chemical formula is $NaHCO_3$. $NaHCO_3$ indicates that one sodium ion combines with one hydrogen carbonate ion. Each hydrogen carbonate ion is formed from one atom of hydrogen, one atom of carbon, and three atoms of oxygen. The subscript "3" indicates that three atoms of oxygen are in one ion. The chemical formula H_2O for water indicates that two atoms of hydrogen and one atom of oxygen chemically combine to form one molecule of water.

$$H + H + O \longrightarrow H_2O$$

Hydrogen (2 atoms) and oxygen (1 atom) chemically combine to form water (1 molecule).

Elements that exist in nature as diatomic molecules have in their formulas a subscript "2" indicating that two atoms of each element are in one molecule. These elements include hydrogen (H_2), nitrogen (N_2), oxygen (O_2), fluorine (F_2), chlorine (Cl_2), bromine (Br_2), iodine (I_2), and astatine (At_2).

©P

1. What is the difference between a compound and a mixture?

2. What are the two major types of compounds? How do the bonds differ in each type?

3. Give an example of a molecular compound.

4. Give an example of a substance held together by ionic bonds.

5. What types of elements join to form molecular compounds? Name three such elements.

6. How is it possible for two different compounds, such as water and hydrogen peroxide, to both be made of the same two elements?

7. Use the diagram below to answer the following questions.

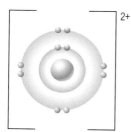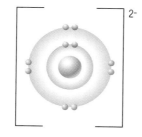

Question 7

(a) What type of diagram is shown?

(b) What type of compound is shown?

(c) What happens to the electrons in the two atoms when the compound is formed?

8. (a) Describe how a salt crystal holds together.

(b) Describe how the atoms in water are held together.

9. Examine the following table of properties of two unknown compounds, X and Y. Which is most likely an ionic compound and which is most likely a molecular compound? Explain your reasoning.

Properties of Unknown Compounds

Property	Compound X	Compound Y
Boiling point (°C)	82	1550
Melting point (°C)	−90	455
Conductivity in solution	poor	good

10. Can compounds have properties different from the properties of the elements from which they are formed? Explain, using an example.

11. For each of the following compounds with the chemical formula given, state the elements and how many atoms of each element are involved in forming the compound.

(a) sulphuric acid, H_2SO_4

(b) sucrose (table sugar), $C_{12}H_{22}O_{11}$

(c) iron(III) oxide, Fe_2O_3

12. Name two compounds that you were familiar with before reading this section. Now that you have completed this section, what have you learned about these two compounds?

Salt and Sugar

Adding sugar to your tea, or salt to your soup, changes the way your food tastes. The sugar or salt will also dissolve to form a solution. That solution may or may not be able to conduct an electric current.

Purpose

To compare the conductivity of different compounds: sodium chloride (table salt) and sucrose (table sugar)

Materials & Equipment

- three 100-mL beakers
- marker
- tap water
- two small spoons
- sucrose (table sugar)
- sodium chloride (table salt)
- battery-operated conductivity tester

Procedure

1. Use the marker to label three 100-mL beakers as water, sucrose, and sodium chloride.

2. Fill each beaker with 50 mL of tap water. Set the beaker labelled "water" aside.

3. Add one small spoonful of sucrose to the second beaker. Use the spoon to stir until the sucrose dissolves completely in water.

4. Use a clean spoon to add one small spoonful of sodium chloride to the third beaker. Use the spoon to stir until the sodium chloride dissolves completely in water.

5. When your solutions are prepared, use a battery-operated conductivity tester (Figure 5.29) to determine whether any of the three samples conduct an electric current.

Question

6. Sodium chloride and sucrose are both shiny white crystals, and both dissolve in water. What evidence shows which of these crystals is an ionic compound?

Pose New Questions

7. What did you find out from this experiment that suggests why it is unsafe to have high-voltage electricity near water?

Figure 5.29 A conductivity tester—the light bulb is lit when an electric current flows.

Molecular Model Kits

In this activity, you will examine the components of a molecular model kit to prepare you to construct simple models. In the kit, balls represent atoms, and sticks represent bonds between the atoms. Carbon is represented by a black ball, oxygen by a red ball, chlorine by a green ball, and hydrogen by a white ball. The number of holes in each ball represents the number of bonds the atom can make with other atoms.

1. Examine the model atoms of carbon, oxygen, chlorine, and hydrogen. Construct as many bonds as you can between the different model atoms.

2. Describe what you observe about the different models you constructed.

Constructing Molecular Models

Chemists use models to represent information about the characteristics of molecules, such as their shape. The shape of a molecule is a good predictor of its properties. In this activity, you will construct ball-and-stick models of simple molecules (Figure 5.30) using a molecular model kit.

Purpose

To represent the molecules of some common molecular substances

---

Materials & Equipment

• molecular model kit

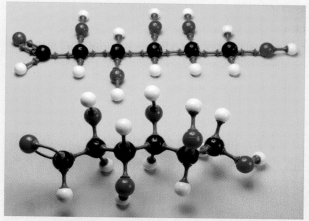

Figure 5.30 A ball-and-stick model of glucose, a type of sugar. Glucose can be straight or zig-zag, as shown here.

Procedure

1. Work in a small group to use the molecular model kit. Your teacher will provide specific information about how to use your particular kit.

2. There are two guidelines that you must follow when constructing molecular models:

   • Each molecule is complete when all the balls are bonded in such a way that all the holes are filled and every connector ends in a hole.

   • It is possible in some cases for more than one bond to exist between the same two atoms.

3. For each of the following, construct the model and then make a sketch of it.

   (a) H_2O (water)

   (b) H_2 (hydrogen gas)

   (c) O_2 (oxygen gas)

   (d) CH_4 (methane, also called natural gas)

   (e) CH_2Cl_2 (a solvent used as a degreaser)

   (f) C_2H_4 (starter material for making polyethylene plastic)

   (g) C_3H_8 (propane, a camp fuel)

   (h) HCl (hydrogen chloride, present in stomach acids)

   (i) H_2O_2 (hydrogen peroxide)

   (j) CO_2 (carbon dioxide)

4. The following molecules can each be assembled in two different ways. Construct and then make a sketch of each molecule.

   (a) C_2H_6O

   (b) C_3H_7Cl

Question

5. Identify the two molecules that represented elements as found in their natural state rather than compounds.

Pose New Questions

6. How do the positions of the holes in each kind of model atom produce a molecule that has a three-dimensional shape?

7. How many atoms does carbon bond with when there is only one bond made per atom? How does the shape of the molecule change as carbon makes more than one bond with other atoms?

Lee Wilson: Research Chemist

Dr. Wilson was the first in a small Métis community in Manitoba to go to university, the first in his family to complete a university degree, and the first Métis student to get a PhD from the University of Saskatchewan. For him, chemistry is not just a research project—it is a source of solutions to problems that touch our lives. Dr. Wilson is an award-winning professor of chemistry at the University of Saskatchewan, where he teaches and conducts research. He hopes his work will make a big difference in medical and environmental science.

Dr. Wilson's special interest is in nanostructured materials. Nanostructured materials are made from components too small to be seen even with a light microscope. These components, which are less than 0.0001 mm in size, are very useful for making membranes with tiny pores. Such membranes can be used as filters to purify water contaminated with toxic chemicals.

The opaque white material looks very ordinary, despite its special properties. Dr. Wilson says that the material acts like a sponge. Instead of trapping water, however, the material traps small particles, such as contaminants.

Personal experience has been a major motivating factor in Dr. Wilson's work. While working in rural Alberta, his father became dangerously ill due to contaminated water and had to have surgery. Dr. Wilson would like to see his research used so that even remote communities can protect their water supplies.

Dr. Wilson feels it is important to be a scientist with a conscience. Scientists should do work that benefits society as a whole, he says.

He also says it is important to follow your passion. "When I have a passion for something, whether it be a problem to solve or an idea of interest, it is the passion that carries me through the hardship, despite how difficult the challenges in solving the problem or learning a new skill may be."

Today he mentors young Aboriginal students participating in science fairs and camps and his own graduate students (Figure 5.31). His advice to young scientists is to get a good education, take lots of science courses, but also take courses in the arts. Scientists need to be able to communicate, he says, not just do research in a lab.

"Get a good grounding in each of the sciences— chemistry, biology, physics, and especially mathematics, because it is a foundational subject in all of the sciences and many future careers.

We live in a complex world with many challenges and today's youth need to empower themselves with education so that they can lead us into the future and seize the opportunities that are available to them," Dr. Lee Wilson says.

Figure 5.31 Dr. Lee Wilson with his students

©P

			Ti = 50	Zr = 90	? = 180
			V = 51	Nb = 94	Ta = 182
			Cr = 52	Mo = 96	W = 186
			Mn = 55	Rh = 104,4	Pt = 197,4
			Fe = 56	Ru = 104,4	Ir = 198
		Ni = Co = 59		Pl = 106,6	Os = 199
H = 1			Cu = 63,4	Ag = 108	Hg = 200
	Be = 9,4	Mg = 24	Zn = 65,2	Cd = 112	
	B = 11	Al = 27,4	? = 68	Ur = 116	Au = 197?
	C = 12	Si = 28	? = 70	Su = 118	
	N = 14	P = 31	As = 75	Sb = 122	Bi = 210
	O = 16	S = 32	Se = 79,4	Te = 128?	
	F = 19	Cl = 35,5	Br = 80	I = 127	
Li = 7	Na = 23	K = 39	Rb = 85,4	Cs = 133	Tl = 204
		? = 45	Sr = 87,5	Ba = 137	Pb = 207
		?Er = 56	Ce = 92		
		?Yt = 60	La = 94		
		?In = 75,5	Di = 95		
			Th = 118?		

Figure 5.32 Dmitri Mendeleev arranged the elements according to certain properties.

Here is a summary of what you will learn in this section:

- The periodic table organizes the elements by their properties, such as the mass of each element's atoms and the element's melting point.

- Atomic number is the number of protons in an atom and uniquely identifies an element.

- Bohr diagrams of the first 20 elements of the periodic table reveal important patterns that relate to the elements' properties.

Patterns Among the Elements

By the 1780s, chemists wondered why some elements, such as oxygen, were gases, while others, such as gold, were metals. To complicate matters, by the 1860s, the list of known elements had grown to 63. No one knew if that list included all the elements that existed or whether there were hundreds or even thousands more that were still undiscovered. Many chemists continued to search for a unifying pattern among the elements.

Then, in 1867, Russian chemist and teacher Dmitri Mendeleev (1834–1907) proposed organizing information about the elements into a table (Figure 5.32). He gathered all the information that he could about the known elements and wrote it down on cards, using one element per card (Figure 5.33). The information included properties such as estimates of the mass of the atoms of each element, colour, density, melting point, and what each element did or did not react with. He then sorted the cards into rows and columns, based on similarities in the elements' properties. This arrangement of cards formed a table, as shown in Figure 5.32. Within Mendeleev's table, and for the first time in history, a complete pattern of the elements began to emerge. In Mendeleev's table, all the cards representing metals ended up on one side, and all the non-metals ended up on the other. Metalloids were in the middle. Even most of the elements that were gases at room temperature were grouped together.

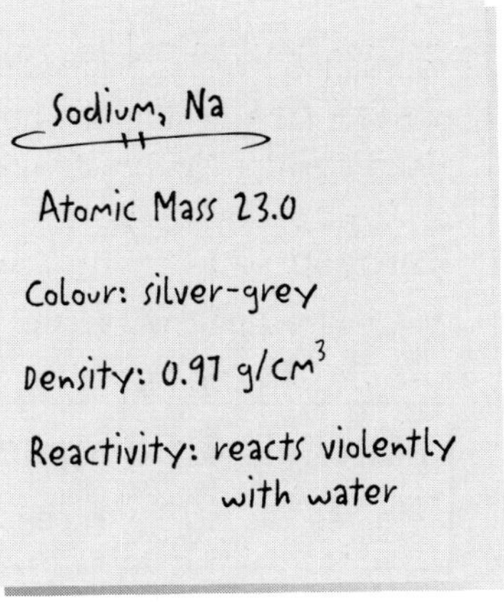

Sodium, Na

Atomic Mass 23.0

Colour: silver-grey

Density: 0.97 g/cm^3

Reactivity: reacts violently with water

Figure 5.33 Mendeleev gathered information on each known element and wrote it on a card.

A Table Based on Properties

Figure 5.34 Dmitri Mendeleev was the first to create a table that logically organized all the elements, including those undiscovered at the time.

Mendeleev knew that some elements were very similar, and it made sense to him to group them together (Figure 5.34). For example, he grouped together sodium, lithium, and other metals that reacted violently with water. Mendeleev had so much confidence in his arrangement that he left a gap in his table if he could not find an element with the right properties to put in a column. The gap represented an element that was yet to be discovered. Other chemists were doubtful.

Then, in 1886, the element germanium was discovered. Its properties were an exact match of the properties predicted for a missing element in Mendeleev's table. This evidence helped convince other scientists that Mendeleev had it right. Today, we use a table based on Mendeleev's table called the periodic table of the elements. Its rearrangement by Henry Moseley is based on the atomic number of the elements (Figure 5.35).

B16 *Quick Science*

Exploring the Periodic Table

Your teacher will provide you with a copy of the periodic table. Within the periodic table, you will look for patterns among the elements' properties.

Purpose

To become familiar with the periodic table

> **Materials & Equipment**
> - a periodic table
> - pencil crayons or highlighters

Procedure

1. Find the element boron (B) and shade it in. Then, with the same colour, shade in all elements that make a diagonal below and to the right of boron, starting with silicon (Si). Finally, shade in germanium (Ge), antimony (Sb), and polonium (Po). These elements are called the metalloids.

2. All the elements to the left of the metalloids, except hydrogen, are classified as metals. All the elements to the right of the metalloids are classified as non-metals. Label the metals and non-metals, but do not shade them.

3. All the elements in the farthest left column, except hydrogen, react violently with water. Shade them the same colour, and label them "alkali metals."

4. All the elements in the column to the right of the alkali metals are slightly less reactive than the alkali metals. Shade them another colour, and label them "alkaline earth metals."

5. Find column 17, and shade all the elements in it the same colour. Label the column "halogens." Find column 18, and shade those elements their own colour. Label them "noble gases."

Question

6. What is the advantage of colouring columns rather than rows?

Pose New Questions

7. What are other patterns in the properties among elements, such as the elements along the rows, that could be found in the periodic table?

©P

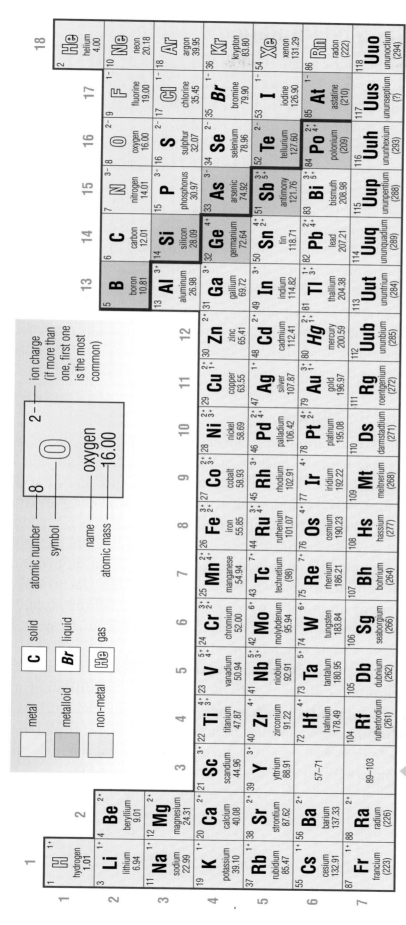

Figure 5.35 The periodic table of the elements

©P

The Modern Periodic Table

The **periodic table of elements** is a chart that places all of the elements in rows and columns. In the modern periodic table, elements are listed from left to right and top to bottom according to a property called atomic number.

Henry Moseley's research on atomic numbers helped explain the irregularities in the location of such elements as potassium and argon and the positioning of the two separate rows of elements near the bottom of the modern periodic table. Moseley proposed that atoms of the same element could have different atomic masses. Such atoms are called **isotopes**. This explained how atomic mass did not order the elements appropriately.

Moseley inspired others to develop the **periodic law**, a generalized description stating that elements arranged in order of atomic numbers show a periodic repetition of properties. His methods also permitted a complete survey of the elements, which showed that, with a few exceptions, the periodic table was complete.

Atomic Number

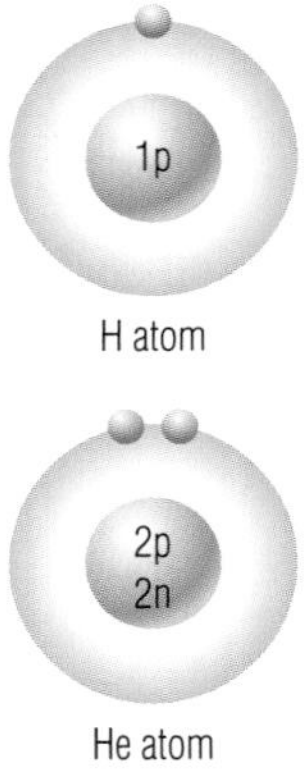

The **atomic number** of an element is defined as the number of protons in the nucleus of an atom of the element. The lowest atomic number is 1, which is the atomic number of the element hydrogen (H) (Figure 5.36). This means that every hydrogen atom has one proton in its nucleus. Hydrogen is placed in the top row and farthest left column of the table. The next element in the periodic table is helium (He), which has atomic number 2. All helium atoms have two protons. Another way to look at it is that any atom with two protons must be a helium atom. In other words, the number of protons in the nucleus of an atom, or the atomic number, determines the element.

Moving down to the next row and back to the farthest left column, the element with atomic number 3 is lithium (Li). Atomic number increases by one with each consecutive element. This increase continues though the entire table until the atomic number is well past 100. No one knows what the highest possible atomic number may be, but as of 2010 it was 118.

Figure 5.36 A hydrogen atom has one proton, and a helium atom has two protons.

©P

Atomic Mass and Ion Charge

Each element has its own square on the periodic table. The information given in the square is not always the same on different versions of the periodic table, but the element's name, symbol, and atomic number are almost always given. Figure 5.37, taken from the periodic table on page 179, shows two other pieces of information: atomic mass and ion charge.

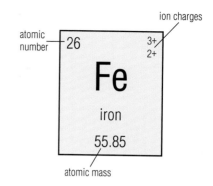

Figure 5.37 Information from the periodic table about iron (Fe)

Atomic Mass and Mass Number

Atomic mass is the average mass of an element's atoms. Atomic mass is given in **atomic mass units (amu)**. From the periodic table, we can see that the atomic mass of hydrogen is 1.01 amu and the atomic mass of iron is 55.85 amu (as shown in Figure 5.37). This means that iron atoms are about 55.85 times heavier than hydrogen atoms, which are the lightest of all atoms.

Atomic masses are always expressed as decimal numbers. One reason is that, except for fluorine, atoms of the same element have different numbers of neutrons. These atoms are isotopes of the element. For example, the most common type of hydrogen atom has one proton and one electron but no neutron. A small percentage of hydrogen atoms have one proton, one electron, and one neutron, and an even smaller percentage have one proton, one electron, and two neutrons. Recall that most of an atom's mass comes from its protons and neutrons. The total number of protons and neutrons in the nucleus of an atom is called the **mass number**. For this reason, isotopes of hydrogen having different numbers of neutrons have different masses, or they differ in their mass number. The atomic mass of hydrogen is an average of these masses.

Atomic mass generally increases in order of atomic number. However, there are a few exceptions to this pattern. For example, iodine (I) has a lower atomic mass than tellurium (Te). Can you find any others?

Ion Charge

As described in section 5.3, ions are formed when atoms or groups of atoms gain or lose electrons. **Ion charge** is the electric charge that an atom takes on when it loses or gains electrons, or ion charge is the charge of the ion formed. Elements with atoms that can form similar ions are grouped together in the periodic table. For example, elements in the first column on the left side of the periodic table all form positive ions of ion charge 1+.

The elements in the middle of the periodic table are called **transition metals**. They include common metals such as iron, copper, zinc, silver, gold, and mercury. The ion charges of these elements cannot be predicted from simple atomic theory. Many of them can form positive ions of different ion charges.

Some elements do not form ions. Helium, for example, does not normally form ions. For these elements, no ion charges are shown in their squares in the periodic table.

Learning Checkpoint

Use the periodic table to answer the following questions.

1. Write the atomic number of each of the following elements.
   (a) C   (b) O   (c) Na   (d) Si   (e) S   (f) Cl   (g) Fe

2. Name the element with the following number of protons in each atom.
   (a) 1   (b) 2   (c) 10   (d) 19   (e) 20   (f) 31   (g) 47

3. Write the atomic mass for each of the following elements.
   (a) H   (b) He   (c) N   (d) F   (e) S   (f) Ca   (g) Ag

4. Determine the number of electrons, protons, and neutrons of an isotope of an element with atomic number 6 and mass number 14.

5. Determine the electric charge on an ion of each of the following elements.
   (a) Li   (b) Be   (c) N   (d) S   (e) Al   (f) I

6. Hydrogen is a non-metal. It is located on the left side of the periodic table. What might be the reasons for placing hydrogen in this position?

7. Describe the general patterns in atomic masses and ion charges in the periodic table.

Periods and Chemical Families

The periodic table has seven horizontal rows. Each of these rows is called a **period**. A number written on the left side of the table identifies each period. For example, hydrogen and helium are in Period 1. Potassium is the first of 18 elements in Period 4.

There are 18 vertical columns in the periodic table, and each represents a different **group** (also called a **chemical family**). The elements within a group share certain physical and chemical properties. Each group has its own number, written at the top of the periodic table. For example, the element carbon (C) is in Group 14. It is also common to refer to a group by the first element in it. Group 14 is also called the carbon group. Some groups have special names (Figure 5.38). We will discuss three of these very important groups in more detail: alkali metals, halogens, and noble gases.

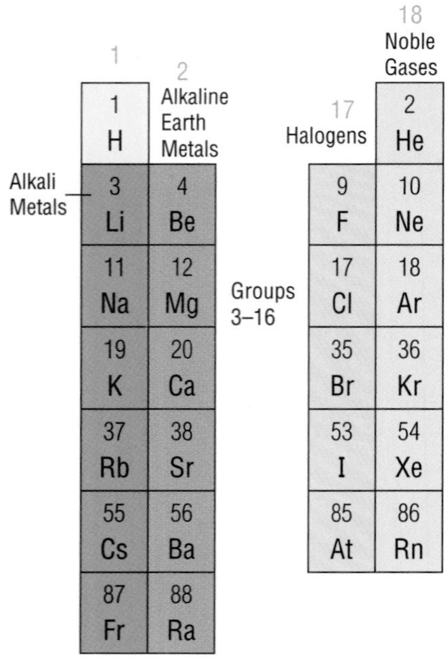

Figure 5.38 Four groups in the periodic table that are known by special names

©P

Properties Within Groups

When we compare the physical properties of elements within groups, a number of patterns become clear. Refer to the periodic table on page 179 as you read about these patterns.

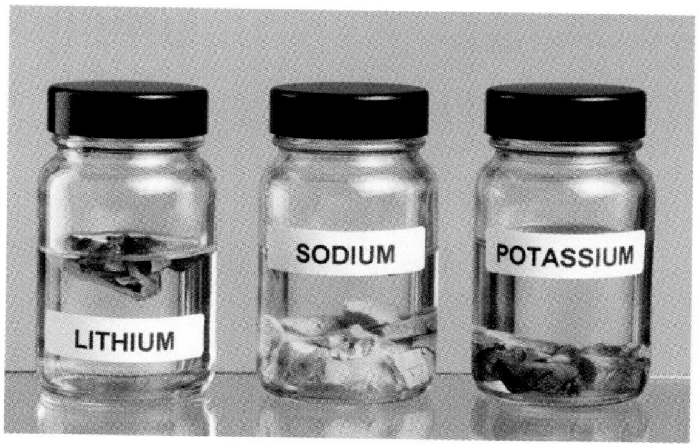

Figure 5.39 Alkali metals are silver-grey in colour.

Alkali Metals (Group 1): Li, Na, K, Rb, Cs

- *Similarities:* All of these metals are silver-grey in colour (Figure 5.39). Like other metals, they are malleable and ductile, and they conduct electricity and heat. However, compared to other metals, the alkali metals have low melting points. They all melt below 181 °C, a temperature easily achieved by most ordinary kitchen ovens. They are all soft enough to cut with a knife. In addition, they all react easily with water and air.
- *Differences:* There is a gradual change in the physical properties in this group from the first element, at the top, through to the last, at the bottom. Moving from lithium to cesium, there is a regular increase in density. The elements also get softer and easier to cut. Lithium's melting point is 181 °C, while potassium's is 64 °C. Cesium's melting point is just 28 °C.

*info***BIT**

Alkaline Earth Metals: Mg, Ca, Sr, Ba

The alkaline earth metals are silver-white in colour. They also show a trend in their physical properties down the group as the alkali metals do. The alkaline earth metals are harder and have a higher density than sodium and potassium. Compared with the alkali metals, they have much higher melting points. Magnesium's melting point is 649°C, while calcium's is over 800°C.

Halogens (Group 17): F, Cl, Br, I

- *Similarities:* All of these elements are non-metals. Each has a noticeable, but different, colour. Although bromine is a liquid and iodine is a solid at room temperature, with slight heating they form gases, like the other halogens. All are very reactive, and chlorine, bromine, and iodine can be used as disinfectants because they kill bacteria and living organisms in water.
- *Differences:* From fluorine, the first element in the group, down through to iodine, the colours of the vapours of the halogens grow in intensity (Figure 5.40). Their melting points also gradually increase from −219 °C for fluorine to 113 °C for iodine.

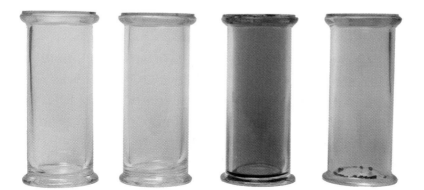

Figure 5.40 The halogens. From left to right: fluorine, chlorine, bromine, and iodine

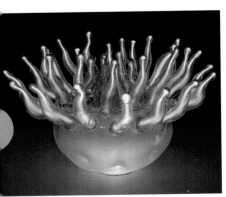

Figure 5.41 This lighted glass sculpture of a sea anemone contains noble gases. As an electric current runs through the gases, they light up, each with a different colour. Some of the gases are denser than the others, making the sculpture different colours in different areas.

Suggested Activity • · · · · · · · · · · ·
B17 Science, Technology, Society, and the Environment on page 189

Noble Gases (Group 18): He, Ne, Ar, Kr, Xe, Rn

- *Similarities:* Although all exist naturally as colourless gases, these elements will glow with bright colours if an electric current is passed through them, as shown in Figure 5.41. None of these gases is chemically reactive except in certain special situations.

- *Differences:* The density of the gases increases steadily, moving from helium through to radon. Balloons filled with helium or neon will rise in the air, with helium balloons rising faster than neon balloons. Argon balloons sink slowly in air. Balloons filled with krypton, xenon, or radon would sink quite quickly in air, with radon balloons sinking the fastest.

Learning Checkpoint

1. Give the names and symbols for the elements found at these locations in the periodic table.
   (a) Period 3, Group 1   (b) Period 2, Group 13
   (c) Period 4, Group 11   (d) Period 5, Group 17
2. Give the period and group for each of the following elements.
   (a) Mg   (b) Si   (c) Cl   (d) He   (e) Au   (f) Pb
3. Compare and contrast the chemical and physical properties of the halogens and the noble gases.

During Writing

Consider the Options

A report presents concise information on a number of options and often makes one or more recommendations. Recommendations allow the reader to consider one option that might be better than another and to trace the reasons for choosing that option back through the information in the report.

Suggested Activity • · · · · · · · · · · ·
B18 Quick Science on page 189

Atomic Models Support the Periodic Table

Mendeleev created his periodic table long before studies of atomic structure revealed the arrangements of subatomic particles. As a result, Mendeleev did not know about atomic number, which is now used to order the elements in the modern periodic table. Instead, he used atomic mass. Similarly, he did not know about electrons or their arrangements within atoms. When electron arrangements are considered, it makes Mendeleev's work all the more remarkable.

Chlorine: A Typical Atom

Atoms of all elements have the same basic structure but different numbers of protons, neutrons, and electrons. Chlorine is an example. A diagram of an atom of chlorine is shown in Figure 5.42. Notice that the number of protons and the number of electrons are equal. This is true of all atoms.

The Nucleus

Modern scientific models of the atom place the nucleus, comprised of protons and neutrons, at the centre of the atom. The nucleus is often enlarged to aid in clarity, as shown at the centre of the chlorine atom, and in the view of the nucleus in Figure 5.42. Depending on the atom, the region outside the nucleus of an atom is 10 000 to 50 000 times the diameter of the nucleus.

- All chlorine atoms have 17 protons. Each proton has a charge of 1+, so the total positive charge in the nucleus is therefore 17+.

- Different kinds of chlorine atoms can have different numbers of neutrons. It is the number of protons in an atom that determines what element the atom is, not the number of neutrons. The most common types of chlorine atoms have 18, 19, or 20 neutrons.

- The nucleus contains 99.99 % of the mass of the atom because protons and neutrons have much greater mass than electrons.

Suggested Activity •···········
B19 Decision-Making Analysis
on page 190

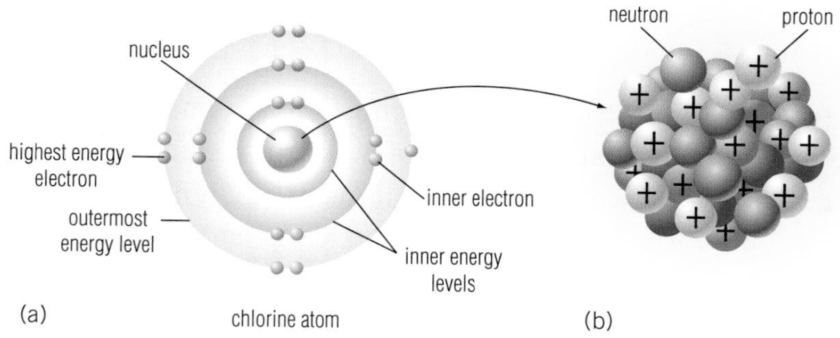

Figure 5.42 (a) A Bohr diagram of a chlorine atom, which contains 17 protons and 17 electrons. The number of neutrons varies between chlorine atoms. (b) A diagram of the nucleus of a chlorine atom

Electrons

Simplified models of the atom show electrons surrounding the nucleus in energy levels. Electrons in higher energy levels have a higher possibility of being farther away from the nucleus. The innermost level, or the first level, can hold a maximum of two electrons. Each of the next two higher levels can hold up to eight. Electrons often exist in pairs.

- The region in which electrons orbit the nucleus occupies more than 99.99 % of an atom's volume.

- Electrons can move between energy levels when energy is applied to or removed from the atom.

- The number and arrangement of electrons in the outermost energy level determines the chemical properties of atoms and the physical properties of elements.

reSearch

People have used various shapes, colours, and arrangements to organize the elements in meaningful ways. Some are shown in Figures 5.44 and 5.45. Search for at least one other version of the periodic table (not shown in this chapter). Compare it with the periodic table on page 179 and find out why elements are arranged or organized in a different way.

Patterns in the Arrangements of Electrons

Figure 5.43 shows Bohr diagrams for the first 20 elements of the periodic table. As you examine the Bohr diagrams, look carefully at the electrons in the outer levels. A very important pattern in the arrangement of electrons is that elements in the same group have the same number of electrons in the outermost level. Notice, in particular, the following points:

- Group 1: Atoms of hydrogen, lithium, and sodium each have one electron in the outermost level. Although hydrogen is not in the same group as the alkali metals, it does share some chemical properties with them because of their similar electron arrangements in the outermost level. For example, they can all form ions with a 1+ charge.

- Group 18: A helium atom has only two electrons in the outermost level, which is the maximum number for the first energy level. Atoms of neon and argon each have eight electrons in the outermost level, the maximum number for the second and third energy levels. The noble gases share many properties because their atoms all have filled highest energy levels.

Suggested Activity • • • • • • • • • • •
B20 Quick Science on page 191

The number of electrons in the highest energy level is not only related to the physical properties of a group of elements, but also related to the ways in which atoms of elements combine to form compounds.

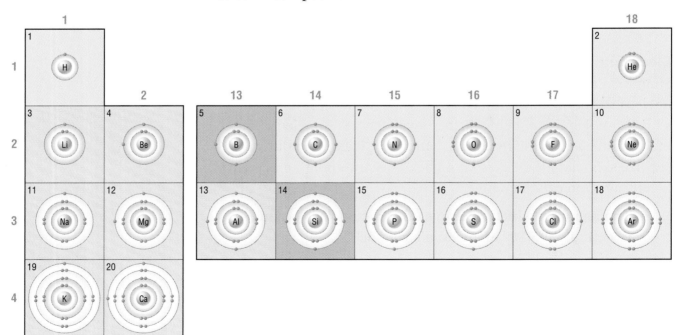

Figure 5.43 A segment of the periodic table showing electron arrangements for the first 20 elements

Organizing the Periodic Table in Different Ways

Scientists continue to organize the elements in different ways. Dr. Theodor Benfey, a U.S. chemist, suggested a spiral version of the periodic table (Figure 5.44). In Dr. Benfey's periodic table, the elements are shown in an unbroken series of their atomic numbers, starting with hydrogen and radiating outward. Figure 5.45 shows another periodic table, known as the physicist's periodic table. This periodic table is three-dimensional and groups the elements according to the energy levels of their electrons.

Suggested Activity •••••••••••
B21 Problem-Solving Activity on page 192

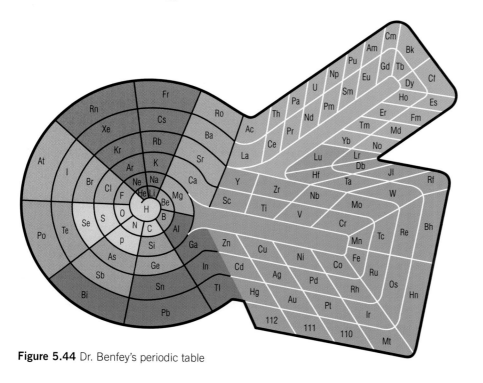

Figure 5.44 Dr. Benfey's periodic table

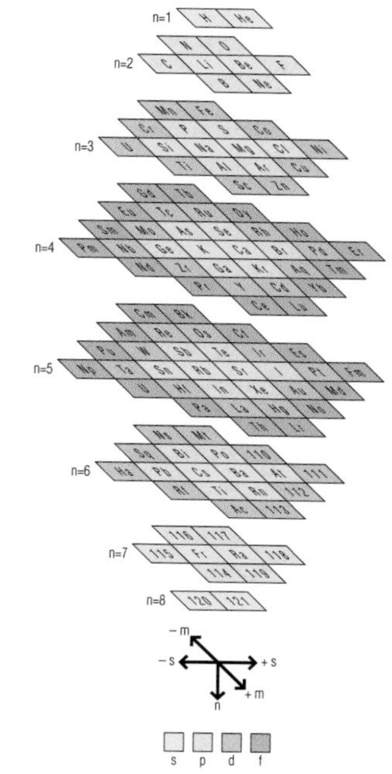

Figure 5.45 The physicist's periodic table

Learning Checkpoint

1. Give the number of highest energy electrons in an atom of each of the following elements.

   (a) hydrogen   (b) aluminum   (c) carbon   (d) oxygen   (e) chlorine

2. For each of the following groups of elements, give the number or numbers of highest energy electrons in the atoms.

   (a) Group 1   (b) Group 2   (c) Group 15   (d) Group 18

3. (a) What is similar about the highest energy electrons for atoms of elements in Period 2?

   (b) What is similar about the highest energy electrons for atoms of elements in Period 3?

4. At room temperature, oxygen is a colourless gas and sulphur is a yellow solid. Why are they in the same group in the periodic table?

5.4 CHECK and REFLECT

1. Name four properties that Dmitri Mendeleev used as criteria for organizing his understanding of elements.

2. Use a periodic table to find how many protons are in an atom of each of the following elements.
   (a) lithium
   (b) nitrogen
   (c) fluorine
   (d) aluminum
   (e) copper
   (f) gold

3. Use a periodic table to name the element with each of the following atomic masses.
   (a) 12.01 amu
   (b) 16.00 amu
   (c) 39.10 amu
   (d) 83.80 amu

4. Name two groups in the periodic table that include elements that conduct heat and electricity.

5. Using hydrogen as an example, explain the difference between atomic number and atomic mass.

6. List two ways in which atoms of different elements are different from one another.

7. What happens to an atom if it loses an electron in the highest energy level?

8. Which of the following atoms typically form negative ions?
   (a) F   (b) Li
   (c) Ne   (d) S
   (e) Al   (f) Be

9. If something occurs periodically—every Monday, for instance—it can be said to occur in a pattern. How do you think the periodic table got its name?

10. How do chemical symbols help scientists from different countries communicate? Why is this important?

11. Use the Bohr diagram below to answer the questions that follow.

Question 11

   (a) What element is shown?
   (b) How many electrons does this atom have?
   (c) How many protons does this atom have?
   (d) What group in the periodic table does this element belong to?

12. Suppose a sample of a metal has a low melting point and reacts easily with water. What group in the periodic table does the element belong to?

13. List three ways that you can use the periodic table in your studies that you did not know about before completing this section.

14. Explain how a scientific law, such as the periodic law, is different from a scientific theory. Use a scientific theory in this unit to help your explanation.

Working with Toxic Elements

In the 18th and 19th centuries, mercury was used in hat making. The mercury produced toxic vapours, which caused symptoms of mercury poisoning in hat makers and in people who wore the hats. Mercury poisoning could impair vision, speech, hearing, or balance as well as cause mood swings and memory loss. The "Mad Hatter" from Lewis Carroll's classic fantasy books about Alice in Wonderland was a cartoon version of a hatter (hat maker) affected by mercury poisoning. Today, laws restrict how mercury can be used.

Other people who work with toxic elements include scientists who study radioactive elements, painters, and pottery makers. Some of the metals that give paints and pottery glazes their bright colours include toxic cobalt, lead, and cadmium.

1. In order to protect the health of workers, how could workplaces limit the use of toxic elements?

2. What types of restrictions would you consider for artists working with toxic elements in their own homes? What questions would you need to answer in order to write a set of guidelines for artists?

3. What steps can people take to work safely with toxic elements?

4. If removing toxic elements from Earth's surface will contaminate the environment, should we do this? What restrictions, if any, would you place on mining for toxic elements? Justify your response.

Drawing Bohr Diagrams

In this activity, you will practise drawing Bohr diagrams of atoms and ions of different elements.

Purpose

To practise drawing Bohr diagrams of atoms and ions

Materials & Equipment
- a copy of the periodic table

Procedure

1. Find hydrogen on the periodic table. Begin a Bohr diagram of a hydrogen atom by drawing a circle to represent its nucleus. Write "1p" to show that there is one proton inside.

2. Draw the energy level around the nucleus as well as the highest energy electron.

3. Find lithium on the periodic table. Begin a second Bohr diagram of a lithium atom. Write the number of protons in the nucleus, and draw the energy levels and electrons in each level.

4. Look up the charge on a lithium ion in a periodic table. Draw a Bohr diagram of a lithium ion.

5. Find sodium on the periodic table. Draw a Bohr diagram of a sodium atom.

Questions

6. How many protons and electrons would be shown in a Bohr diagram of a helium atom?

7. How is a Bohr diagram of a lithium atom different from a Bohr diagram of a lithium ion?

8. Describe the similarities and differences among the energy levels in your Bohr diagrams for lithium and sodium.

Pose New Questions

9. What other ways would be more practical than using a Bohr diagram to show the electron arrangement of an atom with 100 electrons?

Heavy Metals in Fish

Due to environmental pollution, the concentration of heavy metals in fish is on the rise. Some of these metals are toxic to humans. For people who eat a lot of fish, heavy metal contamination is a serious concern.

Initiating and Planning

Many metals are necessary for human health. For example, iron is so important in the diet that some people need to take iron supplements. However, the heavy metals, including cadmium, mercury, and lead, are toxic.

Heavy metal pollution results mainly from industrial processes, such as refining ores, burning fuel, and using nuclear energy. Heavy metals are also used in some types of batteries and computer equipment. When these pollutants are released into the air, they come back down with precipitation. In this way, and from water washing over contaminated landfills, heavy metals get into the water supply. Once in the water, they build up in the food chain. Fish near the top of the aquatic food chain often contain high amounts of heavy metals. Therefore, Health Canada and the Saskatchewan government have set guidelines about how much of different types of fish people should eat to avoid heavy metal poisoning (Figure 5.46). Since heavy metals can harm the fetus, pregnant women are cautioned by the government not to eat certain types of fish from Saskatchewan rivers when the mercury levels in the water are high. Other people are recommended how many servings of certain types of fish they can have per week based on the heavy metal levels.

It is not always clear how much humans are affected by heavy metals in their food. However, scientists have seen an effect on contaminated organisms. Fish stop functioning normally. They seem to be unaware of their natural predators and do not use their ingrained escape-and-evade techniques.

Some fish have trouble recognizing their own offspring, and instead of protecting them, they eat them. This behaviour could have a serious impact on the numbers of some types of fish in the future— as well as the other organisms in their environment.

Heavy metal contaminants have appeared in the food sources of many First Nations people who continue to hunt and harvest animals in the traditional way. Many contaminants, such as elements like mercury, end up in water systems and are later ingested by aquatic life forms, which in turn are digested by larger fish. These larger fish, when harvested and eaten by First Nations people, result in illness or death.

Figure 5.46 Unhealthy fish, such as these, have been collected from water contaminated with heavy metals and petroleum compounds. The deformities and tumours are evidence of possible infection or disease.

In 1975, a Japanese scientist, Dr. Masazumi Harada, first discovered dangerously high levels of mercury in 100 residents of Grassy Narrows, a First Nations reserve in northern Ontario. These people had mercury levels exceeding the safe limits set by Health Canada by more than three times. Dr. Harada's study of other reserves downstream from Grassy Narrows confirmed that people of Grassy Narrows were poisoned. Upon his return to Grassy Narrows in 2004, Dr. Harada found that of the 100 residents in his original study, 43 percent had died from health problems related to mercury poisoning and that Minamata disease, a form of mercury poisoning, continued to affect people from Grassy Narrows and neighbouring reserves.

Other examples of heavy metal contamination exist in Canada as well as around the world. Elders like Julie Pitzel reported that many fishing communities stopped eating as much fish once they learned or discovered that the fish were contaminated with heavy metals. After some time, the fish are now recovering, although not to the same plentiful and healthy levels in and before the 1950s.

Your task is to work with a partner to find out who may be at risk from heavy metals and why. Determine what, if anything, the government should do to protect people from this risk. Use a graphic organizer to keep track of information. After you complete your research, you will present your findings in a poster, an interview, or another form of media.

Analyzing and Interpreting

1. Gather information to help you answer the questions below and complete your overall task.

2. (a) Why might Indigenous peoples and people in remote communities suffer from the effects of heavy metal contamination of fish more than most people in Canada?

   (b) What responsibilities have the polluting companies taken to help these people?

3. What can be done to protect people from heavy metal poisoning from their food?

4. Suppose you go fishing at a pond contaminated with mercury and catch a minnow (a fish at the bottom of the food chain) and a large trout (a fish at the top of the food chain, which eats other fish). Which fish would have a higher concentration of mercury in its body? Explain.

Communication and Teamwork

5. Create an informational poster, a question-and-answer interview that you and your partner can share with the class, or another form of media, giving the three best ways to protect people from heavy metal poisoning.

6. In your research, did a certain type of graphic organizer seem more helpful than another? Explain.

Representing the Elements

In this activity, you will create posters to represent two elements.

Purpose

To construct a graphic representation of elements

Materials & Equipment
- large sheets of paper of various colours
- scissors

Procedure

1. Your teacher will give you two elements to represent. Gather the following information about each element. Add others you find appropriate.
   - colour
   - symbol
   - atomic number
   - atomic mass
   - Bohr diagram
   - physical properties
   - chemical properties
   - how it is obtained
   - how it is used

2. Create a poster to visually represent each element in some way. For example, use paper that has a colour similar to the colour of the element or cut the paper into the shape of an object that contains the element. Write the information from step 1 on each poster.

3. With the class, have all the posters displayed in the classroom, in their appropriate location in the periodic table.

Question

4. Using the periodic table your class created, examine the elements down a group or across a period. Describe any patterns you see.

Pose New Questions

5. What other information about elements should be added to the periodic table on page 179?

Building a Periodic Table

Scientists use models to explain things we cannot see or to display patterns in data.

Initiating and Planning

How can a model represent the patterns in the periodic table?

Materials & Equipment

- large sheets of paper
- ruler
- element cards
- graph paper

Criteria for Success

- The model clearly shows a pattern among elements in the periodic table.
- Elements in your model can be rearranged to represent another pattern in the periodic table.
- The model can be used more than once.

Performing and Recording

1. Collect an element card from your teacher (Figure 5.47).

2. Compare the properties on your card to those of your classmates. Find classmates with cards that have similar element properties. You will form a group with these students.

3. Make a list of the properties your group's elements all share. Share the list with your teacher or class. Once your teacher confirms your list, you will be given a group number.

4. Arrange all of your group's element cards in order of atomic mass.

5. Make a five-by-five grid. Complete it, using the order of the elements in the class. Include the atomic mass for each element in your grid. Write the element's group number at the top of the grid.

Analyzing and Interpreting

6. Use your data on the elements to make a graph of atomic mass versus atomic number.

7. Record any patterns you notice in this graph.

8. Examine the periodic table on page 179. Compare your arrangement of elements with the arrangement of elements in the periodic table. Describe their similarities and their differences.

9. Rearrange your elements based on another pattern of properties. Then repeat step 8.

10. Evaluate your model. Does it meet the Criteria for Success? What are some improvements you could make to your model?

Communicate

11. Return to the guiding question for this activity. Examine the periodic table on page 179. Based on your data and experiences, answer the question. Present your findings to the class in the format of your choice.

12. Did your group work together effectively? What would you do differently next time?

Figure 5.47 Element cards written with information about each element's properties

Courtney Gress: Environmental Professional

Growing up near Estevan, Saskatchewan, Courtney was a first-hand witness to the effects that the coal and oil industries could have on the environment. Her early experiences living in such a resource-rich area helped shape her interest in the environment. Courtney was so curious about her surroundings that she studied all the sciences (physics, chemistry, and biology) throughout high school.

After high school graduation, Courtney attended the University of Regina where she pursued a Bachelor of Science degree, majoring in biology. Courtney studied introductory biology and chemistry, then moved into biological chemistry and organic chemistry, before graduating with honours.

Courtney soon found herself back in the Estevan area working as an environmental professional. She works closely with many of the local oil field companies to maintain environmental management standards in the area. Her work begins with obtaining permits from government agencies for oil and natural gas developments. Much of her work is on-site and involves pre-disturbance assessments, conducting environmental monitoring throughout the exploration process, and testing during the remediation and reclamation process.

The tools that Courtney uses range from simple ones such as a shovel and a camera to more technical pieces of equipment such as pH meters and various computer programs (Figure 5.48). In closing, Courtney states that "science is not about having a wealth of knowledge at your fingertips as much as it is a process. I use process every day to get the data I need. Knowledge of facts is simply a reference."

Figure 5.48 Courtney Gress at work

Key Concept Review

1. What do scientists call the smallest possible amount of a pure substance that can exist?

2. (a) Give an example of an element that is found in nature in the form of atoms.

   (b) Give an example of an element that is found in nature in the form of molecules.

3. Beginning with the innermost energy level in the Bohr model, list the maximum number of electrons that an atom can have in its first three energy levels.

4. List three halogens, and describe a property that they all share.

5. Name four non-metals that are solids at room temperature.

6. Define the term "compound." Give an example.

7. Examine the photograph of mercury at room temperature and answer the questions that follow.

Question 7

   (a) What properties of mercury might have led early chemists to classify it as a metal? Explain.

   (b) What property makes mercury different from most other metals?

8. (a) Name the element that has 43 protons in an atom of the element.

   (b) Name the element that has 66 electrons in an atom of the element.

9. (a) The chemical formula for hydrogen peroxide is H_2O_2. What elements are present in this compound and in what ratio?

   (b) Classify H_2O_2 as an ionic compound or molecular compound and explain your reasoning.

   (c) Name two uses of hydrogen peroxide.

10. Use Figure 5.43 on page 186 to answer the following questions.

   (a) How many energy levels containing electrons does a potassium atom have?

   (b) How many highest energy (outermost level) electrons does a calcium atom have?

   (c) Name the element that has a full outermost level of two electrons.

11. Draw a Bohr diagram of a chlorine atom.

12. (a) List two properties that generally increase, beginning with the first element in the periodic table through to the 100th element and beyond.

   (b) Are there any exceptions to the pattern described in (a)? Explain.

Connect Your Understanding

13. Distinguish between "analytical" and "holistic" ways of thinking by giving an example of each.

14. Based on the structure of ionic compounds, explain why they are usually hard solids with high melting points.

15. (a) Diamond is a pure form of carbon. Name another pure form of this element.

   (b) Name three uses for carbon.

   (c) What are some environmental issues related to using carbon?

16. List the common names for two compounds mentioned in this chapter that you are familiar with from your everyday life. Give the common uses, chemical names, and formulas for these compounds.

17. Use the diagram of benzene below to answer the questions that follow.

(a) Benzene is composed of the elements hydrogen and carbon. What do the different-coloured balls in the diagram represent?

(b) What do the sticks connecting the balls in the diagram represent?

(c) Is benzene an ionic compound or molecular compound? Explain your reasoning.

18. How did Dmitri Mendeleev use the estimated mass of atoms to help him order the elements in a table?

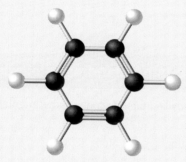

Question 17

19. In the early 1800s, just over 30 elements had been identified. Today, there are more than 100 known elements. Why might there have been such a rapid increase in the discovery of elements?

20. Create a warning poster or public service announcement about an element that can cause harm if improperly used or stored.

Reflection

21. Why is modelling important to scientists? Describe how a scientific model in this chapter has helped scientists better understand the nature of matter.

22. Now that you have studied some theories about atoms,

(a) how has your understanding of the composition of matter changed?

(b) what have you learned about the reasons that scientific models or theories naturally change over time?

23. Briefly describe three ways in which pure elements are used that you did not know about before reading this chapter.

After Writing

Reflect and Evaluate

Choose your suggestions about working with toxic elements or your information piece about heavy metals in fish. Exchange with a partner, read, and provide feedback on how your partner used topic sentences, details, and good flow from one sentence to the next to stay on topic and create unity.

Reflection on Essential Inquiry Questions

How does the composition of matter help scientists explain the various properties of substances? **SI**

How did the discoveries of the structure of matter help scientists develop models of matter? **TPS**

What are some positive and negative impacts of using elements and compounds? **DM**

What did you learn about the different approaches to understanding what makes up the physical world? **CP**

Unit Task

Use your knowledge of the properties of the elements to argue that pure elements should not be used as toothpaste ingredients. Identify elements that you would not want to add to toothpaste.

KEY CONCEPTS	CHAPTER SUMMARY

4 People of all cultures investigate matter according to various properties.

- Ideas about matter can be generalizable or place-based
- Forms of matter
- Classifying matter
- Observing physical properties
- Observing chemical properties
- Usefulness and impact of properties of substances

- Indigenous understanding emphasizes the world being one whole entity and scientific understanding emphasizes how smaller and smaller pieces make up the world. (4.1)
- Scientists mainly produce generalizable ideas and First Nations and Métis peoples mainly use place-based ideas. (4.1 and 4.2)
- Scientists understand matter as being composed of particles. The type of particles and their arrangement in a substance determine its properties. (4.1)
- Elements and compounds are pure substances. Mechanical mixtures, suspensions, and solutions are combinations of pure substances. (4.1)
- Physical properties are characteristics of a substance that can be observed or measured without changing what the substance is. (4.2)
- Chemical properties describe how substances react with other substances or to light or heat and can be observed when chemical changes occur. (4.2)
- Place-based knowledge allowed First Nations and Métis people to survive over thousands of years. (4.2)

5 The periodic table is a tool for organizing scientific understanding of elements.

- Holistic understanding
- Analytical understanding
- Atomic theory
- Atomic models
- Subatomic particles
- Element names and symbols
- Properties of common elements
- Types of compounds
- Chemical bonds
- Chemical names and formulas
- Periodic table
- Properties of chemical groups

- The atomic model continues to be revised based on new experimental evidence or imaginatively new ideas. (5.1)
- Every element is composed of a distinct type of atom. (5.1)
- An atom has a dense nucleus of neutrons and protons, which is surrounded by electrons in different energy levels. (5.1)
- Each element has a standard name and symbol. (5.2)
- Compounds are pure substances composed of atoms of two or more elements that are joined by chemical bonds. (5.3)
- Ions with opposite charges attract each other in ionic compounds, while atoms in molecules share highest energy electrons. (5.3)
- The periodic table organizes the metals, non-metals, and metalloids based on properties such as number of protons in an atom. (5.4)
- The alkali metals share similar properties, such as conductivity, which are different from the properties of the halogens and noble gases. (5.4)
- Bohr diagrams are one way to represent the arrangement of electrons in a model of an atom. (5.4)

VOCABULARY

- adhesion (p. 133)
- chemical change (p. 136)
- chemical property (p. 136)
- chemical reaction (p. 136)
- cohesion (p. 133)
- combustibility (p. 137)
- compound (p. 125)

- element (p. 125)
- mass (p. 124)
- matter (p. 124)
- mechanical mixture (p. 126)
- Medicine Wheel (p. 123)
- physical property (p. 133)

- property (p. 125)
- pure substance (p. 125)
- solution (p. 126)
- suspension (p. 126)
- volume (p. 124)

KEY VISUALS

Adhesion and cohesion of water droplets

Light emitted by a glowing firefly

- alkali metals (p. 183)
- alloy (p. 159)
- atom (p. 151)
- atomic mass (p. 181)
- atomic mass units (amu) (p. 181)
- atomic number (p. 180)
- atomic theory (p. 151)
- bond (p. 170)
- chemical formula (p. 172)
- covalent bond (p. 171)
- diatomic molecule (p. 172)
- electron (p. 152)
- group (chemical family) (p. 182)

- halogens (p. 183)
- ion (p. 170)
- ion charge (p. 181)
- ionic bond (p. 170)
- ionic compound (p. 169)
- isotopes (p. 180)
- lattice (p. 170)
- law (p. 149)
- mass number (p. 181)
- metalloids (p. 160)
- metals (p. 159)
- molecular compound (p. 171)
- molecule (p. 171)
- neutral (p. 170)

- neutron (p. 153)
- noble gases (p. 184)
- non-metals (p. 160)
- nucleus (atomic) (p. 153)
- period (p. 182)
- periodic law (p. 180)
- periodic table (p. 180)
- polyatomic ion (p. 170)
- proton (p. 152)
- relative mass (p. 154)
- subatomic particle (p. 154)
- theory (p. 149)
- transition metals (p. 182)

Halogens: chlorine, bromine, and iodine

Ionic compounds

B22 What Are the Criteria?

Toolkits 3, 7

Task Overview

In this task, you will design a toothpaste. Create a list of criteria for an effective toothpaste, then research ingredients with properties that will help your toothpaste meet those criteria (Figure 5.49). Submit your proposal to your teacher for approval. You will be expected to test the effectiveness of your toothpaste using a model for teeth. You will use graphic organizers to record observations and analyze results. Based on these results, you will present your findings in a lab report or in a presentation. Be sure to include any improvements or modifications you would make to your toothpaste design.

Figure 5.49 Possible materials and equipment to include in your procedure

B23 How Effective Are the Ingredients?

Toolkits 3, 7

Task Overview

In this task, you will be required to research the properties of of the active ingredients found in toothpaste for your toothpaste design. You will then identify your own testable question about how these ingredients contribute to the effectiveness of the toothpaste and design an investigation to answer your testable question. Record your testable question and your procedure and submit them to your teacher for approval. You will then use graphic organizers to record observations and analyze results. Present your findings as a lab report or in a presentation.

B24 What Makes the Best Toothpaste?

Toolkits 3, 7

Task Overview

In this task, you will identify your own testable question to investigate about toothpaste. Your investigation must answer your testable question. Record your testable question and your procedure and submit them to your teacher for approval. You will then use graphic organizers to record observations and analyze results. You will present your findings in a manner approved by your teacher.

©P

Using Key Terms

1. Create a concept map to link the key terms listed below. Add examples of substances, where appropriate.

   - atom
   - electron
   - element (scientific)
   - group (chemical)
   - ionic compound
   - matter
   - mechanical mixture
   - molecular compound

   - molecule
   - neutron
   - period
   - proton
   - pure substance
   - solution
   - suspension

2. Distinguish between a homogeneous mixture and a heterogeneous mixture.

3. What is the difference between cohesion and adhesion?

4. Identify the following as either physical properties or chemical properties.

   (a) Diamonds are hard.

   (b) Gallium will melt in the palm of your hand.

   (c) Wood burns easily.

   (d) Iron is magnetic.

   (e) Some cleaners are corrosive to skin.

5. Use the following list of properties to create a profile of a pure substance or mixture of your choice. Add other terms as needed.

   - boiling point
   - colour
   - combustibility
   - conductivity
   - density
   - ductility

   - hardness
   - lustre
   - malleability
   - melting point
   - reactivity
   - solubility

Reviewing the Big Ideas

6. List at least three cultural ways to make sense of the physical world.

7. Discuss the scientific meaning and an everyday meaning of the term "law." Give an example of each and state on what basis the law is developed.

8. John Dalton described matter as being composed of atoms. How is his 200-year-old atomic model different from the current atomic model?

9. How did J. J. Thomson make use of cathode rays to investigate atomic structure? What did he conclude based on his results?

10. What evidence about an atom did Ernest Rutherford observe, and how did he interpret it?

11. How did Niels Bohr contribute to the understanding of atomic structure?

12. Explain what an "ion charge" is.

13. Is a metal element more likely to form an ion by losing electrons or by gaining them?

14. Give the names and ratios of the elements in the following substances.

    (a) LiCl   (b) Al_2S_3

    (c) AgF   (d) ZnO

    (e) N_2S_3 (f) Br_2

15. Identify each of the substances in the previous question as an ionic compound, a molecular compound, or neither.

16. How are metals, non-metals, and metalloids organized in the periodic table?

17. Give the number of highest energy electrons in an atom of each of the following elements.

(a) hydrogen   (b) aluminum

(c) carbon   (d) oxygen

(e) chlorine

18. Use the diagram below to answer the following questions.

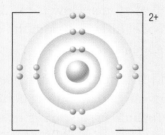

Question 18

(a) What element is shown?

(b) What group in the periodic table does this element belong to?

(c) What is the charge on this ion?

(d) How many highest energy electrons are in a neutral atom of this ion?

Connecting the Big Ideas

19. In two short paragraphs, describe an Indigenous understanding of the physical world and then describe a scientific understanding.

20. Using the language of science, distinguish between the terms "law" and "theory" based on your understanding of the periodic law and atomic theory.

21. Some early philosophers considered elements to be earth, wind, water, and fire. Why do chemists today no longer classify water as an element?

22. What two pieces of information does a formula for a molecule provide?

23. For each of the following, state the type of mixture.

(a) a banana milkshake

(b) water with sugar dissolved in it

(c) tomato juice

24. Which of the following substances will dissolve in water to form a solution that can conduct an electric current?

(a) KCl (b) $C_6H_{12}O_6$

(c) Ne (d) MgO

(e) CH_4

25. Describe two patterns found in the periodic table.

26. (a) What do elements in the same period on the periodic table have in common in terms of structure of their atoms?

(b) How does the atomic structure of the elements change within a period as you read from left to right across the periodic table?

27. How can the manufacture of safe products, such as plastic food containers, result in the chemical contamination of the environment?

28. Name three chemical elements that can be harmful if not handled properly. How are they harmful?

29. Copy the following table into your notebook. Use the periodic table to fill in the blanks.

Information About Elements

Symbol	Name	Atomic Mass	Protons in Atom	Electrons in Atom
			17	
Ca				
	silver			
				10
U				

30. Use the Bohr diagrams below to answer the questions that follow.

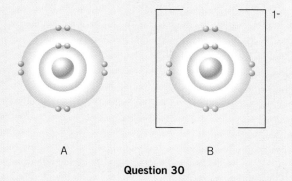

A   B

Question 30

(a) Name the elements shown in A and B.

(b) Did the ion shown in B form by losing an electron or gaining an electron?

(c) Would the atom shown in A likely be found in an ionic compound? Explain.

Using the Big Ideas

31. Suppose you have collected a gas in a test tube. To identify the gas, you light a wooden splint, then blow it out so that it is glowing, and put it in the test tube. What do you predict would happen if the test tube were filled with oxygen gas?

32. How did the development of the atomic model make it easier for people to explain how chemical reactions occur?

33. What are chemical elements, and how are they responsible for the properties of pure substances?

34. Think of one chemical that you know of from each of the following areas that has a positive use in your life: hygiene, food, medicine. Identify the chemical by its common name and, if possible, its chemical name, and state the positive role that it plays.

35. (a) Based on your knowledge about the physical and chemical properties of matter, what kinds of physical and chemical changes can people use to alter matter?

(b) How can we alter matter to meet our needs while improving the conditions of the environment? Explain, using one or more specific examples.

Reflection

36. In this unit, you have learned generalizable ideas produced by scientists, and place-based ideas used by First Nations and Métis peoples. Use an example of each to illustrate the strengths and limitations of each way of knowing.

37. The way in which we apply science and technology impacts the environment. Of the different ways that chemistry can be used to solve environmental problems, describe at least one way that you think is very promising based on your new understanding of the properties of matter.

Reflection on Essential Inquiry Questions

How do properties of matter enable us to differentiate between various substances? **SI**

How have scientists advanced their understanding of the atomic theory? **TPS**

What are the impacts of using various materials to create household, commercial, industrial, and agricultural products? **DM**

How do people from different cultures think about the structure and composition of materials in the physical world? **CP**

Characteristics of Electricity

Lightning around
electrical energy
transmission lines

©P

Big Ideas

6 **Static electric charges collect on surfaces until given a path to escape.**

6.1 The Characteristics of Static Electric Charges
6.2 The Transfer of Static Electric Charges `DI`
6.3 Electrostatics in Our Lives

7 **Current electrical energy is the flow of electrons in a closed circuit.**

7.1 Voltage, Current, and Resistance
7.2 Series Circuits and Parallel Circuits
7.3 Ohm's Law `DI`

8 **We can reduce our electrical energy consumption and use renewable energy resources to produce electrical energy.**

8.1 Renewable and Non-Renewable Energy Resources for Generating Electrical Energy
8.2 Reducing Our Electrical Energy Consumption `DI`

Essential Inquiry Questions

What are static electric charges and current electrical energy and how are voltage, current, and resistance in series and parallel circuits related? `SI`

How do we assess the operating principles, costs, and efficiencies of devices that produce or use electrical energy? `TPS`

What is the impact of electrical energy production and distribution in Saskatchewan? `DM`

What knowledge of electricity do First Nations and Métis peoples have? `CP`

Unit Task

At the end of this unit, you will address some of the Essential Inquiry Questions by completing a Unit Task. Your task will be designing your own lab based on a testable question about static electric charges and current electrical energy; explaining the energy transformations in a device of your choice; or designing an electrical energy conservation plan based on kilowatt-hours of use and electrical energy savings.

©P

6

Static electric charges collect on surfaces until given a path to escape.

Outcomes

By the end of this chapter, you will:

- demonstrate and analyze characteristics of static electric charges and current electricity, including historical and cultural understanding

What you will learn:

- Some First Nations and Métis peoples have an intimate spiritual understanding of lightning in terms of Thunderbird.
- Static electric charges are transferred by friction, contact, and induction.
- Different materials have different abilities to hold or transfer static electric charges.
- Electrical equipment should always be operated safely.
- Many technological devices are designed to improve electrical efficiency or protect other devices by using or controlling static electric charges.

The static electric charge on this Van de Graaff generator has a hair-raising effect on this student.

Key Terms

- charging by contact • charging by induction • conduction
- conductivity • conductors
- electric charges • electrical discharge • electron affinity
- electrons • electroscope
- electrostatics • friction
- grounding • induction
- insulator • neutrons • nucleus
- protons • static electric charge

Before Reading

Determining Importance

Preview the subheadings and images in Chapter 6. Which topics and images are familiar? Which topics and images are unfamiliar based on your background knowledge and experience? The unfamiliar topics and images represent the information that is most important for you to learn. Create a list of learning goals for this chapter based on the information that represents new learning for you.

©P

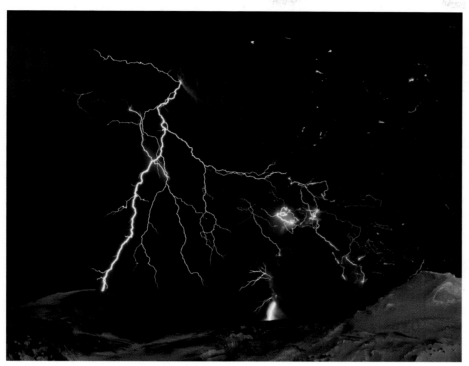

Figure 6.1 Lightning in Iceland's Eyjafjallajökull volcanic eruption

Here is a summary of what you will learn in this section:

- Solid materials are charged by the transfer of electrons.

- When an atom gains electrons, it becomes negatively charged. When an atom loses electrons, it becomes positively charged.

- Electrons can be removed from objects through friction.

- Particles with unlike charges attract each other, and particles with like charges repel each other.

Volcanic Lightning

On April 17, 2010, Iceland's Eyjafjallajökull volcano erupted, spewing volcanic ash, dust, and toxic gases into Earth's atmosphere. The eruption disrupted European air travel for weeks as the dust cloud drifted over the continent.

Lightning is usually associated with rain storms, but bolts of lightning are also found in the middle of ash clouds of active volcanoes (Figure 6.1). While volcanic lightning remains a mystery, it may result from the friction of the particles emitted from the eruption, causing a buildup of electrical charges and then a dramatic discharge of lightning.

In the winter months, some First Nations and Métis people tell stories that explain phenomena, such as lightning and volcanic eruptions. As recently as April 2009, Mount Redoubt in Alaska erupted, and within its blast, a fantastic lightning storm took place. Haida teachings explain that Thunderbird is present in the fiery ash of the volcanoes where lightning strikes. You will learn more about Thunderbird later in this chapter. Every culture, Indigenous or Western, has its own preferred explanations of lightning.

*info*BIT

Haida Stories

Volcanic eruptions contain the power of Volcano Woman. In ancient legends passed down through oral tradition, the Haida people tell the story of a young villager who accidently killed Volcano Woman's son who was disguised as a frog. When none of the villagers took responsibility for her son's death, the volcano destroyed the village.

A Shocking Experience

Have you ever pulled a sweater over your head or removed your hat and felt your hair standing up on a cold winter day? Or maybe you touched a doorknob or a car door handle and got an electrical shock. These examples are caused by electric charges. **Electric charges** are charged particles that exert a force on each other. These charged particles are very small. In fact, there are millions of them on each standing hair in the photo in Figure 6.2.

The buildup of even larger numbers of electric charges can lead to impressive electrical displays. Think of a lightning storm. The large flashes of lightning look similar to the small electric sparks you may have seen when taking off a sweater or touching a doorknob. In fact, they are the same thing, just different in size. They are all examples of electric charges.

Figure 6.2 Electric charges cause strands of hair to repel each other and be attracted to the balloon.

C1 *Quick Science*

Characteristics of Static Electric Charges

In this activity, you will examine the effects of static electric charges on common objects such as confetti, straws, and balloons.

Purpose

To observe static electric charges

Materials & Equipment

- confetti
- plastic drinking straw
- two balloons

Procedure

1. Read the procedure steps, and record your predictions for each step.

2. Sprinkle some confetti in a small area on your desk. Push a plastic drinking straw through your hair several times, then bring it close to the confetti. Record your observations.

3. Inflate two balloons, and knot the ends. Rub one side of each balloon on your hair or clothing. Then, holding the balloons by the knots, bring the rubbed surfaces slowly together. Observe and record the results.

4. Turn one balloon so that its rubbed surface faces away from the other balloon. Again bring the balloons together. Record your observations.

Questions

5. (a) Which objects were attracted to each other?

   (b) Which objects were repelled or pushed away from each other?

6. How did your observations compare with your predictions for each step?

7. What do you think caused the movements that you observed?

Pose New Questions

8. How could you rephrase question 7 in a testable form?

9. What questions could you ask about the materials used in this activity?

Electrically Charged Particles

According to scientists, matter is made up of particles called atoms. Within an atom, there are three types of smaller particles: protons, neutrons, and electrons (Figure 6.3). Protons and electrons are electrically charged particles. **Protons** have a positive electric charge (+), and **electrons** have a negative electric charge (−). **Neutrons** have no electric charge, so they are neutral. The protons and neutrons are in the **nucleus** at the centre of the atom. The electrons are outside the nucleus (Figure 6.4).

In an atom, the number of protons in the nucleus is equal to the number of electrons around the nucleus, so the number of positive and negative charges is equal. This makes an atom neutral. If an atom has gained or lost one or more electrons, it is referred to as an ion.

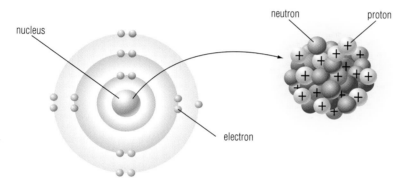

Figure 6.3 In this simplified model of an atom, there are protons and neutrons inside the atom's nucleus and electrons in the area around the nucleus.

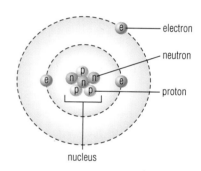

Figure 6.4 In a neutral atom, the number of protons in the nucleus equals the number of electrons around the nucleus.

Static Electric Charges

Objects can become charged when electrons move from one object to another. The electric charge that builds up on the surface of the object is called a **static electric charge**. The charges are "static" because they remain almost fixed in one location on the surface of the object until they are given a path to escape.

Scientists call an object that has more electrons than protons *negatively charged*. They call an object that has more protons than electrons *positively charged*.

Table 6.1 provides some examples of objects that have different numbers of electrons and protons and their charges. You can group objects according to three kinds of charge: positive, negative, and neutral. If a neutral object obtains extra electrons, the object becomes negatively charged. If a neutral object loses electrons, the object becomes positively charged.

Table 6.1

	Number of Protons	Number of Electrons	Charge
O^{2-}	8	10	2−
Na^+	11	10	1+

Friction and the Movement of Electrons

All solid materials are charged by the transfer of electrons. How do atoms lose or gain electrons to become electrically charged? One common cause of electron transfer is friction. **Friction** occurs when objects rub against each other.

When two objects rub together, the force of friction can remove electrons from one object and cause them to transfer to the other object. As one object loses electrons, the other object gains them, as shown by the amber and fur in Figure 6.5.

If you count the electrons in Figure 6.5 (c), you will notice that no electrons are lost during the process of charging. They are simply transferred. The position of the positive charges does not change during the process of charging.

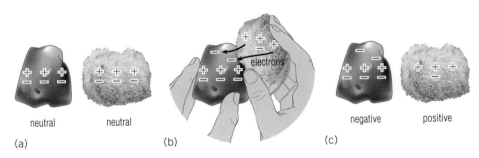

neutral   neutral   electrons   negative   positive

(a)   (b)   (c)

Figure 6.5 (a) The amber and the fur are electrically neutral. (b) If you rub the amber with the fur, electrons transfer from the fur to the amber. (c) As a result, the fur becomes positively charged and the amber becomes negatively charged.

It is important to remember that the transfer of the charges from one object to another is possible because the two objects are rubbing against each other. Both objects are neutral before they are rubbed together. They become charged as a result of the rubbing, which is the force of friction. It is also important to keep in mind that electric charges are not being created. The positions of the electrons in each object change or some electrons move from one object to another.

Electron Affinity

Different substances have different abilities to hold on to electrons. The tendency of a substance to hold on to electrons is called **electron affinity**.

Table 6.2 lists a series of selected materials in order of their electron affinity. This list is referred to as a triboelectric series. You will notice that the higher the material is in the list, the greater the tendency for that material to lose electrons.

Table 6.2 Triboelectric Series

Tend to lose electrons ↑	(+)
	human skin (dry)
	glass
	human hair
	nylon
	cat fur
	silk
	cotton
	steel
	wood
	amber
	ebonite
	plastic wrap
↓ Tend to gain electrons	Teflon®
	(−)

This means that if you rub together two materials listed in the table, you can determine which material will become positively charged and which material will become negatively charged. For example, if you rub nylon and steel together, the nylon will become positively charged and the steel will become negatively charged. The nylon will lose electrons, because it is higher in the table. The electrons from the nylon will be transferred to the steel, making the steel gain electrons and become negatively charged.

Note that there can be a slightly different order for materials such as fur or wood depending on which type of animal the fur is from and which type of tree the wood is from.

infoBIT

Why Is It Called Triboelectric?

The term *tribos* comes from a Greek word meaning "to rub."

Suggested Activity ●···········
C2 Inquiry Activity on page 212

Learning Checkpoint

1. List the three types of smaller particles that make up an atom and describe their locations.

2. What happens when two objects made out of different materials are rubbed together?

3. What term describes an atom's tendency to hold on to electrons?

4. In the term *static electric charges*, what does *static* refer to?

5. In the following pairs, which material is more likely to give up electrons when the materials are rubbed together?

   (a) wood vs. human hair

   (b) plastic wrap vs. steel

   (c) cotton vs. silk

Laws of Attraction and Repulsion

You may have heard the expression "opposites attract" in discussions about people. This is definitely true for electric charges (Figure 6.6). Scientists studying the interaction of objects have observed that when a positively charged object is brought close to a negatively charged object, the two objects attract each other, or pull toward each other. When two objects with the same charge are placed close together, the objects repel each other, or push away from each other.

As a result of data collected and confirmed through many scientific investigations, scientists believe that

- particles with opposite charges attract each other, and

- particles with like charges repel each other.

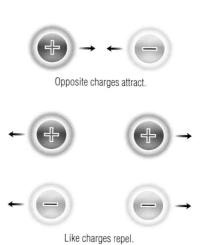

Opposite charges attract.

Like charges repel.

Figure 6.6 If you increase the amount of charge on objects, the attraction or repulsion also increases.

You can use the strategy of visualizing to help you understand the important details of a large amount of complex information. One way you can visualize is to create a picture map. Using the information about the laws of attraction and repulsion, begin drawing pictures to represent the information provided in this section. Add to your picture map as you read about electrical insulators and conductors.

Electrical Insulators and Conductors

Another way to group materials is by their conductivity. **Conductivity** is the ability of materials to allow electrons to move freely in them. Materials that hold onto their electrons and do not allow them to move easily are called electrical insulators. An electrical **insulator** is a solid, liquid, or gas that resists or blocks the movement of electrons, as shown in Figure 6.7 (a). Dry wood, glass, and plastic are all examples of electrical insulators.

Materials that allow electrons to change positions are called **conductors** (Figure 6.7 (b)). **Conduction** is the movement or transmission of electrons through a substance. Examples of conductors include the metals copper and aluminum. These metals are often used in electrical wiring in homes. The wires are coated with plastic, which is an insulator.

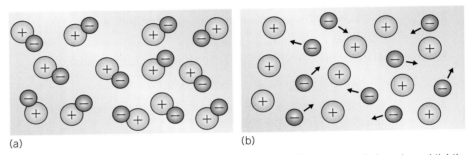

(a)   (b)

Figure 6.7 (a) Electrons in an insulator cannot move freely. The electrons (−) are bound tightly to the nuclei (+) so they resist movement. (b) Electrons in a conductor can move freely. The electrons are not as tightly bound to the nuclei. They can move away from the nuclei.

A Faraday cage is an enclosure made of conducting material that protects its contents from electric charges. Find out how airplanes, cars, and even some specially designed clothes can act as Faraday cages. Conduct your research in the library or on the Internet. Share your findings with the class in a format of your choice.

Some materials allow only some movement of electrons. These are called fair conductors. In a fair conductor, the electrons do not move as freely as in a conductor, but they are not held almost in place as they are in an insulator.

Table 6.3 gives some examples of good conductors, fair conductors, and insulators. There are variations within each category, as some materials are better or poorer conductors than others.

Table 6.3 Conductivity of Selected Materials

Good Conductors	Fair Conductors	Insulators
copper	water with dissolved minerals	rubber
aluminum	moist air	wood
iron	human body	plastic
mercury	carbon	pure water
other metals	soil	metal oxides (for example, rust)

Water as a Conductor

Most water has dissolved minerals in it, making it a fair conductor. This is one reason why you do not want to be in a lake during a thunderstorm. If lightning strikes the lake, the static electric charges from the lightning will be conducted through the water and could injure or kill you. This is the same reason why you should not use water to try to put out an electrical fire (Figure 6.8). You also need to take care not to operate electrical appliances near water or with wet hands. You should never use electrical gadgets near pools, bathtubs, hot tubs, or open water, such as ponds, lakes, or rivers. This can be extremely dangerous and could result in an electric shock causing injury or death.

Figure 6.8 Use an all-purpose fire extinguisher for an electrical fire.

6.1 CHECK and REFLECT

1. (a) Draw a diagram of an atom that has four protons, five neutrons, and four electrons.

   (b) Label each particle with its name and indicate whether it is positive (+), negative (−), or neutral.

2. (a) What is friction?

   (b) Explain how friction can be used to transfer electrons. Use two substances from Table 6.2 on page 208 in your answer.

3. (a) What is the difference between a conductor and an insulator?

   (b) Give one example of a conductor.

   (c) Give one example of an insulator.

4. How would a scientist explain the following observation: a plastic rod that contains a large number of electrons does not have a static electric charge?

5. (a) What does the law of attraction state?

   (b) What does the law of repulsion state?

6. (a) Name two examples of good conductors.

   (b) Name two examples of fair conductors.

   (c) Name two examples of insulators.

7. Copy the table below into your notebook. For each pair, predict which substance becomes more positively charged and which becomes more negatively charged when the two substances are rubbed together. Use Table 6.2 on page 208 to help you make predictions.

Charged Pairs

Pairs	Becomes More Positively Charged	Becomes More Negatively Charged
cotton, steel		
cotton, silk		
human hair, human hands (dry)		
Teflon®, wood		
glass, plastic wrap		

C2 *Inquiry Activity*   Toolkit 2

Investigating Static Electric Charges

If you have ever rubbed a balloon in your hair and stuck it to the wall, you have seen the effects of static electric charges. In this activity, you will investigate the effects of positive and negative charges on each other.

Initiating and Planning

What is the effect of charged objects on each other and on neutral objects?

Materials & Equipment

- two vinyl strips
- clear adhesive tape
- ring stand
- paper towel
- two acetate strips
- beaker
- watch glass
- metre stick

Performing and Recording

1. Copy the following table into your notebook to record your findings. Give your table a title.

Hanging Object	Approaching Object	Predictions	Observations
charged vinyl	charged vinyl		
charged acetate	charged acetate		
charged acetate	charged vinyl		
ruler	charged vinyl		
ruler	charged acetate		

2. Tape one end of a vinyl strip to the ring stand so the strip hangs down. Rub the hanging vinyl strip with the paper towel to charge it.

3. Rub the other vinyl strip with the paper towel, and bring that vinyl strip close to the suspended strip. Record your observations in your table.

4. Repeat steps 2 and 3, using the two acetate strips and the paper towel. Record your observations.

5. Bring one of the charged vinyl strips close to the suspended acetate strip. Make sure the two strips do not touch each other. Record your observations.

6. Place the beaker upside down on the desk or table. Place the watch glass on top of the beaker as shown in Figure 6.9. Balance the ruler so it is lying flat and centred on the watch glass.

Figure 6.9 Step 6 Balance the ruler on the watch glass on top of the beaker.

7. Bring a charged vinyl strip near, but not touching, one end of the ruler. Record your observations.

8. Bring a charged acetate strip near one end of the ruler. Record your observations.

Analyzing and Interpreting

9. Usually, charged vinyl gains electrons and becomes negatively charged, and charged acetate loses electrons and becomes positively charged. How does this information explain your observations?

Communication and Teamwork

10. How would you modify this procedure so that you could identify the type of charge on a charged object? Write a testable question for your new procedure.

11. Write three statements that summarize your observations.

Figure 6.10 The bits of paper are attracted to the statically charged comb.

Here is a summary of what you will learn in this section:

- In charging by contact, an originally neutral object gains the same type of charge as the charged object that touched it.

- In charging by induction, an originally neutral object gains the opposite charge to the charged object.

- Neutral objects are attracted to charged objects.

- Grounding an object transfers electrons between the object and the ground, making the object neutral.

Charged Objects

What does dust on a computer screen have in common with paper on a comb (Figure 6.10)? In both examples, there is attraction between objects with unlike charges. To test whether an object has been charged, you can use an **electroscope**, which is an instrument that can detect static electric charges. The electroscope was invented in 1748 by French clergyman and physicist Jean Nollet.

A metal-leaf electroscope has two very thin metal pieces, called leaves, suspended from a metal rod. The metal rod is attached to a top plate or metal knob. When a charge is transferred to the plate or knob, the charge spreads out over the whole structure, including the leaves. The greater the charge, the greater the separation between the leaves. An electroscope is one of the devices that can be used to study static electric charges. The study of static electric charges is called **electrostatics**.

Using an Electroscope

How do you know when an object is charged? Rather than testing whether an object sticks to something else, you can use an electroscope (Figure 6.11).

Figure 6.11 A metal-leaf electroscope

Purpose

To determine what happens to an electroscope when different charged objects are brought near it

Materials & Equipment

- straw, plastic comb, or ebonite rod
- wool sweater
- metal-leaf electroscope
- glass, acrylic, or acetate rod
- silk fabric

Procedure

1. Charge the straw or comb by running it through your hair, or rub an ebonite rod on a wool sweater.

2. Bring the charged object near, but not touching, the top of the electroscope. Observe the motion of the metal leaves. Record your observations in a chart or by sketching the results.

3. Move the object away and observe the leaves again. Record your observations.

4. Now, touch the charged object to the top of the electroscope. You can rub the object along the top of the electroscope if necessary. Observe the motion of the metal leaves. Record your observations.

5. Move the object away and observe the leaves again. Record your observations.

6. Charge the glass, acrylic, or acetate rod by rubbing it with the silk fabric. Repeat steps 2 to 5 using this charged rod.

Questions

7. What role did friction play in this activity?

8. With your group, explain what happened, using your knowledge about charges. Assume your object had a negative charge placed on it.

9. Write a testable question that could be answered by your observations in this activity.

Pose New Questions

10. What additional procedures and questions could you add to extend your understanding?

Detecting Static Electric Charge

To predict what charge is transferred to an electroscope, you can use a standard set of charged objects, such as ebonite and glass. Ebonite is a hard rubber material that is low on the triboelectric series and readily accepts electrons, as you saw on Table 6.2 on page 208. When ebonite is rubbed with fur, it becomes negatively charged (Figure 6.12 (a)). Glass is high on the triboelectric series and tends to give away electrons. When glass is rubbed with silk, it becomes positively charged (Figure 6.12 (b)).

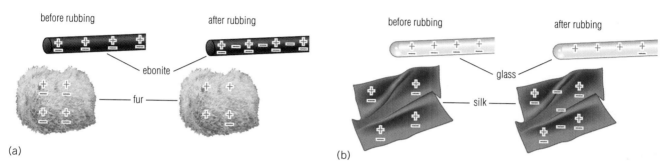

Figure 6.12 To test unknown charges, you can use the known charges on (a) an ebonite rod and (b) a glass rod.

When a negatively charged rod is brought near a neutral electroscope, the electrons in the electroscope are repelled by the rod. The electrons move down into the leaves of the electroscope. The leaves are now both negatively charged, so they repel each other and move apart (Figure 6.13). When the negatively charged rod is taken away, the negative charges in the electroscope are no longer repelled, so they move throughout the leaves, stem, and knob. The leaves drop down, and the electroscope becomes neutral again.

Suggested Activity • · · · · · · · · · · ·
C4 Inquiry Activity on page 220

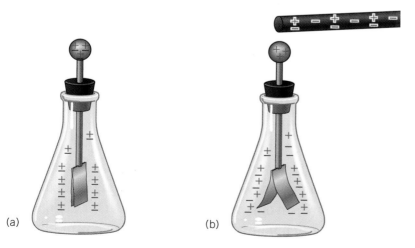

Figure 6.13 (a) The leaves are not separated in the neutral electroscope.
(b) The leaves repel each other when they are charged negatively or positively.

Understanding Terms and Concepts

A Frayer quadrant can help you understand a term or the concept it represents. Divide a rectangle into four sections, and title the rectangle with the term or concept (e.g., Charging by Contact). In the top left section, write a definition of the term using your own words and words from the text. In the top right section, write facts related to the term. In the lower left section, write examples of the term from the textbook. In the lower right section, write ideas or concepts that are not examples of the term.

Charging by Contact

As you learned in Section 6.1, electrons can be transferred through friction. Electrons can also be transferred through contact and conduction. You can charge a neutral object by contact when you touch it with a charged object. **Charging by contact** occurs when electrons transfer from the charged object to the neutral object that it touches. The neutral object gains the same type of charge as the object that touches it because the electrons move from one object to the other (Figure 6.14).

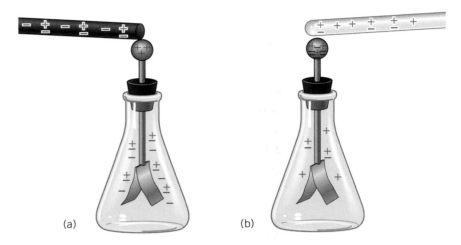

(a)   (b)

Figure 6.14 (a) When a negatively charged object touches a neutral object, electrons move to the neutral object, making it negative. (b) When a positively charged object touches a neutral object, electrons move from the neutral object to the positive object and make the neutral object positive.

Suggested Activities •·········
C5 Inquiry Activity on page 221
C6 Inquiry Activity on page 222

Charging by Induction

Induction is the movement of electrons within an object caused by a nearby charged object, without direct contact between the two objects.

If you rub a rubber balloon on your hair, electrons will transfer from your hair to the balloon, making the balloon negatively charged. The charges stay in a nearly fixed, or static, position on the balloon because rubber is an insulator. When you bring the negatively charged balloon near a neutral wall, the negatively charged electrons on the balloon repel the negative charges on the wall, making that part of the wall a positively charged surface. The balloon is **charging by induction**, or inducing a charge on the wall because it charges the wall without contacting it (Figure 6.15).

When you charge an object by induction, you use a charged object to induce a charge in a neutral object. Then, you ground the newly charged object so it retains its charge. Your newly charged object now has the opposite charge to the one that was on the charging object.

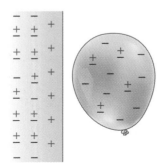

Figure 6.15 The negatively charged balloon has induced a positive charge on the wall's surface without touching the wall.

©P

Grounding is the process of connecting a charged object to Earth's surface. When you connect a charged object to the ground, you provide a path for charges to travel to or from the ground. Figures 6.16 and 6.17 show the process of charging by induction. Grounding occurs in Figures 6.16 (b) and 6.17 (b).

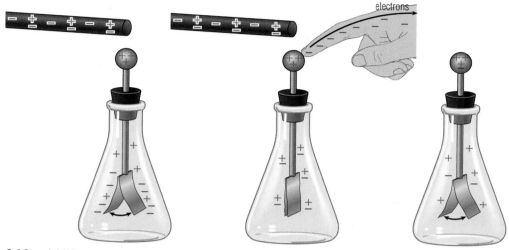

Figure 6.16   (a) When a negatively charged object comes near a neutral electroscope, it repels the electrons in the neutral electroscope.

(b) When you ground the neutral electroscope, you provide its electrons with a path away from the repulsive influence. Some electrons leave the electroscope.

(c) When you remove the ground and the charged object, the electroscope is left with a positive charge because it has lost some electrons.

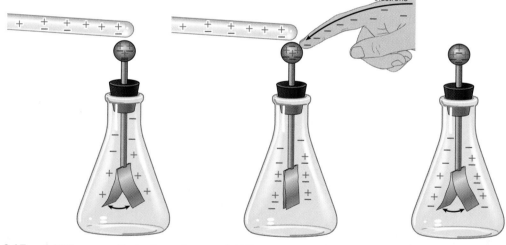

Figure 6.17   (a) When a positively charged object comes near a neutral electroscope, it attracts electrons in the neutral electroscope.

(b) When you ground the neutral electroscope, you provide a path for electrons to go toward the positive influence.

(c) When you remove the ground and the charged object, the electroscope is left with a negative charge because extra electrons are trapped on it.

Electrical Discharge

Once an object is charged, the charges are trapped on it until they are given a path to escape. When electric charges are transferred very quickly, the process is called an **electrical discharge**. Sparks are an example of electrical discharge.

Transfer of charge from girl to door

Transfer of charge from carpet to girl

Figure 6.18 When electrons jump between your hand and a doorknob, you can receive a surprising shock.

reSearch

Sometimes, lightning strikes start from the ground and go up to a cloud. There are also cloud-to-cloud lightning strikes. Find out more about different types of lightning by conducting research in the library or on the Internet. Create a visual display of your findings to share with the class.

Have you ever walked across a carpet and reached for a doorknob only to receive a shock when you created a spark (Figure 6.18)? When you shuffle your feet in slippers or socks on a carpet, electrons are transferred through friction and you build up a static electric charge. When your hand reaches toward the neutral doorknob, the excess electrons transfer due to induction, and you get a shock.

Lightning

Lightning is a very large electrical discharge caused by induction. In a thunderstorm, a charged area, usually negative, builds up at the base of a cloud (Figure 6.19 (a)). The negative charge at the base of the cloud creates a temporary positively charged area on the ground through the induction process (Figure 6.19 (b)). When enough charge has built up, a path of charged particles forms (Figure 6.19 (c)). The cloud then discharges its excess electrons along the temporary path to the ground, creating a huge spark—lightning (Figure 6.19 (d)). This discharge also creates a rapid expansion of the air around it, causing thunder.

Air is normally an insulator. If it were not, lightning would occur every time that clouds formed. For lightning to happen, charges in the clouds must build up to the point where the air cannot keep the charges separated from the ground. Then, the air stops being an insulator and becomes a fair conductor, resulting in a lightning strike.

Earth is a donator or receiver of charge and is so large that overall it is not affected by the electron transfer of huge lightning strikes. As a result, the ground is always considered neutral.

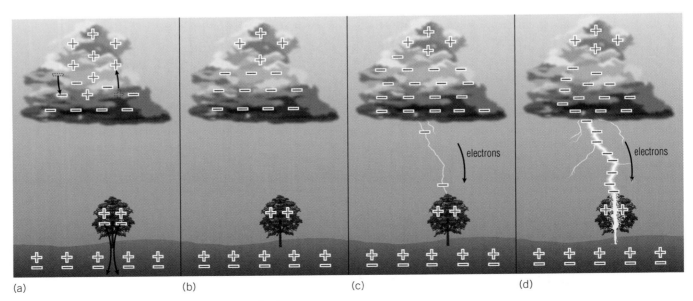

(a) (b) (c) (d)

Figure 6.19 Lightning is an atmospheric electrical discharge.

Electrostatic Generators

Scientists use several devices in the laboratory to study how static electric charges create lightning and other phenomena, such as the static that affects clothes coming out of the dryer.

Early electrostatic generators were called "friction machines" because they used direct contact between different surfaces to create charged areas. A glass sphere or cylinder was rubbed mechanically by a pad to charge it up.

Other technologies, such as the Van de Graaff generator, create charge through friction between the roller and belt and then transfer the charge to a large metal sphere, as shown in Figure 6.20.

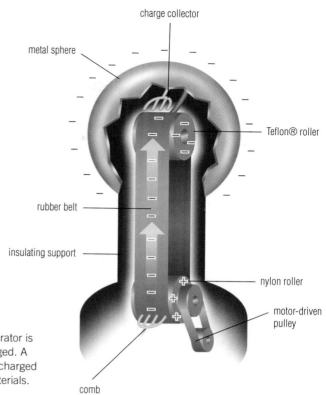

Figure 6.20 This Van de Graaff generator is set up so its dome is negatively charged. A Van de Graaff generator can also be charged positively by using different roller materials.

6.2 CHECK and REFLECT

1. Explain what an electroscope detects.

2. Describe the difference between charging by contact and charging by induction in terms of electron transfer.

3. What is grounding and how is it useful?

4. How are lightning and sparks similar?

5. (a) How do objects become negatively charged using the contact method?

   (b) How do objects become positively charged using the contact method?

6. Explain how an object becomes temporarily charged by induction when a charged object is brought near.

7. Using a sequence of labelled diagrams, explain how a positively charged balloon will stick to a neutral wall. Under each diagram, describe the motion of the charges.

8. How does the process of grounding occur during a lightning strike?

9. (a) The leaves of the charged electroscope shown below move farther apart if a rod with the same charge is brought near. Use your scientific knowledge to explain this observation.

   (b) Give a reason why the leaves move closer together if the rod has the opposite charge to the electroscope.

Question 9

Sorting Materials based on Charges

Materials that tend to lose electrons are higher on a triboelectric series. Materials that tend to gain electrons are lower on a triboelectric series.

Initiating and Planning

How can a variety of materials be sorted based on their ability to gain or lose electrons?

Materials & Equipment

- materials such as wool, silk, aluminum, paper towel, leather, wood, amber, hard rubber, Styrofoam™, plastic wrap, vinyl (PVC), and Teflon®
- metal-leaf electroscope
- known charged object, such as an ebonite rod rubbed on wool to create a negative charge

---

Performing and Recording

1. Make a table like the one below to list your materials, predictions, and results. Give your table a title.

Materials			Prediction of Charge		Actual Charge	
	A	B	A	B	A	B
1.	wool	silk				
2.	wool	aluminum				
3.	silk	aluminum				
4.	silk	paper				

2. In your table, predict what charge each material in each pair will have when the materials are rubbed together.

3. Rub together the first pair of materials, A and B.

4. Touch material A to the knob of the electroscope to charge the electroscope.

5. Use a charged ebonite rod to test the charge on the electroscope by bringing it near the knob. Do not touch the rod to the electroscope (Figure 6.21). Observe the motion of the leaves. Record the charge of material A.

6. Ground the electroscope by touching it with your hand.

7. Charge the electroscope using material B.

8. Use a charged ebonite rod to test the charge on the electroscope by bringing it near the knob. Do not touch the rod to the electroscope. Observe the motion of the leaves. Record the charge of material B.

9. Repeat steps 3 to 8 for each pair of materials.

Analyzing and Interpreting

10. Which materials were good electron receivers and would appear lower on a triboelectric series?

11. Which materials were good electron donors and would appear higher on a triboelectric series?

12. Create a triboelectric series by listing the materials you used in order, according to their electron affinity.

13. Compare your list with the generally accepted list. Suggest reasons for discrepancies.

Communication and Teamwork

14. (a) Write a question about a material that does not appear on the triboelectric series.

    (b) Describe how you could test where this new material would appear on the triboelectric series.

15. Write a testable question for this inquiry.

Figure 6.21 Step 5 To test the charge on the electroscope, bring the charged ebonite rod near it without touching it.

Charging by Contact

You can charge a neutral object by contact when you touch it with a charged object. In this activity, you will investigate what happens when electrons are transferred from a charged object to a neutral object through contact.

Initiating and Planning

What charge does the electroscope gain compared to the charging rod?

Materials & Equipment

- ebonite rod
- glass rod
- wool
- silk
- metal-leaf electroscope

Performing and Recording

1. Make a table like the following to record your predictions, observations, and diagrams. Give your table a title.

Trial		Motion of Leaves	
		Predictions	Observations
A	ebonite rod touching		
	ebonite rod near		
	glass rod near		
B	glass rod touching		
	glass rod near		
	ebonite rod near		

2. Read the procedure, and record your predictions for each step.

Trial A

3. Charge the ebonite rod by rubbing it with the wool. Touch the ebonite rod against the top of the electroscope. Record your observations using a labelled diagram.

4. Rub the ebonite rod with the wool again. Bring it near, but not touching, the top of the electroscope. Record your observations using a labelled diagram.

5. Charge the glass rod by rubbing it with silk. Bring the glass rod near, but not touching, the top of the electroscope. Record your observations using a labelled diagram.

6. Touch the top of the electroscope with your hand. Record your observations using a labelled diagram.

Trial B

7. Repeat steps 3 to 4 using a glass rod charged with silk. Use a charged ebonite rod in step 5. Repeat step 6.

Analyzing and Interpreting

8. (a) Explain why the leaves moved when the ebonite rod touched the electroscope in step 3.

    b) What charge was left on the electroscope?

9. (a) Explain why the leaves moved when the glass rod came near the top of the electroscope in step 5.

    (b) What charge was left on the electroscope?

10. Compare your predictions with your observations.

11. In terms of charge movement, explain in words and diagrams the effect of

    (a) an identically charged rod near the electroscope

    (b) an oppositely charged rod near the electroscope

12. Explain how you would find the charge of an unknown material.

Communication and Teamwork

13. Write a summary statement about the charge the electroscope gains and the charge of the influencing rod that was used in the activity.

Charging by Induction

Charging by induction occurs when a charged object is used to induce a charge in a neutral object and then the charged object is grounded so it retains the charge. In this activity, you will use different charged objects to induce the charge.

Initiating and Planning

What charge does the electroscope receive compared to the charging rod?

Materials & Equipment
- ebonite rod
- glass rod
- wool
- silk
- metal-leaf electroscope

Performing and Recording

1. Make a table like the following. Give your table a title.

Trial		Motion of Leaves	
		Predictions	Observations
A	ebonite rod away		
	ebonite rod near		
	glass rod near		
B	glass rod away		
	glass rod near		
	ebonite rod near		

2. Record your predictions before you begin each trial, and record your observations throughout.

Trial A

3. Charge the ebonite rod by rubbing it against the wool.

4. Bring the ebonite rod near, but not touching, the electroscope. Then, touch the top of the electroscope with your hand.

5. Remove your hand from the electroscope, and then move the ebonite rod away. Observe what happens to the leaves of the electroscope.

6. Bring a charged ebonite rod near the electroscope. Record what happens to the electroscope leaves.

7. Bring a charged glass rod near the electroscope. Record what happens to the electroscope leaves.

Trial B

8. Repeat steps 3 to 7 except start by charging a glass rod against silk in step 3. Use a charged ebonite rod for step 7.

Analyzing and Interpreting

9. (a) Compared to the original rod that was brought near the electroscope, what charge did the electroscope end up with?

(b) How do you know?

10. Explain what happens to the electrons in the electroscope when your hand touches the electroscope.

11. (a) You had to remove your hand first before you moved the rod away. What is a scientific explanation for this action?

(b) What would have happened if you had moved the rod away and then your hand?

12. What other ways could you ground the electroscope?

Communication and Teamwork

13. Summarize the method of charging by induction by using diagrams labelled with the motions of charges.

Figure 6.22 Rock painting of Thunderbird from Wasawakasik Lake, Saskatchewan

Here is a summary of what you will learn in this section:

- Some First Nations and Métis peoples have an intimate spiritual understanding of lightning in terms of Thunderbird.

- Lightning rods are used to prevent damage to buildings.

- Grounding static electric charges can help prevent sparks near flammable fuels and damage to electronic equipment.

- Electrostatic precipitators work by creating charged waste particles and using electrostatic attraction to remove the particles.

Thunderbird

Explanations of the natural world and phenomena, such as lightning and thunder, are transmitted through oral tradition, the passing of stories from one generation to the next. On the Saskatchewan plains, where thunderstorms may suddenly arise and lightning often streaks across the sky, First Nations and Métis peoples have developed a deep spiritual understanding of lightning in terms of Thunderbird (Figure 6.22). Rather than fear lightning, they deeply respect its power.

Thunderbird is found in the legends and teachings of many First Nations and Métis peoples. Thunderbird is often portrayed as a large eagle-like bird. As the herald of spring, Thunderbird brings the rain. Elder Danny Musqua, a Saskatchewan Nakawē (Saulteaux) Elder, explained that his people thought of Thunderbird as a physical and spiritual entity with eyes that blink lightning and a cry that is thunder. However, in special ceremonies called tobacco circles where Elders from his grandfather's time spoke freely, many of them believed that lightning (*waskwanehpigan*) was created by two powerful objects crashing together. Today, First Nations and Métis peoples have two ways to explain the appearance of lightning: *waskwanehpigan* and electrical energy. *Waskwanehpigan* tells us what lightning is in Mother Earth, while electrical energy tells us about how nature works.

During Reading

Determining the Key Idea

Good readers synthesize details from a text to determine the key idea. To do this, you make connections among the important ideas in the text, asking yourself the question, "How does this information connect to that information?" As you read this section, ask yourself how the information on one page connects to the information on another page. What is the single key idea presented on these pages?

Traditional Knowledge Keeper Albert Scott remembers stories that he learned from his Nakawē Elders that uncontrolled lightning occurred as fledgling Thunderbirds learn to fly and control their power. The Nakawē people also have legends surrounding an eternal struggle between Thunderbird and a water snake that resides beneath the ground. A similar legend is told among the Cree people of Saskatchewan, where Thunderbird, *Piyisew* in Plains Cree, born from Mother Earth, fights a great serpent called *Kinēpik* in an attempt to protect the living things on Earth.

C7 *Quick Science*

Lightning: Encounters with a Static Electric Phenomenon

We often see forks of lightning in the sky and hear stories of peoples' encounters with this phenomenon. In this activity, you will use your knowledge of the characteristics of static electric charges to analyze the following story of an encounter with lightning.

Purpose

To analyze an account of a lightning encounter

Procedure

1. As a class, read the following true account of a man's encounter with a lightning strike. Then, discuss the questions that follow.

   A man was digging postholes in a large open field using a 2-m-long steel bar, which he used to pry rocks from the ground. He was working in stormy weather and wanted to finish a bit more work before taking cover. Suddenly, he could feel the hairs on his arms and legs begin to stand up. He threw the steel bar as hard as he could and dove for the ground. Then, he heard a deafening blast of sound. The lightning strike missed him, and he ran for cover. Later, after the storm, he went back to the site. The ground around the bar was blackened, and one end of the bar appeared to have melted.

Questions

2. What did his hair standing up indicate?

3. (a) Holding a steel bar when the lightning struck would almost certainly be lethal. How would a scientist explain the role of the steel bar in this outcome?

   (b) Would it make any difference if the steel bar being held had one end in the ground when lightning struck? Explain.

4. Describe the path the lightning may have taken to result in blackened ground and a melted end of the steel bar.

5. What could the man have done differently in order to be safer during the storm?

6. If you find yourself out in the open during a thunderstorm, you should crouch, keep your feet close together, and stay on your toes. There are scientific reasons for this advice.

   (a) Why should you crouch on your toes?

   (b) Why should you keep your feet close together?

Pose New Questions

7. What questions about lightning has this activity raised for you?

©P

Respect for Lightning

First Nations and Métis peoples' respect for the natural phenomenon of lightning has been integrated into many sacred ceremonies over the centuries. Elder Julie Pitzel remembers teachings from her Elders that the first lightning and thunder in spring heralds the first sweat lodge ceremonies. She was also taught that lightning striking the ground awoke the plants to grow and propagate. As she was taught, Traditional Knowledge Keeper Judy Bear practises a smudging ceremony during the first thunder and lightning in spring.

As a young Métis boy growing up in Green Lake, Elder Peter Bishop was not familiar with First Nations culture, particularly from the south. However, the Métis people of his community learned through observation and experience much practical knowledge about thunderstorms. For example, his people used to shade their windows and mirrors, knowing that lightning was attracted to shiny objects. Elder Peter learned another valuable lesson about lightning striking the nearest tallest object: "During a particularly violent thunderstorm, a bolt of lightning struck a very tall spruce tree close to our home. It travelled down the length to barbed wire my father placed there, knowing it would travel down this wire and strike the ground. We were also told never to swim during lightning storms, knowing that water was a good conductor of electricity."

The power of lightning should be respected. Elders often teach that storms and lightning have more power than humans despite our technologies that have tried to overcome and master them. In this way, we are reminded to be humble. If care is taken, we can enjoy and revere storms and lightning, not fear them.

Lightning Rods

A lightning rod is a metal pole with a wire attached to it that is mounted on the top of a structure. Similar to the barbed wire mentioned by Elder Peter Bishop, the wire runs down the structure into the ground (Figure 6.23). Scientists explain that a lightning rod provides a pathway for lightning, a stream of electrically charged particles, to reach the ground without burning the structure down.

infoBIT

The Names of Lightning

Lightning has many names among the First Nations and Métis peoples of Saskatchewan. Lightning in Plains Cree, *wāsaskotēpayin*, means "fire that falls from the sky" or "lightning that strikes Earth." The Plains Cree use the word *kitōwak* for thunder, which means "to call out," referring to Thunderbird's cry. In Dakota words, Elder Velma Goodfeather teaches that thunder is called *Wakiŋyaŋ hotonpi* and that lightning is *Wakiŋyaŋ tuwanpi*.

reSearch

There are many stories about lightning and thunder in First Nations and Métis cultures. Research these stories and any hidden meanings. Note any similarities and/or differences with Western science principles. Share your findings with the class in a format of your choice.

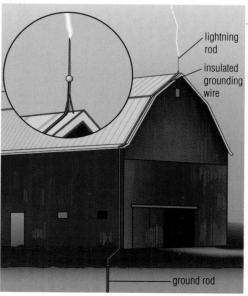

Figure 6.23 The lightning rod redirects the electrical strike away from the barn and harmlessly into the ground.

The stream of electrically charged particles is highly conductive, so if lightning strikes in the area around the building, it is much more likely to strike the lightning rod. This decreases the total amount of electric charge in the building, making it less likely to be struck by lightning. If lightning hits the lightning rod, the flow of electrically charged particles is directed harmlessly down to the ground so the building would not be damaged.

Grounding Static Electric Charges on Vehicles

Friction occurs when two surfaces rub against each other. The surfaces may be solids, such as silk or glass, or they may be gases or fluids, such as air or water. Automobiles and airplanes build up charges through friction between the vehicle's outer surface and the air as the vehicles move. A simple way to prevent static build-up on a car is to use a ground strap (Figure 6.24). However, dragging a strap along the ground would not be a practical solution for airplanes.

Instead, airplanes have needle-like projections, called static discharge rods or wicks, located in various places on the wings and plane body (Figure 6.25). The force of repulsion between charges becomes so strong that charges disperse into the air from the point.

Figure 6.24 Some drivers use a grounding strap to prevent static electric charges from building up on their cars.

Figure 6.25 These needle-like rods on the wing of an airplane disperse static electric charges into the air.

Making Use of Static Electric Charges

Static electric charges can be a nuisance when they cause flyaway hair or sparks in your living room. They can damage electronic equipment and are extremely dangerous when they occur near flammable materials. However, static electric charges can also be useful. Our ability to control and direct static electric charges has allowed us to design technological devices that make use of them to improve our lives.

Spray Painting

Spray painting can be a challenging job. The paint comes out of the spray gun or can at a high speed, so the paint particles bounce off the object being painted, wasting paint. Painting irregular objects or those with a lot of space between their parts, such as a fence or bicycle frame, wastes paint when the paint sprays through the openings.

Electrostatics can help. Figure 6.26 shows how electrostatics are used to paint a car. The paint coming out of the nozzle gains a negative charge through friction. The surface of the car has been given a positive charge. Unlike charges attract, so the paint is attracted to the surface of the car. There is less waste due to bounce and overspray, and the finish is smooth and uniform.

Figure 6.26 Industrial sprayers, such as those used to paint cars, take advantage of the laws of static electric charges.

Suggested Activities •···········
C8 Science, Technology, Society, and the Environment on page 230
C9 Problem-Solving Activity on page 230

re**Search**

Many people have contributed to our understanding of electrical energy. Research one of the following names to find out when these people lived and what they contributed: Benjamin Franklin, Luigi Galvani, Charles-Augustin de Coulomb, Alessandro Volta, James Watt, André-Marie Ampère, Georg Ohm, Robert Millikan, Michael Faraday, Thomas Edison, Nikola Tesla, and George Westinghouse. Conduct your research in the library or on the Internet.

re**Search**

Laser printers make use of electrostatics in the printing process. Find out how a laser printer works. Conduct your research in the library or on the Internet. Make a diagram that shows the steps involved in making a copy using a laser printer and include the role of electrostatics in your sketches.

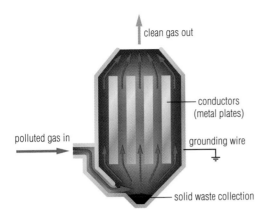

clean gas out

conductors
(metal plates)

polluted gas in

grounding wire

solid waste collection

Figure 6.27 An electrostatic precipitator uses static electric charges to remove particulates from gases in buildings or industrial sites.

Electrostatic Precipitators

An electrostatic precipitator makes use of the laws of static electric charges to clean air (Figure 6.27). The gas discharged from a factory can contain tiny particles of pollutants, called particulate matter. One way to clean the gas before it is released is to send it through pipes that charge the particulate matter negatively. Then, the gas moves through an area that has positively charged plates. The positive plates attract the negative particles and remove them from the gas. These collector plates are cleaned periodically to keep the system running efficiently. Industrial plants that produce cement, steel, lumber, and petrochemicals use similar techniques to remove dust and other particulate matter from the air.

We also use electrostatics in processes that purify and sort materials, such as ore separation in mining, plastics, and paper recycling, and the settling of fine particles suspended in water.

6.3 CHECK and REFLECT

1. It is not safe to take shelter under a tree in a thunderstorm. Use your scientific understanding of lightning to explain what might happen.

2. Explain the importance of lightning in First Nations and Métis cultures.

3. How does the power of lightning remind us to be humble?

4. What is the function of a lightning rod?

5. How is charge build-up reduced on airplanes?

6. Why is it important to ground static electric charges?

7. Large trucks that carry flammable liquids often have a metal wire or chain that drags on the ground. Explain what this prevents.

8. How can neutral pollutant particles be made attractive to the charged plate in an electrostatic precipitator?

9. Describe the devices used on airplanes to protect them from static electric charge build-up.

10. The technician in this photo is using a tool that has insulated handles. Why is this important for working on electronic equipment?

Question 10

11. When spray paint is applied to a car, the paint has a negative charge and the surface of the car has a positive charge. Some processes use a negatively charged paint and a grounded object. Explain why this also works.

©P

Delvin Kanewiyakiho:
Ematawak — Spirit of Thunderbird

For First Nations and Métis peoples, electricity has two meanings. Delvin Kanewiyakiho, a Traditional Knowledge Keeper, describes the arrival of electrical energy to the Little Pine First Nation reserve in the 1950s. His Elders reacted with amazement when electrical energy powered the first light bulb: "The Elders were awestruck. They thought it was amazing that people were able to harness the magic of Thunderbird (Figure 6.28). They were able to use it to produce light. My Elders referred to electricity as something that is mysterious, *Ematawak*, which means 'spirit of Thunderbird.' *Émamahtawak* is the word we use today to describe electricity. I make sense of electricity as a gift of Thunderbird, though in science it is explained as a flow of electrons. It keeps us warm, powers cellphones and iPods, and gives us light."

Delvin considers himself an *Oskapēwos*, which means "helper" in Cree. An *Oskapēwos* is a Knowledge Keeper who trains all his or her life under the tutelage of an Elder to become a keeper of traditional ceremonies. One day, an *Oskapēwos* could be recognized by his or her community as an Elder.

Electrical energy plays an integral role in Delvin's everyday life. Delvin, a savvy user of technology, relies on electrical energy at home and for his work as a teacher. He has a master's degree in education and is a school division consultant. For Traditional Knowledge Keepers like Delvin, a scientific understanding of electrical energy does not conflict with their cultural beliefs about it. But, in the ceremonies where millennia of tradition and spirituality live, electrical energy has no place. Tools used in the sweat lodge, the healing lodge, pipe ceremonies, and the Sun dance, for example, are still done in the traditional way.

"Electricity has made life more convenient. Back then [in the early part of the 20th century], people on my reserve lived in log houses that had dirt floors. While electricity and technology can make life easier, they cannot replace human contact. On a basic human level, [any one person's fixation on] technology can take away from understanding another human being spiritually."

Figure 6.28 When Thunderbird opens its eyes, lightning flashes.

Advertisements for Static Control Products

If you have a problem with flyaway hair, clothes sticking together in the dryer, or dust that will not stick to a mop, chances are there is a consumer product that has been designed to deal with it. For example, people sometimes add an antistatic dryer sheet to a clothes dryer. The dryer sheet adds a thin layer of waxy chemicals to the surface of clothes so there is less friction between the surfaces.

Working in a group, discuss the following questions, and record your answers.

1. Give examples of products that help consumers with static control.

2. Are these products essential for everyday living? Why or why not?

3. (a) What do advertisers say about static in their messages to try to convince you to buy their products? Is this information accurate?

   (b) Do you think advertisers are successful in convincing people? Explain your answer.

SKILLS YOU WILL USE
- Designing, building, and testing
- Suggesting modifications

Create Your Own Electroscope

In this activity, you will design and construct your own electroscope. You will test your device and evaluate its reliability in detecting the presence of static electric charges.

Initiating and Planning

How can we design and construct an electroscope that accurately detects static electric charges?

Materials & Equipment
• clear glass bottle   • cardboard
• paper clip   • scissors
• aluminum foil   • wool
• tape

Criteria for Success

- Your electroscope should have metal leaves that separate when you bring a charged object near it.

- You should be able to order materials from least charged to most charged.

Performing and Recording

1. Use the materials provided to design an electroscope.

2. As a test, charge a glass rod with wool and bring the rod close to the electroscope. The leaves of your electroscope should separate.

3. Create a table to record your observations. Test your electroscope with a variety of charged materials. Record your observations as sketches or written reports, or both.

4. Discharge your electroscope before each test.

Analyzing and Interpreting

5. Which of the materials were most charged?

6. Which of the materials were least charged?

7. How could you modify your electroscope to measure the charge of each material?

Communicate

8. Describe how you designed your electroscope.

9. How could you improve your design?

©P

Rod McEachern: Director, Research and Development, PotashCorp

Figure 6.29 Electrostatic precipitator used to clean dryer exhaust gases in the PotashCorp Rocanville plant

Many industries use electrostatics to help keep pollutants, such as dust and other particulates, out of the air (Figure 6.29). Rod McEachern uses his background in chemistry and his team of engineers and other professionals to help keep PotashCorp efficient and reduce air emissions.

Q: What is your background?

A: I grew up on a small family farm near Sinnett, Saskatchewan. I attended the University of Saskatchewan for 16 years—5 years full-time and 11 years part-time—and received a B.Sc., M.Sc., and Ph.D. in chemistry.

Q: Can you describe your current job?

A: My current position is Director, Research and Development, at PotashCorp. I manage a group of technical professionals who work to ensure that best available technology is used in the processing of potash ores. The group I manage consists of several engineers (electrical, chemical, mechanical, process) as well as a chemist, several chemical technicians, and a maintenance support person.

Our group does research, technology development, and technology transfer in such diverse areas as

- improved process control (distributed control systems, instrumentation, process automation, etc.)
- separation techniques, such as froth flotation, screening, and granulation
- improved product quality
- improved environmental performance of our potash plants, through reduced air emissions and waste management practices
- online equipment monitoring to ensure reliable plant performance

Our group's role is to work with the potash plants to identify needs and areas for improvement. We then assemble technical projects designed to identify solutions to the problems. In many cases, we work with vendors, university researchers, and consultants. Technology development is done through laboratory tests, and pilot plant studies, as well as full-scale plant trials in the potash operations.

Q: How are you using precipitators in the potash industry?

A: Electrostatic precipitators are used in some of our plants to reduce particulates from the exhaust air from our product dryers. The cleaned air is then released to the environment through a stack.

Q: What are some future applications for precipitators in your industry?

A: Reducing air pollution for product dryers is the main application. There may be some future application in reducing the dust levels that are generated by the processing equipment within the plant.

Key Concept Review

1. (a) What are the possible interactions between two charged objects?

   (b) How do a charged object and a neutral object interact?

2. Explain the role of friction in creating a charged object.

3. (a) Two neutral objects, A and B, were rubbed together, resulting in object A being charged positively. What is the charge on B now?

   (b) How do you know?

   (c) Which object, A or B, is likely higher on the triboelectric series?

   (d) How do you know?

4. For the following three electroscopes, explain which way the leaves will move when a charged rod is brought near. Explain your reasoning.

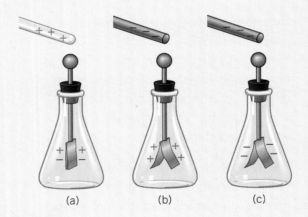

(a)　　　　(b)　　　　(c)

Question 4

5. How would you ground an electroscope?

6. (a) Describe how to leave an object positively charged using the induction method.

   (b) Describe how to leave an object negatively charged using the induction method.

7. (a) Define electrical discharge.

   (b) What is a real-life example of an electrical discharge?

8. Describe a device that uses static electric charges. Include a labelled diagram as part of your answer.

9. Describe a device that protects other devices by controlling static electric charges. Include a labelled diagram as part of your answer.

Connect Your Understanding

10. (a) Explain why a positively charged balloon will stick to a wall just as easily as a negatively charged balloon.

    (b) Would the humidity (moisture content) of the air make a difference in the ability of the balloon to stick to the wall? Explain.

11. Suppose you had a plastic lightning rod that was the same size and design as a metal lightning rod. Would the plastic lightning rod work better than, the same as, or not as well as a metal lightning rod? Explain your answer.

12. Would a negatively charged balloon stick to a metal wall as easily as to a wooden wall? Explain why it would or would not.

13. You have an unknown material that becomes charged when you rub it with silk. You also have a negative ebonite rod and a positive glass rod. How can you determine the charge of the unknown object?

14. If lightning hits a car, the effect is minimal. Explain why.

©P

15. Two identical objects are both charged positively, but one object has about twice as much positive charge as the other object. What would happen to the charges when the two objects are brought together? Explain your answer.

16. (a) How would using a humidifier in a home affect static electric charge build-up?

    (b) Would you need to use a humidifier more in the summer or the winter? Explain.

17. Explain two different actions that could cause static electric charges to build up on a computer.

18. If you wrap plastic wrap on a glass bowl, the plastic wrap will cling to the bowl. Use your understanding of static electric charges to explain why.

19. You run a brush through your hair and wonder if it has become statically electrically charged. Design a test that allows you to determine if the brush has a charge.

20. What materials could be woven into a polyester carpet to prevent a static electric charge from building up on a person walking across the carpet? Explain the reasons for your choice.

21. Suppose a child asks you to explain why there is lightning. Write two simple explanations that you could share with the child. The first is about Thunderbird, the second is about static electric charges. You may wish to include diagrams.

Reflection

22. What role do you think lightning plays in forest fires and the ecology of an area? How do you think this connects with what you learned about Thunderbird?

23. What information from this chapter surprised you or was not what you expected? Explain.

24. (a) How would you rate your participation in the labs you did in this chapter?

    (b) How could you improve your participation?

25. What are two things about static electric charges that you know now that you did not know before you started this chapter?

After Reading

Reflect and Evaluate

Revisit the key learning goals that you set in the Before Reading activity at the start of this chapter. How did the During Reading strategies help you to accomplish your goals? Write a paragraph that summarizes how the reading strategies assisted your learning. Compare your paragraph with a partner's. Add any new insights you gained from reading your partner's reflection.

Reflection on Essential Inquiry Questions

What do you understand about the transfer of electric charges? **SI**

What technologies did you learn about that use static electric charges to improve our lives? **TPS**

What are some impacts of electrostatics on our lives? **DM**

What did you discover about First Nations and Métis understanding of lightning? **CP**

Unit Task

In this chapter, you learned about static electric charges and the role they play in our lives. How can you apply your new understanding to the Unit Task you have chosen?

Current electrical energy is the flow of electrons in a closed circuit.

Outcomes

By the end of this chapter, you will:

- demonstrate and analyze characteristics of static electric charge and current electricity, including historical and cultural understanding

- analyze the relationships that exist among voltage, current, and resistance in series and parallel circuits

What you will learn:

- There are relationships among voltage, current, and resistance.
- Different meters measure electrical energy quantities in different ways.
- Electrical energy is produced, transferred, and converted into other forms of energy, which will help you handle electrical devices safely.
- Series circuits and parallel circuits operate differently and are used in different applications.

Each light bulb in this image of Saskatoon is lit because of the movement of electrons through the wires that connect the bulbs.

Key Terms

- alternating current (AC)
- ammeter • ampere (A)
- battery • circuit • circuit breaker • circuit diagram
- current electrical energy
- direct current (DC)
- dry cell • electric current
- electrochemical cell
- electrodes • electrolyte
- fuse • ground fault circuit interrupter (GFCI) • load
- multimeter • Ohm's Law
- ohmmeter • ohms (Ω)
- parallel circuit • primary cell
- resistance • resistor
- secondary cell • series circuit
- short circuit • superconductor
- switch • transistor • volt (V)
- voltage • voltmeter • wet cell

Before Reading

Learning Vocabulary in Context

This chapter contains many new terms related to electrical energy. Skim and scan Section 7.1 for the ways that vocabulary is supported. Where can you find definitions? How are unfamiliar terms highlighted in the text? What special features explain terms or words? Begin a personal list of unfamiliar terms, adding definitions as you find them in the chapter.

Voltage, Current, and Resistance

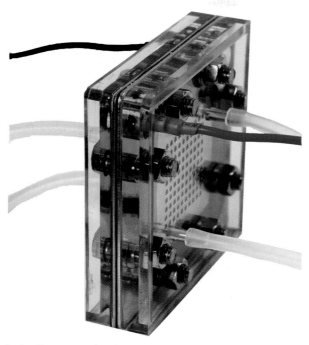

Figure 7.1 A fuel cell converts chemical energy into electrical energy. The fuel cell shown here is only slightly smaller than this textbook.

Here is a summary of what you will learn in this section:

- Voltage is the difference in electric charge between two points.

- Current is the rate of movement of electric charge through a conductor. Resistance is the ability of a material to resist the flow of electric charges.

- An electrochemical cell generates voltage by creating an imbalance of charges between its terminals.

- Models can be mental, mathematical, or a combination. Scientific models can help you communicate your ideas.

Fuel Cells

What do houses, buses, and laptops have in common? They can all be powered using fuel cells.

Fuel cells generate electrical energy from a chemical reaction with a fuel, such as hydrogen (Figure 7.1). Using oil and other fossil fuels, such as coal, for energy produces pollution. Most fuel cells create no pollution and actually produce pure water as a by-product.

A fuel cell is not used up like an ordinary cell (i.e., a battery) would be because as the electrical energy is produced, more fuel is added by taking it from the air. Currently, much of the energy produced by fuel cells is wasted as heat, but their design continues to be refined to make them more efficient.

In 2010, a fleet of 20 Canadian-made fuel cell-powered electric buses began operating in Whistler, BC (Figure 7.2). The buses were fully implemented for the 2010 Olympic and Paralympic Winter Games to be able to manage the huge increase in tourists without a huge increase in pollution. These buses produce 60 percent less greenhouse gases, compared to diesel buses.

Figure 7.2 New fuel cell-powered buses in Whistler, BC

Buses are an excellent choice for fuel cell technology. They do not need an infrastructure of hydrogen fuelling stations as cars would, since they all return to one central depot for maintenance and refuelling. There are many bus systems in such cities as London, Barcelona, and Hamburg in Europe, and Perth in Australia that are already converted to fuel cell technology.

Fuel cells combine oxygen in the air with hydrogen in the cells to power electric vehicles. One day, fuel cells may be used to power smaller devices such as laptop computers. Fuel cells could also be integrated with current power generating stations like wind, solar, and hydro. These stations often produce electrical energy when it is not needed. That electrical energy can be stored in fuel cells for future use.

C10 Quick Science

Light the Lights

In this activity, you will use a combination of wires, light bulbs, and a hand-operated generator to make a bulb light up.

Purpose

To discover how to make flashlight bulbs light up using a hand-operated generator

Materials & Equipment

- five insulated copper wires with both ends bare
- hand-operated generator
- two 2.0-V flashlight bulbs

CAUTION: Disconnect the wires if they get hot.

Procedure

1. Use wire and the hand-operated generator to make one bulb light up. Record your arrangement using a labelled diagram or sketch.

2. Use wire and the hand-operated generator to make two bulbs light up. Record your arrangement using a labelled diagram or sketch.

3. If time allows, try other arrangements for step 1 and step 2.

Questions

4. Describe how to use wire and a hand-operated generator to make one bulb light up. Include a labelled sketch of an arrangement that worked to light up the bulb and one that did not light up the bulb.

5. Describe how to use wire and a hand-operated generator to make two bulbs light up. Include a labelled sketch of an arrangement that worked to light up the bulbs and one that did not light up the bulbs.

Pose New Questions

6. Where do you think the energy comes from to light the bulb(s)?

7. Using your observations from this activity, what testable question could you write that your results from this activity would answer?

8. What other questions do you have about your observations? Write a testable question for an activity that would answer your questions.

Current Electrical Energy

As you saw in Chapter 6, the small static electrical energy discharges you have felt from a sweater is similar to the huge static electric discharges of lightning. Unfortunately, static electric charges are not useful for operating electrical devices. To operate electrical devices, you need a steady flow of electric charge.

Unlike static electric charges and discharges, a flow of electric charge continues to move as long as two conditions are met. First, the flow of electric charge requires an energy source. Second, the electric charge will not flow unless it has a complete path to flow through. This path is called an electrical **circuit**. The flow of electric charge in a circuit is called **current electrical energy**.

Electric Circuits

An electrical circuit includes an energy source, a conductor, and a load. An electrical **load** is a device that converts electrical energy to another form of energy. For example, in Figure 7.3, the light bulb is the load. It converts electrical energy to light and heat energy.

Many electric circuits also include a switch. A **switch** is a device that turns the circuit on or off by closing or opening the circuit. When the switch is closed (Figure 7.3), the circuit is complete and electric charge can flow. An open switch (Figure 7.4) means there is a break in the path, so the electric charge cannot flow through the circuit. The circuit is turned off when the switch is open.

The light switch is a common example of a switch we use every day. It controls the power to the light. Other examples of common switches might also control electric ceiling fans or garage doors.

Suggested Activity • · · · · · · · · · · · · ·
C11 Problem-Solving Activity
on page 245

Figure 7.3 A closed electric circuit

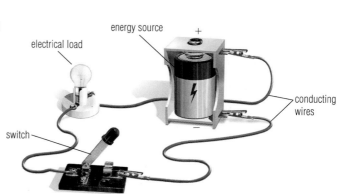

Figure 7.4 An open electric circuit

Voltage

Each electron in a conductor, such as a copper wire, has electrical energy stored within it. When the conductor is connected to an energy source, the electrons flow through the conductor. The energy source provides more energy to each electron, which enables them to move through the conductor.

The difference in electrical energy between two points in a circuit is called the **voltage**. The higher the voltage in a circuit, the greater the stored electrical energy that is provided to each electron.

Measuring Voltage

The voltage in a circuit is always measured between two locations in that circuit. A **voltmeter** is used to measure voltage (Figure 7.5). The voltmeter is showing the difference between the energy levels at the two points (voltage is also sometimes referred to as potential difference). The SI unit for measuring voltage is the **volt (V)**.

Figure 7.5 A voltmeter

How Electrons Transfer Energy in a Circuit

When you turn on the light switch on a wall, you close the circuit and the light comes on immediately. How does the electric charge get from the switch to the light bulb so fast? It may surprise you to learn that individual electrons do not travel from the switch to the bulb when the switch is turned on. Picture electrons in a wire as being like water in the water pipes in your house. The water pipes are normally full of water so when you turn the tap on, water comes out of the tap immediately (Figure 7.6).

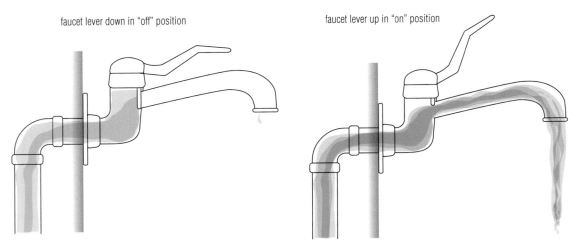

faucet lever down in "off" position   faucet lever up in "on" position

Figure 7.6 Electrons in a wire are like the water in the water pipes in your home. Since the pipes are already full, water comes out of the tap as soon as you turn it on.

Electrons in a wire work in a similar way. When an energy source is connected to a circuit, electrons in the conductor instantly "push" or repel other electrons nearby because of their electric charges.

When one electron moves at one end of the wire, it pushes the next one, which pushes the next one, and so on. This process happens *instantly*. By pushing the first electron, you make the last electron move. That is why when you flip the switch, the light goes on instantly even though the electrons themselves have not moved from the switch to the light bulb.

Current

Electric current is a measure of the amount of electric charge that passes by a point in an electrical circuit in a given time interval. Think of the steady flow of electric current as being like water flowing in a stream. The water keeps on flowing unless its source dries up. As long as the energy source continues, the electrons continue to flow. Because the current flows in only one direction, it is called **direct current (DC)**.

The current that flows through cords plugged into the wall sockets in your home is called alternating current. **Alternating current (AC)** flows back and forth at regular intervals called cycles. This is the current that comes from generators and is carried by the power lines to your home.

Measuring Current

Current in a circuit is measured using an **ammeter** (Figure 7.7). The unit of electric current is the **ampere (A)**. An ampere is a measure of the amount of charge moving past a point in the circuit every second.

*info**BIT***

The Origin of Ampere

"Ampere" and "ammeter" are named in honour of André-Marie Ampère (1775–1836), a French physicist who studied electricity and magnetism.

Figure 7.7 These ammeters show a reading of 0.50 A. The meter on the right has amperes on the scale below the black curved line.

Current Electrical Energy and Static Electric Charge

Current electrical energy differs from static electric charge because current electrical energy is the flow of electrons in a circuit through a conductor. Static electric charge is the electric charge that builds up on the surface of an object. Static electric charge discharges when it is given a path, but does not continue to flow.

Resistance

Resistance is the degree to which a substance opposes the flow of electric current through it. All substances resist electron flow to some extent. As you saw in Chapter 6, conductors, such as metals, allow electrons to flow freely through them and have low resistance values. Low resistance is useful, for example, in power stations that want the maximum of electric current to be conducted to homes and businesses. Insulators, such as plastic and wood, resist electron flow to a greater degree and have high resistance values. In the case of incandescent light bulbs, high resistance is important because the resistance is what causes the light bulb filament to emit light. Resistance is measured in **ohms (Ω)** using an **ohmmeter**. An ohmmeter is usually part of a multifunctional meter called a **multimeter** (Figure 7.8).

When a substance resists the flow of electrons, it converts the electrical energy into other forms of energy, such as heat or light energy. There is still the same number of electrons passing through the circuit, but they each have less energy. The more resistance a substance has, the more energy it gains from the electrons that pass through it. The energy gained by the substance may be radiated to its surroundings as heat, light, sound, or kinetic energy (Figure 7.9).

Figure 7.8 Multimeters can be used to measure voltage, current, or resistance.

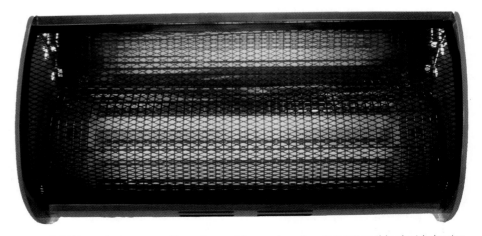

Figure 7.9 When electrons pass through a resistor, such as the element on this electric heater, their electrical energy may be converted to heat, light, sound, or kinetic energy.

Resistance in a Circuit

The more resistance a component has, the smaller its conductance. As you learned in Chapter 6, conductivity is the ability of materials to allow electrons to move freely in them. For example, current in a circuit might pass through the filament in an incandescent light bulb (Figure 7.10). The filament is a **resistor**, which is any material that can slow current flow. The filament's high resistance to the electron's electrical energy causes it to heat up and produce light.

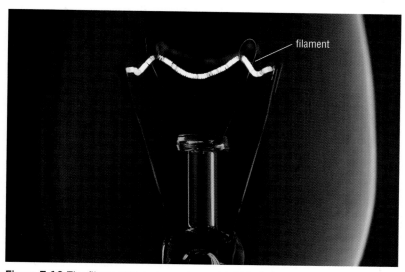

Figure 7.10 The filament in an incandescent light bulb is an example of a resistor.

Superconductors

Superconductivity can be seen in some metals and ceramic materials. Even more than regular conductors, **superconductors** have no electrical resistance below a characteristic temperature. This means that electrons can travel through them freely when they are cooled to temperatures near absolute zero, $-270\,^\circ$C. They can carry large amounts of electrical current for long periods of time without losing energy as heat (thermal) energy. In addition to these extremely low-temperature superconductors, scientists have now discovered that some substances act as superconductors at temperatures above $-243\,^\circ$C. Superconductivity may be used in the future for electrical power transmission. One of its current uses is to make a superconducting magnet in magnetic resonance imaging (MRI) machines in hospitals (Figure 7.11).

Suggested Activities •·········
C12 Inquiry Activity on page 246
C13 Inquire on Your Own on page 247

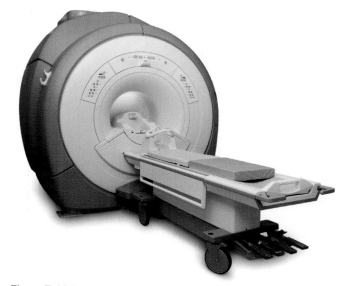

Figure 7.11 This magnetic resonance imaging (MRI) machine uses a superconducting magnet.

1. How is current electrical energy different from the build-up of static electric charges?

2. When you walk into a dark room and turn the light on, do the electrons travel all the way from the switch to the light? Explain your answer.

3. Voltage has been described as similar to the water in the water pipes in your home. What other analogy can you think of that is similar to voltage?

4. What is electric current?

5. What does "resistance" refer to in terms of electron flow?

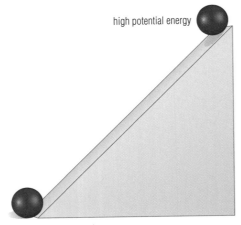

high potential energy

potential energy converted
to another form of energy

Figure 7.12 An electron entering a resistor is similar to a ball at the high end of a ramp, where potential energy is greater.

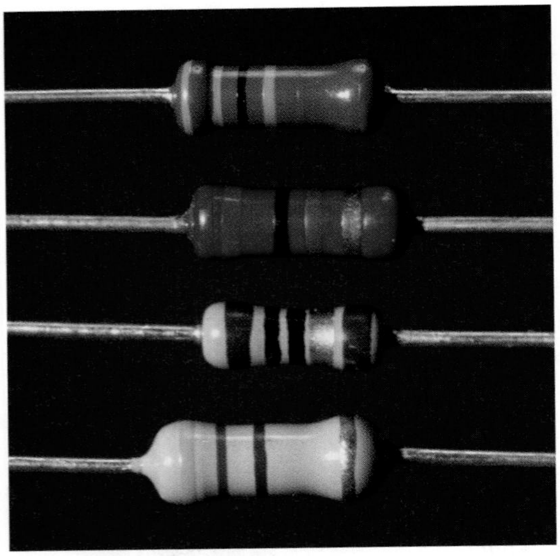

Figure 7.13 Resistors come in many shapes and sizes. The type of material the resistor is made from is one factor that affects its resistance.

Resistors and Voltage

Resistors can be used to cause the electrons to transfer their energy to a different type of energy. When you work with resistors, you should always be aware that they can heat up and cause burns. Use caution when handling them.

In a circuit, electrons have a higher voltage as they enter a resistor compared to when they leave the resistor because they use up some energy in passing through the resistor. You can picture electrons entering a resistor as being at the high end of a ramp, where they have a lot of (gravitational) potential energy. In this analogy, electrons leaving the resistor are at the bottom end of the ramp, where their potential energy has been converted to another form of energy (Figure 7.12).

Types of Resistors

A wide variety of resistors are made for different applications, especially in electronics (Figure 7.13). For example, televisions contain dozens of different resistors.

Resistors are needed in equipment where one power supply is used in different functions, like in your computer. There are many different circuits with different power demands.

A resistor is used if a part of a circuit needs less current than what the power supply is providing. A resistor may also be needed if the current needs to vary. For example, dimmer switches would use a variable resistor. If you lower the light, you are increasing the resistance. Another example would be the volume control for televisions.

©P

Electrochemical Cells

A simple and convenient energy source is a battery. A **battery** is a combination of electrochemical cells. Each **electrochemical cell** is a package of chemicals that converts chemical energy into electrical energy that is stored in charged particles. A simple electrochemical cell includes an electrolyte and two electrodes:

- An **electrolyte** is a liquid or paste that conducts electric charge because it contains chemicals that form ions. An ion is an atom or a group of atoms that has become electrically charged by losing or gaining electrons. Citric acid is an example of an electrolyte.

- **Electrodes** are metal strips that react with the electrolyte. Two different electrodes, such as zinc and copper, are used in a battery.

As a result of the reaction between the electrolyte and electrodes, electrons collect on one of the electrodes, making it negatively charged. The other electrode has lost electrons, so it becomes positively charged (Figure 7.14).

During Reading

Definitions in Context
Often, unfamiliar terms are defined right in the text that you are reading. You do not need to look them up in a glossary or dictionary. Look for the boldfaced words, and then find the definition in the sentence either before or after the term. Add words and definitions to your personal list of terms.

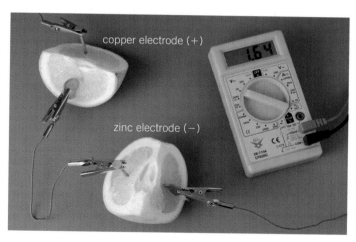

Figure 7.14 The citric acid in the grapefruit is the electrolyte. Electrons collect on the zinc electrode, leaving positive charges on the copper electrode. The meter measures the flow of electrons.

copper electrode (+)

zinc electrode (−)

Wet Cells and Dry Cells

An electrochemical cell that has a liquid electrolyte is called a **wet cell**. Wet cells are often used as an energy source for cars and other motorized vehicles because they are less costly than dry cells and most can be easily recharged. An electrochemical cell that uses a paste instead of a liquid electrolyte is called a **dry cell** or **primary cell** (Figure 7.15). You use dry cells in flashlights, hand-held video game devices, cameras, and watches. A dry cell is a more practical choice in these devices since it can be operated in many different positions including upside down with no concern about the electrolyte spilling.

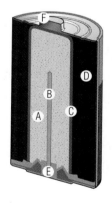

A – zinc powder and electrolyte, where electrons are released

B – electron collecting rod

C – separating fabric

D – manganese dioxide and carbon, where electrons are absorbed

E – negative terminal, where electrons leave

F – positive terminal, where electrons return

Figure 7.15 An alkaline dry cell

Figure 7.16 An electrochemical cell gives electrons electrical energy, or voltage.

Recycling and Re-energizing Dry Cells

Eventually, the chemicals in a dry cell or primary cell are used up and can no longer separate charges. When you are finished using a dry cell, you should recycle it rather than discard it (Figure 7.16). Dry cells can contain toxic materials and heavy metals such as nickel, cadmium, and lead, which are harmful to the environment and living organisms. Household dry cells and batteries are responsible for over 50 percent of all the heavy metals found in landfills. Some dry cells can be re-energized, and are referred to as "rechargeable" or **secondary cells**. Chemical reactions in a rechargeable cell can be reversed by using an external energy source to run electrical energy back through the cell. The reversed flow of electrons restores the reactants that are used up when the cell produces electrical energy. Secondary dry cells can be reused many times and have less impact on the environment than non-rechargeable dry cells. Primary cells are superior in terms of shelf life, as they hold their charge for a longer period of time when not in use. However, secondary cells have greater long-term benefits since they can be used over and over again.

reSearch

Many rechargeable dry cells are available, such as NiCd, NiMH, and lithium ion. Using library or Internet resources, research the different types and compare their composition, lifetime, cost, and ability to hold charges. Display your results in a chart or graphic organizer.

7.1 CHECK and REFLECT

1. What are some examples of electrical loads that you can see in your classroom?

2. Describe the two main components of an electrochemical cell.

3. Explain how electrons flow in a circuit.

4. (a) What device measures voltage?
   (b) What are the units for measuring voltage?

5. (a) What device measures current?
   (b) What are the units for measuring current?

6. (a) What is the function of an electrical load in a circuit?
   (b) List four examples of electrical loads and the type of energy transformation in each.

7. What does resistance refer to in a circuit?

8. What is the role of a resistor in a circuit?

9. Why must a circuit be closed in order for a current to flow?

10. Make a list of similarities between the flow of water and an electric circuit.

11. (a) Using a graphic organizer of your choice, compare the benefits and drawbacks of both primary and secondary cells.
    (b) Referring back to your graphic organizer from (a), which cell would you recommend for a digital camera? Explain.

12. What is the difference between an electrolyte and an electrode?

13. Why should dry cells be recycled rather than thrown in the garbage?

14. What do you now understand about current electrical energy that you did not know before reading this chapter?

Making a Simple Electric Motor

Initiating and Planning

Can an electric motor be built from everyday materials?

Materials & Equipment

- magnet wire
- electrical tape
- scissors
- pliers
- two large safety pins
- wood block
- screws
- screwdriver
- double-sided tape
- magnet
- battery holder with wires
- battery

Performing and Recording

1. First, wind a coil of wire to create the part of the motor that moves (armature). Wind it on a cylindrical form, such as a small battery to keep the shape even.

2. To make the coil hold its shape permanently, twist the free ends and wrap them around the coil a couple of times or use electrical tape to secure the free ends.

3. Hold the wire coil so that it is vertical. Carefully use the tips of the scissors to scrape off the insulation from the top of the wire ends. You may wish to use the wood block to support the free ends.

4. Use pliers to bend two safety pins at the middle to make supports. The safety pins can conduct electrical energy to the armature while the loops of wire on the safety pins can hold it up.

Figure 7.17 Be careful when scraping off the insulation. Only remove the insulation from the top half of the wire.

5. Use the wood block for the base. Use the screws to mount the bent safety pins on the block so that the loops are facing each other and are about 2 cm apart.

6. Use double-sided tape to secure the magnet to the block between the two safety pins (Figure 7.18). Secure the battery holder to the block underneath the magnet. Connect the wires from the battery holder to the safety pins. Insert the battery into the holder. You may need to give the armature a push to get the motor started.

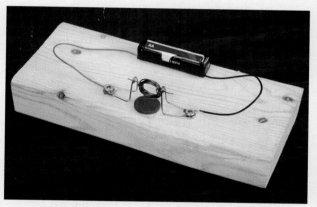

Figure 7.18 Step 6

Analyzing and Interpreting

7. Adjust the angle of the motor so it can work in either a vertical or horizontal position. Draw a diagram of your motor in the different positions.

8. Adjust the shape of the coils and see how they work. Is the coil the best shape? Try squares, ovals, and so on. Make a chart showing each of the shapes you tried and write a short summary of the results underneath them.

9. Vary the number of turns of wire in the coil. Does an odd or even number of turns matter? Does the number of turns determine the speed? Make a chart showing the number of coils and the results.

Communicate

10. Can you make the motor do any work? Demonstrate your results to the class.

C12 *Inquiry Activity*

Toolkit 2

Modelling Voltage, Current, and Resistance

A physical model can help you understand a process or object that may be hidden or too large or small to view directly. Models can be mental, mathematical, or a combination. You can use a scientific model to help you communicate your ideas.

Initiating and Planning

How can you use a model to help you understand the interactions among voltage, current, and resistance?

Materials & Equipment

- 50-cm or longer length of rubber tubing
- water tap and sink
- stopwatch
- 1000-mL beaker

Performing and Recording

1. Create a data table like the one below. Give your data table a title, and use it to record your results.

2. Attach one end of the tubing to the tap. Put the other end into the sink as far from the tap as the tubing will reach without bending.

3. Turn on the water to a medium flow. Record the time it takes for water to exit the tubing.

4. Pinch the end of the tubing, and turn off the water. Keep the end pinched.

5. Simultaneously, turn on the water to a medium flow and release the end of the tubing. Record the time it takes for water to exit the tubing into the sink.

6. While the water is running, pinch the end of the tubing slightly. Observe what happens to the flow.

7. Record the time it takes to fill the beaker using the slightly pinched length of tubing.

8. Record the time it takes to fill the beaker using an open length of tubing.

9. Record the time it takes to fill the beaker using an open length of tubing and the water turned on full.

Analyzing and Interpreting

10. (a) How did the exit times compare for the tubes in step 3 and step 5?

    (b) How would you explain any difference in times?

11. What part of this activity modelled electric current in a circuit?

12. (a) How does the size of the opening in the tubing affect water flow?

    (b) Relate the size of the opening of the tubing to resistance in wires.

13. (a) How does how far a tap is opened affect water flow through the tubing?

    (b) Relate how far a tap is opened to voltage in a circuit.

Communication and Teamwork

14. How did you divide up the tasks in this activity to ensure that all members of your group were included and contributed equally? Would you organize things differently if you were to perform the activity again?

15. How accurately do you think this activity modelled interactions among voltage, current, and resistance? What modifications would make the activity more accurate?

Time to Exit Empty Tube (s)	Time to Exit Pinched Tube (s)	Time to Fill Beaker with Pinched Tube (s)	Time to Fill Beaker with Open Tube (s)	Time to Fill Beaker with Water on Full (s)

SKILLS YOU WILL USE
- Using appropriate equipment and tools
- Designing an experimental procedure

Investigating Conductivity

Question

How do the conductivity of different solutions compare?

Materials & Equipment

- distilled water
- 250-mL beaker
- conductivity tester
- tap water
- salt water
- vinegar
- copper(II) sulphate solution
- other solutions provided by your teacher
- paper towels

Figure 7.19 Conductivity tester

Design and Conduct Your Investigation

Part 1

1. Design a data table to record your predictions and your conductivity readings of the solutions you will test. Give your table a title.

2. Predict which solutions will be the best conductors and which will be the poorest conductors. Record your predictions and the characteristics on which you are basing your predictions.

3. Put 50 mL of distilled water into a 250-mL beaker.

4. Place the metal tips of the conductivity tester in the distilled water (Figure 7.19). Record the conductivity reading of the distilled water in your table. If your conductivity tester is a light bulb, describe the brightness of the bulb.

5. Repeat steps 3 and 4 with 50-mL samples of tap water, salt water, vinegar, copper(II) sulphate solution, and any other solutions your teacher provides for you to use. After each conductivity measurement, empty the beaker as directed by your teacher and rinse it with distilled water. Also, wipe off the tips of the conductivity tester. Make sure that you insert the tips to the same depth in each solution.

6. Clean up your work area. Make sure to follow your teacher's directions for safe disposal of materials. Wash your hands thoroughly.

Part 2

7. Plan an investigation to compare the conductivity of other solutions. Have your teacher approve your plan, and then conduct your investigation.

8. How did you determine whether there were differences in conductivity between the solutions you tested?

9. Rank the substances in order of high conductivity to low conductivity.

10. How did your results compare with your predictions?

11. Make a hypothesis about why there were differences in conductivity between the solutions.

12. Write a summary of your results that answers the question "How does the conductivity of different solutions compare?" Present your findings in the format of your choice.

Figure 7.20 These toy robot dogs are controlled by electric circuits.

Designing Circuits

Computers and devices such as toy robots (Figure 7.20) have complex circuits. Other electrical devices, such as flashlights or hair dryers, have much simpler circuits, often designed in a loop. If you take a flashlight apart, you will probably find a light bulb, some wire, some batteries, and a plastic casing to hold and protect the electrical parts. Flashlights are easy to build with readily available materials and can be assembled efficiently.

However, a simple loop is not always the best design when there are many different components in the circuit. Designers make sure that one component does not depend on another. For example, it would be very frustrating if the toy robot or your computer stopped working completely just because one of its LED indicators went out. These devices have many electrical paths so that if one component stops working, the rest of the device will continue to function.

Tiny Circuits

Conventional switches and other electrical components are practical and convenient for simple electrical devices. However, for the tiny circuits in advanced electronic devices such as computers, transistors must be used instead.

©P

A **transistor** is a tiny device that acts as a switch or amplifier in a circuit. Transistors are often referred to as solid-state components because they are made of solid material with no moving parts. Most transistors are constructed with three layers of specially treated silicon. These layers are arranged so that a small amount of voltage through the middle layer controls a current between the outer layers. In this way, transistors can act as switches.

Microcircuits (also called integrated circuits) are made up of microscopic transistors and other electrical devices. A microcircuit is simply a circuit on an extremely small scale. Microcircuits, or microchips, regularly contain more than a million components per square centimetre (Figure 7.21).

Figure 7.21 A microcircuit is usually called a "chip" or a "microchip."

C14 *Quick Science*

Keep the Lights On

Current exists when a circuit is complete. If there is a break in a circuit, due to a burned-out bulb, for example, the current cannot continue. In this activity, you will investigate how to keep electric charge flowing through a circuit even though one bulb may be burned out or missing.

Purpose

To compare the flow of electric charge in different types of circuits

Materials & Equipment
- D dry cell
- five insulated copper wires with both ends bare
- three 2.0-V flashlight bulbs

CAUTION: Open the circuit if the wires get hot.

Procedure

1. Circuit A: Using any of the materials, determine how to connect three bulbs in a row so they all light up. Make a labelled diagram of your set-up.

2. Circuit B: Connect all three bulbs so that you can remove one bulb without disconnecting the wires and still have the other bulbs stay on. Make a labelled drawing of your set-up.

Questions

3. (a) What would happen to the other two bulbs if you removed one bulb in Circuit A?

   (b) Why would this happen?

4. Why did the other two bulbs stay lit when you removed one bulb in Circuit B?

5. Draw a circuit that would allow you to remove two bulbs and yet have the third bulb stay lit. Have your teacher approve your drawing. If time allows, test your ideas by building the circuit.

Pose New Questions

6. Compare your results with your classmates. Write a testable question that you would like to answer based on the results.

Circuits

A circuit is a pathway that electric current follows. It must be in a complete loop in order for it to work properly. Circuits can be very complicated, but contain the same basic parts. There is a wire to allow the energy to flow, a load to convert the energy, for example, to heat or light, and an energy source (Figure 7.22(a) and (b)). It may also have a switch to open or close the circuit.

Circuit Diagrams

A **circuit diagram** is a model used by engineers and designers in order to design and analyze an electrical circuit (Figure 7.22(c)). They use special symbols that show the components and electrical connections in a circuit. A circuit diagram is not necessarily drawn to scale. Circuits can be tiny, such as in microcircuits, or as large as your home, such as the circuit that connects a light switch, an overhead lamp, and your home's electrical panel.

You can use the symbols in Table 7.1 to draw and interpret circuit diagrams (Figure 7.23). Knowing the basic circuit symbols can help you analyze existing circuits and make it easier to understand where the current flows and how a device functions.

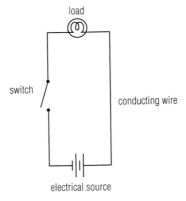

Figure 7.23 The four basic parts of a circuit

Table 7.1 Some Common Circuit Symbols

Symbol	Component	Function
——	wire	conductor; allows electric charge to flow
⊣ⅼⅼⵏ⊢	cell, battery	electrical energy source; longer side represents the positive terminal, shorter side represents the negative terminal
—⊚—	lamp (light bulb)	specific load; converts electrical energy to light and heat energy
—⋁⋁⋁—	resistor	general load; converts electrical energy to heat energy
—⸝⸜—	switch	opens and closes the circuit
—Ⓐ—	ammeter	measures current through a device, connected in series with the device
—Ⓥ—	voltmeter	measures voltage across a device, connected in parallel with the device

Series Circuits

A **series circuit** is an electric circuit in which the components are arranged one after another in series (Figure 7.24). A series circuit has only one path along which electrons can flow. If that pathway is interrupted, the whole circuit cannot function.

The amount of current is the same in all parts of a series circuit. However, if you add more resistors, you increase the total resistance of the circuit. This decreases the current if the voltage remains the same. Adding an extra bulb to a series string of lights makes all the bulbs dimmer.

Electrons use up all their energy going around a series circuit no matter how many loads are in the circuit. Each load will use part of the total voltage, depending on how much it resists the flow of electrons.

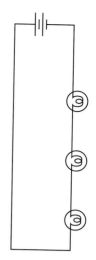

Figure 7.24 A series circuit has only one path along which current can flow.

Parallel Circuits

A simple **parallel circuit** is an electric circuit in which devices are arranged in parallel paths (Figure 7.25), although each electric charge only follows one path. The points where a circuit divides into different paths or where paths combine are called junction points. An interruption or break in one pathway does not affect the other pathways in the circuit. Similarly, adding a new pathway with more resistors does not affect the resistance in any of the other pathways. In fact, adding extra resistors in parallel decreases the total resistance of the circuit. This might seem strange, but think about how much less resistance there is when you drink through two straws instead of one.

Most electrons will follow the path with the smallest resistance. Therefore, the amount of current is greater on the paths with the smaller resistances (Figure 7.26).

Each electric charge has the same amount of energy, and electrons must expend all their energy on the path they are on. This is why the voltage across parallel resistors will always be the same, even though the resistors themselves are of different values.

Table 7.2 on the next page summarizes the characteristics of current and voltage in series and parallel circuits.

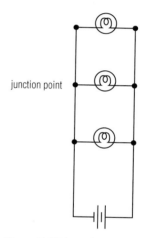

Figure 7.25 In a simple parallel circuit, each component has a parallel path for current.

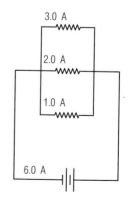

Figure 7.26 Loads of different resistance that are connected in parallel have different currents.

Table 7.2 Voltage, Current, and Resistance in Series and Parallel Circuits

Circuit	Voltage	Current	Resistance
Series circuit	Each load uses a portion of the total energy supplied by the battery.	The current is the same throughout a series circuit.	The current decreases when more resistors are added if the energy remains the same.
Parallel circuit	Each load uses all the energy supplied by the battery.	The current divides into different paths. A pathway with less resistance will have a greater current.	Adding resistors in parallel decreases the total resistance of the circuit if the energy remains the same.

Two Types of Circuits

What happens when one light bulb burns out in a long string of decorative lights? If the set of lights is wired in series, the current must flow through one light before it gets to another light. When one light burns out, all lights go out. The current cannot flow past a burned-out bulb because the pathway is interrupted.

If the set of lights is wired in parallel, the current takes several different paths. If a light on one path goes out, current does not flow on that path. However, there are other paths where the current does flow and lights on those paths remain lit. Series circuits and parallel circuits make up the circuits in your home and school. Some circuits are combinations of series circuits and parallel circuits (Figure 7.27). These combinations help prevent problems such as the refrigerator turning off because a light bulb burned out in a bedroom. It is an important safety feature in a combination circuit to have some switches wired in series, because it is sometimes necessary to turn off the electrical energy in part or all of a home (Figure 7.28).

Suggested Activities • · · · · · · · · · ·
C15 Problem-Solving Activity on page 254
C16 Skill Builder on page 255
C17 Inquiry Activity on page 256
C18 Inquiry Activity on page 257

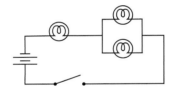

Figure 7.27 A combination circuit. The switch in this circuit can turn all the bulbs on or off.

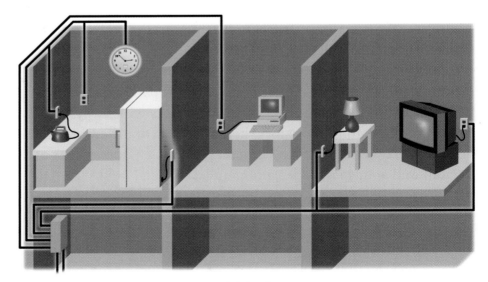

Figure 7.28 A typical home has many parallel circuits.

1. In your own words, define the term *circuit*.

2. Draw the circuit symbol for
   (a) a light bulb
   (b) an ammeter
   (c) a voltmeter

3. Draw a circuit diagram for a circuit that includes a resistor, a switch, conducting wires, and a battery.

4. (a) Draw a circuit diagram of the circuit shown here.

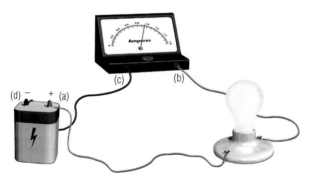

Question 4

   (b) Is this a series circuit or a parallel circuit?

   (c) How do you know?

5. Suppose two pathways in a simple parallel circuit have different resistances. Will the current in each pathway be the same? Explain.

6. What images or memory aids help you remember the differences between series and parallel circuits?

7. Calculate the voltage across the source in each of these circuits.

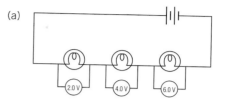

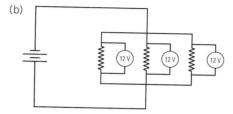

Question 7

8. You have three light bulbs, each with a different resistor. The amount of current through a bulb will affect how much light it emits.

   (a) Will the order in which you hook up the light bulbs in series affect the intensity of light that each emits? Explain.

   (b) What happens when you hook up the bulbs in parallel?

9. Draw a circuit diagram that shows
   (a) three resistors in series
   (b) three resistors in parallel
   (c) one resistor in series and two resistors in parallel

D1

Key Activity

C15 *Problem-Solving Activity*

Toolkits 3, 6

SKILLS FOCUS
- Designing, building, and testing
- Explaining solutions

Off and On

Suppose that all the lights in your home were connected in one simple circuit. When you closed a switch, every light would come on. When you opened the switch, every light would turn off. This arrangement would not be very practical for most uses. Instead, lights can be connected in a circuit in such a way that some can be turned on while others are turned off (Figure 7.29). In this activity, you will investigate how to create such a circuit.

Initiating and Planning

How can a circuit have lights turned on and off individually?

Materials & Equipment

- three or more flashlight bulbs with holders
- connecting wires
- three D dry cells in holders
- switches for each light

CAUTION: Open the circuit if the wires get hot.

Performing and Recording

1. Circuit A: Design and draw a circuit diagram where the three bulbs can be either all on or all off.

2. Circuit B: Design and draw a circuit diagram where each of the three bulbs in the circuit can be turned off and on individually.

3. Circuit C: Design and draw a circuit diagram where two bulbs can be turned off while one stays on.

4. Have your teacher approve your three circuit diagrams. Then, hook up the circuits and test whether they work.

5. Clean up your work area.

Analyzing and Evaluating

6. For each circuit, describe whether the lights were hooked up in series, in parallel, or in a combination.

7. Was the brightness of the lights affected by changing how the bulbs were hooked up? Explain.

Communicate

8. Describe where you would find examples of a series circuit and a parallel circuit.

Figure 7.29 Circuits are carefully designed so that different electrical devices can be operated independently.

Using Equipment Accurately and Safely

Part 1 — Measuring Current

Measuring current involves measuring the amount of electric charge passing a given point in a given time. The current passes through the ammeter where it is measured. The ammeter is hooked in series into the circuit, then the circuit is reconnected and the measurement is taken. Follow these steps to hook up the ammeter.

1. Connect a battery and three resistors in series using a resistor board. Open the circuit.

2. Hook your ammeter in series next to the positive side of the battery. Be sure to connect the positive (red) terminal of the ammeter to the positive (+) terminal of the battery. Connect the negative (black) terminal of the ammeter to the negative (−) terminal of the battery (Figure 7.30). Record the reading.

3. Open the circuit and move the ammeter to immediately beyond the first resistor. Repeat step 2.

4. Repeat step 3 for each resistor.

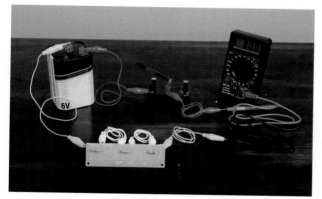

Figure 7.30 Connecting the ammeter in series

CAUTION: Open the circuit if the wires get hot.

Part 2 — Measuring Voltage

5. To insert a voltmeter in a circuit, connect the two wires from the terminals of the voltmeter to opposite sides of the component for which you want to measure the voltage (Figure 7.31).

6. To find the voltage across an electrical source, connect the meter by attaching the red lead to the positive terminal and the black lead to the negative terminal. This allows you to take a reading on both sides of the source. The meter indicates the difference in voltage between the two points.

7. To find the voltage across a resistor or load in a circuit, connect a lead to each side of the resistor or load. Connect the black lead closest to the negative side of the source and the red lead closest to the positive side of the source. This method of connection is called connecting in parallel. By measuring voltage across the resistor or load, you are measuring the voltage drop as the current moves through the resistor or load.

8. Use the voltmeter to test and report on the voltage of a variety of cells and batteries. (Note that 1.5-V batteries almost never actually read 1.5 V.) Compare your readings with the voltage numbers that are written on their labels. If a multimeter is available, use it to repeat your measurements and then compare the results.

9. Connect two or three dry cells in series. Do this by placing them end to end with the positive end of one dry cell touching the negative end of the other dry cell. Predict the voltage reading, and then use the voltmeter to check your prediction.

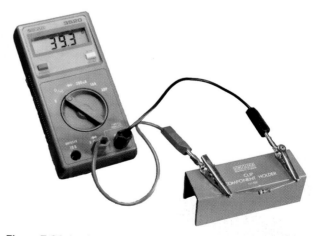

Figure 7.31 A voltmeter connected across a resistor

SKILLS YOU WILL USE
- Observing and measuring
- Recording and organizing data

Series Circuit Analysis

Initiating and Planning

What are the properties of a series circuit?

Materials & Equipment

- 6.0-V battery
- three 100-Ω resistors
- connecting wires
- switch
- resistor board
- multimeter (or voltmeter and ammeter)

CAUTION: Open the circuit if the wires and resistors get hot.

Performing and Recording

Part 1 — Measuring Voltage and Current

1. Create a data table like the one below. Give your table a title.

	Power Supply	Resistor 1	Resistor 2	Resistor 3
Part 1: Current				
Voltage				
Part 2: Current				
Voltage				

2. Construct the circuit shown in Figure 7.32. Keep the switch open until your teacher approves your circuit. Then, close the switch and record the current coming out of the power supply.

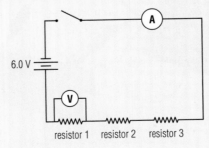

Figure 7.32 Step 2 Construct this circuit.

3. Record the voltage across each resistor and the power supply.

4. Open the switch, and move the ammeter to a position between the first two resistors. Close the switch, and record the current leaving resistor 1.

5. Open the switch, and move the ammeter to a position between the second and third resistors. Close the switch, and record the current leaving resistor 2.

6. Open the switch, and move the ammeter to a position between the third resistor and the source. Close the switch, and record the current leaving resistor 3.

Part 2 — Changing Resistance

7. Open the switch, and remove one resistor. Close the switch. Measure and record the current.

8. Measure and record the voltage across the power supply and across each of the two resistors.

Analyzing and Interpreting

9. State what you noticed in Part 1 about
   (a) the current leaving the resistors in all cases
   (b) the sum of all voltages across the resistors

10. State what happened in Part 2 to
    (a) the current
    (b) the voltages across each resistor
    (c) the sum of the voltages across the resistors

11. What is the effect of adding an identical load in series in a circuit?

12. Did the voltages across any resistors equal the total voltage provided by the source? Explain.

Communication and Teamwork

13. Summarize the properties of a series circuit.

C18 *Inquiry Activity*

Toolkit 11

SKILLS YOU WILL USE
- Using appropriate equipment and tools
- Recording and organizing data

Parallel Circuit Analysis

Initiating and Planning

What are the properties of a parallel circuit?

Materials & Equipment

- 6.0-V dry cell
- three 100-Ω resistors
- connecting wires
- switch
- resistor board
- multimeter (or voltmeter and ammeter)

CAUTION: Open the circuit if the wires and resistors get hot.

Performing and Recording

Part 1 — Measuring Voltage and Current

1. Create a data table similar to the one below. Give your table a title.

	Power Supply	Resistor 1	Resistor 2	Resistor 3
Part 1: Current				
Voltage				
Part 2: Current				
Voltage				

2. Construct the circuit shown in Figure 7.33. Keep the switch open until your teacher approves your circuit. Then, close the switch and record the current coming out of the power supply.

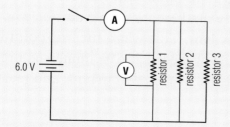

Figure 7.33 Step 2 Construct this circuit.

3. Record the voltage across each resistor and the power supply.

4. Open the switch, and move the ammeter to a position between the first two resistors. Close the switch, and record the current leaving resistor 1.

5. Open the switch, and move the ammeter to a position between the second and third resistors. Close the switch, and record the current leaving resistor 2.

6. Open the switch, and move the ammeter to a position between the third resistor and the source. Close the switch, and record the current leaving resistor 3.

Part 2 — Changing Resistance

7. Open the switch, and remove one resistor. Close the switch. Measure and record the current.

8. Measure and record the voltage across the power supply and across each of the two resistors.

Analyzing and Interpreting

9. State what you noticed in Part 1 about
   (a) the current leaving the resistors in all cases
   (b) the sum of all voltages across the resistors

10. State what happened in Part 2 to
   (a) the current
   (b) the voltages across each resistor
   (c) the sum of the voltages across the resistors

11. What is the effect of adding an identical load in parallel in a circuit?

12. Did the voltages across any resistors equal the total voltage provided by the source? Explain.

Communication and Teamwork

13. Summarize the properties of a parallel circuit.

Here is a summary of what you will learn in this section:

- Ohm's law, $V = IR$, describes the relationship between voltage, current, and resistance.

- In a short circuit, the current does not take the intended path back to its source.

- Fuses and circuit breakers are safety devices.

Figure 7.34 Voltage, current, and resistance have the same relationship in microcircuits in a computer circuit board like this one as they do in the wiring in homes and offices.

Figure 7.35 Georg Ohm (1789–1854)

During Reading

Images Support Understanding

As you read the text, be aware of how the photos, diagrams, or other illustrations support your understanding of new vocabulary. What term or concept is illustrated by the image? How does the image make the concept easier to understand? If you get stuck on unfamiliar terminology, check the images as one way to improve your understanding.

A Fascination with Electricity

The circuit boards in computers work because of the relationships between voltage, current, and resistance (Figure 7.34). These relationships have been understood for about 200 years because of the work of Georg Ohm.

Georg Simon Ohm (Figure 7.35) grew up in Germany in the early 1800s. In high school, he studied physics, chemistry, math, and philosophy. He spent most of his free time playing billiards, ice skating, and dancing with his friends. No one imagined that one day he would be a famous name in science.

After graduation, Ohm went to a private school in Switzerland to teach. Here he taught mathematics and dreamed of studying with great mathematicians at an important university.

Ohm continued to study mathematics. One day, he was asked to instruct in the electricity labs. This was a turning point in Georg Ohm's life. Fascinated by electricity, he immersed himself in the study of the characteristics of voltage, current, and resistance.

Ohm's passion and commitment to his studies led to a deep understanding of how these different electrical concepts were related. Much of what he discovered you have already learned in this unit. He stated these discoveries in what is today called Ohm's law.

Ohm's law established the relationships between voltage (V), current (I), and resistance (R). The symbol for resistance is called the ohm (Ω) in honour of Georg Ohm's work in this field.

C19 *Quick Science*

Voltage, Current, and Resistance

Using the equipment available in your science class, you can investigate the same relationships between voltage, current, and resistance that Georg Ohm did over 200 years ago.

Purpose

To measure how voltage, current, and resistance are related

Materials & Equipment

- 1.5-V dry cell
- resistors, any values from 15 Ω to 50 Ω
- connecting wires
- switch
- resistor board
- multimeter or voltmeter and ammeter

Procedure

1. Create a table like the following to record your data. Give your table a title.

2. Connect one resistor into a simple circuit. If you are using a voltmeter and ammeter, connect these devices as well. Keep your circuit open until your teacher has approved your set-up.

3. Close your circuit.

4. Measure and record the voltage across the resistor.

5. Measure and record the current through the resistor.

6. Record the resistance of the resistor you used.

7. Repeat steps 2 to 6 for different resistors.

Questions

8. Multiply the resistance by the current for each of the trials you completed. What can you infer from your answers?

Pose New Questions

9. If you were going to rewrite this activity, what would you do differently to try and produce different results?

Trial	Resistance (Ω)	Current (A)	Voltage (V)	Resistance × Current
1.				
2.				

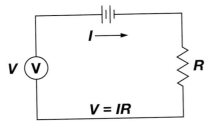

Figure 7.36 Ohm's law states that voltage (*V*) equals current (*I*) times resistance (*R*).

Voltage, Current, and Resistance

Georg Ohm described how voltage and current are affected when one of the values is changed. He determined that the voltage (*V*) in a circuit is equal to the current (*I*) multiplied by the resistance (*R*). Ohm's law states that, as long as temperature stays the same, $V = IR$ (Figure 7.36). In other words,

- the resistance of a conductor remains constant
- the current is directly proportional to the voltage

Table 7.3 and the following examples show how to use Ohm's Law to calculate unknown quantities.

Suggested Activities •·········
C20 Science, Technology, Society, and the Environment on page 264
C21 Inquiry Activity on page 265

Table 7.3 Ohm's Law

Known Quantity	Symbol	Unknown Quantity	Symbol	Unit	Equation
Current, resistance	*IR*	voltage	*V*	V	$V = IR$
Voltage, resistance	*VR*	current	*I*	A	$I = \dfrac{V}{R}$
Voltage, current	*VI*	resistance	*R*	Ω	$R = \dfrac{V}{I}$

Practice Problem

1. A current of 1.5 A flows through a 30-Ω resistor that is connected across a battery. Calculate the battery's voltage.

Example Problem 7.1

A current of 4.0 A flows through a 40-Ω resistor in a circuit. Calculate the voltage.

Given
Current *I* = 4.0 A
Resistance *R* = 40 Ω

Required
Voltage *V* = *x*

Analysis and Solution
The correct equation is $V = IR$.
Substitute the values and their units, and solve the problem.

$V = IR$
$= (4.0 \text{ A})(40 \text{ Ω})$
$= 160 \text{ V}$

Paraphrase
The voltage in the circuit is 160 V.

Example Problem 7.2

A 30-V battery generates a current through a 15-Ω resistor. How much current does the battery generate?

Given
Voltage $V = 30$ V
Resistance $R = 15$ Ω

Required
Current $I = x$

Analysis and Solution
The correct equation is $I = \dfrac{V}{R}$.

Substitute the values and their units, and then solve the problem.

$$I = \dfrac{V}{R}$$

$$= \dfrac{30 \text{ V}}{15 \text{ Ω}} = 2 \text{ A}$$

Paraphrase
A current of 2 A is generated.

Practice Problem

1. A firetruck has a searchlight with a resistance of 60 Ω that is placed across a 24-V battery. Calculate the current in this circuit.

Example Problem 7.3

An electric stove is connected to a 240-V outlet. If the current flowing through the stove is 20 A, what is the resistance of the heating element?

Given
Voltage $V = 240$ V
Current $I = 20$ A

Required
Resistance $R = x$

Analysis and Solution
The correct equation is $R = \dfrac{V}{I}$.

Substitute the values and their units, and then solve the problem.

$$R = \dfrac{V}{I}$$

$$= \dfrac{240 \text{ V}}{20 \text{ A}} = 12 \text{ Ω}$$

Paraphrase
The resistance of the heating element is 12 Ω.

Practice Problem

1. A current of 0.75 passes through a flashlight bulb that is connected to a 3.0-V battery. Calculate the bulb's resistance.

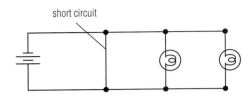

short circuit

Figure 7.37 Current can flow more easily through the wire path than through the light bulb. This creates a short circuit, which could be dangerous.

Figure 7.38 The driver should stay in the truck and wait for help.

Figure 7.39 Some electronic devices, such as this computer, store electrical energy even when the device is not plugged in.

Short Circuits

Sometimes, a wire's insulation breaks down or another problem develops that allows electrons to flow through a device along a different path than the one intended. The device develops a short circuit. A **short circuit** is an accidental low-resistance connection between two points in a circuit, often causing excess current flow (Figure 7.37). Not only do short circuits mean that your electrical device will not work, they can also be dangerous. The conducting wires can quickly become hot from the excess current flow and can start a fire.

One danger from short circuits occurs when a transmission line has been knocked down in a storm or accident. Without a complete path, the electrical energy cannot flow. However, if you come in contact with the wire, the electrical energy will take a path through your body to the ground and seriously injure or kill you. The driver shown in Figure 7.38 is safe as long as he stays inside the truck.

There are times when a technician must short out part of a circuit intentionally by connecting a wire across a load in parallel. The low-resistance wire causes the current to flow through it rather than through the higher resistance device. This allows the technician to work on the device without interrupting the rest of the circuit.

Electrical Safety

All electrical appliances present a risk of electric shock. Always handle electrical appliances properly and observe all safety precautions. Be careful to disconnect the plug before handling an appliance. Some electronic devices, such as computers, retain electric charge even when they are unplugged (Figure 7.39). This is why many electrical devices have a "Do Not Open" warning printed on them. Take the warning seriously, and do not attempt to repair the device yourself. Instead, contact a repair technician.

©P

Fuses and Circuit Breakers

In electric circuits in your home, fuses and circuit breakers act as a first line of defence if something goes wrong. A **fuse** is a safety device in an electric circuit that has a metallic conductor with a low melting point compared to the circuit's wires (Figure 7.40). If the current gets too high, the metal in the fuse melts, and the current stops. This prevents further problems, such as damage to your electrical components or a possible fire. A blown fuse must be physically replaced as it can work only once. This symbol —⌣— represents a fuse in a circuit diagram.

A **circuit breaker** does the same job as a fuse except that the wire inside does not melt. Instead, the wire heats up and bends, which triggers a spring mechanism that turns off the flow of electrical energy. Once the breaker has cooled, it can be reset. Older homes and apartment buildings tend to have fuse panels, whereas modern buildings have breaker panels (Figure 7.41).

Figure 7.40 Examples of fuses. A normal current can pass through a fuse, but a higher than normal current or short circuit will melt the metal in the fuse, breaking the circuit.

Three-Prong Plug

Another safety feature is the three-prong electrical plug, shown in Figure 7.42. The third prong of a three-prong electrical plug connects the device to the ground wire of the building. The ground wire provides a direct path for any unwanted current to the ground. Instead of electrical energy travelling to the metal body of the device and shocking a person using it, the current is directed to the ground. The three-prong plug is now standard for most countries. In North America and much of South America, it is used for electrical devices of 15 amperes at 125 volts.

Figure 7.41 Circuit breakers help prevent electric overloads.

Figure 7.42 One prong in a three-prong plug carries the current to the load, another prong returns the current to the source, and the third prong directs the current to the ground in the case of a short circuit.

Figure 7.43 Ground fault circuit interrupters are part of some electric outlets.

Ground Fault Circuit Interrupter

Some appliances and devices have an added safety feature. A **ground fault circuit interrupter (GFCI)** or residual current device is a device that detects a change in current and opens the circuit, stopping the current (Figure 7.43). For example, if an appliance gets wet while you are handling it and some current starts to flow through the water, the GFCI opens the circuit so there is less chance of injury to you. Remember, it is extremely dangerous to use any electrical device around water.

7.3 CHECK and REFLECT

1. (a) How is current related to voltage in a circuit?
   (b) How is current related to resistance in a circuit?

2. What does Ohm's law state?

3. Copy this table into your notebook, and calculate the missing values of the circuit.

Voltage, Current, and Resistance

V	I	R
0.5 V		50 Ω
	20 A	100 Ω
6.0 V	4.0 A	

4. A 12-Ω bulb is in a series circuit powered by a 6.0-V battery.
   (a) Calculate the current in the circuit.
   (b) If you changed the 12-Ω bulb to a 24-Ω bulb, what current would be drawn from the battery?

5. What is the resistance in the circuit shown here?

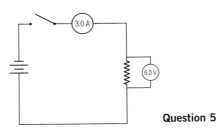

Question 5

6. What is each of these meters called and what does it measure?

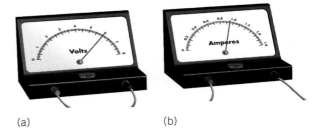

(a)   (b)

Question 6

C20 *Science, Technology, Society, and the Environment*

Electrical Safety

Imagine you have just been hired by SaskPower to help create awareness of electrical safety for kindergarten students.

1. Research electrical safety concerns and, as a class, create a Home Electrical Safety Checklist for home safety.

2. Create an electrical safety poster or brochure that can be shared with a kindergarten class. Be sure to choose electrical safety points that are relevant to young children and to communicate these points in an engaging way.

Investigating Ohm's Law

Initiating and Planning

How are voltage, current, and resistance related?

Materials & Equipment

- four 1.5-V dry cells
- connecting wires
- voltmeter, ammeter
- switch
- two different resistors between 100 Ω and 300 Ω
- resistor board

CAUTION: Disconnect the circuit if the wires or resistors get hot. Have your teacher check the circuit before you close the switch or connect the power source.

Performing and Recording

1. Set up a data table like the one below. Fill in the resistor value for the two resistors you will be using. Examples below are 100 Ω and 200 Ω. Give your table a title.

	Resistor (Ω)	Voltage (V)	Current (A)	Calculated Resistance
1.5 V	1. 100			
	2. 200			
3.0 V	1. 100			
	2. 200			
4.5 V	1. 100			
	2. 200			
6.0 V	1. 100			
	2. 200			

2. Construct the following circuit using resistor 1 and one 1.5-V dry cell (Figure 7.44).

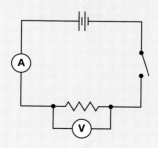

Figure 7.44 The second cell, ammeter, and voltmeter shown in this circuit diagram will be added in step 5.

3. Have your teacher approve your circuit, and then close the switch. Measure and record current and voltage. Open the switch.

4. Replace resistor 1 with resistor 2. Repeat step 3.

5. Connect a second 1.5-V dry cell in series with the first cell in the circuit. Repeat steps 3 and 4, measuring current and voltage for each resistor.

6. Connect a third 1.5-V dry cell into the circuit. Repeat steps 3 and 4.

7. Connect a fourth 1.5-V dry cell. Repeat steps 3 and 4.

8. Calculate your measured resistance for each resistor using $R = \dfrac{V}{I}$.

Analyzing and Interpreting

9. (a) How did your calculated values for resistors compare with their actual values?

   (b) Explain possible reasons for any difference between the two values.

10. Compare your data for all resistor 1 trials. When voltage is increased across a resistor, what happens to the current?

11. Compare your data for all resistor 2 trials. When voltage is increased across the resistor, what happens to the current?

12. What would happen to the current values if you used a resistor with double the value of resistor 2?

Communication and Teamwork

13. By graphing your results, describe the relationship between voltage, current, and resistance. Share your graph with the rest of the class.

14. Explain how your group was able to work together safely to achieve your results.

Key Concept Review

1. Is the circuit below a series circuit or a parallel circuit? Explain why.

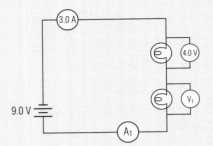

Question 1

2. Draw a circuit diagram of a circuit that includes a battery, an ammeter, and a light bulb with a voltmeter, all properly connected together.

3. How is a parallel circuit different from a series circuit?

4. Are circuits in a home connected in series, in parallel, or in combinations? Explain your answer, using examples of actual rooms in your home.

5. What is the difference between an open circuit, a closed circuit, and a short circuit?

6. A current of 1.5 A flows through a 30-Ω resistor that is connected across a battery. Calculate the voltage of the battery.

7. A 120-V outlet has an appliance that draws 10 A connected to it. What is the resistance of the appliance?

8. Explain, with reference to electron transfer, how an electrochemical cell functions.

9. Explain the benefits and drawbacks of primary and secondary cells.

10. Assume that each resistor in a circuit is of a different value. What type of circuit does each of the following statements describe: series or parallel?

  (a) The voltage is the same across every resistor.

  (b) The voltage varies across each resistor.

  (c) The current varies through each resistor.

  (d) The current remains constant throughout the whole circuit.

Connect Your Understanding

11. Explain the reasons for each of these safety rules.

  (a) Do not poke a knife into a plugged-in toaster to clear out bread crumbs.

  (b) Avoid using an extension cord that is thinner than the cord you are attaching to it.

  (c) When disconnecting an appliance, pull the plug, not the cord.

  (d) Do not plug many electrical cords into one outlet.

  (e) Do not use a kite, stick, or pole close to an overhead wire.

  (f) Make sure your hands are dry before touching any electrical device, cord, plug, or socket.

  (g) Never use a frayed electrical cord.

12. (a) What is dangerous about the situation shown in the picture below?

(b) What should the worker do to be safer?

(c) The drill is plugged into the wall with a three-prong plug. How does the third prong on the plug act as a safety mechanism?

Question 12

13. You want to find the value of an unlabelled resistor. You have a voltmeter, an ammeter, wires, and a battery. How could you find the value of the resistor accurately?

14. An operational definition is one that explains a process and includes clear instructions on how to measure and collect data. For example, the operational definition of the term "weight" would provide instructions on how an item would have its weight measured, including placing the item on a scale. Formulate an operational definition of

(a) voltage

(b) resistance

(c) current

Reflection

15. (a) What do you think is the most useful information you learned in Chapter 7? Explain why.

(b) How might you put your understanding of this information to practical use?

After Reading

Reflect and Evaluate

With a partner, list all the ways that this chapter supports understanding of unfamiliar terms. Revisit your personal list of terms and definitions. Which terms are now more familiar to you? Which terms might you need to review? What strategies will best help you to review those terms? Create two study goals for this chapter based on your understanding of terms.

Reflection on Essential Inquiry Questions

What do you understand about the relationships among voltage, resistance, and currents? **SI**

How do parallel and series circuits affect how electrical energy is distributed and used safely? **TPS**

What are some costs and benefits of different types of cells? **DM**

What knowledge of electricity do First Nations and Métis peoples have? **CP**

Unit Task

In this chapter, you learned that current electrical energy flows in a closed circuit. You also set up parallel and series circuits and learned about the relationships that exist among voltage, current, and resistance. How can you apply your new understanding to the Unit Task you have chosen?

We can reduce our electrical energy consumption and use renewable energy resources to produce electrical energy.

What you will learn:

- The energy consumption and operating costs of various appliances can be measured and monitored.
- There are many social, economic, and environmental impacts of producing electrical energy from renewable or non-renewable sources.
- A plan of action is a good start toward reducing your electrical energy consumption at home.
- Knowledge of electrical energy can help you make intelligent choices and understand complicated debates about global energy issues.

Wind turbines can share the land with crops or grazing animals. A number of wind turbines are often connected together in wind farms to produce electrical energy.

Key Terms
- biomass • efficiency
- EnerGuide • energy efficiency rating • energy grid
- Energy Star • fossil fuels
- generators • geothermal energy • hydroelectrical energy
- kilowatt-hour (kW•h)
- non-renewable • renewable
- sustainable development
- thermonuclear
- transformer • turbine

Before Writing

Get Your Reader's Attention

Good writers want you to be interested in what they have to say. They often use the opening sentence in a paragraph as a hook to get you reading further. Survey the first paragraph under each main subheading in Chapter 8, and decide which one best grabs your attention.

©P

Figure 8.1 The Craik Eco-Centre is located on the edge of the Arm River Valley, overlooking Arm Lake and Craik.

Think Locally

The Cowessess First Nation and the Saskatchewan government are partnering to develop a wind energy project on land southeast of Regina. The turbines will be able to harness winds 70 m to 90 m above ground level, more than 15 m higher than other turbines in the province. The greater height allows the turbines to capture stronger winds and thus produce more electrical energy. The project will also use an experimental new battery that stores electrical energy from the turbine efficiently.

The Craik Eco-Centre is another example of a renewable energy project (Figure 8.1). A **renewable** resource is one that can be reused or replaced, for example, energy from the Sun and wind. A **non-renewable** resource is one that cannot be replaced once it is used up. Examples include coal and oil. The Craik Eco-Centre was designed to use as little energy as possible. The energy that is needed is provided by renewable energy resources.

Figure 8.2 Small-scale hydroelectric generating stations can be a local source of electrical energy.

Local Solutions to Generating Electrical Energy

When you turn on the light in your bedroom, you are using electrical energy that was generated far away from your home. A large- or smaller-scale hydroelectric dam (Figure 8.2) or a coal-burning generating plant is probably the source of your electrical energy. In some areas of Saskatchewan, the source is wind farms made up of giant wind turbines. To build a hydroelectric dam or enough wind turbines to generate electrical energy for a large number of people requires a huge investment in people, money, and equipment. Usually, governments and businesses build these large-scale projects.

C22 *Quick Science*

Renewable Energy Projects in Your Community

Renewable energy projects can be found in many locations throughout Saskatchewan, on public land, private land, and land owned by First Nations and Métis communities. Using print and electronic resources, you and your classmates will learn about examples of these projects.

Purpose

To identify and describe the function of renewable energy projects in your community and on land owned by First Nations and Métis communities

---
Materials & Equipment

- information summaries about renewable energy projects

Procedure

1. Your teacher will provide summaries of projects using renewable resources for generating electrical energy in Saskatchewan.

2. With a partner or small group, select one project to work on.

3. Create a summary of the key features of the project—type of technology used, reason for the project, costs, and value to users and the community.

4. Imagine that you are interested in developing a renewable project for your community. Present your findings to your town council, band council, or your class in an effort to convince them of the potential of your project.

Questions

5. How many different kinds of renewable methods for generating electrical energy did you discover?

6. Are some methods of generating electrical energy more common than others? Why do you think this is the case?

7. What do you think is one reason there are not more renewable energy projects in your community?

8. What examples of renewable energy projects on First Nations and Métis land did you find?

Pose New Questions

9. What questions about renewable energy methods do you have, now that you have completed this activity?

©P

Anthony Sparvier: Engineer in Training, Boundary Dam Power Station

Anthony Sparvier grew up on the Cowessess First Nation and Ochapowace First Nation. He went to the University of Regina to become an electrical engineer and is currently an Engineer in Training at the Boundary Dam Power Station near Estevan (Figure 8.3).

Daily, he is responsible for planning, organizing, and researching projects for electrical (circuit breakers, motors, relays, or transformers), instrumentation (probes, temperature, pressure or flow), or communication (plant control system) equipment.

Q: What advice would you give students who are interested in studying electrical energy?

A: Use your imagination to visualize what you are studying.

Q: How important is imagination in your job?

A: This is very important in my job. I would say that I use my imagination every day at work.

Q: Can you give an example?

A: The greatest examples I can think of are drawings. We use drawings for the projects we work on. As you know, these are interpretations of a physical system and we have to use our imagination and visualize the actual system. We use many different types of drawings, be it electrical schematics [circuit diagrams], one-line diagrams, wiring diagrams, instrumentation loop diagrams, logic diagrams, and safety procedures. We use drawings in combination with the electrical theory we were taught to plan our projects safely and efficiently. A lot of the circuits we work on, we cannot physically see for safety reasons—they can only be opened during an outage—but we have to plan for the project while we are on-line.

Q: Where do you see yourself in the future?

A: When I think of the future, I would picture myself using my experience and education developing or working with newer, cleaner technologies.

Figure 8.3 Boundary Dam Power Station

Figure 8.4 The electrical energy we use in our communities may be produced by massive coils of wire rotating between magnets in huge generators, like this one at the Boundary Dam Power Station near Estevan, Saskatchewan.

Generating Electrical Energy

In 1831, English chemist and physicist Michael Faraday introduced a way to generate a steady supply of large amounts of electrical energy. He demonstrated that an electric current can be generated by moving a conducting wire through a magnetic field, a process called electromagnetic induction. Today, we use electromagnetic induction to generate electrical energy in generators (Figure 8.4). Most **generators** do the same job: they transform the energy of motion (kinetic energy, a type of mechanical energy) into an electric current. The magnets inside a generator are rotated by a **turbine**, which is a machine that usually uses the flow of a fluid, such as a waterfall or fast-flowing river, to turn a shaft. The magnets spin coils of copper wire. This pulls electrons away from their atoms and creates a current in the copper wire.

The electrical energy is delivered to a transmission substation where a **transformer** boosts the generator's voltage for long-distance transmission. The electrical energy is sent through transmission lines to reach cities and towns. The web of interconnections between generating stations, substations, and users is called an **energy grid** or a distribution grid (Figure 8.5). Household voltage is typically 120 or 240 volts. For energy to be useful in a home or business, the extremely high transmission voltage needs to be stepped down again. Transformers step transmission voltages, which may be in the hundreds of thousands of volts, down to distribution voltages, which may be less than 10 000 volts. Generating electrical energy starts with a spinning turbine, but where does the energy come from to spin the turbine?

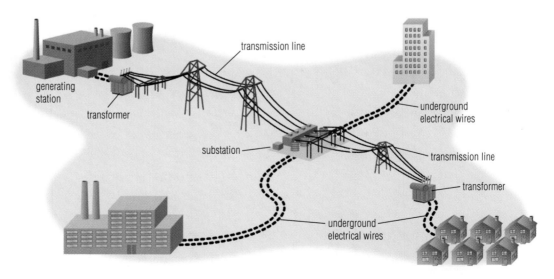

Figure 8.5 An energy grid transfers electrical energy from generating stations to homes, businesses, and factories. The whole grid is a complete circuit.

©P

Using Water to Generate Electrical Energy

Most electrical energy generated in Canada is **hydroelectrical energy**, which means it is generated by harnessing the energy of flowing water. Some hydroelectric stations use fast-flowing rivers to turn their turbines. Other hydroelectric stations, such as the ones at Niagara Falls, Ontario, use the flow from a waterfall to turn their turbines.

Many communities, such as Elbow, Saskatchewan, do not have a waterfall, so a dam may be built across a river to store water in a reservoir (Figure 8.6). The water from the reservoir is directed through a channel called a penstock to a turbine with ridges around it (Figure 8.7). The water turns the turbine, which is connected to a generator.

*info**BIT***

Say Hydro to Water

The prefix "hydro-" comes from the Greek word *hudor*, which means water.

Figure 8.6 The Coteau Creek Hydroelectric Station near Elbow, Saskatchewan

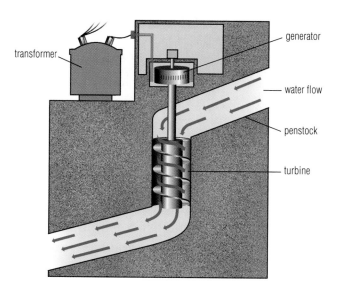

transformer

generator

water flow

penstock

turbine

Figure 8.7 In a hydroelectric generating station, water flows through a penstock. As it flows past the turbine, it causes the turbine to turn. The turning turbine is connected to the generator. The generator converts the mechanical energy from the turning motion of the turbine to electrical energy.

During Writing

Show What You Know

As a writer, you want to convince a reader that you know your topic. Add details, use facts, and present evidence to demonstrate your knowledge.

Using Heat to Generate Electrical Energy

If there are no waterfalls or rivers in your area, what mechanical energy can be used to turn the turbines? One answer is heat, or thermal, energy from steam. In many areas, thermoelectric generating plants use a fuel, such as coal or biomass, to heat water to create high-pressure steam.

Fossil Fuels

Coal, oil, and natural gas are **fossil fuels**, which means they were produced from the organic matter of organisms that lived millions of years ago. Because of how they were created, fossil fuels are non-renewable resources. In Figure 8.8, you can see that a fossil fuel, usually coal, is burned to boil water. The steam is kept under great pressure in pipes, which allows it to reach higher temperatures than normal. The high-pressure steam strikes and pushes the blades on the turbine. Coal is used to fuel the Poplar River Power Station near Coronach (Figure 8.9).

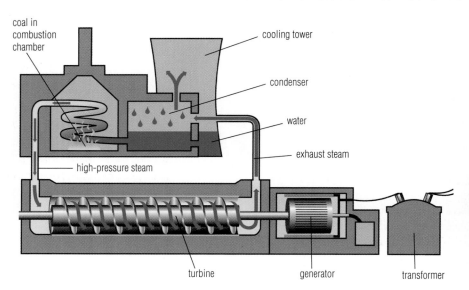

Figure 8.8 A coal-fired generating station

Figure 8.9 The Poplar River Power Station near Coronach is coal-fired.

Biomass

Figure 8.10 Biomass briquettes are made of compressed straw, wood shavings, and oat hulls.

Biomass, a renewable resource, is organic material made up of plant and animal waste. Examples of biomass include wood shavings, peat, straw, nut shells, sewage, and oat hulls (Figure 8.10). In a biomass system, the organic waste decomposes to produce methane gas. The methane can be burned to boil water to make steam, and the steam used to turn a turbine. The most common biomass material used today is wood waste from lumber and from pulp and paper industries.

©P

Nuclear Energy

Electrical energy can also be generated by **thermonuclear** generation through heat energy in nuclear energy stations. In a nuclear reactor, atoms of a heavy element, usually uranium, are split in a chain reaction. This splitting, called nuclear fission, releases an enormous amount of energy. The nuclear fission of just 1 kg of uranium is equivalent to burning about 50 000 kg of coal. The heat energy released by the fission process is used to heat water to produce steam to turn a turbine. Nuclear energy is generally considered a renewable resource. However, the uranium ore necessary to produce fission is not renewable; once it is used up, it cannot be replaced.

Figure 8.11 McArthur River is one of Saskatchewan's uranium mining operations.

Saskatchewan is currently the world's largest uranium-producing region, accounting for about 30 percent of annual world uranium production. There are several uranium mining operations in the province including Eagle Point, McClean Lake, and McArthur River (Figure 8.11). Saskatchewan does not currently use nuclear energy to produce electrical energy, but there continues to be research to determine if it makes sense as a future electrical energy source for the province.

Geothermal Energy

In some places in the world, water, heated by molten rock in Earth's core, rises to the surface as hot water and steam. This renewable energy source is called **geothermal energy**. Geothermal energy sources at or near Earth's surface are hot enough to heat homes and other buildings. However, for generating electrical energy, hotter sources are needed.

High-temperature geothermal sources are found deep in areas where there is volcanic activity. Iceland, with its many active volcanoes and hot springs, uses geothermal energy to produce 19 percent of its electrical energy (Figure 8.12). In Canada, geothermal sources hot enough to be used to drive turbines for electrical energy generation are located in British Columbia. Research is being done to determine how to use geothermal sources cost effectively.

reSearch

The CANDU reactor is a Canadian-invented pressurized heavy water reactor. Identify where active CANDU reactors are being used around the world. Illustrate how a CANDU reactor works, and research how CANDU reactors are similar and different from other nuclear reactors. Conduct your research in the library or on the Internet. Share your information in a format of your choice.

Figure 8.12 This geothermal energy plant is in Thingvellir, Iceland.

Learning Checkpoint

1. What are the differences between renewable resources and non-renewable resources?

2. What is a turbine and how does it operate?

3. Where in Canada are geothermal sources hot enough to drive turbines found?

Other Energy Sources

There are other energy sources that can be used to generate electrical energy. As different technologies continue to be developed and refined, our ability to use these sources economically increases.

Solar Energy

Many people think solar cells are new technology, but the roots of this invention go back to 1839, when French scientist Edmond Becquerel soaked two metal plates in a conducting solution. When Becquerel exposed one of the plates to sunlight, he could detect a small amount of voltage between the plates. He had invented the first solar cell. Solar cells are now made using silicon (Figure 8.13).

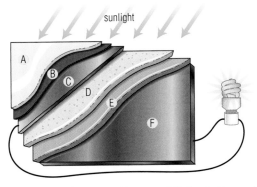

sunlight

A Protective cover glass
B Antireflective coating to let light in and trap it
C Metal contact grid to collect electrons for circuit
D Silicon layer to release electrons
E Silicon layer to absorb electrons
F Metal contact grid to collect electrons from circuit

Figure 8.13 A solar cell has specially treated layers that create current when exposed to sunlight.

Figure 8.14 Solar energy is used to power this pump that draws water for the cattle.

Silicon crystals produce an electric current when struck by light. Solar modules (several cells connected together) and arrays (several modules connected together) have many uses, including heating homes and buildings and powering calculators, livestock watering systems, road signs, and the International Space Station. A solar farm includes arrays of mirrors to focus sunlight onto a liquid that is heated and used to turn water into steam to drive the turbines (Figure 8.14).

Wind Energy

Wind turbines use the renewable energy of moving air to spin their blades, which are connected to a generator. The amount of energy a wind turbine generates depends on how fast the wind is blowing, with approximately 10 km per hour being the minimum for electrical energy generation. The Centennial Wind Power Facility near Swift Current is currently Canada's second-largest wind facility (Figure 8.15). It can produce enough electrical energy to serve about 69 000 Saskatchewan homes. More and more, countries all over the world are harnessing this renewable resource.

Tidal Energy

Tidal energy harnesses the renewable energy of tides to generate electrical energy. North America's only tidal energy generating station is in Annapolis Royal, Nova Scotia, where the powerful tides of the Bay of Fundy spin its turbines (Figure 8.16). The station provides enough electrical energy for about 4500 homes.

Tests are under way in Nova Scotia and also in British Columbia on a promising new technology called a tidal stream generator, which works like an underwater windmill. Other marine energy sources that are being tested include ocean wave energy and ocean thermal energy.

Figure 8.15 The Centennial Wind Power Facility near Swift Current

Figure 8.16 This tidal energy station in Nova Scotia generates electrical energy by using the energy of the water as it rises and falls in the daily cycle of tides.

Learning Checkpoint

1. What are three applications of solar cells?
2. How is a renewable energy source different from a non-renewable energy source?
3. Where is Canada's tidal energy generating station found? Why was this location chosen?

Electrical Energy Production in Canada

Canada is the world's largest producer of hydroelectrical energy, the fifth-largest producer of electrical energy in general, and the second-largest exporter of electrical energy.

However, Canadians need to be aware of the environmental implications of using non-renewable resources. As Figure 8.17 shows, a large part of our electrical energy is generated using non-renewable resources. These resources include coal, uranium (for nuclear energy), oil, and gas. We must decide how to make a transition to using more renewable resources. We need electrical energy, but we also need to generate it wisely.

All of our energy sources are important to Canada because they provide us with flexibility and energy security and help us to become self-sufficient. For example, at one time, Prince Edward Island was completely dependent on outside sources for electrical energy because it does not have fossil fuels, hydroelectrical energy, or nuclear energy. However, the island now produces 18 percent of its electrical energy from wind energy and has become the first place in North America to offer a guaranteed price to anyone—even a homeowner—who produces electrical energy from wind energy.

Across Canada, renewable energy projects for generating electrical energy are under way or being planned. However, as you can see in Figure 8.17, this type of electrical energy generation produced only 0.6 percent of our electrical energy in 2007. It cannot replace our use of non-renewable energy resources for now. To reduce our use of non-renewable resources, we have to find ways to use less electrical energy through technology and by changing our usage habits (Figure 8.18).

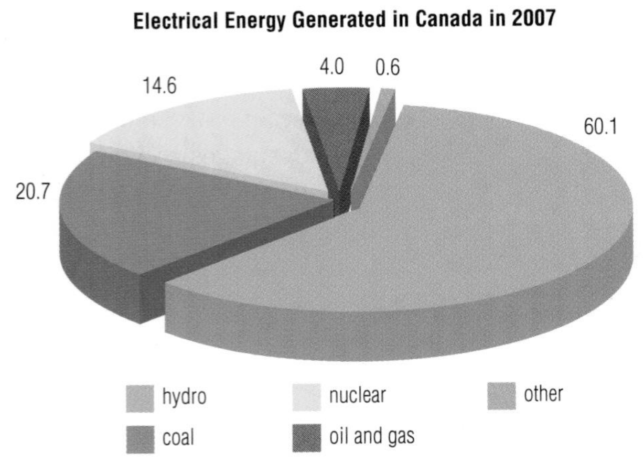

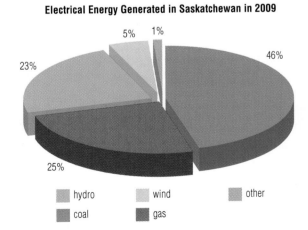

Electrical Energy Generated in Canada in 2007

14.6 4.0 0.6
20.7
60.1

hydro   nuclear   other
coal   oil and gas

Figure 8.17 Methods of electrical energy generation in Canada

Electrical Energy Generated in Saskatchewan in 2009

5% 1%
23%
46%
25%

hydro   wind   other
coal   gas

Figure 8.18 Methods of electrical energy generation in Saskatchewan

©P

A Sustainable Choice

Choosing the right methods for generating electrical energy means finding sustainable solutions. **Sustainable development** is development that meets the needs of the present without compromising the ability of future generations to meet their own needs. If we do not achieve sustainable energy use, future generations in Saskatchewan may not be able to support themselves.

A sustainable approach sometimes requires a different way of using resources. Sustainability may mean no longer using non-renewable resources because they cannot be maintained indefinitely. In the past, fossil fuels were used up quickly to earn money and satisfy consumer demand. Today, we need to reduce our consumption of resources so that they are available over a longer period of time. With renewable energy methods, resources such as solar energy and wind, are available indefinitely.

Figure 8.19 shows the main methods worldwide for generating electrical energy in 2007. Coal, oil, and gas account for 66.6 percent of electrical energy production. These three methods are using non-renewable resources. The other three methods—hydro, nuclear, and other—account for 33.4 percent of the production. Hydro and other methods use renewable energy sources.

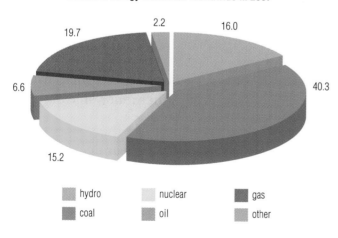

Electrical Energy Generated Worldwide in 2007

2.2
16.0
19.7
6.6
40.3
15.2

■ hydro ■ nuclear ■ gas
■ coal   ■ oil   ■ other

Suggested Activity ● ⋯⋯⋯⋯⋯
C23 Decision-Making Analysis
on page 282

Figure 8.19 This graph shows how the world generated electrical energy in 2007. This graph could become very different during your lifetime.

We may never be able to achieve complete sustainability, but the decisions we make personally and as a society can move us closer to this goal. An example of a personal decision would be to turn off the lights in your bedroom or classroom if you are the last person out of the room. This small action would save on electrical energy use. As you get older, you may make bigger decisions, such as adding solar panels to a house you live in (Figure 8.20). Decisions like these demonstrate you are keeping the goal of sustainability in mind.

Figure 8.20 The people who live in this house are using solar panels to heat their water. This reduces their electrical energy use.

1. What are four methods of generating electrical energy that use heat energy?

2. Explain how a solar cell produces electrical energy.

3. (a) What is the source of most of the electrical energy generated in Saskatchewan?

   (b) What is the source of most of the electrical energy generated in Canada?

4. The photos below show the type of solar cells that are installed on the International Space Station. Why are solar cells used to generate electrical energy on spacecraft?

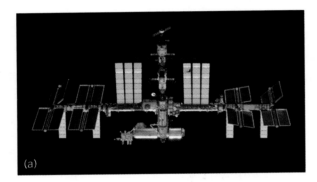

(a)

(b)

Question 4 The International Space Station (a) uses 2500 m² of solar cells (b) to generate its electrical energy.

5. Compare the generation of electrical energy using coal with hydroelectric generation.

   (a) How are the two methods similar?

   (b) How are the two methods different?

6. Suppose that residents of a remote community in northern Saskatchewan decide to use wood as their primary energy source for heating the boiler of the community's electrical generator. They cut down all the trees nearby and stockpile the wood, ready for use.

   (a) What are the advantages and disadvantages of their solution for their energy needs?

   (b) What recommendations would you make to ensure that this community has a reliable long-term energy supply?

7. (a) What information about electrical energy generation did you learn in this section that you did not know before?

   (b) What are two questions that you have about electrical energy generation in Canada?

8. Create a chart that categorizes different energy sources as either renewable or non-renewable.

9. Many people refer to nuclear energy generation as being renewable. Do you agree? Explain why.

Kathryn A. Black: Senior Generation Planning Engineer, SaskPower

As Senior Generation Planning Engineer with SaskPower, Kathryn Black helps decide what electrical energy technologies are right for Saskatchewan.

Kathryn grew up in Regina and decided to take engineering at the University of Regina. She had the opportunity for a co-op work term with SaskPower. During this work term, she was assigned a position at the Poplar River Station near Coronach, one of the largest electrical energy generation stations in Saskatchewan. The experience inspired her to specialize in mechanical engineering so she could come back and work there.

In her current position, she is responsible for looking at ways to produce energy in Saskatchewan. Her group looks at such technologies as wind, solar (Figure 8.21), gas, nuclear, biomass, and coal—all types of ways to generate energy.

Kathryn Black and her team are responsible for looking at these resources and technologies in terms of their technical feasibility—whether they will ever make sense or will continue to make sense to use in Saskatchewan.

Some of the technologies have lots of potential and others are great ideas, but not likely to go far. She needs to use her judgment and engineering skills to review and analyze the technologies. She also is constantly evaluating how other utilities in Canada generate electrical energy. Recently, she looked at all the provinces in Canada and plotted the amount of wind energy they had on their electrical systems compared with SaskPower.

As advice to students, she points out that electrical energy is a very interesting business and SaskPower needs all kinds of skill sets. Kathryn Black says, "Keeping up good grades in school means that your choices will never be limited. Remember, it takes a lot of people with all different skills to keep the lights on in Saskatchewan."

Figure 8.21 A solar farm

Nuclear Energy in Saskatchewan?

Saskatchewan is examining the option of using nuclear energy from CANDU reactors as an electrical energy source. The proposals for the development of nuclear energy have been considered in the past. The nuclear energy station would provide needed electrical energy to Saskatchewan in the future. However, is nuclear energy the best choice?

Initiating and Planning

Two students, Curtis and Kylie, have been researching nuclear energy. The more they have learned about nuclear energy, the more they are convinced of their own viewpoints. However, as both students continued their research, their teacher helped them see that their viewpoints often did not include the views of other stakeholders. A stakeholder is a person or a group of people who have interests and concerns about an issue that might involve economics, or may be personal or moral. The issue of nuclear energy development in Saskatchewan involves the views of many stakeholders (Figure 8.22). Examine the arguments in favour of and in opposition to the development of nuclear energy. Then, from a suggested stakeholder perspective, describe how that person might feel in support of or against nuclear energy development.

Stakeholders

- Government representatives
- Nuclear and mining industry representatives
- Environmentally conscious groups and activists
- Citizens who might live near the area of nuclear energy development
- Biologists and ecologists
- Farmers and ranchers
- Citizens who do not live near the nuclear energy development, but who will be using its electrical energy

OR

Take the role of a stakeholder. Argue for or against the development of nuclear energy from your chosen stakeholder's perspective. For example, how might a biologist argue for or against the development of nuclear energy? What about nuclear industry representatives?

When you undertake the role of a stakeholder, think about First Nations and Métis cultural perspectives. Consider the following questions:

- Does nuclear development and mining greatly harm Mother Earth?
- Does nuclear development create waste that may cause harm to the land and the animals?
- How might nuclear development affect future generations? Elders from some First Nations groups often ask people to consider the impact that their decisions might have on other people seven generations later.
- Does the development of nuclear energy consider the special spiritual relationship that First Nations peoples have toward their land?
- Is the development of nuclear energy considerate of treaty rights and land claims?
- What impact will development of nuclear energy have on the First Nations and Métis peoples, their health, and their traditional ways of life?
- How might the development of nuclear energy bring prosperity to First Nations and Métis peoples?

Figure 8.22 A town hall meeting of stakeholders

In Favour of Nuclear Energy

Supporting facts for nuclear energy in Saskatchewan include the following:

- It is possible to generate a high amount of electrical energy in one single station. Just one station would generate enough energy to provide electrical energy to one million homes.

- The technology is readily available; it does not have to be developed first. The CANDU reactor is a Canadian-designed nuclear reactor. It is one of the most efficient of all the reactors.

- Nuclear energy has a lower fuel cost when compared with coal- , oil- , and gas-fired stations. Even if the costs of processing and enriching the uranium are calculated along with allowances for management and disposal of the waste, the fuel costs are better than those for a coal-fired station or a gas combined-cycle station.

- Nuclear energy has the best safety record of all major energy sources (coal, hydro, natural gas, and nuclear) worldwide.

- A single kilogram of uranium can produce more energy than 200 barrels of oil.

- Nuclear energy stations produce electrical energy through fission of uranium, not the burning of fuels. Consequently, nuclear energy stations do not pollute the air with nitrogen oxides, sulphur oxides, dust, or greenhouse gases like carbon dioxide.

- The uranium isotope required for nuclear fission can be found in Canada.

Opposed to Nuclear Energy

Facts against the use of nuclear energy as an electrical energy source for Saskatchewan include the following:

- Nuclear reactor construction costs are very high. Nuclear reactors take between 12 to 15 years to plan and construct.

- In the process of producing energy, a nuclear reactor transforms its uranium fuel into radioactive waste, which is difficult and expensive to dispose of.

- Some nuclear reactors also pose the remote risk of an extremely serious radiation leak. While such accidents are uncommon, especially in CANDU reactors, they can be catastrophic. Vast land areas would be unfit for living or farming.

- Used fuel from some reactors can be used in bombs, which are loaded with nuclear fuel waste so that the target area becomes heavily contaminated. Because of these hazards, nuclear installations become of interest to terrorists and require extremely heavy security.

- Uranium is a non-renewable resource.

Performing and Recording

1. Research your perspective in the library or on the Internet.

2. Create an ad campaign to support your perspective. Use one or any combination of advertising media to get your point across. Distribute flyers, make posters, record radio spots, or film TV ads.

Analyzing and Interpreting

3. View and critique your classmates' ads. Which ones are the most effective? What facts are included or excluded to support their position?

Communication and Teamwork

4. What is your conclusion about whether a CANDU nuclear energy station should be built in Saskatchewan? Has your position changed by viewing the ad campaign? Explain and justify your conclusion.

Here is a summary of what you will learn in this section:

- Electrical energy consumption is usually measured in kilowatt-hours (kW•h).

- Efficiency is the ratio of useful energy that comes out of a device to the total energy that went in.

- The EnerGuide label shows how much energy an appliance will use in a month of average use.

- Energy Star appliances are the most efficient appliances in their class.

Figure 8.23 Consider how many times a day and how many different ways you use electrical energy.

The Cost of Electrical Energy

Every method of generating electrical energy comes at a cost. There is an environmental cost, which affects the world you live in, and there is an economic cost, which gets passed on to you, the consumer. Each time you plug in an appliance, turn on a switch, or use electrical energy in any way, you are using resources and spending money (Figure 8.23). You can take steps to make better choices about how you use electrical energy. The first step is to understand where, when, and how you use electrical energy.

Most homes and apartment buildings have a meter that tracks how much electrical energy is drawn from the energy grid. Older models of meters have a spinning disk with a black band (Figure 8.24). The more electrical energy that is being used in the house, the faster the disk turns. The energy used is calculated monthly or bi-monthly by reading a set of dials above the disk.

Figure 8.24 Older-style meters have to be read manually.

Newer digital meters, called smart meters, are being installed as part of a major energy conservation effort. The smart meters record electrical energy consumption hour by hour and send the information directly to the electric utility (Figure 8.25). Electrical energy costs are then calculated according to time of use, which includes time of day, weekdays versus weekends, and season.

The cost of electrical energy is higher during peak times, which are the busiest times of the day. When the need for electrical energy is at its peak, electric utilities may have to use less-efficient, more polluting, and more expensive ways to produce electrical energy to meet demand. You can save money on your electrical energy bill by moving activities that are energy-intensive, such as running the dishwasher, to off-peak hours. You can help save resources by reducing your use of electrical energy at all times of the day.

Figure 8.25 Smart meters use wireless and other technologies to send information directly to the utility.

C24 *Quick Science*

Analyzing Home Electrical Energy Use

Every month, we get a bill that charges us for the amount of electrical energy that we have used, yet few of us have any idea what the energy was used for or what we can do to reduce the cost. In this activity, you will investigate the energy use in your home and attempt to find ways to reduce the usage.

Purpose

To identify energy use in your home by examining your electrical devices

Procedure

1. Create a list of all devices in your home that use electrical energy provided by the electric utility or a home generator. Do not include anything powered by batteries, but do include battery chargers.

2. Create a table for your electrical devices that includes columns for each device's average weekly usage, when the device is most often used (time of day, day of week, season), and the estimated electrical energy requirements of the device (low, medium, high). Add enough columns for all the electrical devices in your home. Give your table a title.

3. Complete the table by estimating average usage and predicting the electrical energy requirements.

Questions

4. Which device usages do you think you could reduce?

5. What did this activity show you about your electrical energy usage that you did not realize before?

Pose New Questions

6. How do you think electrical energy use has changed since your parents were your age? How much electrical energy do you think you will be using in 10 years? Will it be more or less than you use today? Explain why.

Electrical Energy Consumption

The electrical energy consumption for a household is equal to the amount of electrical energy used, usually measured in kilowatt-hours. A **kilowatt-hour (kW•h)** is equivalent to the use of one kilowatt in one hour. For example, if the energy (E) used by a microwave is 0.8 kW and the microwave is turned on for half an hour, the electrical energy used is

$$E = 0.8 \text{ kW} \times 0.5 \text{ h}$$
$$= 0.4 \text{ kW•h}$$

One kilowatt (kW) equals 1000 watts (W). A watt is equal to one joule per second. It does not take long for common electrical devices to consume a large number of joules. For this reason, the kilowatt-hour is often used as a unit for energy. To calculate the cost of using an electrical device, multiply the energy consumed in kW•h by the cost per kW•h. In the microwave example above, the consumption of 0.4 kW•h at a cost of 10 cents per kW•h equals 4.0 cents. It may not sound like much, but remember that this was only one event over a half-hour time period. There may also be an electrical energy delivery charge and taxes on top of the charge for use (Figure 8.26).

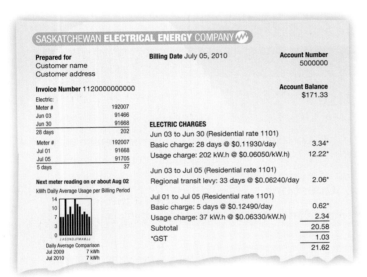

Figure 8.26 A utility bill shows the amount of electrical energy used in kilowatt-hours.

Learning Checkpoint

1. Copy and complete the following table in your notebook. Give your table a title. Calculate the cost of using each appliance over the course of a year. Use a utility charge of 9.7 cents per kW•h.

Appliance	Average Use (hours per day)	Annual Energy Consumption (kW•h)	Annual Cost ($ per year)
Vacuum cleaner	0.1	38	
Hair dryer	0.25	100	
Computer	4.0	520	
Central air conditioning	12 (60 days/year)	1500	

Calculating Percent Efficiency

If you have ever touched a lit incandescent light bulb, you know that it gets very hot (Figure 8.27). An incandescent light bulb uses only about 5 percent of its input energy to create light and converts over 95 percent of its input energy into heat energy. Compact fluorescent lamps (CFLs), however, transform about 20 percent of their energy input into light, so they are more efficient than incandescent bulbs.

5 J light energy

100 J electric energy

95 J heat
(thermal energy)

Figure 8.27 Most of the energy transformed by a light bulb is radiated as heat energy.

The **efficiency** of a device is the ratio of the useful energy that comes out of the device to the total energy that went in. The more input energy that a device converts into usable output energy, the more efficient the device is. Efficiency is usually calculated as a percentage:

$$\text{Percent efficiency} = \frac{E_{out}}{E_{in}} \times 100$$

During Writing

Organize for Impact

When persuasion is the goal, good writers like to create impact at the beginning and end of their piece of writing or presentation. Watch television commercials, especially public service announcements, and note the methods for creating a powerful opener and a convincing closer.

Suggested Activities
C25 Science, Technology, Society, and the Environment on page 291
C26 Inquiry Activity on page 291
C27 Problem-Solving Activity on page 292

Example Problem 8.1

Suppose a light bulb uses 780 J of input energy to produce 31 J of light energy. Calculate its percent efficiency.

Given
Input energy = 780 J
Output energy = 31 J

Required
Percent efficiency = x

Analysis and Solution
Choose the correct equation.

$$\text{Percent efficiency} = \frac{E_{out}}{E_{in}} \times 100$$

Substitute the values and their units. Solve the problem.

$$\text{Percent efficiency} = \frac{31\,\text{J}}{780\,\text{J}} \times 100$$

$$= 4.0\,\%$$

Paraphrase
The efficiency of the light bulb is 4.0 percent.

Practice Problems

1. A car produces 27.5 kJ of useful output energy from 125 kJ of fuel. Calculate the car's percent efficiency.

2. A fluorescent light produces 3.6 kJ of useful light energy from 21 kJ of input energy. Calculate its percent efficiency.

3. A new high-efficiency motor has an input energy of 75 kJ and an output energy of 72 kJ. Calculate its percent efficiency.

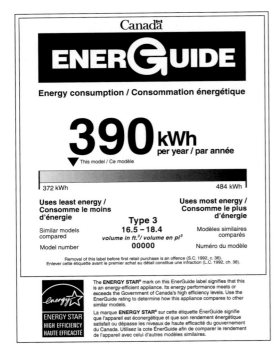
infoBIT

Comparing Efficiency

The **energy efficiency rating** indicates how much electrical energy a device consumes during its operation. By comparing the efficiency of different devices, we can judge both their energy cost and their environmental impact. For example, a front-loading clothes washing machine uses much less electrical energy, washes more clothes per load, and uses less water than a top-loading washer on a per load basis. Another example of improved efficiency is the refrigerator shown in Figure 8.28.

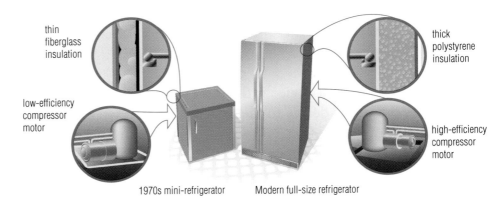

thin fiberglass insulation

low-efficiency compressor motor

thick polystyrene insulation

high-efficiency compressor motor

1970s mini-refrigerator   Modern full-size refrigerator

Figure 8.28 The energy used to run a mini-refrigerator in the 1970s can run a full-size refrigerator today. In the last 25 years, refrigerator efficiency has increased 300 percent.

Read the Label

In Canada, all large appliances, such as stoves, dishwashers, refrigerators, washers, and dryers, have an **EnerGuide** label. This label states how much energy the appliance will use in a year of average use (Figure 8.29). It allows you to compare the energy consumption of different brands and models. The arrow on the long shaded bar on the label below the rating shows the efficiency range of the appliance. If an appliance displays the **Energy Star** symbol seen at the bottom of Figure 8.29, it is one of the most efficient appliances in its class.

How Off Is Off?

If you look at your household devices, you may notice little lights still glowing even when they are switched off (Figure 8.30). These machines are in "standby" mode so that they will restart quickly when you switch them on.

Figure 8.29 You can use the EnerGuide label to compare appliances and determine which are more efficient. For example, you could compare refrigerators that have the same volume but are made by different manufacturers.

Many small appliances, such as computers, televisions, DVD players, and game systems, still use electrical energy—phantom load—even when they are turned off. This phantom energy load can range from a few watts to as much as 20 or even 40 watts per device. To combat phantom load, you can unplug items you are not using or, when replacing items, look for products with the Energy Star rating. These will use less energy both during normal operation and when in standby mode. You can also use power bars with on and off switches to turn off devices when they are not in use. Meters, such as the one in Figure 8.31, allow you to measure phantom load and can tell you which of your household devices are using electrical energy, even when they seem to be off.

Figure 8.30 If the standby light is on, electrical energy is being consumed.

Figure 8.31 An electrical energy monitor lets you measure how much electrical energy is used by appliances or other devices in your home. By tracking which devices are consuming electrical energy, you can save money on your bill.

Energy Conservation Begins at Home

You can make a plan to reduce the use of electrical energy in your home. You can start by asking yourself these questions:

- Are lights being left on in rooms that are not being used? Have you eliminated phantom loads?

- Have you left the computer on while you are at school? Do you sleep the computer when you leave the room?

- Is a lot of hot water being used for long showers?

- Are incandescent light bulbs being used instead of compact fluorescents?

reSearch

Light-emitting diodes (LEDs) are becoming more common for residential and commercial lighting. Often four times more efficient than incandescent bulbs, LEDs last longer and produce very little heat. Using the library or the Internet, research the applications of LEDs that are available now and that are predicted to be available in the near future. Share your findings in a short report or presentation to your class and propose new uses or applications for LEDs.

If we lower our energy demands, we reduce the need to build more generating stations and we avoid greater impact on the environment and major construction costs. Your own personal action plan to reduce energy consumption will make a difference. Reusing and recycling materials, conserving energy, and learning to live responsibly in harmony with our environment are key actions for living in a sustainable way.

8.2 CHECK and REFLECT

1. What does a smart meter measure?

2. (a) A microwave that draws 0.8 kW•h is used for one hour. Calculate the cost of the microwave's electrical energy consumption assuming a cost of 7.5 cents per kW•h.

   (b) Calculate the cost for the microwave if it is used one day for 20 min.

   (c) Calculate the cost of using the microwave for 20 min a day for 30 days.

3. Calculate the percent efficiency of a light source that uses 12.8 kJ of energy and delivers 4.3 kJ of useful light energy.

4. What information is included on an EnerGuide label?

5. What does an Energy Star symbol on an appliance indicate?

Question 5

6. Suppose the standby light on your printer is on even though you have turned the printer off. What does the standby light indicate?

7. Describe how a smart meter is an improvement over older types of electrical energy meters.

8. The costs for electrical energy are higher during peak times. Why do you think this is so?

9. Create an EnerGuide label for an appliance with an Energy Star rating. You can use hypothetical values and names of companies.

10. Why should you compare the efficiencies of appliances before making a purchase?

11. How can we reduce the need to build more generating stations?

12. (a) How has the information in this section helped to make you a better consumer?

    (b) How could you use this information to help you decide which electronic device to purchase?

13. What are three ways you could save electrical energy

    (a) in your home?

    (b) at school?

A Self-Sufficient Energy Community

The 4300 people of Freiamt, a community in southern Germany, wanted to generate their own electrical energy. The community added rooftop solar systems to homes, barns, and garages, and installed wind turbines. The community also has small-scale hydro and biomass generating stations. Some of the generators are jointly owned; others are privately owned.

The community's electrical energy generation has been so successful that each year there is a surplus of about 3 million kilowatt-hours of energy that is sold to Germany's national energy grid.

1. How could you adapt the community's plan to make it suit your community?

2. What do you think are the main points about Freiamt's plan that you could use to gain community support?

D1 Key Activity

Electrical Energy in Your Home

Knowing more about how and when you and your family use electrical energy is a good first step in conservation. Once you have researched your pattern of electrical energy consumption, create a plan to reduce your consumption.

Initiating and Planning

What is my family's pattern of electrical energy consumption annually?

Materials & Equipment
- one year of electrical bills for your home

Performing and Recording

1. Predict what months are the peak periods of electrical energy consumption in your home.

2. Create a table with the following column headings. Give your table a title.
   Actual Electrical Energy Usage (kW•h)
   Adjusted Usage (kW•h)
   Cost of Electrical Energy ($)
   Delivery Charge ($)
   Other Charges ($)
   Total Charges

3. For each bill, break down the different costs and add them to your chart. Total the charges.

Analyzing and Interpreting

4. (a) What does the category "Other Charges ($)" include?
   (b) What does "Adjusted Usage (kW•h)" mean?

5. (a) Graph the data from your table.
   (b) Refer to your graph. During which time periods is your household using electrical energy the most? Why might this be?
   (c) How does this time period compare with your prediction from step 1?

Communication and Teamwork

6. How would you change the bill to make it easier to understand? Do you think that having a bill that was clearer would help people conserve more electrical energy? Explain.

7. Write a summary paragraph explaining the pattern of electrical energy usage in your household.

©P

C27 *Problem-Solving Activity* Toolkits 3, 7

Bringing Electrical Energy to a Province

As a consultant planning for additional electrical energy generating sources for Saskatchewan, your job comprises two tasks. First, it must include new electrical energy generation sources connected to the regional electrical grid. These new sources will help provide a consistent supply of electrical energy to the province. Low-cost and environmentally friendly technologies are preferred. Secondly, you will develop a conservation program to teach people how to reduce their electrical energy consumption.

Initiating and Planning

How can Saskatchewan meet its electrical energy needs responsibly?

Criteria for Success

- The types of generating methods that your group researches must not all be the same.

- Your plan to reduce the consumption of electrical energy in your community must take into account individual, societal, and environmental needs (Figure 8.32).
- Your plans must be environmentally, culturally, and morally responsible. For example, a plan to build a dam across a river will need to consider the effect of creating a new lake, the effect on migrating fish, and how this may impact First Nations and Métis peoples culturally and socially.
- Your plans must be supported by references to existing examples of electrical generation sources. You will need to research your example enough to know what will be necessary to adapt it to your particular location. For example, if an oil-fired generating source is needed, will you be able to use a technology that captures and stores carbon dioxide emissions?

Figure 8.32 What are the individual, societal, and environmental needs for electrical energy in your community?

©P

Performing and Recording

1. As a class, decide on the number of new generating stations that can be planned. Do this by dividing the total number in the class by the size of each planning group.

2. As a class, brainstorm the specific geographical features that may be of use for electrical energy generation in your community. This may involve using only real features in your area, or you may agree to include features not actually present but which will be useful for the purpose of this activity.

3. In groups, brainstorm ideas for electrical energy generation methods. Agree on several options to bring back to the class for discussion. Within your group, also brainstorm ideas for electrical energy conservation in your community.

4. As a class, share the ideas of each group. Remember that methods of electrical energy generation must be varied and must not conflict with each other and must be environmentally responsible. Agree as a class on what type of energy generating source each group will investigate and where on the regional map each generating station will be located.

5. Research a plan for your generating station by examining existing stations or technologies. Research a plan for conserving electrical energy within your community.

6. Design your generating station. Use clearly labelled diagrams.

7. Design a program that clearly details how people in your community can conserve electrical energy and save money.

8. Present your plans for the generating station and for ways to reduce the consumption of electrical energy. Describe how it fits into the overall regional plan with all of the groups' plans.

Analyzing and Evaluating

9. Write an evaluation of your approach to solving this problem.
   (a) Did it work well? Explain.
   (b) What would you have done differently? Explain why.

Communicate

10. Think about your role in the work your group accomplished.
    (a) What do you think was the strongest contribution you made to your group's work?
    (b) How could you improve your contribution to group work in future activities?

11. (a) What do you feel was the most effective aspect of your group's plan?
    (b) How could your group's design have been improved?

Key Concept Review

1. (a) List two non-renewable sources of energy.

   (b) Name an advantage and a disadvantage of using each source.

2. (a) List four renewable sources of energy.

   (b) Name an advantage and a disadvantage of using each source.

3. Describe what happens in nuclear fission.

4. What is sustainability?

5. (a) How do you convert watts to kilowatts?

   (b) How do you convert kilojoules to joules?

   (c) How many joules are in a watt?

6. Suppose you bake a potato in a toaster oven that uses 1.2 kW. The oven is turned on for 25 min. How many kilowatt-hours did it use?

7. (a) If a motor uses 22 000 J while converting it to 13 400 J of useful energy, what is its percent efficiency?

   (b) If a diesel truck produces 47.5 kJ of useful output energy from 125 kJ of diesel fuel, what is its percent efficiency?

8. Give two reasons for reducing energy waste.

9. How can choosing to use a more efficient appliance benefit the environment?

10. What does it mean if an appliance has an Energy Star rating?

11. Answer the following questions by referring to the EnerGuide label shown below.

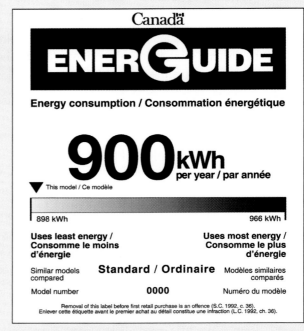

Question 11

(a) What is the energy usage of the rated appliance?

(b) Among similar appliances, which is rated most efficient?

(c) Is the rated appliance efficient? How do you know?

(d) List models similar to the one that is being rated.

Connect Your Understanding

12. Explain why you agree or disagree with the following statement: "A nuclear energy station provides energy using a radioactive source, so a turbine is not needed."

13. A group of Saskatchewan farmers form a co-operative group and build a factory that turns canola into a fuel for generators and cars. Would this energy source be renewable or non-renewable? Explain.

14. Make a labelled pie chart or circle graph showing how electrical energy is used in your home.

15. Is it always a good idea to discard low-efficiency devices? Explain your answer.

16. What could you do to reduce your electrical energy consumption if you lived in
    (a) a house in the country with a large property?
    (b) a mid-size house in the suburbs?
    (c) a small apartment in the centre of the city?

17. Choose an electrical device that you use daily. Identify changes you would make to the design of the device to maximize energy savings. Explain the reasons for your choices. Use a labelled diagram as part of your answer.

18. (a) Create a cartoon that shows at least seven ways that a home loses energy needlessly.
    (b) For each example shown, list a way to reduce that energy loss.

19. Write a paragraph about the photograph below. Include your personal response to the photograph, and explain what the photograph shows about electrical energy generation.

Question 19

20. Think about the businesses in your community. Choose one business that you are familiar with. What are seven practical ways to reduce electrical energy consumption in your chosen business?

Reflection

21. How could you improve the results of your work in the problem-solving and inquiry activities that you did in this unit?

After Writing

Reflect and Evaluate

With your partner, meet with another pair who made a marketing presentation for compact fluorescent lamps (CFLs). Provide positive feedback and helpful suggestions about the others' presentation. How did it hook the audience? Which details, facts, or evidence were most effective in demonstrating knowledge? What were the points that created the greatest impact?

Reflection on Essential Inquiry Questions

What new understanding of current electrical energy and circuits do you have from learning about the production and distribution of electrical energy? **SI**

Why might it be important to assess the costs and efficiencies of devices that produce or use electrical energy? **TPS**

What did you discover about the impact of small- and large-scale electrical energy generation and distribution in Saskatchewan? **DM**

How might different methods of electrical energy production be viewed from a First Nations and Métis perspectives? **CP**

Unit Task

This chapter discussed different methods of electrical energy production as well as the costs associated with electrical energy consumption. What are some new ideas that you have about these topics and how can you apply these to your chosen Unit Task?

UNIT C Summary

KEY CONCEPTS	CHAPTER SUMMARY

6 Static electric charges collect on surfaces until given a path to escape.

• Static electric charges • Conductors and insulators • Charging by friction • Charging by contact and induction • Using and reducing static charges	• When an atom gains electrons, it becomes negatively charged, and when it loses electrons, it becomes positively charged. Particles with unlike charges attract each other, and particles with like charges repel each other. (6.1) • Electrical insulators and conductors are materials categorized by how freely they allow electrons to move. (6.1) • In charging by contact, a neutral object gains the same charge as the object that touched it. In charging by induction, a neutral object gains the opposite charge to the charged object. (6.2) • Neutral objects are attracted to charged objects. (6.2) • Some First Nations and Métis peoples have an intimate understanding of lightning in terms of Thunderbird. (6.3)

7 Current electrical energy is the flow of electrons in a closed circuit.

• Current electrical energy • Electrical circuits • Voltage • Electric current • Direct current • Alternating current • Resistance • Series circuits and parallel circuits • Ohm's law ($V = IR$) • Electrical safety	• Voltage is the difference in electric charge between two points. (7.1) • Current is the rate of movement of electric charge through a conductor. (7.1) • An electric circuit is a path along which electric charges flow. (7.1) • Resistance is how a material resists the flow of electric charge. (7.1) • A circuit diagram is a model of an electric circuit. (7.2) • In a series circuit, the current is constant and the voltages across resistors add up to the total voltage supplied by the energy source. In a parallel circuit, the voltages across loads are constant and the currents on each path add up to the total current leaving the energy source. (7.2) • Ohm's law, $V = IR$, describes the relationship between voltage, current, and resistance. (7.3) • Fuses and circuit breakers are safety devices. (7.3)

8 We can reduce our electrical energy consumption and use renewable energy resources to produce electrical energy.

• Social and cultural consequences • Generating electrical energy • Renewable and non-renewable energy sources • Advantages and disadvantages of energy sources • Percent efficiency $= \dfrac{E_{out}}{E_{in}} \times 100$	• Energy production can have negative and positive consequences for First Nations and Métis peoples. (8.1) • Electrical generators transform kinetic energy into an electric current. (8.1) • Most electrical energy generated in Canada is from hydro- or thermoelectric sources. Other energy sources include biomass, nuclear, geothermal, solar, wind, and tidal. (8.1) • Renewable and non-renewable energy sources have pros and cons. (8.1) • Efficiency is the ratio of useful energy that comes out of a device compared to the total energy that went in. (8.2)

VOCABULARY

- charging by contact (p. 216)
- charging by induction (p. 216)
- conduction (p. 210)
- conductivity (p. 210)
- conductor (p. 210)
- electric charges (p. 206)
- electrical discharge (p. 217)
- electron affinity (p. 208)
- electrons (p. 207)
- electroscope (p. 213)
- electrostatics (p. 213)
- friction (p. 208)
- grounding (p. 217)
- induction (p. 216)
- insulator (p. 210)
- neutrons (p. 207)
- nucleus (p. 207)
- protons (p. 207)
- static electric charge (p. 207)

KEY VISUALS

Static electric charge

- alternating current (AC) (p. 239)
- ammeter (p. 239)
- ampere (A) (p. 239)
- battery (p. 243)
- circuit (p. 237)
- circuit breaker (p. 263)
- circuit diagram (p. 250)
- current electrical energy (p. 237)
- direct current (DC) (p. 239)
- dry cell (p. 243)
- electric current (p. 239)
- electrochemical cell (p. 243)
- electrodes (p. 243)
- electrolyte (p. 243)
- fuse (p. 263)
- ground fault circuit interrupter (GFCI) (p. 264)
- load (p. 237)
- multimeter (p. 240)
- Ohm's law (p. 259)
- ohmmeter (p. 240)
- ohms (Ω) (p. 240)
- parallel circuit (p. 251)
- primary cell (p. 243)
- resistance (p. 240)
- resistor (p. 241)
- secondary cell (p. 243)
- series circuit (p. 251)
- short circuit (p. 262)
- superconductor (p. 241)
- switch (p. 237)
- transistor (p. 249)
- volt (V) (p. 238)
- voltage (p. 238)
- voltmeter (p. 238)
- wet cell (p. 243)

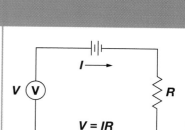

$V = IR$

Circuit diagram

- biomass (p. 274)
- efficiency (p. 287)
- EnerGuide (p. 288)
- energy efficiency rating (p. 288)
- energy grid (p. 272)
- Energy Star (p. 288)
- fossil fuels (p. 274)
- generators (p. 272)
- geothermal energy (p. 274)
- hydroelectrical energy (p. 273)
- kilowatt-hour (kW•h) (p. 286)
- non-renewable (p. 269)
- renewable (p. 269)
- sustainable development (p. 279)
- thermonuclear (p. 274)
- transformer (p. 272)
- turbine (p. 272)

Wind turbine

C28 Design Your Own Electrical Energy Activity

Toolkits 2, 11

Task Overview

In this task, you will identify your own question to investigate and design an activity related to static electric charges and current electrical energy. Your activity must answer your testable question. Record your testable question and your procedure and submit it to your teacher for approval. Remember to include safety as part of your procedure. Then, perform your activity, carefully recording your results in the format of your choice. Present your results and conclusions as a lab report or in a presentation.

C29 Identifying Energy Transformations

Toolkits 7, 11

Question

What energy transformations are involved in the use of electrical devices?

Task Overview

In this task, using an electrical device of your choice, you will explain the energy transformations that are involved in the use of the device. Choose a device that emits heat, light, sound, motion, or magnetic effects, such as a toaster, light bulb, oven, refrigerator, television, hair dryer, kettle, fan, or remote-controlled toy vehicle. Ensure you receive teacher approval for your choice. You must use labelled diagrams and incorporate proper terminology in your report. Explain, with respect to current electrical energy, how the energy transformation occurs.

Figure 8.33 Remote-controlled helicopter

C30 Conserving Electrical Energy

Toolkits 7, 11

Question

How can my family or school conserve electrical energy?

Task Overview

In this task, you will design an electrical energy conservation action plan for your family or school. Remember to take into account how this plan will affect your family or school's needs, such as heating, cooking, heating cold water, and so on. Include in your plan an estimate, based on kilowatt-hours of usage, of how much electrical energy could be saved, using your plan. Extrapolate what this could mean for Saskatchewan if your plan were adopted by every family or school in the entire province.

©P

UNIT **C** Review

Using Key Terms

1. Create a mind map using the following terms. You may add more terms if you wish.

- ammeter
- ampere
- battery
- current
- kilowatt-hour
- load

- ohm
- Thunderbird
- voltage
- resistance
- switch
- voltmeter

Reviewing the Big Ideas

2. (a) You walk across a carpet, touch a metal doorknob, and get a shock. What charge do the particles causing the charge have?

   (b) Use the structure of the atom to explain why these particles have the charge you identified in part (a).

3. Explain the steps you would take to tell the difference between a positively charged object and a negatively charged object.

4. Use a series of diagrams to explain how a charged object attracts a neutral object.

5. Object C is rubbed on object D. The leaves of a negatively charged electroscope temporarily move closer together when object D is brought near.

   (a) What charge does object D have?

   (b) What charge does object C have?

6. (a) When clothes come out of a clothes dryer, they sometimes stick to each other. Explain.

   (b) Name three different ways to reduce this effect.

7. (a) What are the two main components of an electrochemical cell?

   (b) What is the function of each component?

8. Explain the function of the metal rods in the photograph below.

Question 8

9. How has the understanding of static electric charges helped in developing new technologies?

10. Copy and complete the following table in your notebook.

Voltage, Current, and Resistance

Quantity	Definition	Abbreviation	Unit	Symbol
Voltage				
Current				
Resistance				

11. Why does a light bulb light up immediately after you turn on a switch, even if the switch is a long way from the bulb?

12. (a) Use circuit symbols to draw a series circuit with a battery, connecting wires, and two light bulbs.

    (b) Draw a parallel circuit using the same components as (a).

    (c) Describe the difference in current flowing in the two circuits (a) and (b).

13. (a) What is the voltage at V_1 in the circuit below?

(b) What is the current at A_1 in the circuit below?

(c) Is this circuit a series circuit or a parallel circuit?

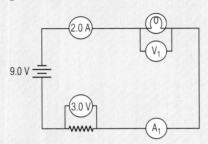

Question 13

14. What does Ohm's law state?

15. If the resistance of a load becomes larger, does the current through the load also become larger? Explain.

16. Why is it a good idea to use fused safety power bars for televisions, computers, and other sensitive electrical equipment?

17. Using examples, describe the difference between renewable and non-renewable energy sources.

18. What are three different electrical energy generating systems you could use if you lived on a small farm?

19. How could you use the EnerGuide and Energy Star labels to help you decide when purchasing appliances or electronics?

20. List five appliances or devices found in the home that consume electrical energy even when they are not in use.

21. What are three benefits of lowering our energy demands?

Connecting the Big Ideas

22. (a) You are standing close to a tall tree when you suddenly see lightning and hear thunder. What should you do? Explain why.

(b) You and a friend have plans to go swimming, but large storm clouds are gathering on the horizon. Should you postpone your plans? Explain.

23. How are a lightning bolt and a spark similar?

24. What understanding of lightning do many First Nations and Métis peoples have?

25. Suppose a more efficient appliance costs more than a regular appliance. Does it make sense to spend the extra money? Explain.

26. Create a sketch, paragraph, or skit using electrical terms in a humorous manner. You should get a "charge" from doing this "potentially" fun exercise at "ohm" or at school.

27. Why are the different kinds of electrical energy generation of concern to First Nations and Métis peoples?

28. The graph below shows the relationship between voltage and current that emerged in tests for a particular resistor. Does this resistor work according to Ohm's law? Explain.

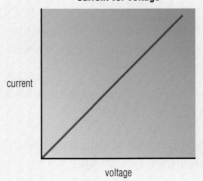

Current vs. Voltage

current

voltage

Question 28

29. For the following situations, explain the safety concern.

(a) A worker carries a large aluminum ladder near overhead hydro lines.

(b) Someone takes the third prong out of a plug in order to use it with a two-prong extension cord.

Using the Big Ideas

30. Copy and complete the following table in your notebook.

Percent Efficiency

Device	Input Energy (kJ)	Output Energy (kJ)	Percent Efficiency
Gas-powered SUV	675	81	
Gas-electric hybrid car	675	195	
Natural gas furnace	110 000	85 000	
Electric baseboard heater	9.5	6	
Alkaline dry cell	84.52	74.38	

Reflection

31. The scientific ideas you learned about lightning are about the physical world. How does this differ from the First Nations and Métis ideas about lightning described in the unit?

32. Nuclear energy is one of the most efficient ways to produce electrical energy.

(a) Why does Saskatchewan not have any nuclear energy stations?

(b) What concerns may First Nations and Métis peoples have about nuclear energy stations in Saskatchewan?

33. Create a graphic representation, such as a mind map or other table, to answer the following questions. Include labelled diagrams if you wish.

(a) What are the costs and benefits associated with the production of electrical energy from renewable and non-renewable sources?

(b) How can electrical efficiencies and savings be achieved through the design of technological devices and practices in the home?

34. Based on the activities you have done in this unit, answer the following questions. Include your personal observations, labelled diagrams, and/or refer to specific activities as part of your answer.

(a) What are the properties of static electric charges and current electrical energy?

(b) What is the relationship between voltage, current, and resistance in an electrical circuit?

35. Has your attitude about how you use electrical energy changed after completing this unit? Explain.

Reflection on Essential Inquiry Questions

What are static electric charges and current electrical energy and how are voltage, current, and resistance in series and parallel circuits related? **SI**

How do we assess the operating principles, costs, and efficiencies of devices that produce or use electrical energy? **TPS**

What is the impact of electrical energy production and distribution in Saskatchewan? **DM**

What knowledge of electricity do First Nations and Métis peoples have? **CP**

Exploring
Our Universe

Silhouetted against
a red background
of dust and gases
is the distinctive
Horsehead Nebula,
surrounded by
brilliant stars.
Nebulae are often
referred to as stellar
nurseries because
it is out of the dust
and gases that new
stars form.

©P

Big Ideas

9 **Celestial objects, phenomena, and interactions are important to people in many different ways.**

    9.1 Human Interest in Space

    9.2 Earth, Moon, and Sun Relationships

    9.3 Our Solar System `DI`

10 **Stars are an important component of galaxies.**

    10.1 Stars

    10.2 Galaxies `DI`

11 **Our understanding of the universe is culturally influenced.**

    11.1 Cultural Explanations `DI`

    11.2 Scientific Theories

12 **Space exploration improves our knowledge and gives us beneficial technologies and has significant costs and hazards.**

    12.1 Space Exploration

    12.2 Benefits of Space Research and Exploration `DI`

    12.3 Costs and Hazards of Space Research and Exploration

Essential Inquiry Questions

How has the way we understand our solar system and universe changed? `SI`

How have we explored the universe and how might we travel and explore the universe in the future? `TPS`

Space exploration is expensive and dangerous. How might the risks and benefits be shared? `DM`

Why is it important to have different ways of knowing about the universe? `CP`

Unit Task

In the Unit Task, you will research space technologies, theories, and accepted knowledge. The tasks include designing a habitable space vehicle; exploring careers related to space science; and expanding your understanding of the solar system and beyond.

©P

9

Celestial objects, phenomena, and interactions are important to people in many different ways.

What you will learn:

- Early cultures and civilizations used celestial patterns for survival, exploration, and spiritual beliefs and rituals.

- Star charts are used to determine the location, appearance, and motion of well-known stars visible in the night sky.

- Astronomical phenomena, such as phases of the Moon, solar and lunar eclipses, and auroras, result from Earth, Moon, and Sun interactions.

- The relative sizes and distances of the major components of the solar system are measured using different units of measure.

This image of our solar system is not to scale.

Before Reading

Making Connections to Prior Knowledge

Skim the titles, subheadings, and illustrations of section 9.1 to get a sense of the key ideas. Scan for terms that you know. Use familiar ideas and terms to create a mind map that connects all of your knowledge about the universe. What you know already will help you connect to new information and ideas.

©P

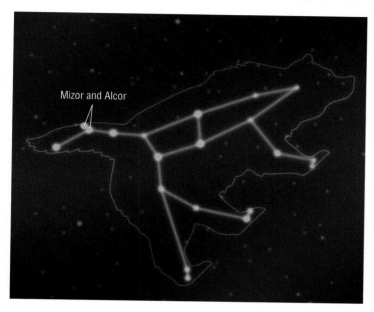

Figure 9.1 The constellation Ursa Major. To many cultures, this star pattern looked like a large bear.

Mizor and Alcor

The View from Earth

Throughout history, humans have been studying the night sky. The study of objects and phenomena in space is called **astronomy**, and people who know and study astronomy are called **astronomers**. What do you see when you look up into the clear night sky? You have probably seen the Moon, the Sun, other stars, and planets, and maybe even a meteor. All the objects in space, including Earth, are known as **astronomical bodies**. A similar term is **celestial bodies**, which refers to all objects we can observe in the sky. The most easily visible celestial bodies are stars. Some stars look as though they are grouped together into patterns. Perhaps the best-known star pattern in the northern hemisphere is the Big Dipper. Different cultures around the world refer to this collection of seven stars by other names. The Lakota people of Saskatchewan have many names for this pattern, one of which is *Oceti Sakowin*, "the seven council fires." For the Lakota, this star pattern has great symbolic meaning. Together, these stars represent the stages of life for both sexes.

The Big Dipper is part of a larger star pattern known as Ursa Major, which is Latin for Great Bear (Figure 9.1). Ursa Major is an example of a **constellation**, a group of stars that, from Earth, resembles a form. Western astronomers have officially listed a total of 88 constellations from collectively used Eurocentric star charts.

Here is a summary of what you will learn in this section:

- Early cultures and civilizations studied celestial patterns with their unaided eye and used their observations to develop calendars, plan hunting and farming activities, navigate across land and oceans, and inspire spiritual beliefs and rituals.
- Astronomy is making sense of the universe that lies beyond Earth.
- Technologies, such as the kamal, the quadrant, and the sextant, were developed to facilitate sea travel.
- The position of celestial bodies can be determined using azimuth and altitude, and declination and right ascension.

infoBIT

Celestial Bodies

The term *celestial bodies* includes all astronomical objects that can be viewed in the sky. It is important to remember that Earth is not a celestial body. We cannot see Earth in the sky while we are standing on it!

reSearch

In most cultures, when people looked up at the night sky, they saw pictures, patterns, and pathways in the stars. These pictures are what we refer to as constellations. Choose a constellation from a particular culture, and research the origins of its story. Present your findings to the class.

Figure 9.2 *Kisci-Okima-Achak, okimāwi anang*, or Vega is one of the three brightest stars in the summer sky, which helps to make the Summer Triangle.

Smaller recognizable star patterns within a larger constellation are known as **asterisms**. The Big Dipper is an asterism.

Constellations are not only patterns of stars. They bear a very special significance for many cultures. For the Lakota, Dakota, and Nakota peoples of Saskatchewan, constellations, such as *Nape* (the hand), teach important sacred lessons. Other constellations told the traditional Lakota people when to travel to wintering grounds and when to conduct sacred ceremonies.

Each First Nations culture has names for stars. For example, *Kisci-Okima-Achak* or the "Great Chief Star" is a Cree name for the star that scientists call Vega (Figure 9.2). This star directs the destiny of all the other stars. The same star is called *okimāwi anang* or "great star" by the Nakawē (Saulteaux).

D1 | *Quick Science*

Reading Star Charts

Star charts are maps that show some or all of the constellations and key stars that are visible from Earth. Stargazers from many cultures use star charts to orient themselves to the night sky.

Purpose

To compare the star charts of different cultures

Materials & Equipment

- Eurocentric star chart
- star charts from various cultures

Procedure

1. Working on your own, select a Eurocentric star chart and one other star chart.

Questions

2. Using the Eurocentric star chart, locate Polaris. Can you find Polaris on the other star chart? Record its name.

3. What constellation is Polaris part of on your Eurocentric star chart? Can you find Polaris in a constellation on another star chart? Record the name of the constellation.

4. Using Polaris as a guide, locate Cassiopeia on your Eurocentric star chart. Does this constellation have an equivalent on your other star chart?

5. Many First Nations and Métis peoples used their understanding of constellations to aid their survival. Explain how specific constellations may have helped them to survive.

Pose New Questions

6. What other cultures' constellations would you like to learn about?

7. Compose a question about one of the constellations and its meanings that you would like to know more about.

©P

Using the Sky as a Calendar

People have always watched and wondered at the Sun and the night sky. Ancient astronomers observed and recorded astronomical phenomena and used their patterns to mark the passage of time and to foretell eclipses and the changing seasons (Figure 9.3).

Many cultures have complex cosmological ideas about the sky. These ideas may be expressed in a story-like way, but they convey important understandings. The Nakawē, or Saulteaux, believe that the *Kise-manito*, or the Great Spirit, created everything. *Kise-manito* gave the Nakawē four celestial gifts. The Sun, which gives and sustains life, represents *Kise-manito*. He lives in the sky to watch over his children. A second gift is Earth, which nurtures life, and is known as Mother Earth. A third gift is the stars, which are the spirits of ancestors. They provide travellers with guidance, not only in the four directions, but in life itself. A fourth gift is the Moon, which represents all the cycles of life.

We pass our understanding of the world from generation to generation. In this way, the Aztecs and Mayans developed accurate calendars over generations of observation and recording. European understanding of the universe during the Renaissance in the 15th century relied heavily on astronomical knowledge gathered by Islamic and Greek astronomers for more than 800 years. In the same way, what we learn about the universe today will be shared with generations of astronomers to come.

Figure 9.3 The Aztec Sun calendar was used by people of Mexico hundreds of years ago. This wheel shows both a 365-day calendar cycle and a 260-day ritual cycle. The two cycles together formed a 52-year "century."

Solstices

Two important annual events for our ancestors were the **solstices**. In the northern hemisphere, the summer solstice, which occurs around June 21, marks the longest period of daylight in the year and represents the start of summer. The winter solstice, which occurs around December 21, marks the shortest day of the year and represents the start of winter. In the southern hemisphere, the solstices are reversed: the summer solstice is near December 21, and the winter solstice is near June 21.

Many cultures held solstice festivals, such as the Chinese festival Dong Zhi, which means "extreme of winter." The Chinese have been celebrating the winter solstice for 2500 years.

*info*BIT

Sacred Knowledge

Knowledge that has spiritual meaning or is rooted in a people's belief system is often called sacred. For many First Nations and Métis peoples, knowledge about the sky is sacred, and so their constellations have sacred significance.

*info*BIT

Sun Stop

The word "solstice" comes from the Latin *sol*, meaning sun, and *stice*, meaning stop.

Using Prior Knowledge

How have different cultures used their prior knowledge to develop ways of predicting seasons? Write down three key statements that describe ways of predicting seasons.

Equinoxes

Another regular phenomenon honoured by early cultures was the twice-yearly equinox. **Equinoxes** occur when the hours of daylight and the hours of night are of equal length. The vernal, or spring, equinox occurs around March 21. The autumnal, or autumn, equinox occurs around September 22. The Mayans of Central America built an enormous cylinder-shaped tower at Chichén Itzá in about 1000 CE to celebrate the equinoxes.

Predicting Seasons

Predicting the approaches of summer and winter was essential to the survival of early peoples. For example, North America has a fairly short growing season, so it was important to know when to plant and harvest crops or prepare for hunting and fishing (Figure 9.4). Many ancient civilizations noticed that the changes in seasons were related to the changing positions of celestial bodies in the sky. Their observations of the position and path of the Sun and stars throughout the year were highly accurate. Using their observations, people developed structures to predict the solstices and equinoxes. Some examples are the Moose Mountain and Roy Rivers Medicine Wheels in Saskatchewan; the Sun Dagger of Chaco Canyon, New Mexico; the Temple of the Sun, Machu Picchu, Peru; and Stonehenge in England (Figure 9.5). These forms of technology remain remarkably accurate.

*info*BIT

Telling the Seasons

The northeast Saskatchewan Cree needed to predict the seasons for harvesting, trapping, and hunting. To tell the seasons, they watched the constellations and the cycles of the Moon. In the spring, they would build weirs at the mouths of rivers and creeks to catch spawning fish. In the fall, they would harvest, trap, and hunt migrating waterfowl.

Figure 9.4 The Moose Mountain Medicine Wheel in Saskatchewan is an example of many created by the First Nations peoples to predict the start of seasonal rites and migrations. This one is dated to 300 CE.

Figure 9.5 Stonehenge in England is estimated to be about 4500 years old.

Using the Sky for Navigation

Before technology such as global positioning satellites (GPS) existed, people used the sky as a guide to their location and directions to where they wanted to go. During the day, the Sun's position could be used for navigation. At night, the stars were used. This form of navigation is called celestial navigation. Most celestial navigation uses Polaris, or the North Star. This star is known by the Cree as *Keewatin*, or the Going Home star. The Cree observed that this star was stationary in the night sky. By keeping the star over their right shoulder, travellers would know they were heading west.

It was not until people began exploring the open seas that there was a greater need for navigation technology. Out on the oceans, there were no landmarks that navigators could use to orient themselves. Arabic sailors used a navigation device called a kamal, a wooden card with a knotted string through it. The number of knots determined the latitude. The kamal did not become widely used because it is only effective near the equator (Figure 9.6).

Later devices, such as the sextant and quadrant, revolutionized sea travel and allowed Europeans to explore other continents. Both the quadrant and sextant measure the angle between the horizon and a celestial body, such as Polaris. Sailors would compare this measurement to a chart to determine their position. You will learn more about these tools in Chapter 12.

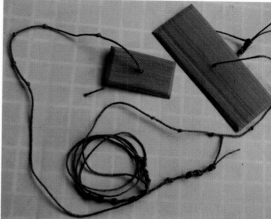

Figure 9.6 Arabic sailors used the technology of the kamal and celestial navigation to travel on the open seas.

Locating Objects in Space

Ancient astronomers needed to develop methods for locating celestial bodies and recording their positions to predict celestial phenomena, such as the changing seasons, and to navigate the open seas. Using their belief that the sky was a solid sphere surrounding Earth with celestial objects fixed on this sphere, ancient astronomers were able to record the location of celestial bodies. The celestial equator is the equator of the celestial sphere, and it aligns above Earth's equator. Although we know the concept of the celestial sphere is not true, we still use the idea to locate objects in space.

To describe the position of objects in space, astronomers use the measurements of altitude and azimuth. Altitude and azimuth describe coordinates. **Altitude** is measured from the horizon (0 degrees) to the point directly overhead (90 degrees), which is known as the zenith (Figure 9.7).

Suggested Activities •·········
D2 Inquiry Activity on page 312
D3 Quick Science on page 313

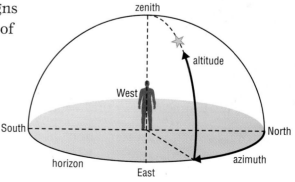

Figure 9.7 The celestial sphere showing altitude and azimuth

The **azimuth** refers to the position of a star from due north moving in a clockwise position. An azimuth of 180 degrees would be due south and an azimuth of 360 degrees would return the viewer to due north.

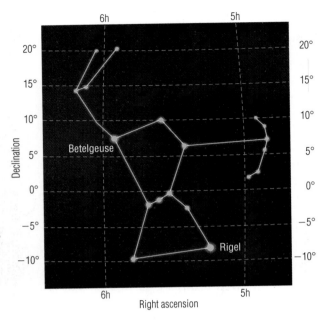

Figure 9.8 The Orion nebula is located at RA 5 hr 35.4 min, decl −5° 27'.

Another way to describe the positions of celestial objects is to use the terms **right ascension**, which would be like longitude, and **declination**, which would be similar to latitude (Figure 9.8). These are both coordinates on the celestial sphere. Right ascension, or RA, starts from the first point of Aries. This point is located where the Sun crosses the celestial equator at the spring equinox. RA increases in magnitude as the observer moves east. RA is expressed in units of hours, minutes, and seconds. These units are used because the night sky rotates once every 24 h.

Declination, or decl, starts from the celestial equator. It is expressed in degrees or minutes and seconds south or north. If it is a northern declination, then the number is positive. If the number is negative, then the declination is southern.

9.1 CHECK and REFLECT

1. List three reasons that early cultures, including First Nations and Métis peoples, had for observing and keeping track of celestial phenomena.

2. How have observations of the natural world helped in the development of calendars?

3. If an alien were to come to Earth, how would we explain constellations to this newcomer? Would the constellations appear the same as on the alien's home planet? Explain.

4. Use your own words to define the differences between solstices and equinoxes in terms of what time of year they occur.

5. Why would the observations of the solstices and equinoxes be so important to various cultures?

6. How could ancient cultures predict the solstices and equinoxes?

7. How have observations of the sky enabled humans to explore and travel?

8. In your own words, explain altitude and azimuth, and how they are used in determining objects in the night sky.

9. How would an astronomer locate a specific star if she or he were only given the right ascension and declination?

10. Why are altitude and azimuth expressed in degrees, while right ascension is expressed in hours, minutes, and seconds?

11. What early forms of technology were used
    (a) for predicting solstices and equinoxes?
    (b) for navigation?

Alfred and Ernestine Cheecham: The Dené Sky

Figure 9.9
The Northern Lights

In Saskatchewan's far north where there may be less than 6 h of daylight on winter days, celestial bodies provide light for the traditional Dené people. During the warmer summer months, the sun bathes the land in its golden light. For millennia, the Dené people of Saskatchewan have made use of these celestial bodies to travel, hunt, and survive. Alfred and Ernestine Cheecham are Elders from Clearwater Dené Nation. Here they share their teachings about the North Star, the Northern Lights (Figure 9.9), and the Sun, through the help of interpreter Jeanne Auramenko.

The Northern Lights, *Yeka Na Ges*, which means "stirring of the surface," are viewed by some Dené communities as ancestral spirits. Elder Alfred explains, "When the northern lights do their dance, you must be respectful and watch their dance. As these ancestral spirits dance, they cause the northern lights. If you mock or try to imitate them, these spirits will take you away with them."

In Dené, the Big Dipper is called *Yeh Da Ghe*, and the Little Dipper is known as *Yan del*.

The Sun has a special place in Dené culture. The Sun's importance is reflected in their stories. The story of Raven and how it stole back the Sun and gave it to the people of the North explains the dramatic changes in winter and summer. Dené Elders forecast the weather through events associated with the Sun, such as sundogs, the sky colours, telling time, and finding directions. The Sun holds a prime position in the natural order, infusing life in all living things. The Cheechams explain that the Sun is the light of the world and it sustains humanity: "Without the Sun, we would have a hard time maintaining our way of life and traditional pursuits like trapping, hunting, and fishing."

The North Star, *Tthen Thoghe*, which means "yellow star," is highly regarded by all Dené communities. The Dené use this star to navigate when they travel by dog team. The North Star guides them to their destination and is like their Sun at night. The lead dog, the head of the dog team, is shown the route once by sniffing the ground and tree peelings. With the help of the North Star, the dog team will lead the rider home. Under the North Star, traps on the trapline are set at night.

Through observation of the sky, the Dené people have survived in one of the harshest environments on Earth.

Using a Star Chart

If you were driving from Greenwater Provincial Park to Tisdale and you passed a small village, you could use a map to find out that you passed Bjorkdale. A star chart works in a similar way. Once you identify one star or constellation, you can identify others.

There are star charts for different seasons and locations. In the northern hemisphere, you can always see Polaris, or the North Star, anywhere and anytime. The Plains Cree know this important marker as *mahikan-acāhkos*, or the Wolf Star.

Initiating and Planning

How can we locate the positions of stars in the night sky?

Materials & Equipment

- star chart
- flashlight with a red light (optional)

Performing and Recording

1. Face south and hold the chart over your head to read it. Using a flashlight that casts a red light will allow you to read your chart without affecting your night vision.

2. Locate the Big Dipper on your star chart. It is part of the constellation Ursa Major. Then, find the Big Dipper in the sky (Figure 9.10). You will see many more stars in the sky than appear on the chart, but the bright stars making up the Big Dipper should stand out.

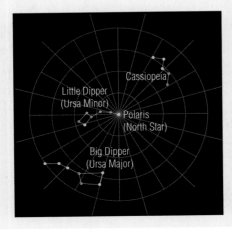

3. After you find the Big Dipper, locate the two stars that make up the outside of the ladle. These are known as the "pointer stars" because they point to Polaris, the North Star. Follow the pointer stars until you see a fairly bright star. This is Polaris. It is always in this position in the sky no matter what the season or the time.

4. Follow along an arc until you reach a group of five stars that forms a big W. (Depending on the time of night and the season, this may look more like an M.) This is the constellation Cassiopeia.

5. Finally, go back to Polaris. It is part of the Little Dipper, forming the last star in the handle. The stars of the Little Dipper are not quite as bright as the stars of the Big Dipper, but they are still easily visible with the naked eye.

Analyzing and Interpreting

6. Describe how you used the Big Dipper to find Polaris, Cassiopeia, and the Little Dipper.

7. If you were unable to find any of these stars or groupings, explain what problems occurred that prevented you from locating them in the sky.

8. The star Sirius is brighter than Polaris. Would it make more sense to call Sirius the North Star, instead of Polaris? Explain your answer.

9. Using your star chart, identify three other constellations in the northern sky.

Communication and Teamwork

10. (a) If you were able to use the star chart effectively in this activity, write one guideline to add to the procedures that would help another student using a star chart for the first time.

    (b) If you were not able to use the star chart effectively, list one or more questions that you would need answered to help you find some or all of the identified objects.

Figure 9.10 Three commonly observed constellations and Polaris

Moon, Where Are You?

The Moon's position in the sky changes from hour to hour and day to day. Recall that the azimuth is a measurement of a celestial body on the horizon and the altitude is the vertical position (Figure 9.11).

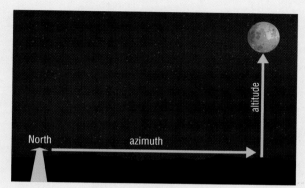

Figure 9.11 Azimuth and altitude are astronomical terms used to determine position.

You do not need any fancy equipment to determine the azimuth and altitude. Your fist is a "handy" instrument. Your closed fist measures about 10 degrees, and each of your fingers is about 2 degrees (Figure 9.12).

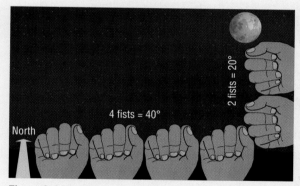

Figure 9.12 It is easy to use your fist to make your measurements.

Purpose

To observe and record the changing location of the Moon using the measurements of azimuth and altitude for a period of two weeks

Procedure

1. Over the next two weeks, you will record information about the position of the Moon. Create a table to record the date, azimuth, and altitude.

2. To measure the azimuth, determine North from your position. Pointing North, extend your arm with your palm down and make a fist. Measure eastward along the horizon by crossing your fists side by side until you reach a point directly below the Moon. If there is a space that is too small to be measured by your fist, use the width of your fingers to measure the space. Record your measurements.

3. To measure the altitude, start at the horizon. Extend your arm with your palm facing sideways and make a fist. The bottom of your fist should be on the horizon. Measure upward by placing your fists one on top of the other until you reach the bottom edge of the Moon. Record your measurements.

4. Continue to observe and record the position of the Moon for two weeks, at approximately the same time each evening.

Questions

5. According to the data you collected, is the Moon's azimuth getting larger or smaller? How does the Moon's altitude change?

6. Create a graph using the azimuth as the *x*-axis and the altitude as the *y*-axis. What information can you discover from the graph? Do you think the graph would be identical if you repeated the experiment in six months? Explain why or why not.

Pose New Questions

7. Many First Nations and Métis peoples, such as the Cree, used the Moon as a calendar. What would you use to create your own calendar based on your observations of the Moon?

8. Consider your results. What new questions do you have about the changing position of the Moon?

Here is a summary of what you will learn in this section:

- First Nations and Métis understandings explain astronomical phenomena, such as changing seasons, eclipses, and auroras.

- Early cultures and civilizations studied celestial patterns with their unaided eye and used their observations to develop calendars, plan hunting and farming activities, navigate across oceans and land, and inspire spiritual beliefs and rituals.

- The movement of celestial bodies in our solar system, including Earth, creates observable patterns, such as Moon phases, and phenomena, such as eclipses.

- The Sun's magnetic field affects the Earth by not only creating auroras at both poles, but may also interfere with or damage equipment. The aurora borealis, or Northern Lights, is understood by First Nations and Métis peoples as a powerful phenomenon.

Figure 9.13 Midnight in the Arctic during the peak of summer

Earth in Motion

If you lived in a region near Earth's equator, you would notice little change from day to day throughout the year in the hours of daylight relative to the hours of darkness. Every day all year long, about 12 h of daytime would be followed by about 12 h of night. The farther north or south of the equator a person lives, however, the bigger the variation he or she sees in daily hours of light over a year.

In the northern hemisphere, we experience the hours of daylight changing in a non-stop cycle, lengthening as we move into summer and shortening as we move into winter. No matter where you live in Saskatchewan, think how different it is at 5 p.m. on a December afternoon compared with 5 p.m. on a July afternoon. The greatest daylight extreme is in Arctic regions, where the Sun does not set some days at the peak of summer and does not rise some days at the peak of winter (Figure 9.13).

©P

The reason for this variation is that Earth spins like a top around a tilted axis, the imaginary line running through Earth. As it spins, Earth also travels around the Sun. These two motions cause day and night, season changes, and what appears from Earth to be movement of the Sun and the stars across the sky.

The Effects of Earth's Motion on Our View of the Sky

Early people were aware that when they observed the position of the Sun and constellations shifting in the sky, a seasonal change was coming.

Purpose

To simulate the relationship between Earth's motion, the position of celestial bodies as viewed from Earth, and the changing seasons

Materials & Equipment

- diagrams of Polaris (the North Star), Cassiopeia, Little Dipper, Big Dipper, Orion, Leo, Scorpius, and Pegasus
- masking tape or thumb tacks

Procedure

1. Your teacher will tape the diagram of Polaris on the ceiling in the centre of the room and tape the diagrams of Cassiopeia, Little Dipper, and Big Dipper around Polaris in their correct orientation.

2. On each of the four walls in the room, tape the following diagrams: Orion (winter) on the west wall, Leo (spring) on the south wall, Scorpius (summer) on the east wall, and Pegasus (autumn) on the north wall.

3. Have one student be the Sun, standing in the middle of the room.

4. Have another student be Earth. Earth stands to the west of the Sun and facing the Sun. In this position, Earth's northern hemisphere is in winter and the time of day on Earth's front is noon. Earth cannot see any stars because the Sun's light is outshining them.

5. Earth slowly turns in a counterclockwise direction until Earth's front experiences midnight. Note which star pattern on the wall Earth can now see and how the Big Dipper is oriented.

6. Repeat steps 4 and 5 for the other seasons by having Earth stand south, east, and north of the Sun.

Questions

7. What motion of the person playing Earth
   (a) represents the passing of one day on Earth?
   (b) represents the passing of one year on Earth?

8. With the person representing Earth rotating counterclockwise, does the Sun rise on the left side or the right side of Earth's face?

9. Explain why different constellations are visible in the evening in different seasons.

10. Why does the orientation of the Big Dipper (Figure 9.14) change with the seasons?

Pose New Questions

11. Consider how the constellations may appear on other planets. Compose a question about their appearance.

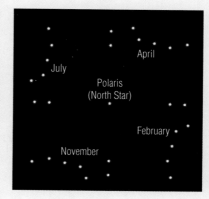

Figure 9.14
The Big Dipper changes its orientation in the sky throughout the year.

Connecting the Known to the New

As you read the text under each subheading, write in your notebook one thing you already know about the topic, two pieces of information that are new to you, and one question you still have about the topic.

info BIT

Traditional Saulteaux Knowledge

The traditional Saulteaux people understand that the Sun walks across the sky. It is important to greet the Sun on its journey with a smile and pure heart, and to say farewell at the end of the day with the same attitude.

Day and Night: Earth's Rotation

The North and South Poles mark the two ends of Earth's axis. One complete spin of Earth on its axis is called a **rotation** (Figure 9.15). A rotation takes almost 24 h.

The daily rotation of Earth on its axis creates day and night. On the side of Earth facing the Sun, it is daytime. Twelve hours later, that same point on Earth faces away from the Sun, and it is night.

Viewed from above the North Pole, Earth spins counter-clockwise. This explains why the Sun always appears to rise in the east and set in the west no matter where you are in the world.

Although it might feel as though the Sun is the object that is moving while we watch from a seemingly stationary Earth, really Earth is spinning like a top around its axis. Standing on Earth, we are carried eastward toward the Sun. We do not feel the motion of rotation because the rotation is relatively slow and the ground and air move with us. Instead, we see the Sun rise. As Earth continues to rotate, the Sun appears to move across the sky until, later in the rotation, the Sun appears to disappear below the horizon, or set. The apparent path of the Sun as it moves through the sky during the year is known as the **ecliptic**.

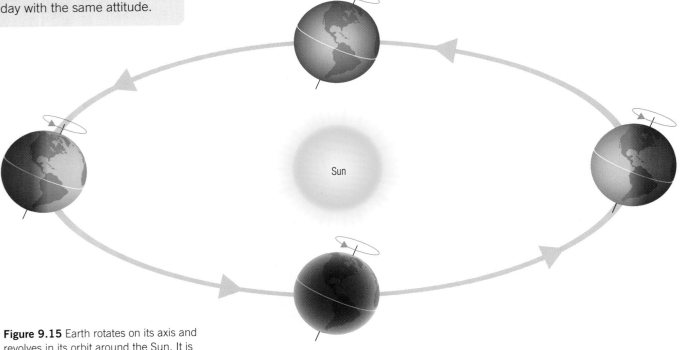

Figure 9.15 Earth rotates on its axis and revolves in its orbit around the Sun. It is daytime on the side of Earth facing the Sun.

Seasons: Earth's Tilt and Revolution

Seasons occur in all parts of the world but differ from region to region. For example, near the equator, there are usually only two seasons: wet and dry. However, in northern and southern regions, such as Canada and New Zealand, there are generally four seasons: spring, summer, autumn, and winter. When it is summer in Canada, it is winter in New Zealand. Six months later, the seasons are reversed.

Some traditional First Nations and Métis peoples of northern Saskatchewan, such as the northern Cree and Dené, observe six seasons. The recognition of six seasons is crucial to survival. Along with spring, summer, autumn, and winter, there are freeze-up and break-up. Freeze-up is the time when the rivers and lakes become frozen as temperatures drop. Break-up is a time when rivers and lakes thaw. Knowledge about changes in the immediate environment, such as freezing and thawing of ice, is called place-based knowledge and is important to survival.

Many people think that the seasons are caused by Earth's being farther away from or closer to the Sun. This is incorrect. In the northern hemisphere, Earth is actually farther away from the Sun in summer than in winter. The changing seasons are the result of Earth's movement around the Sun and Earth's tilted axis (Figure 9.16). Earth's axis is tilted at an angle of 23.5° relative to the imaginary flat surface, or plane, along which Earth orbits the Sun.

Earth travels around the Sun in an elliptical path called an **orbit**. A **revolution** is one complete orbit of Earth around the Sun, a journey that takes one year. The axis of Earth always stays at approximately the same angle, with the North Pole pointing almost exactly toward Polaris. During part of Earth's orbit, the northern hemisphere is tilted toward the Sun. The Sun shines more directly on the northern hemisphere, creating summer. As Earth orbits to the other side of the Sun, the North Pole is still pointed at Polaris, but the northern hemisphere now tilts away from the Sun. The Sun shines less directly on Earth, creating winter. During equinoxes, neither of Earth's hemispheres is more directed at the Sun than the other. This means that, for a time, days and nights are equal everywhere on Earth.

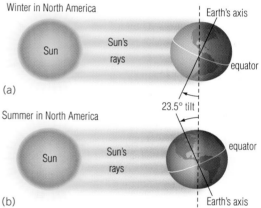

Figure 9.16 (a) The northern hemisphere is tilted away from the Sun, so the Sun shines less directly on it, causing winter. (b) The northern hemisphere is tilted toward the Sun, so the Sun shines more directly on it, causing summer.

Learning Checkpoint

1. Earth rotates and revolves. Explain what each of these actions means. How long does each action take?

2. The axis of Earth is tilted. What is it tilted in relation to?

Earth's Moon

Figure 9.17 An astronaut's footprint on the Moon's surface

Suggested Activity • • • • • • • • • •
D5 Inquiry Activity on page 326

A **satellite** is any object that orbits a planet. A moon is a natural satellite. Artificial satellites will be discussed in more detail in Chapter 12. Earth has only one Moon, which has been featured in stories, songs, and art since humans first looked up into the night sky. Twelve people have walked on the Moon, the last time in 1972. The Moon is smaller than Earth and has no atmosphere and little or no water. On the Moon, an astronaut's footprint can last indefinitely, perhaps as long as a million years (Figure 9.17).

Within a few hundred million years after Earth formed, many scientists believe that it may have been struck by a huge object nearly the size of the planet Mars. The metal core at the centre of the incoming object plunged deep into Earth where it merged with Earth's metallic core. The rocky crusts of Earth and the object mixed, but the momentum of the collision destroyed much of the rest of the material. The larger object cooled down to become Earth. The smaller object, likely formed from material blasted from Earth after the collision, became trapped by Earth's gravitational force, or gravity. It existed first as debris and rubble, but eventually it compacted into a new object, the Moon.

The Moon and Its Phases

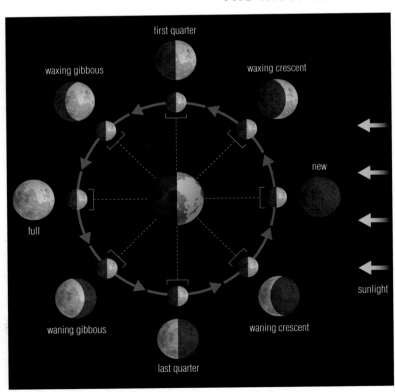

Figure 9.18 The lunar cycle begins with a new moon, grows in size to a full moon two weeks later, and diminishes until the new moon begins again.

The Moon is bright because it reflects the Sun's light. You know from seeing the Moon on different nights how the shape of its bright part changes daily. These changes are referred to as the Moon's phases. The phases of the Moon are caused by the revolution of the Moon around Earth and our changing views of it.

The Moon's phases are classified into eight categories (Figure 9.18).

The full moon occurs when Earth lies between the Sun and the Moon (though not usually exactly between, which would cause an eclipse. Eclipses will be discussed later in this section). In this position, with the Moon on one side of Earth and the Sun on the other, the entire illuminated side of the Moon faces Earth.

Two weeks later when the Moon lies between Earth and the Sun, none of the sunlight reflected by the Moon can reach Earth. This is called a new moon, because over the next two weeks the Moon will become newly illuminated again.

One revolution of the Moon around Earth takes 27 days, 7 hours, and 43 minutes to complete. One complete change of phases is called the lunar cycle.

Eclipses

As Earth revolves around the Sun, and the Moon revolves around Earth, they sometimes line up in such a way that a partial or total shadow of one object is cast on another. Such overshadowing events are called eclipses.

Cultures around the world have ways to describe and explain eclipses. For example, the Eastern Canadian Anishinaabe talk about a young man named *Pikojigiiwizens* whose fine coat made of bird skins was shrunk by the Sun while he slept. Angry *Pikojigiiwizens* used a snare to trap the Sun. When the Sun did not rise, only the mole was brave enough to face the Sun's heat. As the mole chewed away the snare to free the Sun, the mole was blinded. To this day, moles are blind. In Mayan tradition, an eclipse occurs because the god *Ah Ciliz* grows angry and eats the Sun. The Aztecs of Mexico believed that the *tzitzimene*, demons with the faces of women and the bodies of spiders, come down from the heavens to prey on humans during eclipses.

Solar Eclipse

A **solar eclipse** occurs when the Moon lies directly between Earth and the Sun, blocking all or part of the Sun's light to viewers on Earth. For a few minutes, some or all of the Sun seems to disappear. As Figure 9.19 shows, with the Sun shining behind it, the Moon casts a shadow over a small part of Earth.

WARNING: Be sure to watch a solar eclipse through a suitable filter or by projecting the Sun's image onto a screen. Never look at the Sun with the unprotected eye. Without protection, you can permanently damage your vision.

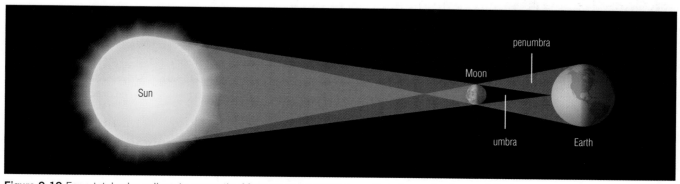

Figure 9.19 For a total solar eclipse to occur, the Moon must be aligned exactly between the Sun and Earth.

Solar eclipses can be partial or total. In a partial solar eclipse, the Sun is only partially blocked from our view by the Moon (Figure 9.20(a)). In the uncommon event of a total solar eclipse, the Moon completely blocks out our view of the Sun (Figure 9.20(b)). Although the Sun is about 400 times the size of the Moon, they appear to be about the same size in Earth's sky because the Moon is so much closer. An annular eclipse occurs when the Sun and the Moon are precisely lined up and only a thin circle of light appears in the sky (Figure 9.22(c)).

 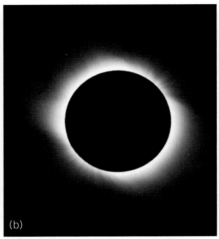 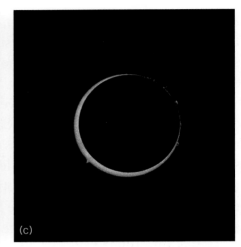

(a) (b) (c)

Figure 9.20 (a) Partial solar eclipse (b) Total solar eclipse (c) Annular eclipse

Lunar Eclipse

A **lunar eclipse** occurs when Earth blocks out the Sun's light shining on the Moon, making the Moon briefly disappear. This happens when Earth lies directly between the Moon and the Sun, as shown in Figure 9.21. Observers on Earth see the Moon pass under Earth's shadow.

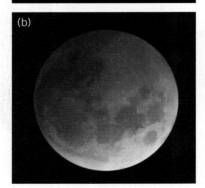

Figure 9.22 (a) Partial lunar eclipse
(b) Total lunar eclipse

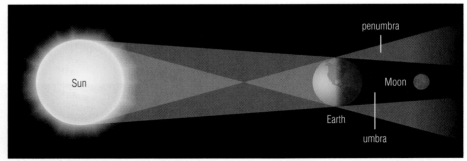

Figure 9.21 For a total lunar eclipse of the Moon, Earth must be aligned exactly between the Sun and the Moon.

In a partial lunar eclipse, the Moon is only partially blocked from our view by Earth's shadow (Figure 9.22(a)). In a total lunar eclipse, Earth's shadow darkens the entire Moon (Figure 9.22(b)).

©P

The Sun

Through history, the Sun has been central to cultures all over the world. In Saskatchewan, the Nakawē understand that the Sun sees all, even through clouds and storms. Because of this and the light the Sun gives—both spiritual and physical—it inspires us to achieve excellence in all we do.

Although the Sun is about 150 million km away from Earth, it is vitally important. The Sun supports almost all life on Earth, and features and phenomena that occur on the Sun have a significant impact on Earth.

The Sun is a star. A **star** is a body of electrically charged gas, or plasma, that emits energy from nuclear reactions taking place in its core. We can see and feel some of this energy as visible light and as warmth. The Sun has a magnetic field that is generated by movement of the plasma deep in its interior. The Sun's magnetic field extends far out into space where it is carried by the solar wind. Four important events that occur on the surface of the Sun are sunspots, prominences, flares, and coronal mass ejections (Figure 9.23). The occurence of these events is linked to the Sun's powerful magnetic field.

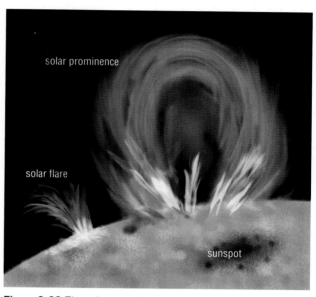

Figure 9.23 Three important solar events

Sunspots

A **sunspot** is a region on the Sun's surface that is cooler than the surrounding areas. Although still very bright, by contrast it looks darker than the surrounding areas (Figure 9.24). Sunspots indicate regions where the magnetic field is extremely strong, slowing down convection. This prevents the plasma from mixing, allowing the region to cool from about 6000°C to 4000°C. Sunspots come and go. The number of them reaches a maximum every 11 years, increasing when the magnetic field strength of the Sun also reaches a maximum level and the Sun's magnetic poles flip.

Suggested Activity •···········
D6 Quick Science on page 327

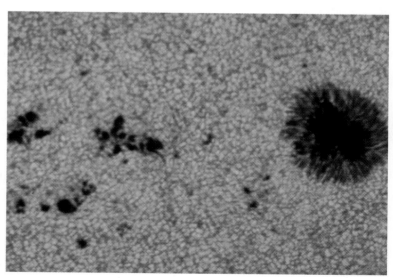

Figure 9.24 The dark zones surrounded by a lighter border are sunspots. Each is larger than Earth's diameter.

Solar Prominences

A **solar prominence** is a large, low energy, curved, bright stream of particles. The curved shape often forms a complete loop as you saw in Figure 9.23 and see in Figure 9.25. The electrically charged plasma in the prominence is shaped by the Sun's magnetic field lines. This makes part of the magnetic field visible. A solar prominence may last for several hours or several weeks.

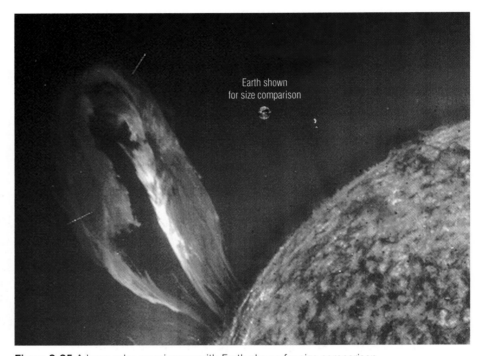

Earth shown for size comparison

Figure 9.25 A large solar prominence with Earth shown for size comparison

Solar Flares

A **solar flare** is a high energy massive explosion at the surface of the Sun. This sudden release of magnetic energy often flings hot plasma out into space, which we see as a long bright filament extending out from the Sun. Solar flares can reach their maximum energy level in just a few minutes and can last several hours.

An extremely powerful kind of flare is called a coronal mass ejection. When this occurs, a large amount of plasma is thrown into space at a speed of more than 1000 km/s. Sometimes, a coronal mass ejection may be pointed directly at Earth. When this plasma stream reaches Earth about three days later, it meets Earth's magnetic field. Our magnetic field protects Earth by diverting much of the plasma away from the planet's surface. This causes natural light displays called auroras, which are described on the next page. Coronal mass ejections can also damage orbiting satellites and electrical transmission lines on the ground.

©P

The Sun's Effects on Earth

As you have read, the Sun warms Earth and supports, directly or indirectly, every form of life on the planet. In addition to these significant influences, there are many other ways the Sun affects our planet. The solar wind and aurora borealis are two of these ways.

The Solar Wind

The tremendous amount of energy at the surface of the Sun produces a thin but steady stream of subatomic particles, or plasma. This constant flow of particles streaming out of the Sun's surface in all directions is called the **solar wind** (Figure 9.26).

During turbulent solar times, electronic equipment and devices on Earth may be damaged by higher-than-normal blasts of charged particles from the Sun. In 1989, geomagnetic storms caused by solar wind destroyed the Hydro-Québec electrical grid, causing many Canadians to go without power for 9 h.

Suggested Activity • • • • • • • • • • •
D7 Science, Technology, Society, and the Environment on page 327

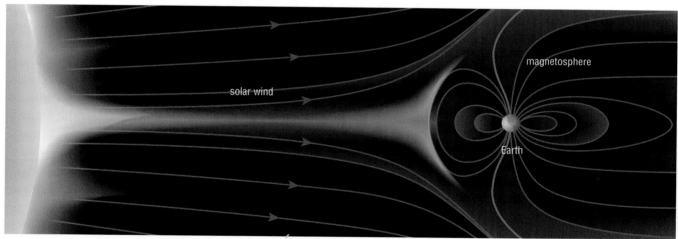

solar wind

magnetosphere

Earth

Figure 9.26 The solar wind crosses space and strikes Earth. Earth's protective magnetic field, called the magnetosphere, deflects most of this solar wind.

The Aurora Borealis

According to scientists, the solar wind is responsible for creating the breathtaking displays of green, yellow, and red light in the skies near Earth's northern and southern regions. In the northern hemisphere, these light displays are called the **aurora borealis** (the Northern Lights). In the southern hemisphere, they are called the **aurora australis** (the Southern Lights).

reSearch

Researchers at the University of Saskatchewan's Institute of Space and Atmospheric Studies are part of SuperDARN. Research SuperDARN and what they study. Present your findings in a method of your choice.

Aurora Borealis Warnings

Sometimes the Northern Lights were seen as warnings by First Nations and Métis peoples. Traditional Knowledge Keeper Judy Bear of the Sweet Grass Cree First Nation was taught by her father that if the Northern Lights were reddish, the Elders would say that there was going to be bloodshed. Reddish Northern Lights appeared just before the North-West Resistance of 1885.

Auroras form as particles from the solar wind are trapped by Earth's magnetic field and are swept toward the North and South Poles (Figure 9.27). The strength of the solar wind affects the shape and size of the aurora in these zones. If the charged particles arrive as solar flares, which often come in cycles, the aurora will appear as very vivid, dancing lights. Changes in the solar wind make the aurora appear to be "dancing" in the night sky.

Many First Nations and Métis peoples understand that the Northern Lights are the spirits of family dancing in the night sky. The round dance (*piciciwin* in Plains Cree) is connected to the aurora. Many believe that when the round dance occurs, the Northern Lights are all around. Some Dené believe the Northern Lights provide them with the caribou and so were important for their survival.

Some Indigenous cultures of Saskatchewan also consider the Northern Lights to be very potent spirits or spirit dancers who, if disrespected, may come down from the sky. First Nations and Métis peoples treat the night sky with respect and speak about it with great reverence and humility. Some Elders express a concern that many young First Nations and Métis peoples have lost their connection to the sacred night sky. Moreover, they believe that townsites and cities that are continually lit have eliminated our ability to see all but the brightest of the stars. They worry that this type of light pollution erodes our relationship with the land and our concept of night.

Figure 9.27 The aurora borealis. The colours are caused by the solar wind interacting with the oxygen in the atmosphere.

1. From Earth, why does the Sun appear to be rising in the east and setting in the west?

2. (a) Explain the connection between the Sun and the tilt of Earth's axis in relation to the seasons.

   (b) How have different cultures detected these seasonal changes?

   (c) Explain why this was necessary to their survival.

3. Describe how the northern Cree and Dené divide one year into seasons. How is it different from how Eurocentric cultures divide the year into seasons?

4. Why do we see only one side of the Moon at all times?

5. The Moon does not have a dense metallic core as Earth does. Instead, it appears to be composed only of the same materials as are found in Earth's outer layers. Based on this information, what conclusion can be drawn about the formation of the Moon?

6. Sketch how Earth, the Sun, and the Moon are arranged on a night when we can see a full Moon.

7. What is an eclipse and how does it occur?

8. Describe the different types of eclipses that can be viewed from Earth.

9. Do you agree or disagree with the statement, "A total eclipse of the Moon by Earth can happen only during a full Moon"? Justify your answer using a diagram.

10. The Sun is a star. Use your own words to write a scientific description of a star.

11. The Sun features significantly in the traditions of the Saulteaux people. Describe one understanding that Saulteaux people have about the Sun.

12. What is the solar wind?

13. Name the solar event shown in each image (a) and (b) below, and explain the cause of each feature.

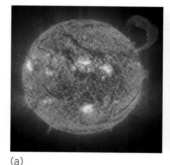
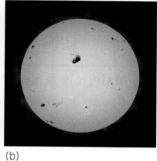

(a)   (b)

Question 13

14. How can a coronal mass ejection from the Sun cause damage on Earth?

15. (a) Explain, according to scientists, what causes the astronomical phenomenon known as an aurora.

    (b) Why is it important to continue to study auroras?

16. First Nations and Métis astronomers use their own observations and cultural perspectives to explain celestial phenomena. Describe some examples of how First Nations and Métis perspectives differ from those of scientists.

The Phases of the Moon

Have you ever noticed a full Moon rising at sunset or setting at sunrise? Does it always happen this way for full Moons? Why are there some times at night when the Moon is not visible and some times in the day when it is visible? Why does the Moon sometimes appear as a crescent? In this activity, you will investigate these questions.

Initiating and Planning

In this activity, you will model the relationships between the Sun, the Moon, and Earth to illustrate the different phases of the Moon. The Styrofoam ball will represent the Moon, you will be Earth, and the light will be the Sun.

Materials & Equipment
- pencil or dowel
- Styrofoam ball
- bright light without a shade

Performing and Recording

1. Insert the pencil partway into the Styrofoam ball to create a model of the Moon. Hold your model of the Moon by the pencil, slightly overhead at arm's length so that your head does not cast a shadow on the model.

2. Have your partner hold up the light in a darkened room (Figure 9.28).

3. With your partner, discuss what position you will have to be in for it to be noon. Once you have decided, rotate to that position. Then, find the correct position for sunrise, sunset, and midnight.

Figure 9.28 Step 2

4. Work with your group to find consensus on how sunrise, sunset, and midnight should be represented in a model.

5. Experiment by moving the model Moon to different locations around your head, always at arm's length. Observe the shadows that appear on the Moon. Compare your observations with those of another group.

6. To model one month of the Moon's movement, hold out the model of the Moon and turn counterclockwise. Note how the shadows on the model change as you move. Discuss your observations with your partner.

7. One last time, follow the Moon through one month of phase changes, this time noting whether you are most likely to view each phase during the daytime or at night.

Analyzing and Interpreting

8. Does a full Moon always rise at sunset and set at sunrise? Explain.

9. Draw three phases of the Moon that are most likely to be seen (a) during the daytime and (b) at night.

10. Why does the amount of sunlight reflected from the Moon to Earth change during a month?

11. First Nations and Métis peoples have different understandings of the phases of the Moon. In small groups, research one of these understandings and share your findings with the class.

Communication and Teamwork

12. Did using models to compare results help with communicating ideas? Explain why or why not.

13. Did you use the same person to compare results or did you compare results with others? Is it better to compare results with a number of individuals or with only one person? Explain.

©P

Sunspots

Scientists have been observing and collecting data about the Sun for a long time. Astronomers in China have been observing sunspots since 28 BCE. The more recorded observations astronomers can make, the more information they will learn. Displaying several kinds of information on the same graph enables you to compare related data in a useful way.

Materials & Equipment
- graph paper
- ruler
- coloured pencils
- tape
- graphing calculator (optional)

Purpose

To graph sunspot data and determine cycles of high sunspot activity

Procedure

1. Your teacher will provide you with yearly sunspot data. Working in a group, divide the data among group members. Each member will be responsible for a section of the data.

2. As a group, decide what scale you will use to construct your graph.

3. Plot your section of data in a line graph.

4. Once individual graphs are completed, tape the graphs together to create a larger graph.

5. Examine the larger graph.

Questions

6. What are some trends shown in the graph?

7. What are the maximums and minimums of the graph?

8. When do you predict the next sunspot maximum will occur? the next minimum?

Pose New Questions

9. Why do you think it is important for scientists to know when there will be high levels of sunspot activity?

10. In addition to sunspot activity numbers, what other aspects of sunspots might astronomers study? Write your answers in the form of testable questions.

Space Weather

The Sun's energy heats Earth and supports all life on Earth. At the same time, however, the Sun poses many challenges for Earth's inhabitants. The plasma that the Sun occasionally spews into space from its turbulent and explosive surface creates what astronomers call "space weather."

When solar storms occur, Earth is bombarded by showers of charged particles. Such events can destroy orbiting satellites and disrupt cellphone service, television programs, and other communications systems.

Sun activity can burn out power grids that supply electricity to homes and businesses. Even the top of Earth's ozone layer, the part of the atmosphere that prevents harmful ultraviolet radiation from reaching Earth's surface, is greatly reduced when Sun activity sends out a blast of streaming particles.

1. Using the library or the Internet, read more about space weather and how sunspot activity and solar storms can affect humans and equipment. Present your findings in a consequence map, or write a news article or weather alert.

- First Nations and Métis understandings explain the origin of Earth and our solar system, and astronomical phenomena, such as meteors.

- Our solar system is composed of the Sun, planets, their moons, and other objects, such as asteroids and comets. Nebular theory suggests that the solar system formed from the leftover gas, dust, and other debris spinning around the newly formed Sun.

- The rocky planets in the inner solar system are Mercury, Venus, Earth, and Mars. The gaseous planets in the outer solar system are Jupiter, Saturn, Uranus, and Neptune.

- Distances in space are measured in astronomical units (AU) and light-years (ly).

Figure 9.29 This life-size alabaster and bronze sculpture by Cree artist Lloyd Pinay shows the Cree peoples' understanding of Turtle Island.

How Our Solar System Formed

First Nations and Métis peoples have a strong oral history that is a record of their knowledge. There are many stories that describe the origin of celestial bodies. Many First Nations and Métis peoples of Saskatchewan, such as the Cree, the Nakawē, and the Lakota, understand that celestial bodies like the Sun, the stars, and the Moon owe their origin to the Great Spirit. The Plains Cree of Saskatchewan simply call this Great Spirit, Creator, or *Kisemanito*. To the Lakota, the Great Spirit is *Wakan*.

The story of Turtle Island and the Sky World is an example of a creation story that explains the existence of Earth (Turtle Island) and the heavens (Sky World). Some Haudenosaunee of Ontario believe that the Great Spirit (*Gehi Mnidoo*) fashioned both the sky and Earth. In the story, a woman fell from the Sky World, a place that existed like a dome over Earth. The animals of Earth, its only inhabitants in that time, rushed to help her, but without any land to rest upon, she would perish. The animals tried to find land and all of them failed, except Toad who dove deep into the ocean and brought up dirt in his mouth. The animals spread the dirt over the great Turtle's back and created North America. Sky Woman cast up a handful of dust from the land, making the stars. Sky Woman then made the Sun and the Moon (Figure 9.29).

©P

The Solar System

Scientists describe our **solar system** as the Sun and all the planets and other celestial objects, such as moons, comets, and asteroids, that are held by the Sun's gravity and orbit around it (Figure 9.30).

Scientists try to understand how our system, as well as other solar systems, have been created to find out whether other Earth-like planets exist in other solar systems in our universe.

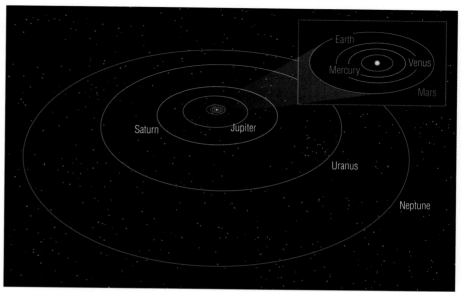

Figure 9.30 A comparison of the orbits of the eight planets in the solar system

---

D8 *Quick Science*

Modelling the Nebular Theory

One of the theories on how the solar system was created is the nebular theory. Similar to how a tornado spins, the nebular theory proposes that dust and gases continued to spin after the Sun was formed, flinging materials out into space, which later formed the planets.

Purpose
To model the nebular theory

Materials & Equipment
- water
- small container
- vermiculite
- stir stick

Procedure

1. Put some water into the container.

2. Add a small amount of vermiculite.

3. Using the stir stick, stir the water and vermiculite mixture so it spins like a whirlpool.

Questions

4. What happened to the vermiculite?

5. What would the vermiculite be similar to in the nebular theory?

6. The planets closer to the Sun are smaller and are made mostly of rock. The planets farther from the Sun are larger and are made mostly of gases. Based on your observations and your understanding of nebular theory, explain how this might have happened.

Pose New Questions

7. Investigate other theories and stories from other cultures of how the solar system may have been formed. Brainstorm how you could model those other theories.

8. Did your observations help you better understand nebular theory? What new questions about the formation of the solar system do you have?

The Nebular Theory

There have been many theories on how our solar system was formed. The most accepted scientific theory on how the solar system was formed is called the nebular theory. A **nebula** is a cloud of dust and gases in space, which scientists believe is an area of star formation. Nebulas are often referred to as stellar nurseries. You will learn more about nebulae in Chapter 10.

The **nebular theory** explains that, after the Sun formed, the solar wind blew against the nebula from which it formed. This pushed the gas and dust away from the Sun. The leftover dust, gases, and other debris in the nebula that remained continued to spin, creating a thin disk around the new star. From within this disk, small bodies began to form, growing into the planets, moons, asteroids, and comets that make up the solar system (Figure 9.31). This process, astronomers believe, is how other star-and-planet systems in the universe have formed as well.

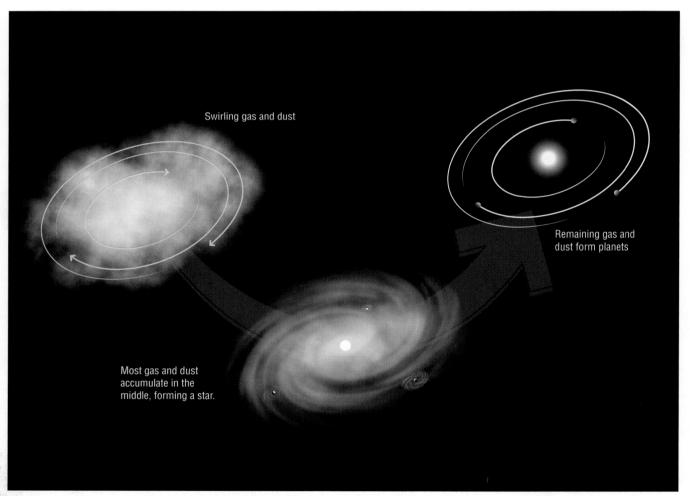

Swirling gas and dust

Remaining gas and dust form planets

Most gas and dust accumulate in the middle, forming a star.

Figure 9.31 The solar system formed when the gas and dust left over from the formation of the Sun continued to spin around the star. Gravity caused the material to clump together and contract, creating a range of celestial objects, from planets and moons to asteroids and comets.

©P

The Heart of the Solar System

As we saw in section 9.2, the Sun is the star at the heart of our solar system. We know the Sun better than any other star in the Universe. The **S**olar and **H**eliospheric **O**bservatory (SOHO), a solar space telescope, has had a clear view of the Sun since 1995. The information it sends back to Earth shows us its fiery nature (Figure 9.32).

A star is defined as a body of gases that is undergoing nuclear reactions and radiates energy. Our Sun is of medium size by star standards and is composed mainly of hydrogen (73 percent by mass) and helium (25 percent by mass). The rest is made up of heavier elements including carbon, oxygen, and iron. It formed in the same way that all stars do, taking shape inside a nebula. The Sun is believed to have first begun shining, or radiating energy, about 5 billion years ago and is expected to continue shining for about 5 billion years more before it runs out of fuel.

Astronomers have estimated the Sun's mass by observing how fast the solar system's planets and other celestial objects orbit around it. Scientists' understanding of how the Sun uses its hydrogen comes from discoveries made in the last century about atomic energy. The nuclear reactions taking place in the Sun are thought to be the same ones that occur in the most powerful kind of atomic weapon, the hydrogen bomb. In both cases, the reaction involves a small amount of hydrogen being converted into helium, which causes a rapid release of tremendous amounts of energy.

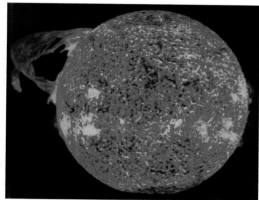

Figure 9.32 Solar events, such as prominences, sunspots, and flares, are of interest to scientists because of their effects on Earth.

infoBIT

Solar Radiation

The Sun radiates energy in many forms, including visible light and ultraviolet (UV) radiation. Some forms of UV radiation can cause sunburn on exposed skin.

The Planets

After the Sun, the next largest astronomical bodies in the solar system are the planets (Figure 9.33). A **planet** is an astronomical body that orbits one or more stars and is capable of forming into a spherical shape under its own gravitational force, or gravity. A planet does not create nor radiate its own energy like a star does. It only reflects the light of the star or stars that it orbits.

Figure 9.33 The solar system. The four rocky planets closest to the Sun were the first to form. The four gaseous planets in the outer solar system took shape later.

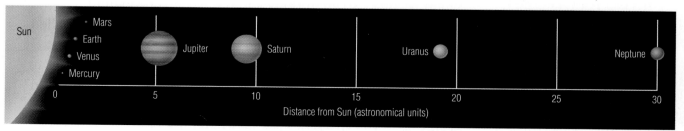

Sun · Mars · Earth · Venus · Mercury   Jupiter   Saturn   Uranus   Neptune

0   5   10   15   20   25   30

Distance from Sun (astronomical units)

The Rocky Inner Planets

As the spinning particles of dust and gas slammed into each other during the early stages of the solar system's formation, some of the particles began sticking together. Larger particles tended to grow faster than smaller ones because they were involved in more collisions. This is similar to a large snowball growing faster when you roll it in sticky snow than a small snowball does.

As these objects got bigger in mass, gravitational forces caused them to contract and bind together even more strongly. Objects orbiting too close to the Sun gradually fell into it, drawn by its gravitational force. However, four large objects lasted and eventually formed the four rocky planets of the inner solar system: Mercury, Venus, Earth, and Mars (Figure 9.34).

Mercury   Venus   Earth   Mars

Figure 9.34 The four rocky planets of the inner solar system

Measuring Distances in Space

The distances in space are so vast that astronomers developed special units of measure. Just as you would not find it practical to measure your school gymnasium in millimetres, it is not practical to measure distances in the solar system in kilometres.

One unit used to measure distances in space is the astronomical unit. One **astronomical unit (AU)** equals the average distance between the Sun and Earth, about 150 million km. Mercury is 0.39 AU from the Sun. This value is less than 1 AU because Mercury is closer to the Sun than Earth is. Mars is farther from the Sun than Earth is. It is 1.52 AU from the Sun.

Outside the solar system, the distance to other celestial objects again becomes so great that even the AU is too small to be a useful unit of measure. Instead, astronomers usually use a unit called the light-year. One **light-year (ly)** equals the distance that a beam of light travels through space in 1 year. It is equivalent to 63 000 AU or 9000 billion km. At the speed of light, you could travel around Earth seven times in 1 s. A trip from the Sun to Neptune at the speed of light takes about 5 h.

infoBIT

Solar Systems

By the 2000s, astronomers had discovered 50 stars that had planets orbiting them.

Suggested Activities •·········
D9 Inquiry Activity on page 342
D10 Inquire on Your Own Activity on page 344
D11 Skill Builder on page 345

D9 Inquiry Activity on page 342
D10 Inquire on Your Own Activity on page 344
D11 Skill Builder on page 345

During Reading

Using Prior Knowledge

Think about holidays or road trips you have taken. What were the destinations? What preparations did you make? How long was each journey? Now, for an imaginary voyage out among the stars, think about the preparations and travel details you would need to consider.

©P

The Four Gas Giants

The solar wind blows gases away from the Sun, but this does not mean that all the gases escape the solar system completely. Just beyond the asteroid belt is the "snow line." On the Sun side of this line, the Sun's radiation keeps water in its gaseous phase. However, out past the snow line, water can cool to form droplets and then freeze.

Astronomers believe that the four largest planets in the solar system may have grown as they did because ice acted as a kind of glue to cause gas and dust particles in the outer regions of the solar system to stick together. In fact, these planets grew much faster than the rocky ones did. The result was the four outer planets: Jupiter, Saturn, Uranus, and Neptune (Figure 9.35).

Jupiter   Saturn   Uranus   Neptune

Figure 9.35 The four gaseous planets of the outer solar system, shown here with the Sun in the background for scale. Had Jupiter been a little larger, nuclear fusion might have started in its core and Jupiter might have become a star.

These planets do not resemble Earth at all. They are often referred to as the gas giants because their atmospheres are made mostly of hydrogen and helium and because they are much larger than the inner planets. Jupiter is so large that several thousand Earths could fit inside it. The planet farthest out in the solar system is Neptune, in orbit 30.1 AU from the Sun.

All of the gas giants are orbited by numerous moons. Jupiter and Saturn each have more than 60 moons (Figure 9.36).

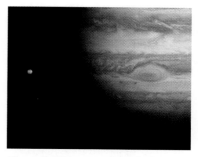

Figure 9.36 Io, one of the Galilean moons of Jupiter, is shown here orbiting the large planet.

Learning Checkpoint

1. Name the planets in the solar system, starting from the Sun.

2. Define an astronomical unit and a light-year. How are they different?

The Rocky Planets

Planet	Average Distance from Sun (AU)	Radius (km)	Mass (Earth mass)	Average Surface Temperature (°C)	Period of Rotation (Earth day)	Period of Revolution (Earth year)
Mercury	0.4	2400	0.1	180	60.00	0.2
Venus	0.7	6100	0.8	470	240.00	0.6
Earth	1.0	6400	1.0	17	1.00	1.0
Mars	1.5	3400	0.1	−60	1.03	1.7

Mercury

Most of what we know about Mercury has been determined from telescope and satellite data. Mercury is the planet closest to the Sun. Its surface is similar to that of the Moon. Mercury has no atmosphere and therefore no protection from being bombarded by asteroids and comets. The scars of millions of years of impacts show this. Other parts of Mercury's surface are smooth, which is probably from lava flowing through cracks in the rocky crust. The temperatures on Mercury vary greatly, from over 400°C on the sunny side to −180°C on the dark side.

Venus

Venus is similar to Earth in diameter, mass, and gravitational force, and is often called Earth's twin. Surface temperatures are kept hot by a greenhouse effect caused by thick clouds. Temperatures can be over 450°C, hot enough to melt lead. The atmospheric pressure is about 90 times that on Earth. Venus's surface cannot be seen by telescope because of its thick cloud cover. The permanent clouds, made of carbon dioxide, often rain sulphuric acid (the same acid found in a car battery). Russia landed a probe on Venus in 1982, but it stayed operational for only 57 min. In 1991, the spacecraft *Magellan* mapped Venus using radio waves (radar). The *Venus Express* orbiter arrived in 2006 and continues to make atmospheric studies. It has found huge canyons, extinct volcanoes, and ancient lava flows. Venus is one of only two planets in the solar system to rotate from east to west, the opposite direction to all the other planets, except Uranus.

Earth

Earth is unique in the solar system for several reasons. It is the only planet where water exists in liquid state. Water covers 70 percent of the planet's surface. It is also the only planet that is at the appropriate distance from the Sun to support life as we know it, a distance called the Goldilocks zone. Earth is protected from solar and cosmic radiation by its atmosphere and its magnetic field. The ozone in the atmosphere screens life on Earth from UV radiation. The magnetic field makes most of the charged particles from the solar wind and cosmic rays stream around the planet, far outside the atmosphere. Earth is one of the few planets in the solar system that has active volcanism.

Mars

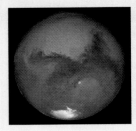

Mars has been studied by telescope for centuries. It is often referred to as the red planet. This appearance is caused by the iron oxides on the planet's surface. Mars has two polar ice caps: one is made up of solely carbon dioxide, and the other is composed of both carbon dioxide and water. The atmosphere is very thin and composed mainly of carbon dioxide. Although the average surface temperature is extremely cold, temperatures at Mars's equator can reach 16°C in the summer. Like Venus and Earth, Mars has canyons, valleys, and extinct volcanoes. Mars is the only other of the rocky planets with a moon, and it has two irregular-shaped moons, Phobos and Deimos.

The Gaseous Planets

Planet	Average Distance from Sun (AU)	Radius (km)	Mass (Earth mass)	Average Surface Temperature (°C)	Period of Rotation (Earth day)	Period of Revolution (Earth year)
Jupiter	5.3	71 000	320	−150	0.41	12
Saturn	9.5	60 000	95	−170	0.45	30
Uranus	19.0	26 000	15	−215	0.72	84
Neptune	30.0	25 000	17	−215	0.67	165

Jupiter

Jupiter has been observed through telescopes since the 1600s, and its four largest moons were discovered by Galileo in 1610. The *Voyager* probes visited Jupiter and many of its moons in 1979, followed by the *Galileo* probe in the mid-1990s. Europa, one of Jupiter's larger moons, may contain liquid water. Jupiter is the largest of all the planets in the solar system. It contains more than twice the mass of all the other planets combined. Jupiter is composed mainly of hydrogen and helium, and scientists speculate that if the planet were only 10 times larger than it is, it might have formed into a star. The Great Red Spot visible on Jupiter is a huge storm in its atmosphere. Jupiter has three very thin rings.

Saturn

Saturn is the second-largest planet in our solar system and has the most distinctive ring system of all the eight planets. Over a thousand rings exist, composed of pieces of ice and dust that range in size from grains of sand to house-sized blocks. In 1610, the astronomer Galileo saw Saturn's rings with his primitive telescope, though he initially thought they were a group of planets. *Voyager 1* and *Voyager 2* flew by Saturn in 1980 and 1981, respectively. In late 2004, the *Cassini* spacecraft arrived at Saturn and dropped a probe onto Titan, the largest of the planet's moons. Saturn, like Jupiter, is composed mostly of hydrogen and helium. Because of the planet's quick rate of rotation, wind speeds at Saturn's equator have been estimated at over 1800 km/h.

Uranus

Voyager 2 has given us most of our close-up information about Uranus, last sending data back to Earth in 1986 before it left the solar system. Satellite and telescope analyses have provided other interesting details. Uranus has one of the most unusual rotations in the solar system. Its axis of rotation is tilted toward the plane of its orbit, making it appear to roll during its orbit. Uranus is composed mainly of hydrogen and helium. Methane in its atmosphere gives the planet a distinctive blue colour. Uranus has a large ring system and 17 moons. When scientists observed the orbit of Uranus to be different from what they had calculated, they searched for an eighth planet.

Neptune

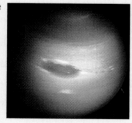

In 1846, scientists found Neptune. About a century and a half later, *Voyager 2* flew to Neptune to collect more information. The composition and size of Neptune make it very similar in appearance to Uranus. Composed of hydrogen, helium, and methane, Neptune is bluish in colour as Uranus is. Very little of the Sun's energy reaches Neptune, which gives off about three times more energy than it receives. This planet has the fastest wind speeds in the solar system, 2500 km/h. Like all the other gas giants, Neptune has its own ring system, as well as eight moons.

A Different Theory on Solar System Formation

Astronomer Alan Boss proposes another theory of solar system formation. He believes the nebular theory does not explain the formation of the planets Uranus and Neptune. Although these planets are considered gas giants, they both have large rock and ice cores with a thin gas layer.

Boss's theory states that the formation of the outer planets was affected by another young star nearby. According to Boss, this star was much larger than the Sun, extremely hot, and emitted extreme UV radiation. The Sun's gravity created a protective zone. Jupiter became the largest planet because it was fully protected. Saturn is smaller because it is located between the two star zones and had some of the available material diverted by the competing stars away from Saturn's formation. Neptune and Uranus were closer to the larger star and similarly had materials stripped away from their formation. What was left condensed to form those two planets. The other star died and the Sun, along with our forming solar system, was pushed out of the nebula and sent to a calmer part of the galaxy (Figure 9.37).

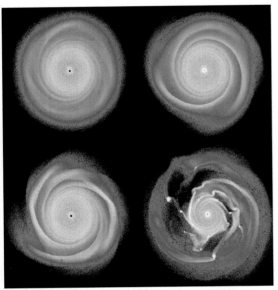

Figure 9.37 This model of solar system formation supports Alan Boss's theory.

Other Objects in the Solar System

Many smaller objects exist in the solar system besides the eight planets. These include moons, comets, dwarf planets such as Pluto, and tiny grains of dust and ice. Some objects held by the Sun's gravity are as far as 50 000 AU away, which is one-quarter of the way to the next nearest star.

The Asteroid Belt

Between the inner rocky planets and the outer gas giants lies a huge band of billions of rocks, spread out in a vast ring circling the Sun at a distance of about 3 AU (Figure 9.38). These rocks are **asteroids**—metallic, rocky bodies without atmospheres that orbit the Sun but are too small to be classified as planets. This ring of rocky debris is known as the **asteroid belt**.

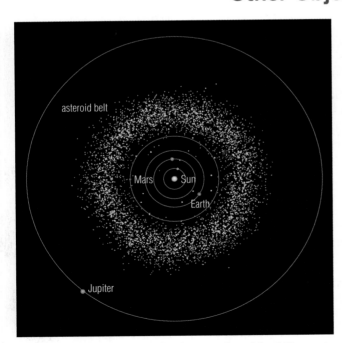

Figure 9.38 The asteroid belt lies between the orbits of Mars and Jupiter.

Asteroids are classified according to their chemical composition and albedo. Albedo, or how bright objects appear, is a measure of how well they reflect the Sun's light. Asteroids can range in size from 1000 km in diameter to the size of pebbles. Most asteroids are less than a kilometre in diameter.

Scientists' understanding of asteroids comes from Earth-based remote sensing (telescopes) and space probe fly-bys. Astronomers study asteroids for a number of reasons. One of these reasons is that many celestial bodies have hit Earth and the Moon. It is widely believed that 65 million years ago, a comet or asteroid hit Earth at three impact sites (Figure 9.39). The impact and the effects of the impact are believed to have caused the mass extinction of the dinosaurs.

Figure 9.39 This crater in Arizona, US, measures about 1.2 km in diameter and is thought to have been created by an asteroid 24 m in diameter.

Some scientists looking for Earth-like planets in other star systems are doing so by looking for the presence of an asteroid belt around the star. If there is such a band, this might indicate that rocky planets are orbiting the star as well.

The analysis of asteroids has given us the estimated age of the solar system. This is why asteroids are often known as "fossils." By the 1950s, scientists had found a way to determine the age of many asteroid specimens. The oldest ones were dated at 4.56 billion years old. Since Earth would have formed at the same time as the asteroids did, researchers have used this asteroid-dating technique to date Earth. As it took time for the asteroids to form, the Sun and solar system are currently estimated to be about 5 billion years old.

Dwarf Planets

Dwarf planets are similar to planets in that they orbit the Sun and have a roughly spherical shape, but unlike planets, they have an unusual orbit or orbit in a zone that contains many other objects. Scientists are still debating the definition of dwarf planet and which objects should be classified this way.

*info*BIT

Close Call

On March 23, 1989, an asteroid that was 400 m wide came within 640 000 km of Earth. The asteroid and Earth missed being in the same spot by 6 h.

*re*Search

In 2000, the first space probe ever to orbit an asteroid reached 433 Eros in the asteroid belt. Eros measures 33 km by 13 km. Find out the purpose of the mission to Eros and whether it succeeded in its task.

There are millions of small objects besides Pluto orbiting the Sun. Some are larger than Pluto, but most are smaller. Together, they create a thin disk that, like the asteroid belt, forms a ring around the entire solar system. About 25 of these are large enough, however, to be considered dwarf planets.

Similar to asteroids, dwarf planets are believed to have been created when the solar system formed. Using improved technologies, astronomers are able to gather more data about the dwarf planets. It is believed that the dwarf planet HL Tau b will one day become an actual planet. Scientists refer to these dwarf planets that are still forming as protoplanets. It will take a lot of time for this to occur, but by recording data, the question of how planets actually form may be answered.

Figure 9.40 Most comets have been orbiting the Sun in the Oort Cloud for billions of years. Because of their composition, they are often referred to as "dirty snowballs."

Comets

The most distant region of the solar system is the Oort Cloud. It lies about 50 000 AU from the Sun. It consists of billions of fragments of ice and dust, and is a major source of comets. A **comet** is a celestial object made of ice and dust, often called a "dirty snowball," which travels in an elliptical orbit around the Sun. When a comet nears the Sun, the Sun heats the comet, causing some of its ice particles to break away. Carried away from the Sun by the solar wind, these icy particles spread out into a tail millions of kilometres long and are lit up by reflecting the Sun's light (Figure 9.40).

Comets can sometimes be seen from Earth, passing slowly across the sky over several days. The brightness of a comet depends on two things: how close the comet is to the Sun, which controls the comet's activity, and how close the comet is to Earth. In 1910, when Halley's comet passed Earth, it was very bright and impressive. However, in 1982, it was not as bright. This was because the comet was about three times farther away from Earth than it was in 1910 (Figure 9.41).

Astronomers have been recording the appearance of comets since 2000 BCE. Scientists believe that comets were created from the same nebula that formed the planets.

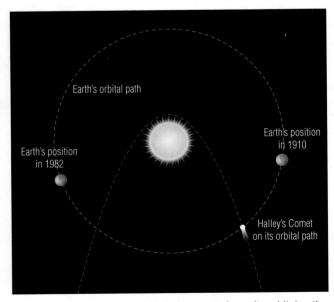

Figure 9.41 This diagram of Halley's comet shows its orbital path. Note that this diagram is not to scale.

These same compounds or molecules are the building blocks of life. Some believe that the ice that surrounds comets plays an important role in the creation of oceans and atmospheres. It is not just the components of comets that astronomers are interested in. Comets and asteroids orbit the Sun just like the planets do. As a comet or asteroid comes close to Earth, there is the possibility that it will fall from orbit and collide with Earth. Astronomers have developed the Torino Scale to help communicate the possibility of such a collision. The scale ranges from 0 to 10, where 0 indicates little or no impact and 10 is a collision that would cause global climatic change. Evidence shows that a comet or asteroid hit Earth 65 million years ago in the Yucatán Peninsula, in Mexico. This impact caused global tidal waves, worldwide firestorms, dust storms, and massive earthquakes. Scientists believe that these events caused the extinction of the majority of species on Earth, which included the dinosaurs.

infoBIT

Halley's Comet

The most famous comet is Halley's comet. Edmond Halley not only discovered the comet, but did the mathematics that predicted that the comet returns every 75 to 76 years.

Meteors and Meteorites

Also visible from Earth are meteors that streak brightly through Earth's atmosphere in seconds. You may have heard of meteors referred to as "shooting stars," although they are not stars. Meteoroids are small pieces of rock or metal that travel throughout the solar system with no fixed path. They are thought to be similar in origin to asteroids and comets. A **meteor** is a meteoroid that, upon entering Earth's atmosphere, collides with gas molecules. The particle becomes wrapped up in heated air, and as a result, the surface material is vaporized. Most meteors are not much bigger than a grain of sand. However, larger meteors may create a fireball brighter than the planet Venus, one of the brightest objects in the night sky. If a meteor does not burn up completely and strikes Earth's surface, it is called a **meteorite** (Figure 9.42).

We can usually see meteors when they are at an altitude of between 80 and 120 km above Earth. Faster particles tend to shine brighter at higher altitudes. Sometimes, these particles will leave a trail behind that lasts for a few seconds to minutes. For the Blackfeet Nation of Montana, a meteor event was an omen. It meant that either a great sickness would affect the tribe that winter or that a great chief had passed away.

Suggested Activity •··········
D12 Quick Science on page 345

Figure 9.42 Pieces of a meteorite were found in west-central Saskatchewan after a meteor lit up the night sky on November 20, 2008. The 10-t meteor exploded in the air and the debris covered a 20-km^2 area.

Figure 9.43 Up to 60 meteors per hour are visible during the Perseid meteor shower.

Under a dark sky, a person can see anywhere from two to seven meteors on any night of the year. A greater than usual number of meteors can be seen during celestial events known as meteor showers. One of the best-known meteor showers is the Perseid meteor shower (Figure 9.43). The Perseid meteor shower begins in mid-July and peaks in the second week of August, when the Saskatchewan night sky is covered by the streaks of these "shooting stars."

9.3 CHECK and REFLECT

1. How are First Nations descriptions of the creation of the solar system reflective of the traditional environment in which these different groups lived?

2. Explain the difference between a planet and a star.

3. Why do scientists use AU and ly for measuring distances? Do they use AU and ly for the same measurements? Explain your answer.

4. Using the nebular theory, explain why the rocky planets would be closer to the Sun than the larger gas giants.

5. Which planets are the inner rocky planets, and which are the gas giants? List them in order, starting with the planet closest to the Sun.

6. Compare and contrast the two scientific theories on the formation of the solar system.

7. What is an asteroid, and why are scientists interested in studying them?

8. Explain why the presence of an asteroid belt around other stars besides the Sun might provide evidence that other Earth-like planets exist.

9. In 2008, Canadian astronomers were the first to capture an image of three planets orbiting a star far from the solar system. Make a sketch to illustrate the accepted theory of how a star-and-planet system such as this formed.

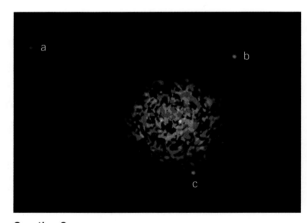

Question 9

10. What is the difference between a dwarf planet and a protoplanet?

11. What affects the brightness of a comet?

12. What is the Oort Cloud and where is it? Why might scientists be interested in studying it?

13. What is the difference between a meteor and a meteorite?

©P

Vance Petriew: Comet Discoverer

It is August 18, 2001, and once again the evening sky shows why Saskatchewan is known as the Land of the Living Skies. For Vance Petriew, it would be a life-changing night. He was attending the Annual Star Party at Cypress Hills Provincial Park when he looked through his telescope and became the first human to discover a comet in the year 2001.

Of the 20 comets that were discovered in 2001, only two were discovered by humans. The rest were discovered by computer-assisted telescopes.

At first, Vance was not sure what he had found, so he asked his friend, Rick Huziak, to take a look. They soon realized that it was a comet. It had a bright nucleus but no tail. The pair took detailed information and made a call to the International Astronomical Union to report their findings.

The next day, they were asked by Dan Green to observe the comet again that evening. Green was having astronomers from North America and Europe also make and record their observations. At this point, Vance was convinced that someone else had discovered the comet before him, but he was able to see the comet for a brief three minutes when the cloud-covered sky opened up.

It was not until Petriew returned to Regina that he learned that indeed, he had discovered a comet. His discovery was actually confirmed by Alan Hale, the co-discoverer of the comet Hale-Bopp. Further observations revealed that the comet has an elliptical orbit that stretches from Earth (0.95 AU) to Jupiter (5.3 AU). The period, or the time it takes the comet to return, is 5.5 years. However, there will be times when the period will be 7 years. This is because the comet is affected by Jupiter's gravitational pull.

What makes this discovery so amazing is that Vance Petriew is an amateur astronomer. Usually, amateur astronomers play important roles in confirming and gathering information about celestial bodies, but not discovering comets (Figure 9.44). Vance has always been interested in astronomy and even taught astronomy labs as a student at the University of Saskatchewan, but he is a computer consultant during the day. According to Petriew, astronomy is one of the last sciences that any person can study in which exciting discoveries can be made without being in a laboratory.

Figure 9.44 An amateur astronomy club in Cypress Hills Provincial Park, Saskatchewan

D9 *Inquiry Activity*   Toolkit 8

SKILLS YOU WILL USE
■ Observing and measuring
■ Recording and organizing data

Calculating Astronomical Distances

Our universe is ever expanding, and so the distances used to describe it are extremely large. Scientists use units, such as light-years (ly) or astronomical units (AU), to make these distances easier to work with.

The light-year is used for describing distances outside our solar system. It can sometimes take millions of years for light to reach Earth. If you consider that light travels 300 million metres per second, how far are these objects that take a million or more light-years for the light to reach us? We know that a light-year is the distance it takes light to travel in one year. Because light travels at a speed of 300 000 km/s, in one year, light will travel 9.46 trillion km. For example, the Milky Way is about 100 000 light-years across (Figure 9.45).

The astronomical unit is used for describing objects within our solar system. An astronomical unit (AU) is the distance between Earth and the Sun. One astronomical unit is equal to approximately 150 000 000 kilometres. For example, Venus is 0.7 AU from the Sun.

Initiating and Planning

How are scientists able to work with such large numbers when dealing with the huge distances between objects in space?

Materials & Equipment

- calculator
- pencil and paper
- ruler

Procedure

1. Copy Table 9.2 on the next page into your notebook.

2. Determine the AU equivalent using equivalents or ratios. 1 AU = 150 000 000 km. Use the data from pages 334–335, look up the AU for each of the planets in our solar system, and determine the distance in kilometres.

   For example, Mercury:

   $$\frac{1 \text{ AU}}{150\ 000\ 000 \text{ km}} = \frac{0.4 \text{ AU}}{x \text{ km}}$$

   Cross multiply:

   1 AU (x km) = (0.4 AU)(150 000 000 km)

   or 1 AU (x km) = 60 000 000 km AU

   Isolate the unknown, in this case, divide:

   $$\frac{60\ 000\ 000 \text{ km AU}}{1 \text{ AU}} = x \text{ km}$$

   The unknown distance is 60 000 000 km.

3. Repeat this calculation for the other solar system planets. Record your results in your table.

4. Determine the time it takes light to travel from the Sun to each of the planets using the light equivalent. Because the distance between the Sun and the planets is relatively small compared to universe distances, use the ratio 300 000 km = 1 s.

   Again, use Mercury as an example. The distance from the Sun to Mercury calculated in step 1 is 60 000 000 km.

   $$\frac{300\ 000 \text{ km}}{1 \text{ s}} = \frac{60\ 000\ 000 \text{ km}}{x \text{ s}}$$

   Just as in step 1, cross multiply:

   300 000 km (x s) = 60 000 000 km (1 s)

   and then isolate the unknown

   $$(x \text{ s}) = \frac{60\ 000\ 000 \text{ km s}}{300\ 000 \text{ km}} = 200 \text{ s, or } \frac{200 \text{ s}}{60}$$

   s/min = 3.33 min

5. Repeat this calculation for the other planets and record your results in your table.

Analyzing and Interpreting

6. In your opinion, is it easier to use astronomical units (AU) or kilometres when discussing the distance between planets? Support your answer.

7. Examine the time it takes light to travel from the Sun to the outer planets. What can you deduce about the temperature of those outer planets from this information?

8. Think about this activity. How could you explain why there is a delay when receiving information from probes that explore the solar system or even from the equipment that explores Mars, one of our closest neighbours?

9. Imagine that you are an astronomer who is observing a probe sent to Jupiter. As the probe approaches Jupiter, you notice that it is 30 min from crashing into the planet's surface. Based on your calculations, can you save the probe if you immediately send a signal telling it to turn on its rockets and veer away from the planet? Assume that Earth and Jupiter are aligned on the same side of the Sun.

Communication and Teamwork

10. Create a poster or model of our solar system, but use astronomical units (AU) or the time needed for light to travel to the planets as a base for your scale.

Figure 9.45 The Milky Way galaxy is about 100 000 light-years across.

Table 9.2

Planet Name	Distance from Sun (in millions of kilometres)	AU Equivalent (in astronomical units)	Time Needed for Light to Travel from the Sun
Mercury	60	0.4	200 s or 3.33 min
Venus		0.7	
Earth		1	
Mars		1.5	
Jupiter		5.3	
Saturn		9.5	
Uranus		19.0	
Neptune		30.0	

A Model of the Solar System

Understanding relative size and distance on the scale of the solar system is a difficult task. Models are helpful tools for scientists to show comparisons between objects. In this activity, you will create a model or a graphic representation of the solar system with correct scales for planet and Sun diameters and distance of planets from the Sun.

Question

How can you model the scales for planet diameter and distance from the Sun?

Design and Conduct Your Investigation

Part 1 — Planet and Sun Diameters

1. Working in a small group, brainstorm ways that you can model planet size. As you consider and discuss your options, think about:

   - What materials or equipment will you need for your model?

   - Are the materials or equipment readily available in the sizes and quantity you will need?

   - How big will your model need to be? You may wish to review the data from pages 334–335 to determine a scale for relative planet size (diameter). You may also need to conduct research for any missing information you will need.

   - What other elements do you need to include?

3. Select a design and write a procedure to build your models. Include a list of materials and equipment you will need.

4. Ask your teacher to approve your designs before beginning construction.

5. Build your models according to your design. Make sure to document any changes you make to the procedure or the materials and equipment list.

Part 2 — Planet Distances from the Sun

6. Working in your groups, discuss ways to model distances of planets from the Sun. Consider:

   - What model type would be an appropriate choice to show relative distances?

   - How much room will you need for your model? Refer to the data on pages 334–335 and do additional research as required.

   - What materials or equipment do you need for your model?

   - What else should you include?

7. Complete steps 3 to 5 for your model on relative distance.

Part 3 — Combining Relative Size and Relative Distance into One Model

8. In your groups or as a class, review your models for relative planet and Sun size and relative distance.

9. Brainstorm ways that the two models could be combined to effectively show an accurate scale model of our solar system.

©P

Math Scaling

A mathematical scale is a ratio between units of measure. Scales are used to show something in larger or smaller form, but in the same proportions as the original. For example, to map your neighbourhood, you would have to create a scale to show the relative distances between streets and buildings accurately. You might set your scale at 1 cm = 50 m or 1 cm = 200 m.

Imagine you are building a scale model to show the distance from Earth to the Oort Cloud, 50 000 AU from the Sun. Earth is 1 AU from the Sun, and the model you want to make places Earth at 1 m. Where would you need to place the Oort Cloud in your model? You would need to determine the model distance x to represent 50 000 AU.

1. Write an equation that compares the real distances on the left side with the model scale distances on the right side.

$$\frac{50\ 000\ AU}{1\ AU} = \frac{x}{1\ m}$$

2. Simplify the left side by cancelling the units and doing the division.

$$50\ 000 = \frac{x}{1\ m}$$

3. Multiply both sides by 1 m.

$$50\ 000 \times 1\ m = x$$
$$50\ 000 = x$$

The model scale distance of the Oort Cloud is 50 000 m, or 50 km.

Solve the following scale distances (x):

4. The distance from your home to a store is 2 km. The scale distance is 10 cm. The distance from your home to a library is 3 km. What is the scale distance to the library?

5. The distance from the Sun to Earth is 1 AU and from the Sun to Jupiter is 5.2 AU. The scale distance from the Sun to Earth is 8 cm. What is the scale distance to Jupiter from the Sun?

6. Think about the example of the Oort Cloud and Earth. Our original calculation had us making a model that was 50 km in size. How could you make a model that might fit inside your school, or even your classroom? Support your answer, using math scaling calculations.

The Differences between Asteroids, Comets, Dwarf Planets, and Meteors

There are many similarities among asteroids, comets, dwarf planets, and meteors. Each of these celestial objects also has its own characteristics.

Purpose

To examine the similarities and differences among asteroids, comets, dwarf planets, and meteors.

Procedure

1. Create a Venn diagram using four circles. Label the circles Asteroids, Comets, Dwarf Planets, and Meteors.

2. Use this chapter and research in the library or on the Internet to complete your Venn diagram.

Questions

3. What do asteroids, comets, dwarf planets, and meteors have in common?

4. What is/are unique characteristics of each of these astronomical bodies?

5. Why are scientists so interested in studying these objects?

Pose New Questions

6. The Chinese have been observing comets for centuries. What would you like to find out about observations made in the past?

Key Concept Review

1. How was the observation of the sky important to the survival of the First Nations and Métis peoples?

2. Are the constellations the same when viewed from all locations on Earth and at all times? Explain your answer.

3. What is the difference between a celestial body and an astronomical body?

4. What is the relationship between an equinox and a solstice?

5. How do scientists use the terms declination, right ascension, altitude, and azimuth?

6. What is the difference between the revolution and the rotation of a planet?

7. Describe what is meant when we say that the Moon is a satellite.

8. (a) What causes the changing phases of the Moon?
   (b) How many main phases of the Moon are there?

9. What are the causes of eclipses?

10. Name the process occurring in the core of the Sun that gives it its ability to shine.

11. Solar prominences are huge arcs and often form complete loops on the surface of the Sun. Explain why.

12. What is the solar system?

13. Briefly explain what an astronomical unit and a light-year are, and how these units of measure are used.

14. How have scientific astronomers used asteroids to estimate the age of the solar system?

15. What are dwarf planets? How are they different from protoplanets?

16. Why are comets of such interest to astronomers?

17. Compare and contrast meteors and meteorites.

Connect Your Understanding

18. Why might constellations vary with different cultures?

19. Is the scientific understanding of constellations and asterisms in the sky and on star charts misleading? Explain.

20. First Nations and Métis peoples used observations of the natural world around them as a way to know the changing of the seasons. How did they use the sky as a way to indicate the change in seasons?

21. Your friend claims that summer occurs because Earth moves closer to the Sun. Is your friend correct? Explain why and make a sketch to illustrate your answer.

22. Earth has several other kinds of motion besides rotation and revolution. Like the axis of a spinning top changing the direction in which it points, Earth's axis of rotation slowly changes direction, though the axis will still be tilted at 23.5°. This motion is called precession. Research precession, including how long one complete cycle takes and where Earth's axis points now and where it will point later. Present your findings in the format of your choice.

23. What are some positive and negative effects that the Sun can have on Earth?

24. All cultures respect the importance of the Sun to life on Earth. With advances in technologies, humans have learned much more about how the Sun affects Earth. Discuss the variety of ways the Sun affects life on Earth.

25. Many First Nations people respect the aurora borealis. Explain their reason for doing this. How might this respect be linked to their survival?

26. Briefly name and describe the two theories on the formation of the solar system discussed in this chapter. Compare their similarities and differences.

27. How does the distance from the Sun directly affect the composition of the planets in the solar system?

28. The four gaseous outer planets are by far the largest planets in the solar system. What might be one explanation for how they grew to be much larger than the four rocky inner planets?

29. Suppose a gaseous planet half the size of Saturn were discovered. Where in the solar system do you think it would be located? Give a reason for your answer.

30. When an asteroid strikes Earth, it can cause great damage. A pair of asteroids simultaneously crashed into the Canadian Shield on the east side of Hudson Bay about 290 million years ago as shown in the image below. Suggest how it might have happened that the two asteroids crashed at the same time.

Question 30

31. The star Aldebaran, visible from Earth, lies about 65 ly away from us. What is the minimum amount of time that would be required to send a message to Aldebaran and receive a reply (assuming someone was there to receive the message and respond)?

Reflection

32. This chapter focused on the solar system and Earth's place in it. We have learned much about our solar system with improved technologies over time. Do you think that people should continue exploring our own solar system or should they now be focusing their attention beyond our solar system? Explain your thoughts on this.

After Reading

Reflect and Evaluate

How did making connections to your prior knowledge about space and the universe help you to understand new ideas and information? On your mind map, highlight at least five connections between your "old" knowledge and the "new" knowledge that you learned in this unit. Share these connections with a partner.

Reflection on Essential Inquiry Questions

How has our understanding of the relationships among the celestial bodies of our solar system changed? **SI**

How have stars guided exploration? **TPS**

How does an understanding of the relationships of celestial bodies help people on Earth? **DM**

How do different cultures explain and use the stars? Did their explanations of the stars and the phenomena related to stars guide their explorations? **CP**

Unit Task

In this chapter, you have learned about not only what is in our solar system, but also possible ways it was formed. These formation theories could also apply to other systems in our galaxy. It is possible that many of the celestial bodies in our solar system could be found elsewhere. Brainstorm some ways that you could apply this knowledge to your Unit Task.

10

Stars are an important component of galaxies.

Outcomes

By the end of this chapter, you will:

- examine how various cultures, past and present, including First Nations and Métis, understand and represent astronomical phenomena

- inquire into the motion and characteristics of astronomical bodies in our solar system and the universe

- analyze scientific explanations of the formation and evolution of our solar system and the universe

What you will learn:

- Early cultures and civilizations recorded observations of star life stages and explanations of the universe.

- The formation and life cycles of stars, including the Sun, help us understand the formation of not only the solar system, but galaxies as well.

- Different types of stars are classified according to mass and life cycle.

- Galaxies have specific shapes and contain star clusters, black holes, and dark matter.

A collision between two spiral galaxies NGC 6050 and IC 1179 in the Hercules constellation

Before Reading

Determining Importance

When information seems far beyond your experiences, you must determine its importance to you. Skim the bulleted items on this page and the next. Then, write two statements about how the solar system and the formation of stars are important to you.

Key Terms

- binary system • black hole
- dark matter • galaxy
- magnitude • protostar
- quasars • supernova
- universe

©P

Figure 10.1 This 14th century illuminated manuscript shows an astronomer using a sighting tube, a precursor to the telescope, used to sight Polaris to aid in telling time.

Here is a summary of what you will learn in this section:

- First Nations and Métis understandings explain the origins of the universe and astronomical phenomena such as the Milky Way and supernovas.

- A star forms inside a nebula as gravitational forces pull dust and gas together, creating a spinning, contracting disk of material in which nuclear fusion begins. Stars are classified according to their colour, luminosity, and temperature.

- Stars have life cycles during which they form and then evolve in one of three main ways.

Looking Back in Time

Every major culture has astronomers, people who investigate the universe and the objects in it. The **universe** refers to everything that physically exists—the entirety of space and time, and all forms of matter and energy. Long ago, astronomers had only three aids to help them understand the wonders of the universe: sharp eyesight, their current understanding, and an ability to make detailed observations (Figure 10.1). Today, highly powerful and sensitive instruments allow astronomers to peer farther and farther into the universe and to gather information about the celestial bodies and phenomena in it. Supercomputers can analyze the incoming data from 100 000 stars at the same time.

When astronomers observe a faraway astronomical body, the distance they are looking across is so vast that they are really looking back in time. Light takes time to travel. When you look at your hand, for example, you see it not as it is, but as it was a few billionths of a second ago. At short distances, this delay is insignificant. However, when you are looking far into space, the delays begin to add up. For example, it takes about 1.5 s for the light from the Moon to reach Earth. Therefore, we always see the Moon as it was 1.5 s ago. The planet Jupiter, farther from Earth than the Moon is, appears to us as it did 45 min before.

Figure 10.2 The Andromeda galaxy. In 3 billion years, our descendants will see a galaxy rise in addition to a sunrise when Andromeda eventually collides with the Milky Way.

All the thousands of distant twinkling stars we can see from Earth even without a telescope are part of the galaxy we live in, the Milky Way. A **galaxy** is a collection of hundreds of billions of stars that are held together by gravitational forces (Figure 10.2). The distance from the Milky Way to the other galaxies is extremely great. Scientists have also found that, with a few exceptions, all galaxies are moving farther away from ours and from each other. These are incredible thoughts, yet scientific evidence supports them and many other intriguing conclusions about the nature of our universe.

D13 *Quick Science*

A Map of the Universe

The universe is so large that it can be difficult to comprehend all the astronomical bodies and their relationships to each other. A map can help you visually show objects' relationships to each other and their relative positions in space.

Purpose

To list all the objects you know that exist in the universe and show their relationships to each other by arranging them on a map

Materials & Equipment

- poster paper or newsprint
- felt pens

Procedure

1. Working in pairs or a small group, brainstorm a list of all the different kinds of astronomical bodies you know about.

2. Copy the labels shown in Figure 10.3 onto the sheet of poster paper.

3. Arrange the objects from your list in the order you might encounter them on a trip that begins at Earth and continues to the most distant reaches of the universe (or as far out as you

know about). If you know the shape of each object or a symbol to represent it, draw that. Do not concern yourself with trying to make your map to scale. Label each object.

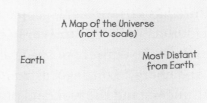

Figure 10.3 Step 2

4. Post your map on a wall in the classroom.

Questions

5. Compare your map with that of other groups. How do they differ? How are they similar?

Pose New Questions

6. What new objects did you learn about during this activity?

7. Compose a question about an object that is new to you, or one you find interesting, that you want to have answered by the end of this chapter.

8. What challenges are there in using a piece of paper to map space?

©P

More than a Ball of Plasma

Stars are hot balls of plasma that shine because nuclear reactions are taking place at their core. When stars die, they explode and blow most or all of their matter into space. Some of that matter comes together in a way that makes a solar system. This means that the atoms in every human being today came from earlier stars that once existed in our part of the Milky Way. You are made of atoms that are very, very old.

Elders also tell about the stars in the night sky. Some First Nations and Métis creation stories talk about human spirits coming from the stars, and when a human dies their spirit returns to the night sky as a new star. The idea that humans come from the stars is shared by many scientists and some Elders, although the details differ.

Another First Nations and Métis idea is that we are all related to everything in Mother Earth. This idea has new meaning when we think about the scientific idea that our Earth and everything on it comes from the same earlier star in the Milky Way—we are all related to an early star by sharing the particles produced in that star.

Measuring a Star's Brightness

It is easy to think that all the stars forming a constellation or asterism lie at the same distance from Earth, as though drawn on a celestial sphere. In fact, the stars in a constellation vary greatly in their distances from Earth, with some being many times farther away than others. They only appear to be twinkling from a flat surface because they are of similar brightness.

The brightness of a star is known as its **magnitude**. Some of the brightest stars in the night sky will have a magnitude of -1, and as the numbers get larger, the stars are less bright (Figure 10.4). A star with a magnitude of 0 will be brighter than a star with a magnitude of 1.

This system was created by ancient Greek astronomers Hipparchus and Ptolemy. They divided the stars they could see into six magnitudes, but as technology changed, so did the divisions of magnitude. The Hubble Space Telescope can detect stars as faint as 30 magnitude! The use of magnitude allows astronomers to determine how far away a star is and the current stage of its life cycle.

Figure 10.4 This time-lapse image shows supergiant Polaris, the North Star. It is more massive than the Sun and 1000 times brighter.

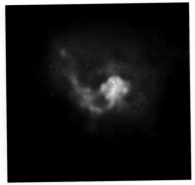

Figure 10.5 The Centauri system. Proxima Centauri, Earth's nearest star after the Sun, is part of this system.

Other than our Sun, the nearest star to Earth is Proxima Centauri. It is part of a group of three stars that orbit each other, called the Centauri system (Figure 10.5), located about 4.3 ly away from our solar system. Although Proxima Centauri is the closest star to Earth after the Sun, it isn't the brightest star we can see at night. The brightest star visible from Earth is Sirius, even though it is nearly twice as far from us as the Centauri system. Sirius is brighter because it is a different kind of star than the Centauri stars.

Binary Star Systems

The Centauri system, aside from being our closest star neighbour, is interesting in another way. It is a multiple star system. Well over half of the star systems that astronomers have observed have two or more stars. A system with two stars is called a **binary system** (Figure 10.6). (Centauri is a trinary system because it has three stars.) If the stars are close enough together, it might be possible for planets like ours to orbit all the way around both or all of them. Some astronomers suggest that Earth-like planets orbiting around tightly bound binary stars might be more common than our one-star system.

Figure 10.6 Albireo is an example of a binary star system. When viewed by the unaided eye, Albireo looks like a single star. A telescope shows that it is really made up of two stars.

How a Star Is Born

Compared with the life span of humans, the life span of stars is extremely long. All stars form from the dust and gases inside a collapsing nebula (Figure 10.7). A nebula's collapse can be triggered by a disturbance such as the gravitational attraction of a nearby star or the shockwave from an exploding star.

Figure 10.7 Stars are "born" in nebulae, such as the Eagle nebula shown here, with its aptly named Pillars of Creation region (inset).

Inside a collapsing nebula, the region with the greatest amount of matter will start to draw material toward it through gravitational forces. This is where the star will form (Figure 10.8 (a)). Material falling inward to the core has excess energy. This energy causes the central ball of material to begin to spin (Figure 10.8 (b)). Extremely high pressures build up inside the ball, which in turn causes the tightly packed atoms to heat up. As the temperature climbs, the core begins to glow. This is a protostar (Figure 10.8 (c)). A **protostar** is a star in its first stage of formation.

Eventually, the temperature of the spinning protostar rises to millions of degrees Celsius. This is hot enough to start nuclear fusion reactions, in which the hydrogen nuclei combine to form helium. Over tens of thousands of years, the energy from the core gradually reaches the outside of the star. When that occurs, the fully formed star "switches on" and begins to shine.

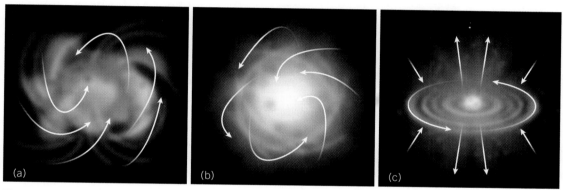

Figure 10.8 (a) As a region of a nebula collapses in on itself, gravitational forces start pulling dust and gas together into small masses. (b) As a mass grows, it begins a cycle of heating up, spinning, contracting (pulling inward), heating, and so on. (c) The result of this process is a protostar.

The Life Cycle of Stars

A century ago, astronomers could tell that many different kinds of stars existed. What they had not yet discovered was that stars have a predictable life cycle just like all living things do.

How a star evolves in its lifetime depends on the mass it had when it originally formed. Astronomers describe stars in three general mass categories: low, medium, and high. Low mass stars burn more slowly than high mass stars, so their life span is longer and their temperatures are cooler. Red dwarf stars, such as Gliese 581, are low mass stars. They emit dim, reddish light. Conversely, high mass stars burn hotter, brighter, and bluer than low mass stars. Supergiant stars, such as Polaris and Betelgeuse, are examples of high mass stars. Medium mass stars are in between. Our Sun is an example of a medium mass star.

Suggested Activity • • • • • • • • • •
D14 Problem-Solving Activity
on page 359

Life Cycle Comparison of Different Star Masses

A low mass star advances through different phases than a high mass star does. Look at Figure 10.9 and Table 10.1 to examine how the mass of a star affects its life cycle.

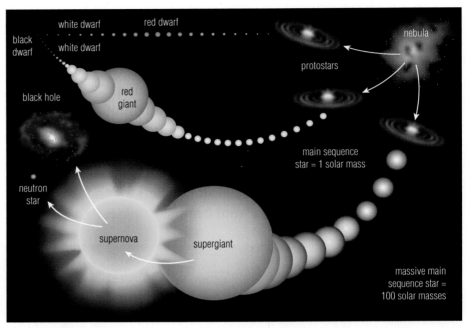

Figure 10.9 The three main life cycles of stars. What cycle a star goes through is determined by what mass the star first develops after its formation in a nebula.

Table 10.1

Star Mass	Example	Life Span (years)	After the Hydrogen Runs Out	Becomes . . .
low	Gliese 581	100 billion	collapses and cools	white dwarf
medium	Sun	10 billion	collapses, but the collapse causes the temperature and pressure to increase enough to start nuclear fusion again, this time using helium as fuel. Once the helium runs out, the new star collapses and burns out.	red giant
high	Betelgeuse	< 7 billion	similar to a medium mass star, but it goes through many cycles of collapse, and nuclear fusion re-starts. Eventually, new elements, such as iron, are formed in its core.	supergiant

Figure 10.10 The stars in this binary system differ in colour, luminosity (brightness), and surface temperature.

Learning Checkpoint

1. Using diagrams, describe the process of the "birth" of a star from collapsing nebula to when it begins to shine.

2. Betelgeuse has a magnitude of −7.2. Sirius has a magnitude of +1.4. Explain which star is brighter.

Classifying Stars

As the life cycle of stars shows, there are many types of stars. Some differences among them include what colour they are, how bright (or luminous) they are, and even what their surface temperature is (Figure 10.10).

The Hertzsprung-Russell Diagram

In 1919, two astronomers, Ejnar Hertzsprung and Henry Norris Russell, sorted and plotted thousands of stars according to three characteristics: colour, luminosity, and surface temperature. They wanted to find out whether any patterns might emerge that would tell us more about the nature of stars.

The plotted data revealed that very clear relationships existed among star properties. Figure 10.11 shows a version of what is called the Hertzsprung-Russell diagram. In it, the stars are arranged as follows:

- by colour — Red stars are plotted on the right, and blue stars are plotted on the left. Other stars, such as the yellow Sun, are plotted in between.

- by luminosity — The brightest stars are plotted at the top, and the dimmest stars are plotted at the bottom. A star with a luminosity of 100 is 100 times brighter than the Sun.

- by surface temperature — The hottest stars are plotted on the left, and the coolest stars are plotted on the right.

Suggested Activity •···········
D15 Inquiry Activity on page 360

During Reading

Comparing Important Ideas

As you read about the life cycle of stars, create a table to compare the different types. Note the types of stars, their names, examples, and two important facts about each type. Which type of star has the longest life? Which type always comes to a violent end?

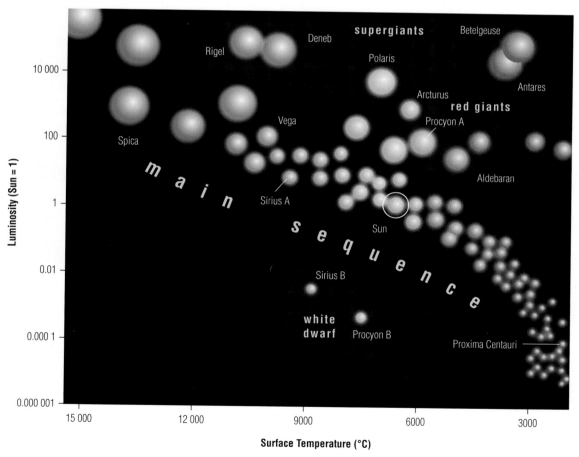

Figure 10.11 The Hertzsprung-Russell diagram represents thousands of stars based on colour, luminosity (brightness), and surface temperature.

The Hertzsprung-Russell diagram shows many patterns based on the three properties of colour, luminosity, and surface temperature. For example, the star data forms a distinct band that stretches from the top left of the diagram to the bottom right. This is called the main sequence. The Sun is a main sequence star. These stars are thought to be in the stable main part of their life cycle. They have evolved to this stage since formation, but will gradually either cool and die out or expand before exploding.

Groups of stars that do not appear along the main sequence are often near the end of their lives. At the bottom centre of the diagram are white dwarfs, such as the star Procyon B. They are white because they are hot, but dim because they are small. White dwarfs are cooling and will eventually become black dwarfs. At the top right of the diagram are red giants, such as Aldebaran, and super-giants, such as Betelgeuse (Figure 10.12) and Antares. The outer layers of these stars are cool and appear red, but they are bright because they are so large. All of these giants will eventually explode.

Figure 10.12 Betelgeuse is a red supergiant. It is so huge that if it were in the solar system where the Sun is, it would reach nearly all the way to Jupiter's orbit.

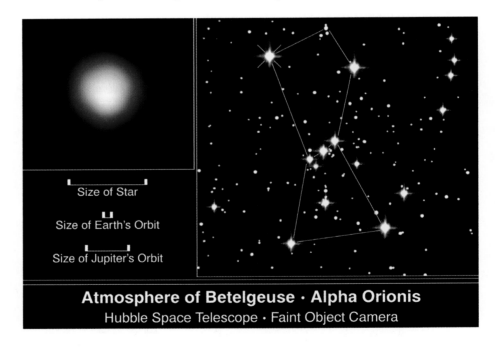

Size of Star
Size of Earth's Orbit
Size of Jupiter's Orbit

Atmosphere of Betelgeuse · Alpha Orionis
Hubble Space Telescope · Faint Object Camera

Supernovas: The Violent End of High Mass Stars

A star might exist for millions or even billions of years before it goes supernova. A **supernova** occurs when a high mass star explodes. The explosion releases huge amounts of energy, some of which is visible as bright light. This light fades over time. When a supernova occurs, the explosion forms the heavier elements, such as iron and nitrogen. These heavier elements create not only the celestial bodies, but life itself. Humans and other animals need iron to make blood cells, and Earth's soil needs nitrogen to support plant life.

©P

The amount of heavier elements in a star's core will affect how long a supernova will produce light. For example, the fusion of iron does not release energy. If too much of the core of a star is made up of iron, the star—which may have been shining continuously for more than 7 billion years—will "turn off" in minutes. With no fuel left, the star collapses one final time. This collapse is so fast and intense that the core of the star heats up to many hundreds of millions of degrees and explodes (Figure 10.13).

(a)

(b)

Figure 10.13 In 1987, Canadian astronomer Ian Shelton photographed the explosion of the brightest supernova seen by anyone since the invention of telescopes. The images here show supernova 1987A before the explosion (a) and after (b).

The blast is directed both outward and inward. The outward blast sends these heavy elements far out into space. Some of the debris and elements from the old star create new nebulae. Nebulae are often called star nurseries because stars develop from their dust and gas.

The inward blast causes the atoms in the star's core to compress and collapse. The remaining core after a supernova explosion faces one of two outcomes:

- *Neutron stars* — A star 10 to 40 times the Sun's mass will become a neutron star. The compression and collapse of the core forms neutrons, particles that are at the centre of most atoms. When the star's core becomes little more than a ball of neutrons about 15 km across, it is called a neutron star. Neutron stars are made of the densest material known (Figure 10.14).

- *Black holes* — A star greater than 40 times the mass of the Sun will become a black hole. A **black hole** is a region of space where gravitational forces are so strong that nothing, not even light, can escape. After exploding as a supernova, the star's core is under so much gravitational force that nothing can stop its collapse, not even the formation of neutrons. In this case, the effect of gravitational forces is so great that all nearby matter and energy, including light, start to fall into a single point and form a black hole.

Figure 10.14 A neutron star. Imagine Mosaic Stadium, Regina, being filled with steel and then the steel being compressed to fit inside a 20-L fish tank. That represents the density of the matter in a typical neutron star.

Figure 10.15 These petroglyphs (rock drawings) on the walls of Chaco Canyon in Arizona record the supernova event that created the Crab Nebula.

In 1054, Chinese and Arab astronomers recorded a celestial event four times brighter than Venus that lasted 23 days. In the southwestern United States, observations of this supernova were recorded by the Anasazi people. They illustrated this celestial event in petroglyphs in Chaco Canyon (Figure 10.15). The remnants of this supernova now form one of the best-known nebulas, the Crab Nebula (Figure 10.16).

Figure 10.16 The Crab Nebula (M1), in the Taurus galaxy, is one of the best-known remnants of a supernova.

10.1 CHECK and REFLECT

1. In your own words, define the words *universe* and *galaxy*. What relationship exists between the two?

2. Astronomer Carl Sagan once said: "We are star stuff." In your own words, explain what he may have meant by this statement.

3. What do scientists mean when they discuss the magnitude of a star?

4. What would be known about two stars, one with a magnitude of 2 and the other with a magnitude of 4?

5. Why are astronomers interested in studying binary star systems?

6. What is a protostar?

7. What process must occur inside a forming star before it begins to shine?

8. Explain how the colour of a star is related to its
   (a) luminosity
   (b) surface temperature

9. How are stars classified according to the Hertzsprung-Russell diagram?

10. Explain the important concept about stars revealed by the Hertzsprung-Russell diagram.

11. What is a supernova? Why might astronomers be interested in this astronomical event?

12. Design your own star. In your design, provide details about your star's colour, mass, and life cycle. Include diagrams in your explanation.

©P

SKILLS YOU WILL USE
■ Making technical drawings
■ Carrying out a plan

Life Cycle of a Star

In some ways, a star is like a living thing. It is "born" and eventually—and often dramatically—"dies." This process takes millions of years to complete, so scientists can never observe the entire process in their lifetimes. When objects are extremely large or processes take huge amounts of time, scientists use models to try to understand what is happening.

In this activity, you will create a model of the life cycle of a star. To be able to observe this process, the model you will create will be a flipbook. A flipbook is a simple animation technique. Pictures are drawn that show small, yet important, changes. When these pictures are placed in order and "flipped" through, it will appear as though the process is actually happening. Using a flipbook approach, you will be animating the life cycle of a star.

Initiating and Planning

How can we model the life cycle of a star?

Materials & Equipment
- 15–20 (7.62 cm × 12.7 cm or 3" × 5") unlined recipe cards
- crayons, markers, or coloured pencils
- heavy-duty stapler

Performing and Recording

1. Choose a type of star and plan the illustrations you will need to illustrate its life cycle. You may wish to do quick thumbnail sketches on a separate piece of paper. Remember, in a flipbook, the picture you draw is only slightly different from the previous picture and the picture that follows.

2. Once you have your plan in place, draw your pictures on separate recipe cards (Figure 10.17).

3. As you complete each drawing, place your pictures in order and flip through them to ensure the book is coming together the way you planned. Revise your plans as required.

4. When you are confident your flipbook is complete, place your pictures in order and staple them together. Be sure to place the staple(s) only near one edge. You must be able to flip through your book.

5. Exchange flipbooks with a classmate. Use his or her flipbook to answer the questions below.

Analyzing and Interpreting

6. What are the characteristics of a star?

7. What is the relationship between the age of a star and its mass?

8. How is the temperature of a star related to the colour of that star?

9. When the temperature of a star decreases, then its gas pressure also decreases. Gravitational forces are then stronger than the gas pressure. This makes the star unstable. As you look at the flipbook, what can you infer will happen next?

10. What do you think, based on your flipbook observations, will occur at the end of the star's life cycle?

Communicate

11. How is the flipbook a good model of the life cycle of a star? Why is it not a perfect model?

12. How could you make the flipbook a better model? Is there a better way to model the information?

Figure 10.17 Step 2

Using a Hertzsprung-Russell Diagram

To make a Hertzsprung-Russell (HR) diagram, you must use the luminosity and temperature of stars.

Astronomers use a scale called absolute magnitude to measure the luminosity, or brightness, of a star. The brighter a star appears, the lower the absolute magnitude.

To determine the temperature of a star, astronomers use a telescope with two different filters, blue (b) and yellow (v). The filters block out all light except for the blue and yellow. Astronomers then subtract the yellow magnitude (v) from the blue magnitude (b) to produce a value known as the b-v colour. Stars with higher b-v colour have lower temperatures.

Initiating and Planning

How do luminosity (absolute magnitude) and temperature (b-v) relate to a star's life cycle?

Materials & Equipment
- pencil
- graph paper
- three different coloured markers

Performing and Recording

1. An HR diagram is similar to a traditional graph. Examine Table 10.2. On the sheet of graph paper, plot the luminosity, or absolute magnitude, of the stars on the y-axis.

2. Plot the temperature, or b-v colour, on the x-axis.

3. Using different coloured markers, circle any groups or patterns of stars.

4. Compare your graph with the HR diagram on page 355. Create a chart to identify which stars are supergiants, red giants, main sequence stars or dwarfs, and white dwarfs.

Analyzing and Interpreting

5. How do giants differ from the dwarf stars in the main sequence? Why do you think these stars are different?

Table 10.2

Star Name	Absolute Magnitude	b-v Colour
Sun	4.8	0.63
Sirius	1.4	0
Canopus	−2.5	0.15
Arcturus	0.2	1.23
Alpha Centauri	4.4	0.71
Vega	0.6	0
Capella	0.4	0.08
Rigel	−8.1	−0.03
Procyon	2.6	0.42
Betelgeuse	−7.2	1.85
Achernar	−1.3	−0.16
Hadar	−4.4	−0.23
Acrux	−4.6	0.24
Altair	2.3	0.22
Deneb	−7.2	0.09
Regulus	−0.3	−0.11
Castor	0.5	0.03
Spica	−3.2	−0.23
Becrux	−4.7	−0.23
Adhara	−4.8	−0.21
Pollux	0.7	1.0

6. Compare our Sun to the other stars on the diagram. How does its luminosity and colour compare to the average star on the diagram?

7. How are supergiants, red giants, and white dwarfs different from and similar to each other? Create a Venn diagram to show your answer.

8. Is your HR diagram an accurate representation of the majority of stars? Explain.

Communication and Teamwork

9. Brainstorm another way you could present the information you found from the graph analysis. Present your information to the class.

©P

Figure 10.18 Spiral galaxy M81

Here is a summary of what you will learn in this section:

- Galaxies, which have four types of shapes, contain about 200 billion stars each and usually have a supermassive black hole in the centre.

- Galaxies contain star clusters and black holes.

- Quasars, which are the brightest objects in the universe, are created by energy being fed into black holes.

- Dark matter makes up 90 percent of matter in the universe.

Neighbours in the Universe

As you learned earlier, a galaxy is a system of stars, dust, and gas held together by gravitational forces. Galaxies with more dust tend to produce more new stars, because stars form from dust and gases present in nebulae. Some galaxies, thought to be very ancient, have almost no dust because it has been used up in star-making.

The farthest galaxies we can see may also be the oldest, because the light has taken so long to reach us. Astronomers think that the stars of these galaxies were possibly larger than the largest stars that exist today. If that were the case, then those stars had short, hot lives, usually ending in supernova explosions. Gravitational forces pulled the material together again, repeating the cycle of star formation, explosion, and spreading of new elements into space.

Galaxies are commonly classified according to their shape: spiral, barred spiral, elliptical, or irregular.

Spiral and Barred Spiral Galaxies

Spiral galaxies are named for the spiral-shaped arms that radiate out from the galaxy's centre (Figure 10.18). About half of all spiral galaxies, including the Milky Way, have what appears to be a bar across them (Figure 10.19). These are called barred spiral galaxies.

Figure 10.19 The barred spiral galaxy known as NGC 1300

Figure 10.20 The giant elliptical galaxy ESO 325-G004

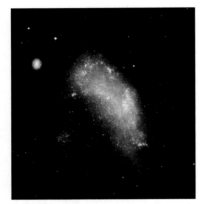

Figure 10.21 The irregular galaxy NGC 1427A

A wave moving outward from the central regions of the galaxy causes the gas and dust to compress into arm-like bands that rotate around the central hub. A typical spiral galaxy completes a full rotation about once every 300 million years. New arms continually form as older ones disappear or change shape. Gravitational forces keep the spirals from flying apart.

Elliptical Galaxies

Elliptical galaxies have shapes ranging from almost spherical to football-shaped (Figure 10.20), or long and cylindrical, like a pencil. Such galaxies are thought to result when two or more galaxies, such as spiral galaxies, merge. The largest galaxies in the universe are elliptical.

Elliptical galaxies contain very little dust. This means they have fewer young stars than spiral galaxies do. Many of the stars in elliptical galaxies are extremely old.

Irregular Galaxies

Galaxies without a regular shape are called irregular galaxies (Figure 10.21). The distorted form of an irregular galaxy may be because the galaxy collided with another one or got close enough to another galaxy so that its gravitational forces drew stars away.

D16 *Quick Science*

Hunting for Galaxies in the Hubble Ultra Deep Field

The Hubble Ultra Deep Field image reveals several thousand galaxies. In this activity, you will become more familiar with the variety of galaxy shapes that occur.

Purpose

To identify and classify galaxies

Materials & Equipment
• image of the Hubble Ultra Deep Field
• handout showing galaxies of different shapes

Procedure

1. Study the image of the Hubble Ultra Deep Field. Use the handout to help you identify as many kinds of galaxies as you can. Count and record the number of each type.

2. Some galaxies will appear as a tiny dot, too difficult to classify. Count as many of those as you can and record them as unclassified.

Questions

3. Calculate the percentage of each type of galaxy you identified, including unclassified galaxies.

4. Based on your results, which type of galaxy is the most common? Which kind is the least common?

5. Suggest why some galaxies were large enough for you to classify, while others were too small.

Pose New Questions

6. What other information would you like to learn about galaxies? How could you answer your questions?

©P

Our Galaxy: The Milky Way

Often, we can look up into the night sky and see so many stars that they are blurred together and look like spilled milk, thus giving our galaxy its name (Figure 10.22). This view of the Milky Way is the result of the billions of stars that lie along a fairly flat disk of stars revolving around the centre of the galaxy. The dark smudgy line along the band is dust. This dust obscures our view into the centre of the galaxy. However, we are able to view stars at the very centre of our galaxy by using telescopes that detect infrared light (heat) rather than visible light, because infrared light is not blocked by the space dust.

Figure 10.22
The Milky Way

The Milky Way is often called the Spirit Road by many First Nations and Métis peoples of Saskatchewan. The stars are understood to be the spirits of ancestors that have passed on. The Cree people call the Milky Way *cīpay-mēskanaw*—the ghost, spirit, or skeleton road. They understand that this swath of stars is a path that spirits follow to the next world. In Cree, the word *ahcāhk* or spirit is used synonymously with the word for star. The Lakota view the Milky Way as a pathway to *Wanaghiyata*, the promised home of departed souls. The Lakota call the Milky Way *Wanaghi Tachanku* or "trail of the spirits." They understand that where the Milky Way splits, or forks, is where the departed are judged on the life they had led and how they will spend the afterlife. Some First Nations communities understand that these ancestors journey on the Spirit Road toward Creator.

The Nakawē (Saulteaux) people have a different understanding of the Milky Way. They call the Milky Way *anango mikana*, which means "flight of the birds" or "migration." Nakawē Elder Danny Musqua explains that the stars that make up the Milky Way help birds and insects migrate along the star track from north to south at specific times of the year.

*info***BIT**

The Milky Way

The word "galaxy" comes from an ancient Greek word *galaktos*, meaning milk.

*info***BIT**

Spiral Galaxies Views

Most of the images we have of spiral galaxies show them from a top view. This is because, from the side, a spiral galaxy looks like a thin disk.

*info***BIT**

Distant Galaxy

As better telescopes are developed, astronomers continue to discover galaxies that are farther and farther away. The most distant galaxy discovered so far is 13.2 billion light-years away. It is called UDFj-39546284. It is more commonly referred to as redshift 10 galaxy candidate.

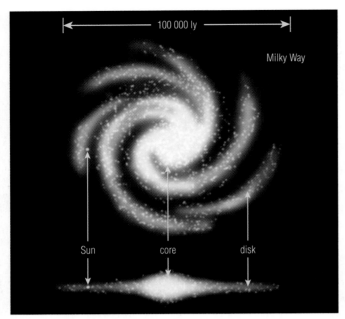

Figure 10.23 A top view and a side view of the Milky Way galaxy

Suggested Activities •·········
D17 Inquiry Activity on page 368
D18 Inquiry Activity on page 369

The Milky Way is about 100 000 ly in diameter and about 2000 ly thick at its widest point, near the core (Figure 10.23). Such a size is very difficult to imagine. The solar system, which is enormous compared to the size of Earth, is very tiny compared to the whole Milky Way galaxy. While light from the Sun takes about 5 h to reach the most distant planet in the solar system, Neptune, that same light would take 100 000 years to cross the entire Milky Way. We cannot see the entire Milky Way directly because our solar system is inside it.

Galaxy Clusters

Many of us have played the game of writing out our full address, from the street name and number to the city or town, province, country, Earth, and finally, Milky Way. In fact, your universe address does not end there.

If you could get out beyond our own galaxy and look back at it, you would see that the Milky Way is part of a group of about 20 galaxies. Such a group is called a galaxy cluster, and the one containing the Milky Way is known as the Local Group (Figure 10.24). More than 2 trillion stars may lie inside the cluster. The Local Group is part of the Local Cluster of galaxies, and that in turn is part of the Local Supercluster.

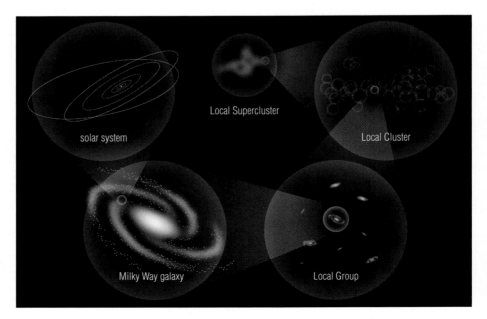

Figure 10.24 Galaxies tend to occur in groups called galaxy clusters. Galaxy clusters in turn form groups called superclusters. According to astronomers, there may be more than 100 billion galaxies in the universe.

Other Objects in Galaxies

When astronomers look at galaxies, both near and far away, they are looking at more than just stars, dust, and "space." There are other objects that exist that are components, or parts, of a galaxy. There are also objects, based upon collected data, that can only be inferred by astronomers.

Star Clusters

Galaxies contain distinct groupings of stars known as star clusters. A star cluster is a concentration of stars in a relatively small region of space. Star clusters occur in two broad types. One is an open cluster, which contains a few hundred to a few thousand stars. Open clusters are among the youngest star groups in a galaxy. The other type of star cluster is a globular cluster, which contains hundreds of thousands of stars, drawn together in a spherical form by the stars' gravitational forces (Figure 10.25). Globular clusters are the oldest star groups in a galaxy.

Figure 10.25 A globular cluster of stars

Black Holes

Through studies of hundreds of thousands of galaxies, astronomers now believe that each galaxy contains at least one supermassive black hole at its centre (Figure 10.26). As you learned earlier in this chapter, a black hole is a region of space where gravitational forces are so strong that nothing, not even light, can escape. The evidence for the existence of black holes is strong. For example, at the centre of the Milky Way, a number of stars can be seen rapidly orbiting around a point in space that seems to have nothing in it. Scientists believe that this spot is almost certainly a black hole.

Figure 10.26 Artist's concept of a black hole

A black hole mainly affects its surroundings through its tremendous gravitational pull. Its gravitational force is so strong that it can pull a star right into it (Figure 10.27). This completely collapses the atoms in the star. The mass of the star is added to the black hole's original mass, increasing the mass and gravitational pull of the black hole. It has been estimated that the Milky Way's black hole has been pulling stars in for at least 7 billion years. Currently, the black hole has a mass equal to about 3 million stars of similar size to our Sun.

Figure 10.27 A region of space containing a black hole, as photographed by the Hubble Space Telescope

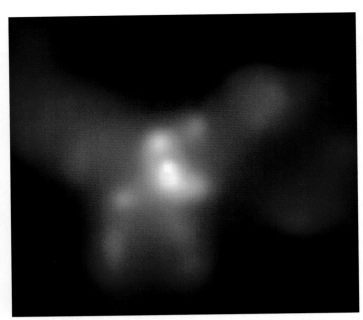

Figure 10.28 In the central region of galaxy NGC 6240, two black holes are visible (shown here in blue). This galaxy was formed by two small galaxies colliding.

Astronomers speculate that when galaxies collide, the black hole at the centre of each one gradually moves toward the other. After hundreds of millions of years, they will merge, with their masses combining into a single supermassive black hole. Figure 10.28 shows the two black holes at the centre of a galaxy that resulted from the collision of two smaller galaxies.

Quasars

In the 1950s, astronomers began using radio telescopes. A radio telescope forms a sort of picture using the naturally occurring radio wave energy coming from objects. The radio waves give scientists clues as to the composition of astronomical objects. Radio telescopes provided scientists with data that enabled them to identify a quasar for the first time. **Quasars** are believed to be the brightest and most distant objects in the universe. In the 1960s, scientific astronomers believed they were actually stars because they emitted huge amounts of energy. On average, they burn energy equivalent to a trillion Suns.

As technology improved, scientists soon learned that these objects were not stars. They began to believe that quasars were actually the centres of distant galaxies and that quasars themselves were supermassive black holes. The brightness of the quasar is due to energy being fed to the black hole. As it is "feeding," energy is emitted. Because of the incredible distances between quasars and Earth, these objects are still a mystery to astronomers.

Dark Matter

Although there are billions of astronomical bodies in space, even more astounding is that astronomers speculate that those objects add up to less than 10 percent of the total matter in space. At least 90 percent of the universe may be filled with matter that is not even visible. Scientific astronomers have named this dark matter. **Dark matter** refers to matter in the universe that is invisible because it does not interact with light or any other kind of radiation. Because of this, dark matter is invisible to direct observation by telescopes.

For a long time, astronomers have been puzzled by the unexpected motion of many galaxies. It appears as though gravitational forces are affecting them, yet the amount of visible mass (for example, stars, moons, gas, and dust) does not seem to be enough to cause it. For example, the stars in the Milky Way revolve around the galaxy's centre at such high speed that we would expect them to be flung off, just like a spinning water sprinkler sends drops of water flying out in all directions. However, evidence shows that the Milky Way is not coming apart. Astronomers have concluded that it is being kept together by the gravitational force of an enormous amount of matter that we cannot see directly (Figure 10.28). Today, most of the gravitational force in the universe is thought to be produced by dark matter.

Figure 10.29 By observing how matter in this galaxy cluster bends light rays, astronomers were able to compute and map out where they believe the dark matter (shown by the dark blue ring) is distributed in the cluster.

10.2 CHECK and REFLECT

1. Why do galaxies with more dust than other galaxies generally produce more new stars?

2. How is the distance of galaxies from Earth related to the age of the galaxy?

3. Compare and contrast the characteristics of different types of galaxies.

4. How did First Nations and Métis peoples explain their observations of what scientists call the Milky Way?

5. Are star clusters and galaxy clusters the same? Explain.

6. What are some differences between open star clusters and globular star clusters?

7. What is the relationship between black holes and galaxies? Why is this relationship of interest to astronomers?

8. Why were quasars originally thought to be stars? What are they really?

9. What is dark matter and why is it invisible to direct observation by telescopes?

10. Write your full address, including all the astronomical pieces up to the universe.

D17 *Inquiry Activity*   Toolkit 7

Modelling the Distances between Galaxies

The distance from the Milky Way to its nearest neighbouring galaxy, Andromeda, is vast: 2.5 million ly. Yet compared with the distances to other galaxies in the universe, Andromeda seems right next door to us. In this activity, you will create a scale and plot the distance to several galaxies on a local map, setting the distance from the Milky Way to Andromeda at 1 m.

Initiating and Planning

How can we model the distance from the Milky Way to seven other galaxies?

Materials & Equipment

- paper or notebook
- photocopy of a map of the local area around your school
- calculator
- ruler
- markers
- photograph of Hubble Deep Field

Performing and Recording

1. Copy the data from Table 10.3 into your notebook.

2. Using the data provided in the first three rows, estimate the model distance for the remaining four galaxies and record these distances in the table.

3. Mark an X at any point on the map of the school area to represent the Milky Way galaxy. Label it.

4. Following the map's scale, measure 1 m on the map in any direction and plot this second point. Label it Andromeda galaxy.

5. Continue plotting all but the galaxies shown in the Hubble Deep Field photograph. The direction to each galaxy is not important, just the distance.

Analyzing and Interpreting

6. In your own words, describe the universe composition using the map as an example.

7. Estimate how far your map would have to extend to include the galaxies in the Hubble Deep Field.

8. Why do you think what we know about the universe is so limited? Suggest a technology that could be invented to overcome this limitation.

Communication and Teamwork

9. How could you use your model to teach someone about the distances between galaxies?

Table 10.3 Seven Galaxies and Their Real and Model Distances from the Milky Way

Appearance	Galaxy	Distance (ly)	Model Distance (m)
	Andromeda galaxy	2.5 million	1
	Magellanic galaxy NGC 2366	12.5 million	5
	Sombrero galaxy	38 million	15
	Antennae galaxies	90 million	
	Seyfert's Sextet	190 million	
	Cartwheel galaxy	620 million	
	Galaxies in Hubble Deep Field	10 000 million	

D1 Key Activity

D18 *Inquiry Activity*

Toolkit 9

SKILLS YOU WILL USE
- Observing and measuring
- Drawing conclusions

An Ever-Growing Crab

A supernova sends out a massive amount of energy. This energy is released in knots or clumps. These clumps can be 10 times the mass of our Sun and travel at a speed of thousands of kilometres per second. From Earth, we can see these knots for a really long time, sometimes centuries. As these knots move away from the centre of the explosion, the cloud that is formed is a nebula. We can determine how much a nebula is growing and its age by tracking the energy knots.

Initiating and Planning

To determine the age of a nebula and how much it has expanded over time

Materials & Equipment

- two images of the Crab Nebula, one from 1956 and one from 1999
- calculator
- ruler
- graph paper

Performing and Recording

1. In a small group, examine the two images of the Crab Nebula. You should be able to see the filaments and knots of gas throughout the nebula. Note any differences you see between the two pictures. It is these changes that will help you determine the age of the nebula.

2. Near to the centre of the nebula is the pulsar, or the collapsed core of the original exploded star. Measure in centimetres the distance of each knot from the pulsar. You should find 11 knots on each picture. HINT: Measure each knot in both images before measuring the next knot.

3. Calculate the difference in distances between the knot and the pulsar in 1956 and in 1999. The difference is the expansion of the nebula. Look at the numbers you calculated. Is the amount of expansion close (around 10 percent) or is the difference greater?

4. On graph paper, plot the expansion of each knot versus its distance from the pulsar in the 1999 image. Draw a line of best fit for your graph.

5. To find the age of the nebula, you will first need to find out how much it has expanded over time, or its expansion rate. Calculate the time elapsed between the images to the nearest 0.1 years. Divide the expansion amounts calculated in step 3 by the time difference to determine how many centimetres/year the nebula has expanded.

6. Using your expansion rate, you can determine the age of the nebula. If rate = distance/time, then time = distance/rate. Use the expansion rate you calculated in step 5 and the distance of each knot from the pulsar in the 1999 image to determine the age of the nebula.

7. Calculate the average age of the nebula from the ages determined from the 11 knots from 1999.

Analyzing and Interpreting

8. If the image of the nebula was taken in 1999, in what year did the nebula explode?

9. The images of the nebula were scaled to each other. This means that one centimetre was the same physical distance in both images. Why would this be important?

10. What do you believe is the reason for the relationship between the pulsar and the speed of expansion you may have found on your graph?

11. It is believed that the Crab Nebula exploded in 1054. How close was your answer?

Communication and Teamwork

12. How much do you feel you can rely on your group member(s) to complete the required task(s)? Did everyone just do tasks on their own, or did the group collaborate?

13. How effectively did you communicate with the group? How would you change the way that you communicated with your group member(s)?

Key Concept Review

1. Identify one similarity among the understandings of First Nations and Métis peoples and scientists.

2. If two stars appear to have the same magnitude, are they the same distance from Earth? Explain.

3. Explain how the study of distances of stars and planets is really a study of the past.

4. What is the relationship between the mass of a star at its birth and its life span?

5. Briefly describe the life cycle of our Sun, according to scientists.

6. List the three key properties of stars used to construct a Hertzsprung-Russell diagram.

7. High mass stars end their existence in an explosion that can produce two possible results. Name and describe the two possibilities.

8. What are the differences between a protostar and a supernova?

9. Identify the type of galaxy in each of the photos below.

(a)   (b)

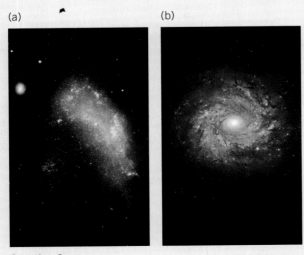

Question 9

10. Relate black holes to star life cycles and galaxies.

11. How is the amount of dust within a galaxy important to the structure and formation of a galaxy?

12. Why do some galaxies have a lot of dust in them, while others have little or none?

13. Describe some of the First Nations and Métis explanations of the Milky Way.

14. Compare and contrast the two different types of star clusters.

15. Why is dark matter so important to the formation of galaxies?

Connect Your Understanding

16. Summarize how a protostar might become a black hole.

17. How would you use a Hertzsprung-Russell diagram to determine where a star is in its life cycle?

18. What would be the approximate colour, luminosity, and surface temperature of the following stars on the Hertzsprung-Russell diagram? You may wish to make reference to the larger Hertzsprung-Russell diagram in Figure 10.11 on page 355.

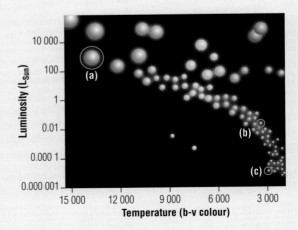

Question 18

19. Suppose you can see two stars of equal brightness in the night sky. One star appears to be yellow in colour, and the other star appears to be blue. Which star is closer to Earth? Explain your answer, making reference to the Hertzsprung-Russell diagram in Figure 10.11 on page 355.

20. Different cultures explained the appearance of supernovas. Explain why these events might have had a cultural importance.

21. Technically, no photographs of black holes can be taken. Explain why this is the case.

22. What information do scientists use to classify different types of stars?

23. How is the formation of stars similar to the formation of galaxies?

24. Discuss the importance of gravitational forces in the creation of galaxies.

25. Imagine you are an astronomer and you are asked to identify a galaxy. What would be the characteristics you would look for?

26. Explain why scientists believe that the galaxies that are the farthest away from Earth are also the oldest.

27. What do the distances between galaxies and their components reveal about the universe?

28. Compare and contrast the formation of our solar system to the formation of galaxies.

29. In your own words, explain how quasars and black holes are related.

30. Dark matter is matter that is invisible. Describe how scientists have inferred its existence.

31. How has our understanding of stars and galaxies changed over time? Use specific examples to support your answer.

Reflection

32. Do you think that the use of the words *nursery*, *birth*, *life cycle*, and *death* provides a reasonable analogy to the explanation of star formation? Explain.

33. How have your ideas about the size and structure of galaxies been changed by what you read in this section? Explain.

34. Do you think that events, such as supernovas, in neighbouring galaxies, and even in galaxies far away, influence humans on Earth? Explain your ideas.

After Reading

Reflect and Evaluate

Work with a partner to list all the strategies you have learned for determining or finding important ideas. Create a tip sheet for other students in the class on how to find important ideas. Exchange your tips with another pair of students and then post your sheet in the classroom, with the teacher's permission.

Reflection on Essential Inquiry Questions

What is the relationship between a star's colour, luminosity, and surface temperature and its life cycle? How has this understanding developed? **SI**

Why is it important to understand astronomical bodies, such as stars and black holes, when developing technologies for exploring our universe? **TPS**

As we explore the universe, who should have access to that knowledge? **DM**

What observations of the universe were made by First Nations, Métis, and other cultures? **CP**

Unit Task

In this chapter, you have learned about the life cycle of different types of stars, and about the different shapes and objects, such as black holes and quasars, of the galaxies found in our universe. How could this knowledge be important to the completion of your Unit Task?

11

Our understanding of the universe is culturally influenced.

Outcomes

By the end of this chapter, you will:

- examine how various cultures, past and present, including First Nations and Métis, understand and represent astronomical phenomena

- inquire into the motion and characteristics of astronomical bodies in our solar system and the universe

- analyze scientific explanations of the formation and evolution of our solar system and the universe

What you will learn:

- First Nations and Métis understandings describe and explain some astronomical phenomena including the origin of the universe.

- Astronomy is making sense of the universe that lies beyond Earth, both from holistic and cultural viewpoints and from scientific viewpoints.

- Astronomical bodies have unique characteristics and composition, which may affect how they interact with one another.

- Improved technology and observation has lead to the development of different theories on how the universe and our solar system may have formed.

- Ongoing space research continues to be important.

The Hubble telescope found this very young, still-forming galaxy, almost 12.8 billion light-years from Earth. Astronomers believe it started to form just 700 million years after the Big Bang occurred.

Before Reading

Monitoring Understanding

Good readers keep track of places where their understanding of new words or ideas breaks down, and they use strategies to improve their understanding. Preview the Key Terms and the subheadings for section 11.1. Make predictions about places where you may have difficulty understanding the ideas.

Key Terms
- apparent retrograde motion
- Big Bang theory
- electromagnetic radiation
- electromagnetic spectrum
- geocentric models
- heliocentric model
- orbital radius • red-shifted
- spectral lines • spectral shifting • spectroscope
- spectrum

©P

Figure 11.1 The giant Pan Gu holds the egg of the universe, which is often shown as the yin and yang symbol. According to Chinese ideas, when the egg was cracked open, the universe was created.

Here is a summary of what you will learn in this section:

- Astronomy differs among cultures. For instance, scientific astronomy is figuring out from observations how the physical universe works. Indigenous astronomy is coming to know what is beyond Mother Earth and involves making sense of the universe in a cultural context.

- Throughout history, humans in many different cultures around the world, including First Nations and Métis, have explained the universe based on their worldview, what they believe, and what they are able to observe.

Explanations for the Origins of the Universe

Ancient cultures used their observations and traditional understanding to explain the world around them, including how the universe was created.

In Chinese culture, for example, believed that the universe began as a big, black egg. Inside the egg was Pan Gu, who was the first living being and creator (Figure 11.1). When he cracked open the egg, the clear part of the egg floated up and became the heavens, and the rest of the egg became Earth. When Pan Gu died many, many years later, his eyes became the Sun and the Moon and his hair and beard became the stars in the sky.

The understanding of the Cree people in Saskatchewan attribute the creation of the universe, Sun, other stars, and Earth to Creator. Some creation stories do not necessarily describe the creation of the universe, but they detail a great flood event prior to the creation of humans. Cherokee Thomas King, in his book *Green Grass, Running Water*, notes, "In the beginning, there was nothing. Just the water."

Creation of the Universe

There are many different cultural understandings from all over the world about how the universe was created. Researching ideas unfamiliar to us helps us learn more about the universe.

Purpose

To explore creation stories from different cultures

Procedure

1. Research a creation story from a culture of your choice. Cultures may include
   - Africa: Maasai, Zulu
   - Asia: Hindu, Japanese, Korean, Mongol
   - Central and North America: Aztec, Cree, Dené, Lakota, Mayan, Navajo
   - Middle East: Babylonian, Jewish/Christian, Persian
   - Pacific: Australian Aborigine, Hawaiian, Maori
   - South America: Incan

2. Often, cultural understandings are part of an oral tradition. In keeping with that tradition, assume the role of a storyteller and share your story.

Questions

3. After listening to the different stories, write a one-page mini-essay that answers the following questions:

(a) What are the similarities between stories? Why might these similarities exist?

(b) What do the stories tell you about the culture they are from?

(c) What may have influenced the creation of these stories? These influences may include the environment, politics, technology, and society.

(d) How might these stories influence the everyday lives of the people in the respective cultures?

Pose More Questions

4. As you have learned, oral storytelling is a common way different cultures tell their creation stories, but there are many other ways to express or tell those same stories. What ways can you think of that a culture might use? Give an example in your answer.

5. What questions do you have about the origin of the universe that were not answered by the creation story you researched?

Suggested Activity •··········
D20 Quick Science on page 377

Other Ways of Knowing the Universe

Similar to the Cree, the Dené of northern Saskatchewan believe that Creator made the universe and everything in it. Their spiritual accounts, called *Üæqhzé*, explain their place within the universe and creation.

In Saskatchewan, First Nations and Métis peoples have rich creation stories, which explain their people's origin and their place in the universe. Nakawē people, who are descendants of the Anishinabe from Ontario who migrated west long ago, have similar stories. Elder Danny Musqua, a Nakawē Elder, recounts the shared creation story of the Anishinabe and Nakawē peoples. Creator is both mother and father. Elder Danny's people understand that the physical universe came from the woman spirit, which in turn came from Creator. The universe, explains Elder Danny, is the physical expression of the Mother's spirit.

It is the woman spirit that gave life to all four corners of the universe and then, in turn, created Earth. Thus, the Nakawē call our planet Mother Earth. People originate as spirits who reside with Creator, but then are transformed into physical bodies in order to understand what it means to be made physical. People live in the physical world to learn about it until they find their way back to the spirit world.

According to Albert Scott, a traditional Knowledge Keeper from the Kinistin Saulteaux First Nation, there are four levels above Earth. The first level has the stars and the sky we can see. Long ago, Creator's helpers looked down from the fourth level. They saw only disorganization. One of the helpers said, "Watch me," and created the sky and what scientists call the universe.

The ancient Egyptians believed that in the beginning, there was a chaotic and endless ocean called Nu. From this chaos, Amen-Renef, or "He Whose Real Essence Is Unknown," created himself. Once created, he was known as Atum. He created the air god, Shu, and the water goddess, Tefnut. Shu and Tefnut had twins: Nut, who represents the sky, and Geb, who is Earth. The importance of Nut and Geb can be seen in the paintings inside of tombs that show both the heavens and Earth (Figure 11.2).

The Egyptians believed that the goddess Nut's body was the sky. Her body acted as a shield against the chaos that lay beyond her, beyond what the ancient Egyptians could see. Nut protected the ordered cosmos of this world. Every evening, as the Sun set, the Sun god Ra entered her mouth only to be reborn the next morning at sunrise. The Sun and the god Ra were very important to the Egyptians. They believed the Sun was the centre of the universe.

Figure 11.2 The goddess Nut covers Earth and protects all its inhabitants. Her fingers and toes touch the four directions. The Egyptians believed that stars, which cover her body, come from Nut.

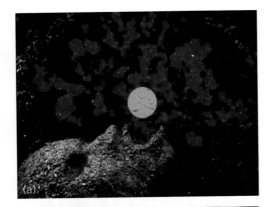

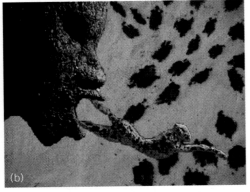

Figure 11.3 According to Boshongo stories, the god Bumba created Earth and the heavens, and humans by vomiting.

Like the Egyptians, the Boshongo people in the Congo also believed that in the beginning, there was a single entity who existed in a dark, watery place. According to the Boshongo, the god Bumba was surrounded by nothing but water and darkness. One day, Bumba had pains in his stomach. The pains became worse and worse. He vomited up the Sun, and there was suddenly light all around (Figure 11.3). The heat from the Sun made the water evaporate, creating the clouds and causing the water to recede and show the edges of the world. He vomited again, this time producing the Moon and the stars that give light at night. He was still in pain, and this time he vomited nine creatures: the leopard, the crested eagle, the crocodile, a little fish, the tortoise, lightning, the white heron, a beetle, a goat, and humans. From these creatures, all the other creatures came into existence.

Culture has not only influenced the creation of stories, it has also influenced the development of Eurocentric science. In the next section, you will learn about specific scientific theories.

11.1 CHECK and REFLECT

1. (a) Using a Venn diagram, identify similarities and differences among the creation stories you studied in this section.

   (b) Why do you think that there are similarities and differences among the creation stories of different cultures?

2. Think about the environment that you live in. Create a story about the creation of the universe based upon the observations you make about where you live.

3. How is the Egyptian creation story reflective of their belief in reincarnation?

4. Why do you think humans, regardless of culture, have attempted to explain the origin of the universe?

5. In the shared creation story of the Anishinabe and Nakawē peoples, Elder Danny explains that the physical universe comes from the woman spirit. How is this understanding reflected in the way the Anishinabe and Nakawē peoples refer to planet Earth?

6. The Cree, Egyptian, and Boshongo creation stories share the element of water. What other creation stories do you know that involve a beginning with water? What might be some explanations for these similarities?

7. What creation story did you find the most surprising? Explain why.

D20 *Quick Science*

Cosmology and Art

In the past and still today, different cultures use different methods to explain the universe and humanity's role in it. The study of the universe and our role in it is called cosmology.

Scientists publish scientific papers with their explanations of cosmology, and other cultures use art forms, such as dance, songs, paintings, or architecture. For example, the Cheyenne used symbols and colours to represent the creation of the universe and the Cheyenne role within that universe (Figure 11.4).

Figure 11.4 Artist Mike Schwab painted this bag with symbols that derive from traditional Cheyenne cosmological symbols. The design has a personal, private meaning for the artist.

Procedure

1. Using the library or the Internet, research different ways that cultures used art to represent their knowledge of cosmology.

2. From your research, present examples of how cultures have combined cosmology and art. Present your finding, or create an example of the type of art used by a culture. Be sure to explain the link between the cosmology and the art form.

Questions

3. Why do you think there are so many examples of cosmology in art?

4. How are the art forms influenced by the natural world?

5. Why do you think art has been used to convey knowledge?

6. What modern examples of how cosmology influences art are present in Canadian society?

7. Are there other ways, other than art and scientific papers, in which our beliefs or knowledge about how the universe has been created have been expressed? Explain your answer.

Pose New Questions

8. What questions do you have about the origin of the universe that are not answered by your findings?

9. Choose a classmate's presentation. What questions do you have about the culture's beliefs that he or she presented?

Here is a summary of what you will learn in this section:

- The Big Bang theory of the formation and expansion of the universe is consistent with known laws of the universe.

- The red shift of spectral lines in the light we see from galaxies shows that the light's wavelengths are getting longer, meaning that other galaxies are moving away from us.

- The cosmic background radiation in the universe, now mapped, is thought to be leftover energy from the moment the universe first formed.

- Today, scientists' understandings are based upon a heliocentric, or Sun-centred, model.

Figure 11.5 The Hubble Space Telescope was named for astronomer Edwin Hubble.

Explaining the Origin of the Universe

Edwin Hubble was an American astronomer who was one of the first scientists to study galaxies (Figures 11.5 and 11.6). Between 1918 and 1929, two of his major findings changed astronomy. First, he confirmed that many other galaxies existed beyond the Milky Way. Second, he found that almost all galaxies are moving away from each other. These observations helped to support the proposal made in 1927 by Belgian priest and physicist Georges Lemaître that the universe is expanding. Both of these ideas would lead astronomers and physicists to develop theories on how the universe may have formed.

More people recognize Hubble's contribution because he had evidence to support his ideas. The evidence Hubble used to reach his conclusions came from measuring the distance from Earth of 46 galaxies and the speed of their movement. Hubble closely examined each galaxy's light spectrum. When white light passes through a prism, it is separated into a continuous rainbow known as the visible light **spectrum**. In science, a spectrum refers to the separation of radiation, such as light, into different wavelengths. This is pluralized as spectra, or sometimes as spectrums.

The measurements of different light spectra helped support Hubble's theory. Evidence from thousands of observations of galaxies has confirmed his findings. Hubble's work remains the foundation of modern understanding of the nature and origin of the universe.

Figure 11.6 American astronomer Edwin Hubble (1889–1953) using the 100-inch (250-cm) telescope at the Mount Wilson Observatory, Los Angeles, California, in 1937

Using a Spectroscope

A device called a **spectroscope** enables us to split a light sample into its component colours, or spectra. Each element produces its own unique light spectrum. By studying light spectra, scientists can determine the composition of different astronomical bodies, even if those sources are extremely far away.

Purpose

To build a spectroscope to observe and compare the spectra of different light sources

---

Materials & Equipment

- utility knife
- cardboard box
- CD or DVD
- protractor
- tape
- duct tape (optional)

- various light sources: compact fluorescent lamps (CFLs), incandescent bulbs, "black light" tubes, spectrum tubes for different elements
- coloured pencils or markers

Procedure

1. Use the utility knife to carefully cut a slit on one side of the box.

2. On the opposite side of the box, carefully cut an opening large enough to hold the CD. This is your viewing area (Figure 11.7).

3. Place the CD into the opening you made in step 2. Use your protractor to be sure that the CD is placed on an angle of 60 degrees.

4. Tape the bottom of the CD to the box.

5. You may wish to use duct tape to cover part of the eyepiece for better viewing.

6. Using your spectroscope, observe the CFL. Record the order of the colours and any black lines that appear.

7. Repeat step 6 using different light sources.

Questions

8. Pure white light produces a spectrum that is a continuous rainbow. How is it different from the spectra produced by other light sources?

9. What differences did you notice among the spectra produced by different light sources?

10. (a) Which kind of light source produced the most distinct spectrum?

    (b) Explain why you think that was the case.

11. If you used element spectrum tubes, how did the spectra produced by the tubes differ from the spectra produced by the light sources?

12. The spectra produced by different light sources are like fingerprints. The pattern of lines can be used to identify if certain elements are present. How could knowledge of the spectra of light created by particular elements help an astronomer determine the composition of a distant star or galaxy?

Pose New Questions

13. What other uses could you use a spectroscope for? What do you think you could learn from using it?

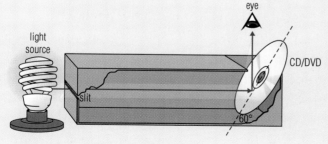

light source / eye / CD/DVD / slit / 60°

Figure 11.7 Diagram of CD spectroscope

Evidence for the Big Bang Theory

From the light spectrum of each galaxy he studied, Hubble was able to determine the speed at which each galaxy was moving away from our own. Then, for those same galaxies, he separately determined the distance between each one and the Milky Way. Plotting both the speed and the distance measurements together, Hubble discovered a clear relationship between the two. The farther away a galaxy was, the faster it was moving away.

These findings, along with observations of many other scientists of the time, gave further support to Lemaître's idea that the universe is expanding. Out of this and the work of many other physicists, mathematicians, and other scientists of the day, came one of the most remarkable theories of the 20th century. The theory, which came to be called the **Big Bang theory**, states that the universe formed when an infinitely dense point suddenly and rapidly expanded in a single moment. All the matter and energy that exists today was created during the early minutes of that hot, rapid expansion. Most of the credit for the Big Bang theory goes to Russian-American physicist George Gamow and American mathematician Ralph Alpher.

It is now commonly accepted by scientists that the universe formed 13.7 billion years ago. That moment marks the beginning of the universe and also the beginning of time. Today, at several research facilities around the world, scientists are trying to recreate various aspects of the conditions that might have existed in the early moments of the universe (Figure 11.8). In this way, they hope to gain a better understanding of the origin of everything within the universe.

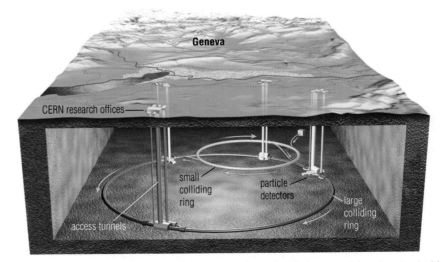

Figure 11.8 At CERN in Switzerland, scientists are trying to break down particles of matter inside a 27-km-long "supercollider" (shown here in blue), located deep in the ground. These experiments may reveal how the smallest particles of matter were created when the universe first formed.

An Ever-Faster Expanding Universe

Scientists compare the expansion of space to the expanding surface of a balloon as it is inflating. Just as dots drawn on a balloon separate from each other as the balloon expands, so clusters of galaxies are moving away from each other as space opens up between them.

The effects of the expansion of space are so small that our Milky Way galaxy is not moving away noticeably from our nearest galaxy neighbour, Andromeda. Gravity and other forces are strong enough to keep these objects together. However, between clusters of galaxies is an immense amount of empty space. This is where the tiny effects of the expansion of space add up.

In the last 20 years, data from the most distant galaxies show that the rate at which the most distant galaxies are receding from our view is increasing. In other words, not only are galaxies moving away from us, but they are doing so at an ever-faster rate (Figure 11.9).

Figure 11.9 This spiral galaxy is NGC 4526; the small, bright spot is Supernova 1994D.

Learning Checkpoint

1. What is a light spectrum?

2. What two findings of Edwin Hubble changed astronomy?

3. What does the Big Bang theory explain?

The Wave Nature of Light

How can a light spectrum tell us whether a galaxy is moving away from us? First, we need to understand the nature of light. Light is a form of energy. Scientists have two ways of explaining how light travels: in waves or as energy parcels called photons. The wave form of energy is called **electromagnetic radiation**.

Figure 11.10 shows the full known **electromagnetic spectrum**, from radio waves with very long wavelengths, to gamma rays with very short wavelengths. Humans can only see a small fraction of the electromagnetic spectrum, a rainbow of colours known as the visible light spectrum. Each of the different colours of the visible light spectrum, from red through to yellow and green and on to violet, varies in wavelength. The wavelength of red light, for example, is longer than the wavelength for blue light. Technology enables us to detect other forms of electromagnetic radiation that are not readily visible to humans.

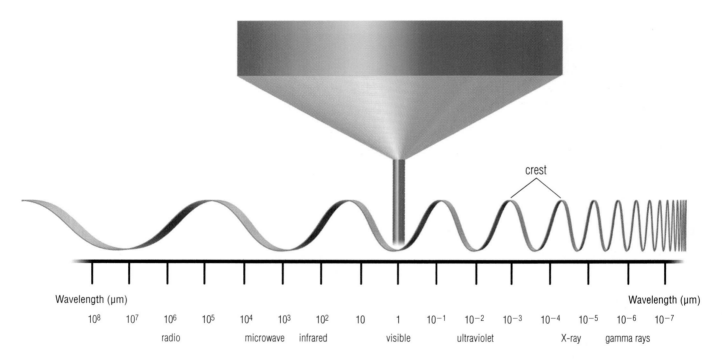

Figure 11.10 The electromagnetic spectrum. Objects in space emit a great variety of electromagnetic energy.

Analyzing the Movement of Light Waves

To understand the movement of light waves in space, consider waves in a lake. Light waves move in a similar way to the waves on the surface of water. Picture a duck floating on a calm lake.

Gentle movements of the duck create ripples on the water surface that spread out evenly all around the duck (Figure 11.11(a)) in a circular pattern. The wavelength of these ripples is measured as the distance from the crest of one wave to the crest of the next.

As the duck moves, the ripples in front of it compress and the wavelength shortens. At the same time, the ripples behind the duck stretch out and the wavelength gets longer (Figure 11.11(b)) in a more elliptical pattern. Even if you could not see the duck directly and could only see the ripples on the water, you would still be able to tell whether the duck was moving toward you or away from you.

In a similar way, observing the light emitted by a galaxy allows scientists to measure the light's wavelengths to determine whether the galaxy is moving and in which direction. This phenomenon is called the Doppler effect.

Figure 11.11 By observing the pattern made by the waves, we can tell whether an object is moving and whether it is moving toward or away from us. (a) When an object is hardly moving (stationary), its waves radiate out evenly in all directions. The distance between each wave, or wavelength, is the same. (b) When the object is moving, the waves in front of it become compressed (the wavelength shortens) and the waves behind it stretch out (the wavelength lengthens).

Analyzing the Colour of Light Waves

Another characteristic of star or galaxy light that astronomers analyze is spectral pattern. When astronomers sample the light from a star or galaxy, a series of dark lines appears across its light spectrum. These **spectral lines** look similar to the bar code you see on retail products. Spectral lines are created as each gas that makes up a star absorbs some of the light energy. Each element does this in a different way, creating its own particular pattern of spectral lines (Figure 11.12). Because astronomers can see the spectral lines of hydrogen in the spectra of nearly all celestial objects, it is clear that hydrogen is present throughout the universe.

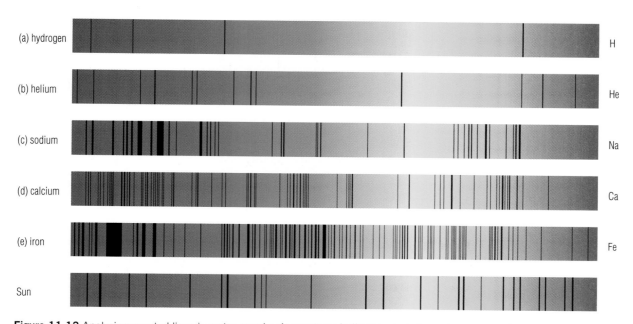

Figure 11.12 Analyzing spectral lines in a star or galaxy's spectrum indicates what elements are present.

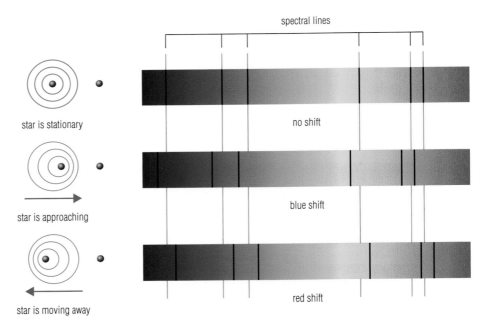

infoBIT

Seeing Colours

Most humans are trichromatic, which means we have three receptors in our eyes to see colour. Organisms that have four receptors are known as tetrachromats. They are able to see more of the electromagnetic spectrum than the average human. These include birds and some insects and reptiles. There are some humans, mostly women, who are tetrachromats as well. Some humans can be bichromatic or colour-blind. Both these conditions in humans are genetically caused.

Hubble and other astronomers noticed that for all of the galaxies Hubble was studying, the spectral lines were shifted. **Spectral shifting** is the change in position of spectral lines to the left or the right of where they normally are in the spectrum of a light source that is not moving. In all of Hubble's observations, the spectral lines were shifted toward the red end of the spectrum.

Recall that red light has a longer wavelength than blue light at the other end of the spectrum. When light's wavelength is increased, the wavelength moves toward the red end of the visible spectrum, or is **red-shifted**. This change in wavelength can be explained by the Doppler effect. Recall the moving duck and the wavelength patterns it produces: wavelengths in front of the duck get shorter and wavelengths behind the duck get longer. Because the light spectra were red-shifted—that is, the light spectra wavelengths were longer—Hubble concluded that the galaxies were moving away from the Milky Way (Figure 11.13).

If Hubble had instead found that the spectral lines were shifted to the blue end of the galaxies' light spectra, he would have concluded that the wavelengths were shorter and more compressed. Just as with the duck example, shorter wavelengths between the observer and the moving object would have meant that the galaxies were moving toward us, not away.

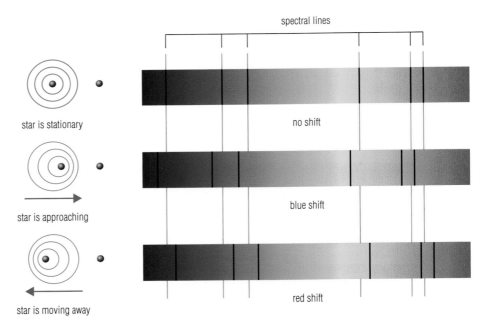

spectral lines

star is stationary — no shift

star is approaching — blue shift

star is moving away — red shift

Figure 11.13 If the spectral lines in the light from a star or galaxy occur toward the blue end of the light spectrum, it means the observer is seeing short wavelengths. This "blue shift" indicates that the star or galaxy is approaching the observer. However, if the spectral lines occur toward the red end of the light spectrum, it means the observer is seeing long wavelengths. This "red shift" indicates that the star or galaxy is moving away from the observer.

When Hubble and other astronomers found this red-shift pattern in an increasing number of galaxies, it supported the idea that the universe was expanding. Since then, much more evidence has been collected.

The Keck telescope in Hawaii is one of the largest optical telescopes in the world (Figure 11.14). Astronomers recently used the Keck telescope to conduct a red-shift survey of galaxies, repeating Hubble's work. This newer survey, called DEEP2, measured the light from 60 000 galaxies instead of 46. The results of the DEEP2 survey supported and added to Hubble's original work.

Figure 11.14 The Keck telescope in Hawaii

Radiation Maps: More Evidence

A critical question related to the Big Bang theory remained unanswered. The theory stated that the very early universe was extremely hot and filled with short-wave gamma ray radiation. Then, as the universe rapidly expanded, it cooled and the wavelength of the radiation lengthened. The radiation became lower energy types, including X rays, ultraviolet, visible light, infrared, and microwaves.

So, asked scientists, if the theory describing this series of events was reasonable, then where was the energy that should have been left over from the very early moments of the formation of the universe? Their prediction was that all of space should contain evidence of this radiation. Scientists set about to look for evidence of this residual radiation.

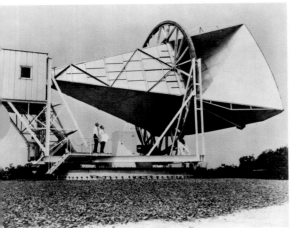

Figure 11.15 It was while using the Horn Antenna, located in New Jersey in the United States, that radio astronomers Penzias and Wilson unexpectedly discovered the microwave background radiation present in every part of the sky.

In 1965, two researchers, Arno Penzias and Robert Wilson, made a big discovery—a discovery they were not even looking for (Figure 11.15). Their new microwave antenna, intended for use in telecommunications, detected that the entire sky was bathed with microwave energy. It came from every direction, not just from individual stars. This energy is often called cosmic background radiation. Scientists believe it is the energy left over from the massive and split-second expansion of the universe from a single point some 13.7 billion years ago.

In 1992, the **Co**smic **B**ackground **E**xplorer satellite (COBE) made detailed maps of the background radiation collected from the most distant parts of the visible universe. This was followed in 2006 when the Wilkinson Microwave Anisotropy Probe (WMAP) took even more precise measurements of the radiation and created a much-enhanced map (Figure 11.16).

Both the COBE and the WMAP results showed that the spectrum of the background radiation precisely fits the predictions consistent with the Big Bang theory.

In science, although a theory can be supported by evidence, it is never considered to be proven correct. If new evidence conflicts with a theory, scientists may need to rethink or revise the theory. This happens quite often. This is why there are so many theories and so few laws in the field of science. In this way, the COBE and WMAP surveys not only back up the Big Bang theory, but they also show that other theories of the formation of the universe cannot be supported. One of the theories not supported is the Steady State theory, which suggests that the universe is infinitely old and that matter and energy constantly enter and leave the universe at equal rates. To date, the Big Bang theory continues to be the only theory for the universe's formation that is supported by the entire body of scientific information gathered so far.

Figure 11.16 The universe's cosmic background radiation, mapped by the Wilkinson Microwave Anisotropy Probe (WMAP). The tiny variations in the radiation are thought to indicate hot regions, now mostly empty space, and cooler regions, where matter could collect to form the first galaxies.

Learning Checkpoint

1. What is wavelength? How is wavelength related to energy?

2. In your own words, define spectral shifting.

3. What is cosmic background radiation?

Explaining Planetary Motion

In addition to developing theories that explain the origin of the universe, humans have also attempted to explain the motions of celestial bodies and our place in the solar system. From our perspective on Earth, everything in the sky appears to be in motion. The Sun rises and sets. The Moon, in its ever-changing phases, travels across the sky. Planets shift against a background of stars. Even constellations appear to change position.

Just as we use what technology and science we have to answer questions about the world around us, so our ancestors used the knowledge and technology they had to make sense of the constant change they observed in the sky. Not surprisingly, it appeared to early observers that all celestial bodies revolved around Earth.

Geocentric Model

More than 2000 years ago, the widely held belief among astronomers was that Earth sat at the centre of the universe. The ancient Greeks are best known for their models of the universe. The Ionians (6th to 4th century BCE) are credited with the idea that nature moves in predictable ways, and were the first to build models based on observations, not on supernatural explanations. The Ionian philosopher Anaximander proposed that Earth was a cylinder at rest in the centre of the universe. This cylinder was surrounded by one or more spherical shells with holes in them. These holes appeared as stars because there was a fire that lay beyond the outer sphere. Models that have Earth at the centre of the universe are called **geocentric models**, or Earth-centred.

The philosopher and astronomer Aristotle is often mistakenly credited with the geocentric model. Although his model helped to explain how some objects, such as the Sun, Moon, and five planets, revolved around Earth (Figure 11.17), in his model, there were 53 transparent rotating spheres above Earth. The Sun, Moon, and planets were embedded into these spheres. The stars were formed from a fifth element, called quintessence, which was considered incorruptible and eternal and lay beyond the spheres.

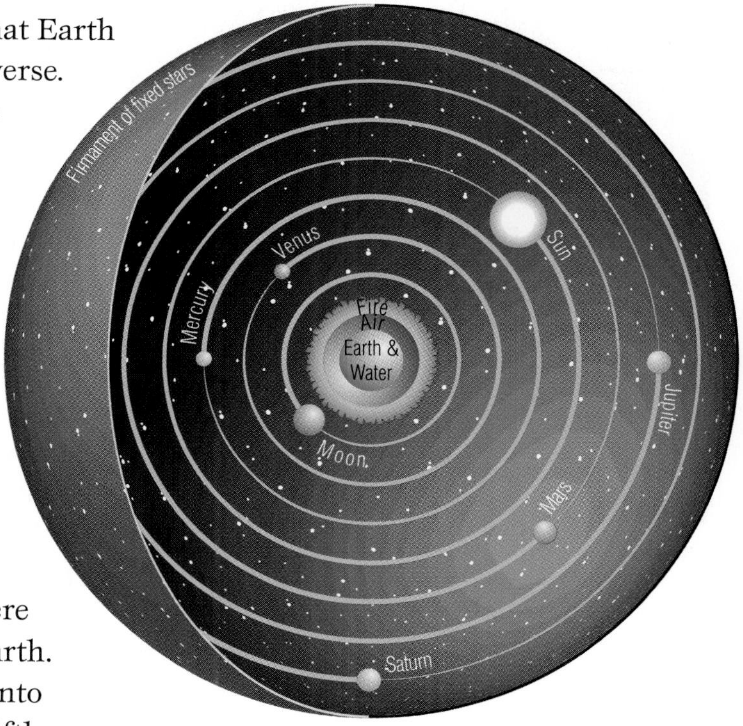

Figure 11.17 In the geocentric model, Earth was at the centre and stars were thought to be fixed to the inside of the "celestial sphere," like stars glued on the unmoving ceiling of a dome. Over time, with improved observations, this model was shown to be wrong.

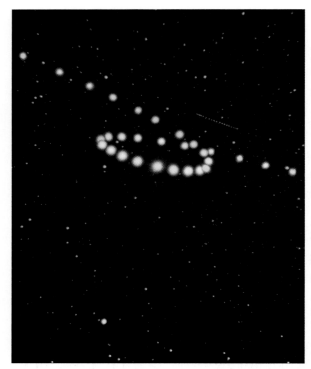
Figure 11.18 This composite image of Mars was taken in 2003 over the course of two months. It clearly shows the phases of the planet in apparent retrograde motion.

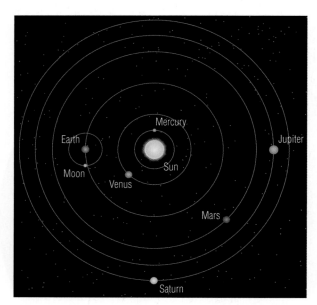
Figure 11.19 The heliocentric model of the solar system put the Sun at the centre of the universe. At the time, it was considered to be an outrageous idea.

The geocentric model continued to be developed by early scientists, including the Greek astronomer Ptolemy in the 2nd century BCE. Ptolemy's model enabled the forecasting of many astronomical phenomena, such as the changing phases of the Moon. Still, some observations of planetary motion were puzzling. You know that the Sun moves across the sky along a path known as the ecliptic. Planets also appear to follow a path close to the ecliptic. However, Mars, Jupiter, and Saturn appear to loop backward for a period of days or weeks before resuming their normal path (Figure 11.18). This apparent backward motion is a celestial phenomenon known as **apparent retrograde motion**. Various astronomers proposed changes to the geocentric model to explain apparent retrograde motion, but most of these adaptations were extremely complicated.

Heliocentric Model

The geocentric model of the solar system was accepted for almost 2000 years. The **heliocentric model**, which places the Sun at the centre, had been proposed by the Ionian Greeks as far back as 500 BCE. Nicolaus Copernicus (1473–1543) reintroduced a simplified heliocentric model (Figure 11.19) in about 1530, based on Ptolemy's observations but not Ptolemy's geocentric model. Copernicus's model placed the Sun, stationary, near the centre of the solar system and everything revolved around the Sun, including Earth. This was a very radical idea at the time. Within the next 150 years, a new generation of scientists provided solid evidence for a slightly more complex heliocentric model. Notable among these scientists were the renowned Galileo Galilei (Italy), Johannes Kepler (Germany), and Sir Isaac Newton (England).

Two key ideas about planetary orbits helped add support to the heliocentric model. One was the relationship between a planet's orbital radius and its speed of orbit. The other was the fact that planetary orbits are elliptical and not circular.

©P

Orbital Radius

In the heliocentric model, all planets orbit the Sun in the same counterclockwise direction but at different distances. A planet's distance from the Sun is called the planet's **orbital radius**. The shorter the orbital radius, the faster the planet moves in its orbit. Therefore, Earth, which is closer to the Sun than Mars, orbits the Sun more quickly than Mars. This is not just because Earth's orbit is shorter than Mars' orbit. Earth is also moving faster than Mars. In turn, Mars is moving faster than Jupiter, the next planet out from the Sun. This pattern is true for all the planets, dwarf planets, and even asteroids in the solar system. The reason is that the farther an object is from the Sun, the weaker is the effect of the Sun's gravity on that object.

Apparent Retrograde Motion

The differences in orbital speeds explain why Mars, Jupiter, and Saturn sometimes appear to have retrograde motion to an observer on Earth. Earth orbits the Sun faster than the other three planets. For example, at times, Earth overtakes Mars in its orbit around the Sun. It appears to an observer on Earth that Mars is moving eastward across the sky, stopping, and moving westward before stopping again and resuming its eastward motion (Figure 11.20). This change in direction is just an optical illusion. To help visualize how apparent retrograde motion occurs, imagine you are in a track race. You pass three other runners, not only because you are moving faster, but also because you have the inside turn position. When you pass the other runners, they appear to be moving backward relative to you.

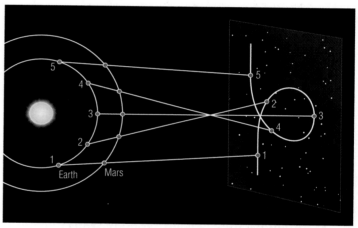

Figure 11.20 About every two years, Earth catches up to Mars and passes it. This makes Mars appear to lag for a while, tracing a backward path against the starry background.

Geocentric models attempted to account for apparent retrograde motion but were too complex. Heliocentric models, however, were better able to explain apparent retrograde motion. This was key evidence in support of heliocentric models of the solar system.

Elliptical Orbits

Early heliocentric models could still not predict planetary motion very accurately. These models assumed that planets had a circular orbit. A circle has a single focus point—the centre. If the Sun were placed in the centre, astronomers' predictions of planetary motion did not match their observations.

reSearch

Earth's orbit is elliptical, which means that the distance between Earth and the Sun changes as Earth moves through its orbit. The shape of the orbit itself has also changed, and because of this, the date when Earth is closest to the Sun has also changed. Research how this affects the length of the year over time.

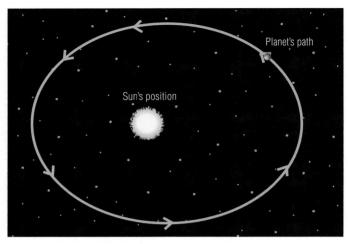

Figure 11.21 The planets orbit the Sun in slightly elliptical, not circular, orbits.

In 1609, German mathematician Johannes Kepler finally came up with the next piece of the puzzle. Using detailed observations made by Danish astronomer Tycho Brahe, Kepler realized that the orbits of the planets were ellipses (Figure 11.21).

An ellipse is somewhat like a slightly flattened circle. Unlike a circle which has only one focus point, an ellipse has two focus points. If the Sun were placed at one of the two focus points, then astronomers' predictions and observations matched. This was another key piece of support for the heliocentric model.

Today, all astronomical observations continue to support the heliocentric model of our solar system. It is also the guide we use when studying other star-and-planet systems.

11.2 CHECK and REFLECT

1. List Edwin Hubble's two main discoveries. How did they change the way astronomers thought of space beyond our universe?

2. According to the Big Bang theory, how did the universe originate?

3. When we view a celestial body from Earth, how we view and track the object often depends on the shape of the object's orbit. Using Kepler's explanation of orbits, explain the differences in the shape of the orbits in our solar system.

4. What does the visible light spectrum refer to?

5. Why is the understanding of the wave nature of light important to astronomers?

6. What is the difference between spectral shifting and red shifting?

7. What information can be gathered by observing space for spectral shifting?

8. How does the idea that the universe is expanding relate to the observation that the spectra from distant galaxies are red-shifted?

9. How is it possible to know that the element hydrogen exists throughout the universe?

10. Explain how the discovery and mapping of cosmic background radiation gave scientists evidence in support of the Big Bang theory.

11. Astronomers often use models to explain theories.

    (a) In your own words, explain what an astronomical model is.

    (b) Why might scientists need to use models?

12. What is the main difference between geocentric models and heliocentric models?

13. Using the geocentric and heliocentric models as examples, explain how theories may change based upon the work of other scientists.

14. In your own words, define *apparent retrograde motion*. How many celestial bodies are involved in apparent retrograde motion? Explain.

©P

Modelling Planetary Motion

Astronomers proposed different models of planetary motion to help explain celestial phenomena, such as the changing phases of the Moon and apparent retrograde motion. Two very important ideas in the development of models of planetary motion are orbital radius and elliptical orbits.

Question

How can you model celestial phenomena using geocentric and heliocentric models of planetary motion?

Design and Conduct Your Investigation

1. Working in small groups, brainstorm ideas about how you will create geocentric and heliocentric models of the solar system. As you generate ideas, consider the following questions:
   - Which celestial bodies will you need to include in your model?
   - How big does your model need to be? Does it have to be to scale?
   - How will the celestial bodies in your model maintain consistent orbital distances from the centre?
   - How can you ensure that celestial bodies travel at a consistent speed?
   - How will you record celestial phenomena as viewed from the position of Earth? Can cameras be used?
   - How can you incorporate the ideas of orbital radius and elliptical orbits into your model?

3. Select a design and write a procedure to build your models. Include a list of materials and equipment you will need.

4. Ask your teacher to approve your designs before beginning construction.

5. Build your models according to your design. Make sure to document any changes you make to the procedure or the materials and equipment list.

6. Test your design by modelling a few rotations. Adjust your design, making note of any changes you make.

7. Use your design to model the changing phases of the Moon and the apparent retrograde motion of Mars, Jupiter, and/or Saturn. How can these phenomena be explained according to the geocentric model? the heliocentric model? If necessary, adjust the design of your models and make note of any changes you make.

8. Present your final geocentric and heliocentric models in the format of your choice. Describe the celestial phenomenon you chose and show how your models explain the celestial phenomenon.

9. Consider how you could refine your investigation if you were to repeat it. Discuss your suggestions with your group or as a class.

Key Concept Review

1. How are First Nations and Métis peoples' ideas of the creation of the universe based on their knowledge of their environment?

2. Using the creation of the universe as an example, explain how a person's culture may influence their explanations of the world around them.

3. Why do scientists find the use of models so important?

4. What did Edwin Hubble discover about the motion of the 46 galaxies he first studied?

5. How did Hubble's discovery provide evidence for what Georges Lemaître had proposed about the universe?

6. How old is the universe thought to be?

7. Does red light in the visible light spectrum have a longer or a shorter wavelength than blue light?

8. (a) Make a sketch to illustrate what scientific astronomers mean when they say that light from a distant galaxy is red-shifted.

   (b) What does a large red shift indicate about a galaxy's motion?

9. Explain how cosmic background radiation supports the Big Bang theory of how the universe formed.

10. (a) Scientific astronomers have learned in recent decades that the most distant galaxies from the Milky Way are moving away from us. Use the library or the Internet to research the rate at which these galaxies are moving away from the Milky Way.

    (b) What does your answer to part (a) suggest about the universe?

11. Imagine you are standing on a shore and there is an invisible duck swimming on a calm pond. For each example (a) and (b) shown below, state whether the duck is swimming toward or away from you. Explain how you know the direction of its movement.

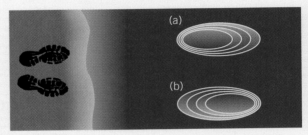

Question 11

12. What technological development played an important part in gathering support for the heliocentric model? How was it helpful?

13. Describe the geocentric and heliocentric models of the universe in terms of the position and movement of the Sun, Earth, and the stars.

14. Explain how elliptical orbits and better explanations of apparent retrograde motion provided evidence to support the heliocentric model of the solar system.

Connect Your Understanding

15. You have learned two scientific theories: the Big Bang theory and the heliocentric model of the solar system. Choose one theory and explain how this theory was developed. Be sure to include observations that were made, developments in technology, and evidence that supports the theory. Present your findings using a format of your choice, such as a graphic organizer, timeline, written paper, or presentation.

©P

16. Most evidence collected by scientists so far supports the Big Bang theory of the origin and formation of the universe. All other scientific theories to explain the origin have so far largely been disproven by scientific evidence. If you were a scientist, would you agree or disagree with the statement: "The Big Bang theory is correct because it is the last theory standing"? Explain the reason for your answer.

17. Scientists speculate that trillions of years from now, galaxies will have moved away from our galaxy faster than their light can reach us. Our region of space, like all other regions, will be left in the dark. Is this something we should plan for on Earth? Explain.

18. Humans have attempted to explain the origin of the universe and our place in it from both cultural and scientific perspectives. How are the explanations similar? How are they different?

19. Another type of retrograde motion is retrograde rotation. Use library or Internet resources to research retrograde rotation and which planets undergo this type of retrograde motion. Present your findings in the format of your choice, such as a poster, written report, or presentation.

Reflection

20. Think about the activities in this chapter that you carried out. Make a list of the ones you did or observed your teacher demonstrating. Beside each activity, write down two points you learned from it that have helped you better understand the concepts presented in the text.

21. Many of the activities in this text suggest that you brainstorm in a small group or as a class. What benefits do you think a group approach offers in terms of helping to advance ideas about a topic?

22. For each of the following topics, describe three facts that you learned in this section that you did not know before:

(a) formation of the universe

(b) structure of the universe

(c) evolution of the universe

After Reading

Reflect and Evaluate

Summarize the "improve your understanding" strategies you learned to use in this chapter. Working with a partner, create a tips sheet for other readers about improving understanding when they are reading. Add other strategies that you have used successfully to understand what you read.

Reflection on Essential Inquiry Questions

How has the way we explain what is occurring in our solar system and universe changed? What has caused these changes? **SI**

How do different understandings of the universe affect how we explore it? **TPS**

How have advances in technology lead to different theories on how the universe may have formed? **DM**

How is making sense of the universe culturally influenced? **CP**

Unit Task

Technology is now allowing humans to explore our solar system and universe in new and exciting ways. As more information is gathered, our knowledge grows. Canada is not only a leader in development of space technology, but also a contributor to the understanding of our universe. How will a greater understanding of the creation or nature of the universe be useful in completing your Unit Task?

12

Space exploration improves our knowledge and gives us beneficial technologies and has significant costs and hazards.

What you will learn:

- Humans throughout history, including First Nations and Métis peoples, have interpreted their observations of the universe and used that knowledge to aid them in everyday life.

- Canada has made significant contributions to space research, technology, and exploration.

- The importance and benefits of space exploration often outweigh the costs, hazards, and issues surrounding it.

- Exploring the universe gives us a greater understanding of its nature while also advancing the development of technologies for use on Earth.

Astronaut Stephen K. Robinson is mounted on the end of the Canadarm2 robotic arm to make repairs to the International Space Station in orbit around Earth.

Before Writing

Signalling Organizational Patterns

Good writers give signals to the reader about the way text is organized. They use dates and sequencing words (such as *first*, *next*, *then*) to indicate time order for a chronological or sequential account. Often, in scientific writing, writers will also use a problem-solution pattern, describing a problem and suggesting possible solutions. Skim section 12.1, and decide which type of organizational pattern is used.

Key Terms
- artificial satellite
- geostationary orbit
- microgravity • spinoff

Figure 12.1 An artist's concept of *Pioneer 11* in flight against the backdrop of Saturn's rings. *Pioneer 11* is expected to be approaching a star in the constellation Aquila in about 4 million years.

Here is a summary of what you will learn in this section:

- Throughout history, humans have explained phenomena in the universe based on what they are able to observe.

- As telescopes, space probes, and other technologies have advanced, humans have been able to explore farther out into space. Such observations provide evidence that leads us to different conclusions about our understanding of our solar system and the universe.

Into the Frontier of Space

In 1972, the space probe *Pioneer 10* was launched by the National Aeronautics and Space Administration (NASA), the U.S. agency responsible for the country's space program. The mission of this unpiloted spacecraft was to fly past Jupiter and continue on to the outer solar system. *Pioneer 10* transmitted images of Jupiter back to Earth that revealed details humans had never been able to see before. The probe continues to travel through space, but no signals have been received from it since January 2003. By August 2009, Earth-based telescopes tracking *Pioneer 10* saw that it was already more than 1000 times farther from the Sun than Earth. If nothing interferes with its progress, it could pass the star Aldebaran in about 2 million years.

In 1973, *Pioneer 11* was sent on a similar mission as its sister probe with the added task of capturing images of Saturn (Figure 12.1), as well as Jupiter. No communication has been received from the probe since 1995.

Space probes *Voyager 1* and *Voyager 2* were launched in 1977 to study Jupiter, Saturn, and the outer solar system. *Voyager 1* is the most distant human-made object in space (Figure 12.2). By February 2011, Voyager 1 was 116.082 AU away.

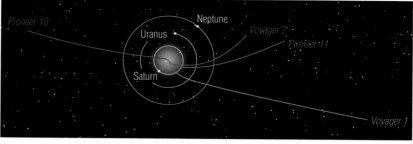

Figure 12.2 The current location and direction of travel of the *Pioneer 10* and *11* space probes, as well as *Voyager 1* and *2*

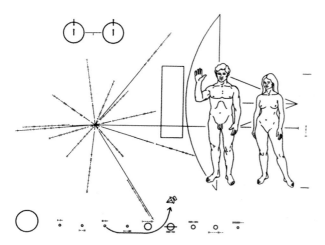

Figure 12.3 Peaceful greetings on the plaque aboard *Pioneer 10* and *Pioneer 11*

Both *Pioneer* craft have now left the solar system and are travelling into space like two ghost ships. The two *Voyager* craft continue to transmit data to Earth, but their future will be like that of the *Pioneer* probes. Still, the purpose of all four craft has not entirely ended. Aboard each *Pioneer* probe is an engraved plaque showing a man and woman, the solar system, and other basic information to indicate where Earth is located (Figure 12.3). Aboard each *Voyager* probe is a "golden record," with recorded sounds and pictures of Earth.

D23 *Quick Science*

Greetings from the People of Earth

Each of the *Pioneer* space probes that have left the solar system carries the plaque shown in Figure 12.3. It is hoped that other life forms that think enough like humans might find one of the probes and be able to use the plaque's information, even millions of years from now, to locate Earth.

Purpose

To examine the implications of sending information about humans into space

Procedure

1. Working in a small group, read through the following questions. Discuss each question within your group, and record your answers in point form. If there are differences of opinion within your group, be sure to note them as well.

2. When you have discussed all the questions, be prepared to share your answers with the class.

Questions

3. What does our sending information like this out into space suggest about our own ideas of the universe?

4. What does the plaque information assume about the nature of any aliens who might acquire it?

5. If you were to design your own plaque, what would you put on it? Explain.

6. If the plaque can last a million years, will it outlive the human race? Explain your answer.

7. Would aliens capable of finding the plaque already know about Earth because of our radio transmissions?

8. Is the most likely finder of the plaque going to be future human space travellers who have forgotten their early roots? Explain your answer.

Pose New Questions

9. What would you like to know about the life forms that may find the plaque?

10. What issues could there be if the plaque is found? What if it is not found?

The Evolution of Astronomers' Tools

The idea that humans could send spacecraft such as *Pioneer 11* and *12* so far away to gather information about the universe would have been unimaginable a century ago. Still, today's accomplishments in technology and scientific astronomy are built on the observations, engineering prototypes, and scientific problem-solving skills of the past.

Astronomy has been around for at least 4000 years. Early on, astronomers used their eyes to observe celestial objects. Step by step, our understanding of space and Earth's place in it has progressed, thanks in large part to the improvement of the tools available to observe, record, measure, and analyze what we see.

As you read in Chapter 9, humans are very inventive and have developed tools over the centuries to help them better understand astronomical phenomena. Sundials, for example, have been used for more than 7000 years to measure the passage of time (Figure 12.4). Ancient Egyptians invented a device called a merkhet to chart astronomical positions and predict the movement of stars. In the second century, Egyptian astronomers designed a tool called a quadrant to measure a star's height above the horizon (Figure 12.5). For centuries, Arabian astronomers used the astrolabe to make accurate charts of star positions. In the 14th century, astronomer Levi ben Gerson invented the cross-staff to measure the angle between the Moon and any given star. With each of these innovations, astronomers made new discoveries and gained more knowledge about what they were seeing.

Figure 12.4 The upright part of a sundial casts a shadow onto the face of the dial. The position and movement of the shadow provide an accurate way to track time, at least during sunny days.

Suggested Activity •············
D24 Science, Technology, Society, and the Environment on page 401

quadrant

astrolabe

cross-staff

Figure 12.5 The inventiveness of astronomers led them to develop many tools to help them observe, record, and measure celestial activity.

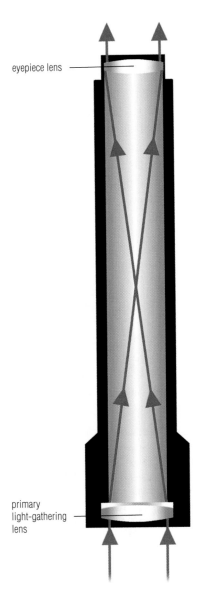

eyepiece lens

primary
light-gathering
lens

Figure 12.6 A refracting telescope

Telescopes

Optical Telescopes

The invention of the telescope in the Netherlands in the late 16th century was a technological breakthrough that revolutionized Western astronomy. Suddenly, astronomers such as Galileo could see more in the night sky than ever before. Telescopes detected exciting details about Earth's closest planetary neighbours and revealed the existence of other astronomical bodies in the solar system. With the telescope, astronomers learned that what lay beyond Earth was greater than they had ever imagined.

The first telescope was a simple refracting telescope. Refracting telescopes use two lenses to gather and focus starlight (Figure 12.6). However, there is a limit to how large a refracting telescope can be. Lenses larger than 1 m in diameter warp under their own weight and distort images, like trying to look at objects through the bottom of a pop bottle.

Reflecting telescopes use mirrors instead of lenses to gather and focus light (Figure 12.7). At one end of a reflecting telescope is a large concave mirror made from glass-like material that is coated with a thin layer of metal. The metal, such as aluminum, is polished to a shiny finish so that it can reflect even the faintest light. Reflecting telescopes are often located high on mountaintops to get the clearest view possible of the night sky.

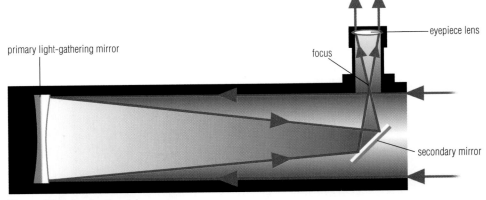

primary light-gathering mirror

eyepiece lens

focus

secondary mirror

Figure 12.7 A reflecting telescope

Figure 12.8 The Canada-France-Hawaii Telescope is located on Mauna Kea, Hawaii, the tallest mountain in the world.

Ground-based Optical Telescopes

An example of a ground-based, or Earth-based, telescope is the Canada-France-Hawaii Telescope (Figure 12.8). In 2007, it detected the most distant black hole yet discovered in the universe, nearly 13 billion ly away. It was detected because the telescope was able to view glowing gas falling into the hole.

©P

Space-based Optical Telescopes

All ground-based telescopes are still at the mercy of the weather. Clouds, humidity, and even high winds can interfere with stargazing. For this reason, telescopes positioned high above Earth's atmosphere have a tremendous advantage over ground-based telescopes.

Canada's space telescope, **M**icrovariability and **O**scillations of **St**ars (MOST), launched in 2003. MOST is the size of a suitcase and has a mirror only 15 cm across (Figure 12.9). Despite its tiny size, it has amazing capabilities. It can detect hidden features on the inside of stars by recording vibrations that occur on their surface. Its two-year mission was so successful that it has been used to analyze planets that are not visible to even the best ground-based telescopes.

The Hubble Space Telescope is a reflecting telescope that orbits about 600 km above Earth. Launched in 1990, the Hubble is a cylinder just over 13 m in length and 4.3 m in diameter at its widest point. Gradually, it will be phased out of service.

By 2014, the Hubble will be replaced by the James Webb Space Telescope (Figure 12.10). Located 1.5 million km from Earth, the James Webb will get even clearer images of more remote objects than the Hubble.

The James Webb telescope will gather infrared emissions, allowing scientists to "see" objects from the farthest and earliest galaxies. Infrared is able to see through the immense amounts of dust present in the universe. These dust clouds can block visible light making some objects impossible to see. The infrared signatures of astronomical bodies can be detected through these dust clouds. As well, some objects that only emit small amounts of light will now be visible because of their infrared emission.

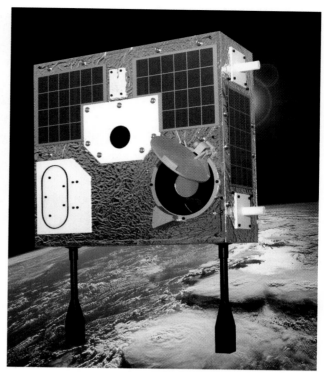

Figure 12.9 Canada's MOST space telescope can image planets in other solar systems.

Figure 12.10 Model of the James Webb Space Telescope. The James Webb Telescope will use infrared light to detect objects even through dust clouds.

info**BIT**

Canadian Contributions

Canadians played an important role in the James Webb telescope. Canadian engineers developed the Fine Guidance Sensor, used for adjusting the telescope, and Tunable Filter Imager, used for an imaging technique called coronagraphy.

Figure 12.11 The four curved mirrors of the Chandra X Ray Telescope are able to observe the X rays from particles up to the last millisecond before they fall into a black hole.

For examining objects that emit huge amounts of energy, such as supernovas, black holes, and quasars, scientists use X ray telescopes. Instead of gathering visible light, like a traditional telescope, these telescopes gather X ray wavelengths. Because X rays cannot pass through Earth's atmosphere, these telescopes are used on rockets, balloons, or satellites. In 1999, the Chandra X Ray Observatory, which is stationed in Earth's orbit, became operational, giving incredible images that are improving our understanding of the universe (Figure 12.11).

Radio Telescopes

Optical telescopes collect visible light. Radio telescopes detect and record radio waves emitted by stars, galaxies, nebulae, and even some planets. Studying radio waves emitted by objects in space gives astronomers data that are not available from the visible spectrum.

Astronomers use radio telescopes to collect signals and focus them (Figure 12.12). Sophisticated electronics and computers then allow the collected information to be mapped.

Figure 12.12 The world's largest radio telescope, at the Arecibo Observatory in Puerto Rico. Its dish measures 305 m in diameter.

Radio telescopes have several advantages over optical telescopes. Radio waves are less affected by weather and can be detected during the day and at night. They are also not distorted by clouds, pollution, or the atmosphere as light waves are.

As well, it was radio telescopes that detected cosmic background radiation, the microwave radiation that scientists interpreted as evidence for the Big Bang theory.

Using radio telescopes, astronomers have also detected quasars, enormously powerful energy sources at the edge of the visible universe (Figure 12.13). As you learned in Chapter 10, quasars put out as much energy as an entire galaxy but may be no larger than a solar system. Astronomers continue to study quasars using radio telescopes.

Figure 12.13 This image of 3C186 reveals a very distant quasar.

12.1 CHECK and REFLECT

1. How have scientists used space probes to gather information?

2. Name three tools developed and used by astronomers before the invention of the telescope.

3. Compare and contrast reflecting and refracting telescopes.

4. If a telescope with a larger lens can capture better images, why are there no extremely large refracting telescopes?

5. What are some reasons that observatories are built on remote mountaintops?

6. Radio astronomers can make observations at any time during the day, but optical astronomers are limited to making their observations at night. Explain why.

7. Using a Venn diagram, compare the types of information collected by the three types of telescopes: ground-based optical telescopes, space-based optical telescopes, and radio telescopes.

8. Discuss how the development of technology has helped not only with new discoveries, but with our understanding of space.

9. Using what you learned about the three featured space telescopes, explain why there is a need to improve the instruments that modern-day astronomers use.

10. This section includes two activities that differ in purpose and skills focus. Comment on the difficulties and successes you experience in carrying out the activities.

D24 *Science, Technology, Society, and the Environment*

Ancient Astronomers

In this activity, you will discover the contributions of ancient astronomers. Many of these discoveries and observations influenced the culture, building structures, and religion of these ancient peoples.

You will research three of the following cultures:

- First Nations and Métis
- Babylonians
- Chinese
- Egyptians
- Greeks
- Incas
- Mayans

Present your findings in essay format, writing a minimum of three paragraphs for each of the groups. Discuss what discoveries were made by each of the groups and how these discoveries influenced that group's culture.

Figure 12.14 This photograph, named "Earthrise," was taken by the Apollo 8 crew during their historic mission to orbit the Moon in 1968. Although this photo is usually presented with the Moon appearing at the bottom, this orientation is how the Apollo 8 astronauts saw it. It is generally considered the most influential photograph ever taken.

Earthrise

Until 1968, we on Earth did not really have a good sense of what our home planet looked like from the viewpoint of far away. The image shown in Figure 12.14, however, changed humanity's view of Earth. This picture was taken from the *Apollo 8* spacecraft that orbited the Moon in 1968, carrying three astronauts. For the first time, humans saw their small blue-and-green planet against the darkness and depth of space.

"Earthrise," as the image came to be known, appeared around the world on newspaper front pages, magazine covers, and postage stamps. It was this picture that helped people realize that our planet does not have infinite resources and that even the seas and the atmosphere are finite. The main purpose of the *Apollo 8* program was to advance our exploration of the Moon. Yet, the true legacy of the mission was that it helped billions of people gain a greater appreciation of their home, the planet Earth.

The Origins of the World

People from all over the world have used the oral traditions of storytelling to pass knowledge from one generation to another. These stories provide explanations of the world around us. Creation stories are an important part of different cultures, as they explain how the world came into existence and humans' place within it. We also use science fiction and fantasy literature to help us understand and explore ideas on how and why we and the universe exist.

Purpose

To identify the common characteristics of the origins of the world from various cultures

Materials & Equipment

- poster paper or newsprint
- felt pens
- reference materials on various creation stories
- Internet access (optional)

Procedure

1. Complete a KWL chart about what you currently know about different origin myths.

2. You will be assigned a specific area of the world. Conduct research on an origin story of a culture in that area.

3. When you have found your story, answer the following:

   - What is the main topic or theme of the story?
   - Who are the main characters of the story?
   - What is the sequence of events?
   - What are the lessons learned in the story?

4. In a small group, share the story.

5. Complete a placemat organizer (Figure 12.15) to find the similarities and differences among the stories you have heard. Each outer section shows the differences between the myths, while the inner section shows the similarities.

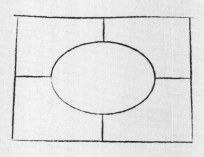

Figure 12.15

6. As a group, choose one of the stories from your group to present to the class. This could be done as a play, mural, song, interview, or dance.

Questions

7. After seeing other groups' performances, explain how these stories help to make sense of the origin of the world.

8. Compare your organizer with those of other groups. How do they differ? How are they similar?

9. Why do think these similarities exist even though they come from different cultures?

10. Whom do you think the stories were created for? Explain your answer.

Pose New Questions

11. What questions do you still have about some of the stories you heard?

12. What modern examples of stories about the origin of Earth from different media do you know of?

Major Advances in Space Exploration

Space exploration began as soon as humans gazed upward. Before long, humans longed to explore space themselves. To make the journey, they needed to develop some form of transportation.

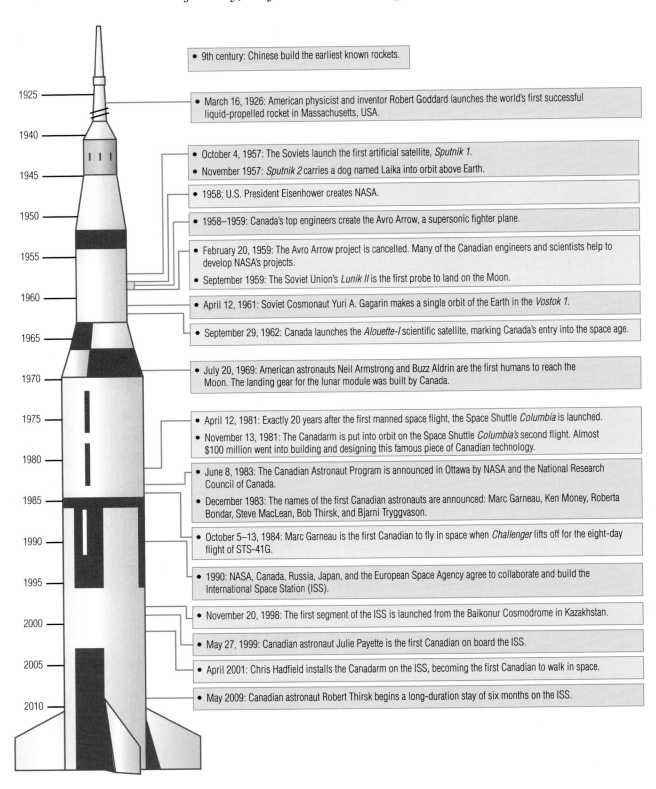

- 9th century: Chinese build the earliest known rockets.

- March 16, 1926: American physicist and inventor Robert Goddard launches the world's first successful liquid-propelled rocket in Massachusetts, USA.

- October 4, 1957: The Soviets launch the first artificial satellite, *Sputnik 1*.
- November 1957: *Sputnik 2* carries a dog named Laika into orbit above Earth.

- 1958: U.S. President Eisenhower creates NASA.

- 1958–1959: Canada's top engineers create the Avro Arrow, a supersonic fighter plane.

- February 20, 1959: The Avro Arrow project is cancelled. Many of the Canadian engineers and scientists help to develop NASA's projects.
- September 1959: The Soviet Union's *Lunik II* is the first probe to land on the Moon.

- April 12, 1961: Soviet Cosmonaut Yuri A. Gagarin makes a single orbit of the Earth in the *Vostok 1*.

- September 29, 1962: Canada launches the *Alouette-I* scientific satellite, marking Canada's entry into the space age.

- July 20, 1969: American astronauts Neil Armstrong and Buzz Aldrin are the first humans to reach the Moon. The landing gear for the lunar module was built by Canada.

- April 12, 1981: Exactly 20 years after the first manned space flight, the Space Shuttle *Columbia* is launched.
- November 13, 1981: The Canadarm is put into orbit on the Space Shuttle *Columbia's* second flight. Almost $100 million went into building and designing this famous piece of Canadian technology.

- June 8, 1983: The Canadian Astronaut Program is announced in Ottawa by NASA and the National Research Council of Canada.
- December 1983: The names of the first Canadian astronauts are announced: Marc Garneau, Ken Money, Roberta Bondar, Steve MacLean, Bob Thirsk, and Bjarni Tryggvason.

- October 5–13, 1984: Marc Garneau is the first Canadian to fly in space when *Challenger* lifts off for the eight-day flight of STS-41G.

- 1990: NASA, Canada, Russia, Japan, and the European Space Agency agree to collaborate and build the International Space Station (ISS).

- November 20, 1998: The first segment of the ISS is launched from the Baikonur Cosmodrome in Kazakhstan.

- May 27, 1999: Canadian astronaut Julie Payette is the first Canadian on board the ISS.

- April 2001: Chris Hadfield installs the Canadarm on the ISS, becoming the first Canadian to walk in space.

- May 2009: Canadian astronaut Robert Thirsk begins a long-duration stay of six months on the ISS.

Space Transportation Technologies

The science of rocketry has sent humans on round trips to the Moon and sent robots to investigate our neighbouring planets. It has also launched the Hubble Space Telescope and, in 2014, it will send the James Webb Space Telescope into space. For the past few decades, four main types of spacecraft have been used:

- Rockets lift small capsules containing crew, equipment, or satellites into orbit and beyond. The new generation of human space flight spacecraft is the *Orion* crew exploration vehicle (Figure 12.16).

- Space shuttles transport personnel and equipment to orbiting spacecraft. The space shuttle was first used in 1981 and was instrumental in the building of the International Space Station.

- Space stations are orbiting spacecraft that have living quarters, work areas, and all the support systems needed to allow people to live and work in space for extended periods.

- Space probes are unmanned craft that carry out robotic exploration of space.

Figure 12.16 The first *Orion* crew exploration vehicle is due to begin servicing the International Space Station by 2015.

The International Space Station

The International Space Station, assembled in space in several stages since 1998, orbits at 400 km above Earth. It is the largest spacecraft ever built. One of Canada's most significant contributions to the space station has been the Canadarm2, shown on the opening page of this chapter. This robotic device can move astronauts and equipment around as they work outside the space station. It can also bend around corners and grasp objects with its computer-controlled "fingers."

Space Probes

One important technology for space exploration is the space probe, which is a robotic spacecraft that explores celestial bodies or even distant galaxies. These probes are launched from Earth and may take months or years to reach what they are to observe.

Many probes have been launched by different space agencies. Some explore planets, such as *Mariner 10*, which explored Mercury. Others have multiple purposes, such as *Pioneer 10*, which was the first spacecraft to travel through the asteroid belt on its way to Jupiter.

re*Search*

There have been many achievements and spinoff benefits to human space explorations as well as sacrifices and tragedy. Starting with Laika, the Russian space dog, research the costs of space exploration that cannot be measured in dollars and cents.

Suggested Activity •·········
D26 Science, Technology, Society, and the Environment on pages 412–413

The probe Near Earth Asteroid Rendezvous (NEAR) Shoemaker's mission was to orbit and then land on an asteroid. It was launched in February 1996 and landed in 2001. Astronomers learned much about the composition and properties of asteroids and how asteroids interact with other celestial phenomena, such as solar wind. This information could not have been gathered without the probe.

Currently, some of the most interesting probes are the ones being sent to Mars. In preparation for a possible manned mission, we need to gather as much information as possible. Canada has played an important role on these missions. For example, Canada's meteorological station aboard the *Phoenix* Mars Lander studied the climate and environment and discovered snow forming in the atmosphere of the red planet, as well as ice!

Benefits of Space Research

Space research and exploration are constantly revealing new details about the size and complexity of the universe. This knowledge helps improve our understanding of Earth, our solar system, and the origins of everything around us.

At the same time, many of the technologies invented to advance space research and exploration are now aiding us in our everyday lives on Earth. From faster, safer airplane trips to the widespread availability of cellphone communication and improved fire-fighting equipment (Figure 12.17), we see the spinoffs of space research all around us. A **spinoff** is a secondary effect or product of a thing or an activity.

Product Technologies

Many items, materials, and systems first created for a space application have been put to practical use on Earth. For example, astronauts even in low orbit in space are at risk of receiving harmful levels of radiation emitted by the Sun. As a result of research into how to protect astronauts from such exposure, we now have better radiation detectors on Earth and better ways of shielding people during radiation-related medical treatments. From cancer treatments and pacemakers to mechanical insulin pumps and flat-screen televisions, the technological benefits created by space research are now everywhere in our daily lives.

Figure 12.17 The fire-resistant suits and compact breathing apparatus used today by firefighters are spinoffs from innovations developed for astronauts.

All of these innovations, many developed for use in the International Space Station, got their start fulfilling a purpose in space exploration.

Table 12.1 lists some of the spinoff applications of space technology. Opportunities for the economic development of space resources are also being investigated today, including such ideas as offering tourist space flights, building hotels on the Moon, and mining minerals on asteroids.

Table 12.1 Space Exploration Spinoff Products

Product	Purpose for Space Exploration	Example of Spinoff Use on Earth
Dehydrated food	To provide astronauts with meals for long flights	Portable camping food; emergency food supply; food storage
Miniaturized computers and robotics	To equip space vehicles and probes	Emergency response robots, such as those that inspect explosive devices
Scratch-resistant plastic coatings	To protect astronauts' helmet visors	Coating for plastic eyeglass lenses that increases scratch resistance up to 10 times
Memory foam (an open-cell foam that evenly distributes the weight of a load)	To pad aircraft and spacecraft seats to buffer astronauts from the impact of landings	Motorcycle and bicycle seats (Figure 12.18); pillows and mattresses for bedridden patients to reduce bed sores
Antibacterial water filter	To provide clean drinking water for astronauts	Household water purification filters
Infrared thermometer	To measure the temperatures of stars	Medical thermometers that can measure body temperatures faster and more accurately (Figure 12.19)
Ionization smoke detector	To detect possible fire outbreaks on board spacecraft	Sensitive household smoke detectors

Figure 12.18 Modern comforts, such as padded bicycle seats, are a spinoff of space research.

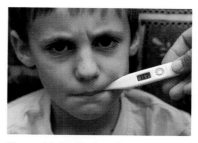

Figure 12.19 Modern thermometers are another space research spinoff.

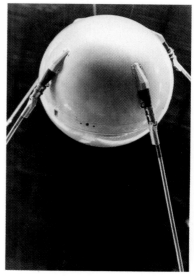

Figure 12.20 *Sputnik 1*, launched in 1957, had a radio transmitter on board that could be picked up by shortwave radios.

Satellite Technologies

Perhaps the greatest single impact on global society has occurred with the development of artificial satellite technologies. In Chapter 9, you saw that moons are satellites of their respective planets, sometimes referred to as natural satellites. An **artificial satellite** (or, simply, satellite) is a human-made device placed in orbit around Earth or another celestial object. The first satellite was launched in 1957 by the former Soviet Union (Figure 12.20). It was only the size of a football, and its purpose was to demonstrate that sending a device into orbit was possible.

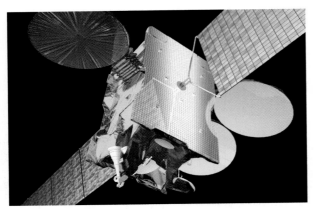

infoBIT

Anik Satellites

In the Inuit language, *anik* means "little brother."

Communications Technologies

Canada was the third country in the world to launch a satellite. Canada's first satellite, *Alouette 1*, collected data about the extreme upper regions of the atmosphere, where many future satellites would be placed. Canada also launched a series of Anik satellites beginning in 1972. *Anik 1* transmitted 12 television channels to large ground stations across the country. The signals were then rebroadcast by regional ground-based transmitters already in place. The Anik satellites were particularly important in connecting Canada's northern communities with the rest of the country. The use of these satellites was innovative and set a trend for future communications satellites worldwide.

Today, communications satellites circle the globe. *Anik F3* was launched by Telesat Canada in 2007 (Figure 12.21). It occupies a geostationary orbit above Earth. A **geostationary orbit** is one in which a satellite orbits Earth at the same rate as Earth rotates. This makes the satellite appear stationary (staying still) when viewed from the ground, and enables receiving antennas to be permanently pointed to one spot in the sky. *Anik F3* has a mass of 5900 kg, which is 10 times the mass of the original *Anik* satellite. It provides broadcast and broadband Internet services across North America.

Figure 12.21 *Anik F3*, a Canadian communications satellite launched in 2007

Figure 12.22 With more than two dozen satellites in orbit, there are at least three above the horizon, relative to a person's location on Earth, at any one time.

Tracking Devices

The Global Positioning System (commonly referred to as GPS) is the most widely available tracking system today. It relies on a group of satellites that transmit low-energy microwave signals (Figure 12.22). These signals are picked up by small receivers in hand-held devices (Figure 12.23). A GPS receiver can show you your location and, if you are walking or in a vehicle, show how fast you are moving and in what direction. Today, GPS is widely used for commercial applications, map-making, agriculture, surveying, wildlife research, and personal use.

Figure 12.23 The computer in a GPS receiver calculates your position and displays it on the receiver's screen.

©P

Remote Sensing and Digital Imaging

When a series of clouds drift by on a sunny day, it is not possible to see from the ground that these clouds may be part of a weather pattern that covers half a continent. When waves lap ashore on the beaches of the Great Lakes or James Bay, it is not possible to notice decades-long patterns such as changes in average water level. On the other hand, one satellite image may show the changes in air quality right across a continent, or measure the effect of flooding or forest fire damage across a whole region. Only from the vantage point of space can the entire view of an 800-km hurricane be seen with its advancing storm front on the outside to the quiet centre of its eye.

Satellite imaging can show changes over time. Many satellites remain operational for decades, allowing the collection and archiving of data for later analysis. Earth observation satellites already show us the results of the constant slashing and burning of the world's rainforests, as shown in Figure 12.24, and the presence of a hole in the protective ozone layer. Long-term monitoring provides data to help us assess the impact of human populations on landscapes and oceans.

In viewing Earth, satellite observation equipment must make a trade-off between how much of Earth it can observe at one time and the amount of detail in the image. A high-resolution image can show individual buildings, roads, cars, and even people. However, the higher the resolution, the longer it takes to cover a given area. For the assessment of natural disasters due to hurricanes, flooding, and volcanic activity, medium-resolution instruments covering a wide area are used.

During Writing

Match Organization to the Purpose and Audience

Once writers know their purpose and audience, they can choose an organizational pattern. Should it be cause and effect, problem-solution, or time order/sequential? Think about this as you carry out the writing task for STSE C26.

(a)

(b)

Figure 12.24 The same area of rainforest shown (a) several years ago and (b) today. Note how the forest cover has changed.

Envisat (for "environmental satellite"), launched by the European Space Agency, is part of a network of satellites operated by various nations around the world to observe Earth. Launched in 2002, the *Envisat* satellite is packed with an array of sensors for studying the atmosphere, the oceans, land surfaces, and ice (Figure 12.25).

Figure 12.25 *Envisat* image showing three of the Great Lakes

Figure 12.26 The GOCE satellite in orbit

Real-Time Imaging

Not all satellites observe Earth by taking pictures. For example, the GOCE satellite (**G**ravity Field and Steady-State **O**cean **C**irculation **E**xplorer), launched in 2009 by the European Space Agency, makes measurements of the subtle variations in Earth's gravity (Figure 12.26).

The strength of the gravitational force field sensed by a passing satellite is affected by the distribution of matter beneath it. For example, the existence of a mountain range below a satellite increases the gravity slightly. Similarly, a mountain located under the sea would also affect the gravitational force. It is expected that the GOCE satellite will advance human understanding of ocean circulation, sea-level change, climate change, volcanoes, and earthquakes.

As improvements are made to sensing technology, data integration software, and broadband speed, researchers expect that soon data from many different satellites can be combined at once. This will make it possible to view current and past conditions on Earth. Such data will likely be available directly from the Internet, and may even be a hybrid of direct photography as well as computer overlays of information. Several sources on the Internet provide imaging now, some of which is freely accessible, such as mapping information (Figure 12.27).

Figure 12.27 Images like this of the Parliament Buildings in Ottawa are available free on the Internet.

Even today, the millions of images taken over several years can be combined to show the "full picture" of Earth. Examples of interpreted real-time images include those showing Earth without cloud cover or at night, with population centres, burning rainforests, and natural gas flares all visible (Figure 12.28).

Figure 12.28 Earth's population centres are clearly visible at night from space, as shown in this composite image.

reSearch

Complete coverage of Canada's lands and oceans is being made by a group of satellites called the RADARSAT Constellation. Find out the role of these satellites in maritime surveillance, disaster management, and ecosystem monitoring.

1. Name three spinoff products mentioned in this section that you have used. Explain the products' connection to space exploration.

2. In your own words, define *artificial satellite*.

3. List and briefly describe four different functions of satellites.

4. What is a geostationary orbit? Why might a satellite be placed into a geostationary orbit?

5. The satellite image below shows a river emptying into a coastal area. What information might be revealed if scientists were to observe this area from space over several decades?

Question 5

6. What information about Earth can be found by making sensitive measurements of variations in Earth's gravity?

7. Briefly explain how a GPS receiver determines a location.

8. Suppose that high-resolution colour images of the surface of Earth are made and stored electronically. Computer software can analyze each image pixel by pixel, as well as count pixels, such as those representing water instead of land. Suggest ways the data from these images could be used in

   (a) monitoring the health of rainforests

   (b) surveying changing crop yields over time

   (c) converting usable agricultural land into cities

9. List five important ways in which Canada has contributed to, and participated in, space research, technology, and exploration.

10. In a small group, brainstorm products that you think may have been developed for use in space research or exploration. For the next week, keep a Space Technology Spinoff in My Life record. List each potential spinoff product and why you think it should be classified as a Space Technology Spinoff.

D26 *Science, Technology, Society, and the Environment*

Canadian Contributions to Space Research, Technology, and Exploration

For over 150 years, Canada has actively contributed to space research, technology, and exploration. Many individuals and organizations are involved. The federal government sponsors the Canada Space Agency and also provides financial support to many projects related to space research.

Also active are Canadian universities, research and development organizations, and private companies and industry working in a range of fields, including aeronautics, satellite technology, and telecommunications.

Today, Canadian astronomers, astronauts, robotics engineers, and dozens of other science and technology specialists collaborate with colleagues around the world to advance human understanding of space.

In this activity, you will research the extent of Canada's contributions in one particular area and then present your findings to the class.

Procedure

1. Working in a small group, choose one of the following categories to research:

   • Canada and Satellite Technology

   • A Timeline of Canada's Work with the ISS

   • The History of Canada's Astronaut Program

   • Current Areas of Research by Canadian Astronomers

   • The David Florida Laboratory (Figure 12.29)

   Alternatively, suggest an area of Canadian contribution to space study that you would like to research. Ask your teacher for approval before you begin.

Figure 12.29 The David Florida Laboratory near Ottawa

2. With your group, brainstorm questions about your topic and what sources you will use for your research. Options for research sources include the Internet, books, journals, documentaries, and interviews with people who have special knowledge.

3. Conduct your research, making notes and gathering relevant photographs, artwork, and other materials to include in your report. Work with your group to develop an outline for the report. Assemble your findings and decide how best to summarize and report them.

4. In preparation for your presentation, discuss the implications to Canadian society that your topic has, or will have, in future. Some of the questions you should discuss may include the following:

   • What are benefits of your topic? What are some costs?

   • Do the benefits outweigh the costs?

   • Should Canada, with such a small population compared to other countries involved in space exploration, be so heavily involved with your topic area? Why or why not?

5. Develop your group's report as a computer presentation, video, or webcast. Be sure to include your group's discussion on the implications of topic area to Canadian society in your presentation.

6. Present your key findings to the class.

Questions

7. Based on your group's research findings, explain what most impressed you about that aspect of Canada's contributions to space research, technology, and exploration.

8. Based on the research and reporting of other groups, explain what most impressed you about those aspects of Canada's contributions.

9. Should Canada continue its space research? Should the Canadian government increase, decrease, or maintain its current level of funding for space research?

Dr. Robert (Bob) Thirsk: Adventure on the ISS

Dr. Robert Thirsk's fascination with human space flight influenced his educational path from a very young age. He has degrees in medicine, engineering, and business.

In 1983, Dr. Thirsk saw an ad in the paper that would change his life forever. Canada was looking for astronauts! Over 4000 individuals applied, and Thirsk was one of the six chosen to represent his country.

Each astronaut candidate has to complete a training program before earning the title of astronaut. The training is physically and mentally demanding. It includes wilderness training, underwater lab work, classroom time, and using simulators.

In 1996, Robert Thirsk fulfilled a lifelong dream as a payload specialist aboard the space shuttle on mission STS-78 (Figure 12.30). He was in space for 17 days, performing life and material science experiments.

Two years later, Dr. Thirsk was assigned to NASA's Johnson Space Center. In addition to his mission specialist training, he also worked as a CAPCOM (Capsule Communicator). The CAPCOM is the only person who communicates directly with astronauts while they are in space.

In 2009, Dr. Thirsk was the only active astronaut of the original six Canadian astronauts, and his second trip into space would be beyond anything he would have dreamed. He was selected to spend 6 months as a permanent crew member on the International Space Station (ISS) (Figures 12.31 and 12.32).

Throughout his career, Dr. Robert Thirsk has been a space pioneer. While he was on the ISS mission, he became the first Canadian to fly onboard a Russian Soyuz spacecraft, to stay in space an extended period of time, and to have the longest spaceflight of more than 125 million km. He also was part of the team that participated in Canadarm's first-ever capture of a space vehicle, Japan's HTV.

In view of all his accomplishments, the future of the Canadian Space Program still excites Dr. Thirsk. He says, "The next Canadian space generation, who are now in the high schools of our nation, are going to help define our place in the universe. I can't wait to see what they'll do."

Figure 12.30 The STS-78 mission patch features an eagle. Both mission badges were designed by Tsimshian artist Bill Helin.

Figure 12.31 Canadian astronauts Julie Payette and Robert Thirsk aboard the International Space Station

Figure 12.32 The ISS mission patch for Expedition 20/21 features a Thunderbird.

Here is a summary of what you will learn in this section:

- Space research and exploration are very costly, and travel into space involves a high degree of risk.

- While space exploration offers extensive benefits to humans, there are many ethical, political, and environmental issues to be assessed and balanced against the benefits.

- Living in the microgravity of space poses special risks to human health.

Figure 12.33 When such enormous problems as poverty are affecting millions of people on Earth, can we justify spending billions of dollars on space research and exploration? This is just one aspect of space study that is up for debate.

Questions About Space Exploration

There is no doubt that space exploration is exciting. There is also no doubt that we on Earth benefit greatly from space research and technology spinoffs, in addition to gaining valuable knowledge about the universe. At the same time, however, there remain many hard questions to ask and debate given the enormous amounts of money, time, and resources that countries spend on studying celestial objects and sending equipment and people into space (Figure 12.33). In the United States, space research and exploration programs cost billions of dollars every year.

As more countries become involved in exploring space, many issues and questions have arisen concerning the use and responsibility for space and its resources (Table 12.2 on page 416). For example, who owns space? Who is entitled to claim its resources, such as land or the mineral deposits on the Moon (Figure 12.34)? Is it right to spend billions of dollars to send a few people into space when millions of people on Earth do not have clean drinking water? Who is responsible for cleaning up the space environment?

All of these ethical, political, and environmental issues will grow as matters of debate in the coming decades as we expand our interest in space research, exploration, and development.

Figure 12.34 Before selling a piece of property, you must own it first. Who owns the land on other planets or moons?

Table 12.2 Examples of Issues Related to Space Research, Exploration, and Development

Issue		
Ethical	**Political**	**Environmental**
• How can we justify space exploration to expand human knowledge and understanding? • Do we have a right to alter materials in space to meet our needs? • Should we ensure that space resources will be used for the good of all humans and not to further the interests of only one nation or group?	• Who owns space and its resources? • Who will determine how space will be used? • Under what circumstances should weapons be allowed in space?	• Who is responsible for protecting space environments from alteration? • Who is responsible for cleaning up "space junk" (the equipment no longer used in space but left there in orbit)? • Meteorites have caused great environmental damage. Why, then, might it be irresponsible not to explore space to ensure the survival of Earth's inhabitants?

D27 *Quick Science*

Who Owns Space?

Today, there are over a dozen space agencies in the world (Figure 12.35). As travelling into space becomes more common, questions arise about the nature of our journeys.

Figure 12.35 The Indian Space Agency's first mission to the Moon landed in October 2008.

Purpose

To brainstorm some of the ethical, political, environmental, and economic issues connected to the ownership of space

Procedure

1. Read and answer the following questions.

2. In a class discussion, share your answers to each of the questions.

3. Summarize your answers. Did any of the answers you had in step 1 change because of your classmates' ideas? Do you think your ideas might have changed the views of others?

Questions

4. Do the resources of a moon, planet, or asteroid belong to the nation that is the first to land on it or claim it?

5. Should space resources be owned only by nations rich enough to be able to afford the costs of reaching those resources?

6. If we journey to other planets, should we go as ecotourists, only to observe the planet, leaving it in the condition we found it, or as pioneers, to settle and change the planet to meet human needs?

7. First Nations and Métis peoples believe that humans do not own anything and that everything belongs to Creator. How would you address this viewpoint, and yet ensure that all people have equal access to space?

Pose New Questions

8. What questions would you ask the United Nations to help create guidelines for countries to follow for space exploration?

9. What questions would you ask differing nations to help you ensure they all had equal access to resources?

©P

Hazards of Travelling in Space

We have only taken baby steps when it comes to exploring our solar system and beyond. Space exploration is a very high-risk undertaking. The space environment is not "life friendly." Many hazards lie beyond Earth's protective atmosphere. For example, both people and equipment face exposure to damage from intense solar radiation (Figure 12.36). There is also the potential for damage or total destruction from colliding with a comet, asteroid, or other objects.

Humans have learned to live in very extreme and varied environments on Earth and even on the International Space Station orbiting Earth. Still, many unforeseen risks and hazards remain. Accidents related to space travel may result not only in loss of human life, but in immense economic loss and the loss of countless years of work. In 1967, the three-member crew aboard *Apollo 1* died during a training exercise when fire broke out on board the spacecraft. In the same year, a Russian cosmonaut died on re-entry into Earth's atmosphere when the capsule's parachute failed to open. Two space shuttle accidents have occurred, one on launch in 1986 (Figure 12.37) and the other on returning from orbit in 2003. Seven crew members died in each incident. After each disaster, crewed space programs were suspended until the causes were found and fixed.

Equipment such as satellites and space probes to other planets are expensive. Both the Russians and Americans lost Mars probes shortly before the craft arrived at the planet. In both of those cases, hundreds of millions of dollars and thousands of hours of labour were lost.

Nevertheless, human curiosity in learning about space persists. Rather than back away from space exploration, space agencies around the world have continued to fund new projects, balancing risks and costs against potential benefits as best they can.

Figure 12.36 Crew members on board the International Space Station wear Russian-made spacesuits to protect them from hazards such as radiation.

Figure 12.37 The space shuttle *Challenger* broke up 1 min after launch because fuel leaked through faulty O-ring seals and ignited. Seven crew members died, including Christa McAuliffe, an elementary school teacher.

Challenges of Living in Space

People travelling and working in space do not need an Earth-like environment simply for comfort, but for survival. Humans have orbited Earth, flown far into space, landed on the Moon, and returned safely home. We are now hoping to put a human—not just a robotic machine—on another planet for the first time.

Scientists believe we now have the technology to send a group of astronauts to Mars and back. This would not be a typical week-long mission for space shuttle astronauts, nor would it be like the six months that astronaut Robert Thirsk spent in the International Space Station. Astronauts going to Mars would be gone for two to three years. Such long missions would pose many challenges. The physical environment is harsh. Living in confined quarters for such a long period of time can be stressful.

As well, the long-term effects of microgravity on humans are still unknown. **Microgravity** is the condition when gravitational forces are greatly reduced to almost zero. On Earth, gravity gives us our feeling of weight. This feeling is greatly reduced when a person is in orbit. Microgravity is often likened to a feeling of weightlessness, similar to what you may have felt briefly on an elevator or an amusement park ride that drops quickly.

Challenges of the Physical Environment

Space is a vacuum with no air or water. It also presents many hazards for spacecraft and its occupants, including the damaging effects of cosmic rays and solar radiation and the risk of being hit by space debris (Figure 12.38).

Furthermore, because there is no atmosphere in space, temperatures can range from unimaginably cold in shadows to extremely hot in the full Sun. No atmosphere also means that the gases that keep us alive on Earth, such as oxygen, do not exist in space. Neither does the pressure of the atmosphere, which keeps our bodily fluids from boiling at room temperature.

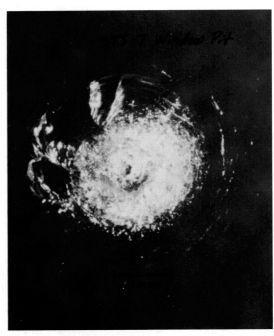

Figure 12.38 Damage to a spacecraft window from colliding with a small piece of space debris

Challenges of Confined Living

Long trips in a confined living space may lead to psychological problems. Imagine spending every minute of every day with one or two people for two years. Now, imagine spending those two years in an enclosure not much bigger than your classroom. Stepping outside for a break is not an option.

Suggested Activity •••••••••••
D28 Science, Technology, Society, and the Environment on page 421

Challenges of Microgravity

To stay in space for extended periods, the human body must physically adapt to a microgravity environment. On Mars and the Moon, the force of gravity is weaker than on Earth. People standing on Mars would feel only one-third of their weight on Earth. On the Moon, they would feel only one-sixth their normal weight.

Microgravity's Effects on the Body

Extended periods of microgravity cause changes in the human body that can have a negative effect on a person's health. For example:

- The heart, which is mostly muscle, does not have to pump as hard as it normally does to circulate blood. This causes the heart to weaken (Figure 12.39).

- The leg muscles used for walking and lifting are not used as much. As a result, these muscles start to weaken. Studies aboard the International Space Station show that within a relatively short time, a person can lose 40 percent of his or her muscle mass.

- Bones have much less pressure on them than normal. This causes them to lose minerals, which in turn leads to the bones weakening. Astronauts may lose bone mass at a rate of about two percent per month in microgravity.

- Red blood cell production in the body declines and the body's immune system weakens, increasing a person's risk of becoming infected.

Figure 12.39 Experiencing microgravity looks like fun, as these astronauts in training show, but the effects can be damaging to the body.

Reducing the Effects of Microgravity

Astronauts exercise in space to help keep fit (Figure 12.40). On board the International Space Station, crew members spend at least one hour each day doing cardiovascular training (exercising their heart and circulatory system), as well as an hour of resistance training (like weightlifting). During the first few space missions that lasted more than a month, it was discovered that those who did not exercise while in space could not stand up for a few days after returning to Earth.

Figure 12.40 An astronaut exercising in the Destiny laboratory of the International Space Station

Suggested Activities •·········
D29 Problem-Solving Activity on page 422
D30 Decision-Making Analysis
on pages 424–425

A number of the health conditions caused by microgravity appear to be similar to those that happen when humans age. Studies of health effects related to microgravity may lead to better care of the elderly, such as improved treatments for osteoporosis, a common type of bone degeneration. Canadian scientists, including Dr. Nicole Buckley, head of Life and Physical Sciences at the Canadian Space Agency, and also from Saskatchewan, have been leaders in this area of study.

Challenges of Visiting Mars

Getting spacecraft and astronauts safely to Mars, and someday beyond the inner solar system, will be a difficult task. The metal hull of spacecraft cannot effectively shield astronauts from solar radiation for a flight that will take years. Some plastics, such as those being developed for new spacesuits, have more than 10 times the shielding ability of metal. Without this protection, the crew would be at greatly increased risk of cancer.

The atmosphere on Mars is only about 1/100th the pressure of Earth's and does not contain oxygen. Sandstorms are also common on the planet. Because the atmosphere on Mars will not support life, a protective suit will be necessary for anyone leaving the controlled environment inside the landing craft. Current spacesuits will not do the job. They are bulky and heavy, making them very difficult to move around in. In addition to the challenges of building protective spacecraft and suits, scientists have to figure out how to supply the mission. This will include fuel and water supplies. A facility to live in will also have to be assembled, with air, heating, cooling, and other life-support systems installed.

Just as important as figuring out how to build and ship all of this material will be planning how to transport the astronauts on the return trip to Earth.

As well, NASA has investigated the effects of people living together in cramped quarters for extended periods. In 2007, it set up the Flashline Mars Arctic Research Station (Figure 12.41). A crew of seven lived together there for four months. The only time they were allowed to leave the facility—dressed in mock spacesuits—was to practise tasks related to geology.

What we learn from astronauts spending time on the ISS and travelling to the Moon, and possibly Mars, will one day help humans in their exploration of the outer regions of our solar system, other galaxies, and beyond.

infoBIT

Return to the Moon

Humans have not stood on the Moon since NASA's Apollo 17 mission in 1972. However, in February 2011, 29 teams began a race to land a robot on the Moon for a $30 million prize. Canada is one of the 17 countries participating in the race. The Google Lunar X PRIZE expects to award the winning prize sometime in 2015.

Figure 12.41 The Flashline Mars Arctic Research Station on Devon Island in Nunavut. The facility sits at the edge of a 23-km-diameter impact crater made when an asteroid struck Earth 39 million years ago.

1. Space research and exploration raise many concerns. For each of the broad categories below, write two questions that are being debated these days.
   (a) ethical
   (b) political
   (c) environmental

2. The First Nations and Métis peoples believe that they cannot own the land. They believe that they are the keepers of Earth for future generations and the decisions that they make must be based upon those beliefs. Should humans apply this idea to space? Justify your answer.

3. (a) What are some advantages to sending robotic probes rather than people into space?
   (b) What are some advantages to sending people into space rather than robotic probes?

4. In your own words, define *microgravity*.

5. How are astronauts able to minimize the effects of microgravity?

6. Adjusting to living in microgravity conditions poses many challenges for astronauts. Describe some of the more serious negative effects on health for humans living for extended periods in a microgravity environment.

Question 6

7. What might be some other challenges of living in space or on Mars that were not described in this chapter?

8. What preparations are needed to make the human exploration of Mars a reality?

D28 | *Science, Technology, Society, and the Environment*

Sharing a Small Place in Space

In addition to the environmental hazards that humans face in space exploration are many psychological challenges in sharing confined quarters with fellow travellers for long periods of time. For example, a one-way trip to Mars would take about 12 months, and a one-way trip to Jupiter would take a minimum of 2 years.

1. Use tape, chalk, string, or other material to mark a 4 m × 4 m square on the floor. Imagine that this outlines the size of the spacecraft that will be your home for the next year as you travel to Mars.

2. Stand in the square with five other classmates. For about 1 min, move around with your fellow astronauts as best you can in the space provided.

3. Return to your desks and, with your group, think about all the problems that could arise during a long trip in this type of confinement. List the potential problems you identify. Then, for each one, suggest a solution.

4. After you finish, compare your problems and solutions with those noted by other groups. What were some similarities? What were some differences?

D29 *Problem-Solving Activity*

The Effects of Space Travel on Human Health

Space travel puts humans in extreme environments where they experience everything from tremendous force exerted on them during the rocket launch to almost no force during their time in microgravity. Our ability to stay oriented—that is, knowing the directions of up, down, left, and right—is the result of visual cues from our eyes and balancing cues from our inner ears. Without gravity, the balance cues conflict with our visual cues, causing disorientation.

You are part of a group of mission specialists who will research the effects of extreme conditions on humans during space flight. Your Earth-based research, simulating changes that the human body may undergo during a flight, will be used to prepare astronauts for their first journey into space.

Initiating and Planning

How can humans safely travel in space?

Criteria for Success:

The research team must

- present an approved plan for carrying out experiments

- show what observations they made to back up their conclusions about the effects of space flight on the body

Performing and Recording

1. As a class, brainstorm ideas on forces that the human body might feel and how it might respond to different phases of space flight, such as a high-velocity launch, microgravity in orbit, and the loss of a sense of up or down. For example, will an astronaut shrink under microgravity? What might happen to an astronaut's sense of balance after he or she floats upside down?

2. In small groups, brainstorm various experiments you could conduct to test the effects discussed in step 1. Examples include measuring leg diameter under different conditions such as standing or being upside down against a wall (Figure 12.42); and simulating the effect of increased blood flow

to a person's head during launch by having him or her lie on an incline with feet higher than the head.

3. Select three effects that might occur on the human body, and plan a procedure to test each one. Consult your teacher if you need ideas.

4. Make a list of the materials and equipment you will need for each procedure.

5. Present your procedures and materials and equipment lists to your teacher for approval.

6. Once your procedures are approved, perform the tests and record your observations.

7. Repeat experiments as time permits to get the most reliable data possible. As you work, you may discover ways to improve your testing procedures. Discuss any changes with your teacher before modifying your procedures.

Analyzing and Evaluating

8. Based on your observations, how might space travel affect the human body?

9. How well did your procedures simulate the conditions of space travel? What were some limitations? How could they be improved?

Communicate

10. Report your results on an information poster, in a slide show presentation, or by other means.

11. How effective was your team listening to each other and sharing information? What worked well? What could be improved?

Figure 12.42 An astronaut in microgravity having the diameter of her leg measured

Dr. Julia Green-Johnson:
Feeding Our Astronauts

"Knowledge is of two kinds. We know a subject ourselves, or we know where we can find information on it." — Samuel Johnson

"If you have knowledge, let others light their candles at it." — Margaret Fuller

These words describe Dr. Julia Green–Johnson's outlook on her life and her work. Growing up in Porcupine Plain, Saskatchewan, her parents encouraged her to be interested in science and helped her to believe that she could meet any challenge that faced her. It was not until Mr. Sweeney's grade 10 biology class that she became hooked on science and began her journey to become a microbiologist. Today, she is part of the science faculty at the University of Ontario Institute of Technology. A major part of her job is to conduct research.

Most of her research is on how the immune system and microbes work together, and because of her expertise, she has been working with the Canadian Space Agency. The project involves looking at what people eat to promote health. "Probiotics," or good bacteria, are being grown in soy, which is then fermented (Figure 12.43). The effects of the fermented soy product on the immune system are then examined.

One challenge of human space travel is meeting the nutritional needs of individuals working in space.

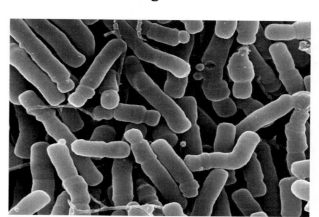

Figure 12.44 Dr. Green-Johnson and her team are working with several different strains of Lactobacillus, including *Lactobacillus rhamnosus.* Electron micrograph courtesy of Dr. Sandy Smith, Dept. of Food Sciences, University of Guelph.

Dr. Green–Johnson says, "Nutrients in the diet affect how well the immune system works. There is still much to learn about how different nutrients do this and how they interact. For space travel, it will be essential to have ways to keep the immune system functioning at its optimum level (Figure 12.44)."

But, there may be additional benefits. According to Dr. Green–Johnson, "Developing a fermented food product that would have health benefits for astronauts also means it would have benefits for everyone else, so I believe this work has strong potential for real-world application." Understanding how these types of food products work should translate into knowledge that can be used by anyone.

"We have great resources in Saskatchewan with respect to science and learning—and we have spirit! I remember a mentor telling me that people from Saskatchewan have a reputation for being good at mediating and making things work. Certainly growing up in rural Saskatchewan, one learns a lot about coping with what you have, and making it work!"

Figure 12.43 Soybeans have been grown in Saskatchewan since 1898.

Our Mess in Space: The Growing Problem of Space Debris

"Space junk" is an unfortunate legacy of humans venturing into space. Since we started sending rockets, satellites, and various craft into space, the problem of human-made items left behind in low orbit and geostationary orbit around Earth has risen dramatically. Like the garbage dumps we have created here at home, the whole outer envelope around the planet at an altitude of between 200 and 35 000 km has been slowly filling up with space junk (Figure 12.45).

Space junk ranges from broken bits off old rockets and all types of spacecraft to non-operating satellites, abandoned nuclear power units, and even small tools and cameras dropped by astronauts working outside their spacecraft.

Since 1957, more than 4500 missions have been sent into space. Each one has left behind its own bits of debris. Estimates put the total number of pieces of space junk of 10-cm diameter and larger at about 17 000. Smaller fragments number in the millions.

This accumulation of junk creates many problems, usually in the form of collisions. While small bits of debris are very hard to detect in space, they travel at lethal velocities of tens of thousands of kilometres per hour.

For example, a piece of metal less than 1 mm in diameter can move at more than 10 times the speed of a bullet.

When debris in the space environment collides, it does so at such high velocity that even a tiny bolt or bit of broken antenna can pierce a spacecraft hull or section of a satellite or crack a telescope mirror (Figure 12.46). The damage can result in equipment not working (for example, knocking out communications signals to Earth) and requiring costly repairs. Worse is the risk of catastrophic effects on human life if crewed spacecraft are seriously damaged. Collisions are therefore enormously costly, create even more debris, and pose a threat to the life of humans in space.

In February 2009, two satellites collided over Siberia. One was a communications satellite owned by a company in the United States. The other was an old Russian satellite no longer in use. The collision destroyed both units, creating a debris field of more than 600 pieces scattered in the region of the impact. Not all collisions of space junk occur between two objects as large as these.

However, the number of collisions is increasing annually as the amount of space junk increases. Every collision results in more debris, as larger parts break up into even smaller bits. In turn, more debris results in more collisions.

Both the space shuttle and International Space Station are constantly being bombarded by tiny pieces

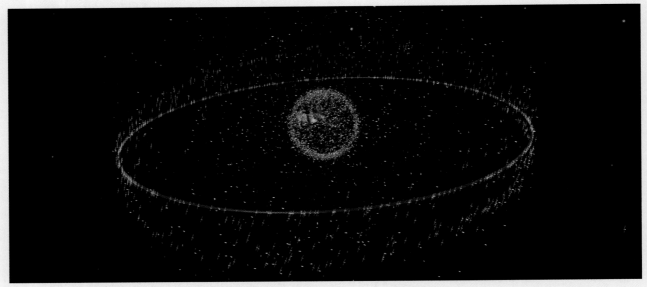

Figure 12.45 This image shows vividly the cloud of trackable objects cluttering what was once a space free of human-made material.

©P

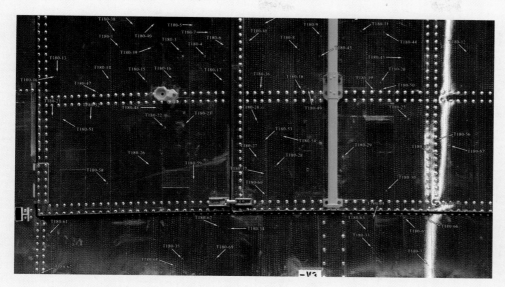

Figure 12.46 Every nick, dent, and scratch on this old section of the Hubble Space Telescope is marked in yellow. Constant collisions with small space debris mean that repairs must be made regularly.

of space debris. Maintenance is done regularly to repair and patch the damage. More than 80 windows on the space shuttle have had to be replaced during its period of operation. While the space station is usually able to alter course to avoid colliding with large tracked objects, it is constantly being struck by smaller objects.

Over the last decade, several space and research agencies, including those in the United States and Russia, have been keeping track of space debris, 10 cm to 1 m in diameter, using radar and optical equipment. Maps produced by the German-based European Space Operations Centre, an arm of the European Space Agency, show the extent of the debris.

Initiating and Planning

What is the best solution for dealing with the growing space debris problem now and in the future?

Performing and Recording

1. Read through the information presented. In a small group, use the following questions to analyze the issue.

   - What do you think about the issue of space debris? How pressing a problem is this?

   - Who should take responsibility for the debris that exists in space today? Is it acceptable to just leave it in "graveyard orbits" in space?

   - What should be done to manage the hazards posed by the debris?

   - What solutions can you suggest for reducing the problem in the future?

2. As a group, decide whether additional information would help you answer the questions above and evaluate the issue. If necessary, perform additional research using Internet or library resources.

3. Summarize your conclusions and recommend what actions, if any, should be taken.

4. Organize and summarize your conclusions and recommendations in one of two formats: a short written report or an electronic presentation.

Analyzing and Interpreting

5. Listen to other groups' views in a class discussion. Re-evaluate your group's conclusions and recommendations. Did any of the arguments made by others persuade you to reconsider your view? Explain why or why not.

Communication and Teamwork

6. Good recommendations clearly describe an action and who is responsible for taking that action and by when. Reread your group's recommendations and revise them if necessary to be clearer.

Key Concept Review

1. Explain the similarities and differences between a refracting telescope and a reflecting telescope.

2. Give three advantages of space-based optical telescopes over ground-based optical telescopes.

3. What is the difference between optical telescopes and radio telescopes? What are the advantages of each?

4. Name four types of spacecraft that have been used to carry equipment, animals, or people into space.

5. Give one example of a spinoff benefit from space-related research or technology that now has

   (a) an environmental use

   (b) a medical use

   (c) a domestic use

6. (a) What is the name of one of Canada's most significant contributions to the International Space Station?

   (b) What does the item named in (a) do?

7. Name four risks associated with space exploration. How can we avoid or reduce these risks?

8. Why must astronauts be in top physical shape before, and during, their time spent in space?

9. Name and describe four functions of satellites.

Connect Your Understanding

10. Explain how the invention of the telescope helped the science of astronomy.

11. Humans can explore space using telescopes, probes, and manned spacecraft. List some pros and cons for each.

12. List five spinoffs from space-related research and exploration that benefit you in your daily life.

13. Using three examples, explain what the following statement means: "Modern satellites have become excellent tools to help us better understand and manage Earth, its resources, and its environment."

Question 13

14. Research some challenges not presented in this chapter that would be faced by crew members making a long space flight to another planet, such as Mars. How can these challenges be overcome?

15. Many movies, television shows, and books explore the possibility of permanently living in space. What might be some challenges of living permanently in space?

16. How do advancements in technology assist in space exploration and our understanding of space?

Reflection

17. In this chapter, you read about many of Canada's contributions to space research, technology, and exploration. Name an area of Canada's contributions that you would like to find out more about. Explain why that area is of particular interest to you.

18. In what ways could many First Nations beliefs on ownership be applied to space and its exploration?

19. Discuss why the concept of globalization has become essential for the continued exploration of space.

20. Many costs and benefits of space exploration were discussed in this chapter. Do you feel we as humans and Canadians should continue to explore space? Explain your answer.

21. In this section, several of the activities encouraged you to assess the pros and cons of space research and exploration. Did you change your opinion about any of the issues as you discussed them with others in your class? If so, in what way was your opinion changed and what arguments persuaded you to change?

After Writing

Reflect and Evaluate

The human brain likes to find patterns in the stars, the seasons, and even in textbook chapters. Types of patterns in text organization include time order, problem-solution, and cause and effect. Write a short paragraph explaining how knowing about patterns of text organization helped you in understanding what the writer was requesting in various activities in this chapter. Exchange your reflection with a partner and discuss.

Reflection on Essential Inquiry Questions

How have human observations of the universe contributed to their everyday lives? **SI**

How has Canada contributed to space exploration? **TPS**

How can the costs and hazards of space exploration be justified and shared? **DM**

Why is expanding our knowledge of the universe important? **CP**

Unit Task

As you learned in this chapter, humans face an enormous number of hazards when they venture into space. The extreme environment beyond Earth and on other celestial bodies, including moons, asteroids, and planets, puts people at high risk of harm or even death. It also puts equipment at risk of damage or complete destruction. In addition, all of the work that goes into researching, building, and developing technologies, as well as training and preparing crews to go into space, is very costly. Yet, between our desire to gain more knowledge about the universe and our ability to apply space-related technologies to improving life on Earth, the push to continue investing in space exploration remains strong. How does understanding some of the hazards and benefits of space exploration affect your Unit Task?

KEY CONCEPTS	CHAPTER SUMMARY

9 Celestial objects, phenomena, and interactions are important to people in many different ways.

- Early human views of the universe
- Celestial navigation
- Earth-Moon-Sun interactions
- Formation of the solar system
- Solar system components

- Early cultures and civilizations, including First Nations and Métis peoples, studied celestial patterns to develop calendars, plan hunting and farming activities, navigate, and inspire spiritual beliefs and rituals. (9.1)
- The movement of objects in our solar system, including Earth, creates observable patterns, such as Moon phases, and phenomena, such as eclipses. (9.2)
- The Sun's magnetic field affects Earth by creating auroras at both poles, and it may interfere or damage equipment. (9.2)
- The solar system is composed of the Sun, planets, their moons, and other objects such as asteroids and comets. (9.3)

10 Stars are an important component of galaxies.

- Formation and life cycle of stars
- Galaxies

- At the start of its life cycle, a star forms inside a nebula. Stars are classified according to their colour, luminosity, and temperature. (10.1)
- Galaxies contain about 200 billion stars and usually have a supermassive black hole in the centre. Galaxies usually clump together in clusters. (10.2)

11 Our understanding of the universe is culturally influenced.

- Cultural and scientific views of the universe
- Big Bang theory
- Red shifting in light spectra
- Expanding universe
- Heliocentric model of the solar system

- Throughout history, humans in many different cultures around the world, including First Nations and Métis peoples, have explained the universe based on their worldview, what they believe, and what they are able to observe. (11.1)
- The Big Bang theory of the formation and expansion of the universe is consistent with known laws of the universe. (11.2)
- The red shift of spectral lines in the light we see from galaxies shows that the light's wavelengths are getting longer, meaning that other galaxies are moving away from us. (11.2)
- Scientific understandings are based upon a heliocentric, or Sun-centred, model. (11.2)

12 Space exploration improves our knowledge and gives us beneficial technologies and has significant costs and hazards.

- Technologies used to observe and explore space
- Benefits of space exploration
- Canadian contributions to space exploration
- Costs and hazards of space exploration

- As telescopes, space probes, and other technologies have advanced, humans have been able to explore farther out into space. Such observations lead to new understanding of our solar system and the universe. (12.1)
- Space research and exploration expand our knowledge of the universe while also producing many technological spinoffs that have practical applications on Earth. These advancements have costs and hazards. (12.2)
- Canadian organizations and individuals make significant contributions to space technology, research, and exploration. (12.2)
- While space exploration offers benefits, there are many ethical, political, and environmental issues to be balanced against the benefits. (12.3)

VOCABULARY

KEY VISUALS

- altitude (p. 309)
- asterisms (p. 306)
- asteroid belt (p. 336)
- asteroids (p. 336)
- astronomers (p. 305)
- astronomical bodies (p. 305)
- astronomical unit (AU) (p. 332)
- astronomy (p. 305)
- aurora australis (p. 323)
- aurora borealis (p. 323)
- azimuth (p. 310)
- celestial bodies (p. 305)
- comets (p. 338)
- constellation (p. 305)
- declination (p. 310)
- dwarf planets (p. 337)
- ecliptic (p. 316)
- equinoxes (p. 308)
- light-year (ly) (p. 332)
- lunar eclipse (p. 320)
- meteor (p. 339)
- meteorite (p. 339)
- nebula (p. 330)
- nebular theory (p. 330)
- orbit (p. 317)
- planet (p. 331)
- revolution (p. 317)
- right ascension (p. 310)
- rotation (p. 316)
- satellite (p. 318)
- solar eclipse (p. 319)
- solar flare (p. 322)
- solar prominence (p. 322)
- solar system (p. 329)
- solar wind (p. 323)
- solstices (p. 307)
- star (p. 321)
- sunspot (p. 321)

The Hubble Ultra Deep Field

- binary system (p. 352)
- black hole (p. 357)
- dark matter (p. 366)
- galaxy (p. 350)
- magnitude (p. 351)
- protostar (p. 353)
- quasars (p. 366)
- supernova (p. 356)
- universe (p. 349)

The Pillars of Creation in the Eagle nebula

- apparent retrograde motion (p. 388)
- Big Bang theory (p. 380)
- electromagnetic radiation (p. 382)
- electromagnetic spectrum (p. 382)
- geocentric models (p. 387)
- heliocentric model (p. 388)
- orbital radius (p. 389)
- red-shifted (p. 384)
- spectral lines (p. 383)
- spectral shifting (p. 384)
- spectroscope (p. 379)
- spectrum (p. 378)

The Hubble Space Telescope

- artificial satellite (p. 407)
- geostationary orbit (p. 408)
- microgravity (p. 418)
- spinoff (p. 406)

The Canada-Hawaii-France Telescope

D31 Design and Build a Space Vehicle   Toolkits 3, 5

Question

How can you make a habitable space vehicle that could support human exploration of our galaxy?

Task Overview

In this task, you will research the requirements for a habitable space vehicle that will be able to travel to a destination within or beyond our solar system.

Once you know what is needed for human survival in space, you will design your vehicle and build a prototype that shows what will be needed to support human exploration of space. Your report should include a description of the vehicle's destination, a description of the challenges the vehicle will have to overcome, and an analysis of what space "weather" conditions you would monitor.

Figure 12.47 Orion exploration vehicle, 2015

D32 Space Career Search   Toolkits 5, 6

Question

In Canada, what careers and/or training are related to space science?

Task Overview

Most people associate space science with astronomers and astronauts, but many Canadians are unaware of how other people in varying occupations work directly with the Canadian Space Agency, the National Research Council, and a variety of industries involved in space research and exploration. In this task, you will conduct research on which occupations assist in Canadian space contributions. You must find out what training for these careers is necessary.

D33 Design an Inquiry or Research Project   Toolkits 2, 5

Task Overview

In this task, you will identify your own question about our solar system or beyond to investigate and determine a procedure to follow to answer your question.

If you design an inquiry, be sure to create a hypothesis to answer your question, and be sure to identify the variables you will control and which ones you will measure. Write your procedure and have your teacher check it. Carry out your task and analyze your data.

If you design a research project, be sure to create a thesis statement to answer your question. Remember to check your sources for reliability and bias.

Using Key Terms

1. Create a concept map to organize all the terms in the list below.

- artificial satellite
- astronomical unit
- Big Bang theory
- celestial object
- galaxy
- light-year
- nebula
- planet
- protostar
- revolution
- rotation
- solar system
- solstice
- spectral shifting
- spinoff
- star
- supernova

Reviewing the Big Ideas

2. Why are constellations important to First Nations and Métis peoples?

3. First Nations and Métis peoples traditionally developed calendars based upon their observations of the natural world. What observations were used to create their calendars?

4. List four different types of galaxies, and sketch the general shape of each one.

5. Give two pieces of evidence that support the Big Bang theory of the formation of the universe.

6. Sketch the three main stages in a star's formation.

7. Explain what has to happen inside a high-mass star to cause it to turn into a supernova.

8. The Hertzsprung-Russell diagram plots stars according to what three stellar properties?

9. Describe one of the theories of how the solar system formed.

10. (a) Name the astronomical phenomenon shown in the image below.

    (b) Explain what causes it to happen.

Question 10

11. Is it the rotation or the revolution of Earth that is part of the cause of the seasons? Explain.

12. Define *apparent retrograde motion*. What causes retrograde motion?

13. Explain the significance of the following in terms of hours of day and night:

    (a) summer solstice

    (b) winter solstice

    (c) equinox

14. Does Mars or Saturn have the greater orbital radius? Explain. How does this affect its orbital speed?

15. (a) What is the gravitational condition shown in the image below?

    (b) Define that condition.

    (c) Describe four ways that this gravitational condition affects the human body.

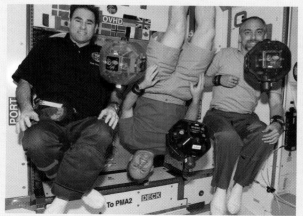

Question 15

Connecting the Big Ideas

16. Discuss how, for First Nations and Métis peoples, observing the sky was not just important for survival, but important spiritually.

17. Galaxy NGC 4256 has a supernova occurring inside it. Astronomers calculate that this exploding star lies 55 million ly from Earth. The image here was taken in 1994. How many years ago did the star actually explode?

Question 17

18. Explain why astronomers think that the farthest galaxies we can see may also be the oldest in the universe.

19. Describe the life cycle of
(a) a low mass star
(b) a medium mass star

20. If all of the asteroid belt's material were combined, it could make a planet about the size of rocky Mercury. However, there is one main reason that such a development will never occur. With reference to the diagram below, suggest what that reason is.

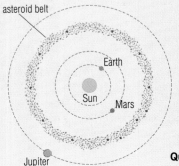

Question 20

21. Why is the length of a year on Earth not the same length as a year on all the planets in the solar system?

22. The largest refracting telescope ever built and still in use has a large glass lens almost 1 m in diameter. Suggest why larger refracting telescopes have not been built.

23. Critique the following statement: Until humans invented the telescope about 500 years ago, they had no tools or other means of studying celestial motion or celestial objects.

24. (a) Optical telescopes collect visible light. What does a radio telescope detect and collect?
(b) What piece of evidence in support of the Big Bang theory did radio telescopes detect?

25. Use the Hertzsprung-Russell diagram in Figure 10.11 on page 355 to answer the following questions.
(a) What colour is each of the following stars?
  (i) Rigel
  (ii) the Sun
  (iii) Aldebaran
(b) How many times brighter than the Sun is Betelgeuse?
(c) What is the surface temperature of Procyon A?
(d) Which stars have a higher surface temperature: yellow or red?
(e) Red stars normally have low luminosity. Explain how a red star such as Betelgeuse can be one of the brightest stars in the sky.

26. Many countries, such as China as shown below, now have their own space agency. As more countries look to space and its resources as a new frontier, what issues arise?

Question 26 Astronaut Zhai Zhigang making China's first spacewalk. He was launched into space in 2008 on a Chinese-built rocket and spacecraft.

Using the Big Ideas

27. Development of the Canadarm and Canadarm2 is one way that Canada has supported international efforts to explore and learn about space. Such undertakings require extensive co-operation and teamwork at the national level. The robotic Canadarm technology was developed by a private Canadian aerospace company, with the financial support of the federal government. Other partnerships in Canada between government, research institutes, universities, and industry continue to help advance space technologies, research, and exploration.

(a) Why do you think it is advantageous for Canada to contribute space technologies to international projects rather than to pursue space exploration by itself?

(b) Can scientific knowledge and technologies related to the study of space develop and advance without the sharing of knowledge?

28. The discovery of other star-and-planet systems in the universe helps support the theory of how the solar system formed. Explain.

29. Why is it important for society to consider and assess the range of benefits, costs, and hazards related to space research before making decisions to continue with space exploration?

30. Describe how Edwin Hubble's findings about the motion of galaxies helped support the Big Bang theory of the formation and evolution of the universe.

Reflection

31. (a) Has your opinion about the value of space research and exploration changed since you began this unit? Explain.

(b) This unit describes or refers to many different career areas in the field of space research and exploration. Have any of the areas you read about inspired you to find out more about what the work might involve? If so, ask your teacher for assistance in learning more about that area.

Reflection on Essential Inquiry Questions

How has the way we understand the universe changed? **SI**

How has the universe been explored in the past and present? How might we explore the universe in the future? **TPS**

How should the risks and benefits of space exploration be shared? **DM**

Why is it important to have different ways of knowing about the universe? **CP**

Toolkits

Contents

©P

Safety Symbols

Safety symbols identify potential hazards. When you see any of the following symbols, either in this book or on a product, take extra care.

Safety Symbols in This Book

Some activities in this book have symbols to help you conduct the activity safely. Look for these symbols at the beginning of activities.

 When you see this symbol, wear goggles or safety glasses while doing the activity.

 This symbol tells you that you will be using glassware during the activity. Take extra care when handling it.

 When you see this symbol, wear an apron while doing the activity.

 When you see this symbol, wear insulated gloves to protect your hands from heat.

 This symbol tells you that you will be working with sharp objects. Take extra care when handling them.

 When you see this symbol, wear gloves while doing the activity.

 This symbol tells you that you will be working with wires and power sources. Take extra care when handling them.

 This symbol tells you that you will be working with fire. Make sure to tie back loose hair. Take extra care around flames.

WHMIS Symbols

These are symbols you might see on the materials you use in your classroom. You will see them occasionally in the Materials and Equipment lists for activities when a substance that needs a warning is used. These symbols are called Workplace Hazardous Materials Information System (WHMIS) symbols. They are placed on hazardous materials used at job sites and in science classrooms.

They may also be on other manufactured products bought for home use. A container may have one or more of the symbols shown below.

compressed gas

biohazardous infectious material

dangerously reactive material

corrosive material

oxidizing material

flammable and combustible material

poisonous and infectious causing immediate and serious toxic effects

poisonous and infectious causing other toxic effects

Hazard Symbols for Home Products

You have probably seen some of these hazard symbols on products at home. They are a warning that the products can be harmful or dangerous if handled improperly. These hazard symbols have two shapes: a triangle or an octagon. A triangle means that the container is dangerous. An octagon means that the contents of the container are dangerous. Here are four of the most common symbols.

 Flammable Hazard: The product could ignite (catch on fire) if exposed to flames, sparks, friction, or even heat.

 Toxic Hazard: The product is very poisonous and could have immediate and serious effects, including death, if eaten or drunk. Smelling or tasting some products can also cause serious harm.

 Corrosive Hazard: The product will corrode clothing, skin, or other materials and will burn eyes on contact.

 Explosive Hazard: The container can explode if it is heated or punctured.

The Inquiry Process of Science

Scientists are always asking a lot of questions. They are always inquiring. They want to understand why the things they observe, and wonder about, happen. Experiments are important tools scientists use to help them answer their questions.

The diagram below shows a planning process for an experiment.

Hints

- Answers may lead to additional questions. New questions often lead to new hypotheses and experiments. Do not be afraid to ask questions, or to rethink the ones you have already asked.

- Science grows when scientists ask questions, answer them, and are willing to question those answers. Scientific knowledge is always growing and changing.

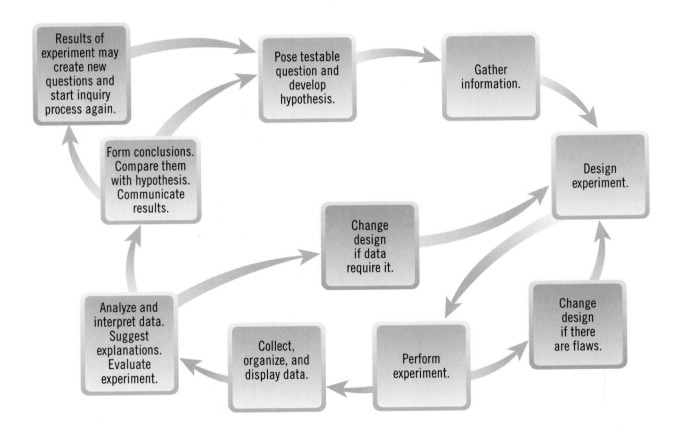

Pose a testable question and develop a hypothesis.

Asking questions is easy. Asking questions that are testable is more challenging. Scientists usually ask testable questions because they lead to verifiable, repeatable, and reliable answers. Here are a few examples.

- How does the concentration of laundry detergent in wash water affect the cleanliness of clothing?

- How do different temperatures affect the growth of seedlings?

- How does the amount of moisture affect the growth of mould on bread?

Notice how the causes—the detergent, temperature, and moisture—are things that you will change. For example, you can use different concentrations of detergent, different temperatures, and different amounts of moisture. Causes are the independent or manipulated variables. They are factors that you change when you investigate a testable question.

The results will change depending on the causes. For example, some clothes may become cleaner than others, or not clean at all depending on the concentration of laundry detergent. Some seedlings may grow better than others, or some might not grow at all depending on the temperature. Some bread samples may have lots of mould, some may have less, and some might not have any depending on the amount of moisture. Results are the dependent or responding variables. They change because of the independent variable.

When you ask a testable question, you should include only one independent variable in your question. This allows you to see the effect of that variable on the dependent variable.

Once you have posed a testable question, you can develop a hypothesis. A hypothesis is a way of restating a testable question so that it gives a reasonable, possible answer. Basically, a hypothesis is a possible explanation of the reason things have happened. It may be written in the form of an "If ... then" statement that states the relationship between the independent and dependent variables.

Here are hypotheses for the testable questions outlined on the previous page.

- If the concentration of the detergent is high, then clothing will become cleaner because more dirt is removed.

- If the temperature is decreased, then the seedlings will not grow as well because they will not be able to germinate.

- If the amount of moisture is increased, then the bread will get mouldier because mould needs moisture to grow.

Hint

A hypothesis is an early step in the experiment-planning process. Your hypothesis can turn out to be "right," but it might not always. The purpose of the experiment is to test the hypothesis.

Gather information.

With your classmates and your teacher, you can discuss what you already know about the testable question and then, you can think about what else you would like to know. For example, you could conduct some research to find out about the relationship between temperature and germination of certain types of seeds. You might also consider reading about other factors that affect seedling growth. Your information gathering can help you generate ideas about your testable question and may even lead to new questions.

Design the experiment.

When you develop a procedure, you need to ask yourself some questions. Your answers to these questions will help you plan a fair and safe experiment. Here are some questions you should think about. These questions are answered for the seedling experiment.

- **Which independent variable do you want to investigate?** The independent variable is temperature.

- **How will you measure this variable (if it is measurable)?** You can measure temperature with a thermometer or a temperature probe.
- **How will you keep all other variables constant (the same) so they do not affect your results?** In other words, how will you control your experiment so it is a fair test?

  To control the experiment, these variables should be kept constant: the amount of light the seedlings receive; the amount and temperature of water applied to the seedlings; the kind of soil the seedlings are planted in.
- **What materials and equipment will you need for the experiment?** The materials would include seedlings, soil, growing pots or containers (same size), water and a watering can, a light source, a thermometer or a temperature probe, and a ruler or other measuring device.
- **How will you conduct the experiment safely?** Some of the safety factors to consider include putting the seedling pots in a place where they would not be disturbed, washing your hands after handling the materials, and making sure you do not have any allergies to the soil or seedlings you use.
- **How will you set up the procedure to get the data you need to test your hypothesis?** You could divide your seedlings into groups (e.g., three seedlings for each temperature) and grow each group at a certain temperature. You would keep track of how much each seedling in a group grew over a specified amount of time (e.g., four weeks) and calculate the average for the group.

Perform the experiment.

Follow all safety procedures.

If you are working in a group, make sure all members understand tasks before you begin.

Use the appropriate materials and equipment needed to test your hypothesis. Make sure that only one variable is changed at a time as you follow the procedure. Address any problems and change the procedure or design, if needed.

Collect, organize, and display the data.

You can work together with classmates and your teacher to decide, or to make a plan, as to how you will present the data you will collect. Depending on the kind of experiment you have planned, you may choose to record the data in the form of a chart or table, a labelled sketch, notes, or a combination of these. For example, a good way to record the seedling data would be in tables like the following one (one for each week of the experiment).

Week 1: Height of Seedlings Grown at Different Temperatures

Temperature (°C)	Height of seedling 1 (cm)	Height of seedling 2 (cm)	Height of seedling 3 (cm)	Average height (cm)
20				
15				
10				

Hint

Analyzing the data you collect is the only way you have to assess your hypothesis. It is important that your record keeping be organized and neat.

©P

Analyze and interpret the data. Suggest explanations. Evaluate the experiment.

Scientists look for patterns and relationships in their data. Often, making a graph can help them see patterns and relationships more easily. (See Toolkit 9 for more about graphing.)

A graph of the seedling data would show you if there were a relationship between temperature and growth rate.

Hint

If you have access to a computer, find out if it has the software to help you make charts or graphs.

Form conclusions. Compare them with the hypothesis. Communicate your results.

Usually, forming a conclusion is fairly straight-forward. Either your data will support your hypothesis or they will not. Either way, however, you are not finished answering your testable question.

For example, if the seedlings did not grow as well in cooler temperatures, you can conclude that your data support your hypothesis. But you will still need to repeat your experiment several times to see if you get the same results over and over again. Doing your experiment successfully many times is the only way you and other scientists can have confidence in your data and your conclusions.

If your data do not support your hypothesis, there are three possible reasons why.

- Perhaps your experimental plan was flawed and needs to be re-assessed and possibly planned again.

- Perhaps your data collection was not accurate.
- Perhaps your hypothesis was incorrect and needs to be re-assessed and modified.

For example, if the seedlings grew better in the lower temperatures, you would have to re-think your hypothesis, or look at your experiment for flaws.

You would need to ask questions to help you evaluate and change your hypothesis, your plan, or your data collection. For example, you could ask: Do certain seedlings grow better at lower temperatures than others? Do different types of soil have more of an effect on growth than temperature?

Every experiment is different and will result in its own set of questions and conclusions.

Hint

You could also enlist the help of your classmates. If others have completed the same experiment and got the same results, the conclusions are likely more reliable. If not, the hypothesis must be modified. Scientists often work this way to compare results.

©P

Scientists generally share the results of their inquiries in order to add to the overall knowledge about a topic. One method they commonly follow is by summarizing the problem they studied, how they studied it, what they learned, and what it means. They may write a formal report that includes their purpose, procedure, hypothesis, observations, analysis, and conclusions. Other times, they may share their results in a less formal manner, but still include drawings, charts, or graphs to support their points.

When communicating your results in a report, use the guidelines below to help you.

Tell readers why you did the work.

Use a heading such as "Introduction" or "Purpose." Explain the purpose of your report and provide any background information needed for your report. State your testable question in this section.

State your hypothesis.

Under a heading such as "Hypothesis," state your hypothesis. Your hypothesis is your explanation based on data, observations, and other information you collected. It must indicate the relationship between the independent and dependent variable.

List the materials and equipment used.

Title this section "Materials and Equipment." List all the materials and equipment you used. Remember to include the exact amounts of materials used. You may also wish to include diagrams to show the equipment set-up.

Describe the steps of your experiment.

Under a heading called "Procedure," include detailed descriptions of the steps you followed when conducting your experiment.

Show your experimental data.

Under a heading such as "Data" or "Observations," use tables, diagrams, and any other visual aids to show the data you collected. If you performed the experiment a few times, give results for each trial.

Analyze and interpret your results.

Interpret and analyze the data you collected. Calculations, graphs, diagrams, or any other visual aids may be needed. Explain any calculations or graphs that you used to help explain your results.

Form conclusions.

This section can be called "Conclusions." Explain what your tests and experiments showed. Explain whether your results were predicted by the hypothesis. Describe how you might adjust the hypothesis based on what you learned from your results, and how you might test this new hypothesis.

The Problem-Solving Process for Technological Development

When you plan an experiment to answer a testable question, you follow a process. The same is true for designing a model or prototype that solves a practical problem.

The diagram below shows a planning process for solving a practical problem.

Choose a practical problem to solve.

This involves recognizing what the problem is. For example, suppose you observe that a rope bridge across a ravine at a local park is unstable and swings back and forth when crossed. This might be fine for people who want a thrill, but you find that most people are not comfortable crossing the bridge and do not get to enjoy one of the nicer areas of the park. You wish there were a way to make the bridge more stable so more people would use it. That is the situation or context of the problem.

When you understand a situation, you can then define the problem more exactly. This means identifying a specific task to carry out. In the situation with the bridge, the task might be to build a new bridge or add support to the existing bridge.

Gather information.

With your classmates and your teacher, you can discuss what you already know about the problem and then, you can think about what else you would like to know. For example, you could conduct some research to find out about bridge design or the strength and cost of different materials.

Conducting research may involve reading books and magazines, searching the Internet, interviewing people, or visiting stores. It all depends on what you are going to design.

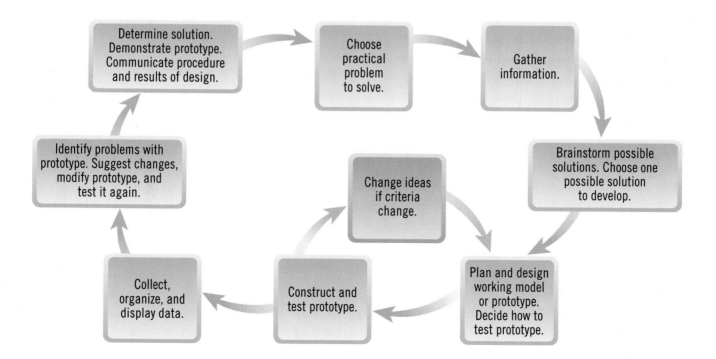

One idea for the rope bridge would be to anchor the bridge with strong rope or thick metal wire to large rocks or to the hillside at either end of the bridge. Sketches and diagrams would help to generate different ideas for the bridge design.

Brainstorm possible solutions. Choose one possible solution to develop.

When you brainstorm, remember to relax and let your imagination go. Brainstorming is all about generating as many ideas as possible without judging them. Record your ideas in the form of words, mind maps, sketches—whatever helps you best.

You have defined the problem and now you must look for solutions. But how will you know when you have found the best possible solution? Before you start looking for solutions, you need to establish your criteria for determining what a successful solution will be.

One of your criteria for success in the bridge example would be the completion of a stable bridge. The criteria you choose do not depend on which solution you select—whether to reinforce the old bridge or build a new bridge. In this case, whatever the solution, it must result in a stable bridge.

When you are setting your criteria for success, you must consider limits to your possible solutions. For example, the bridge may have to be built within a certain time, so rebuilding completely may not be possible. Other limitations could include availability of materials, cost, number of workers needed, and safety.

If you are building a product or device for yourself, you may set the criteria for success and the limitations yourself. In class, you, your class-mates, and your teacher may decide as a group.

Hint

Always consider safety. This includes safe handling and use of materials and equipment, as well as being aware of possible environmental impacts of your ideas. Discuss with your teacher and fellow students how your solution might affect the environment.

Hint

Humans have been inventors for tens of thousands of years—so take advantage of what has already been developed. When you are solving a problem, you do not have to "reinvent the wheel." See how others have solved the same problem before and use their efforts as inspiration. You can also look for ways to "build upon" or improve on their ideas.

Plan and design a working model or prototype. Decide how to test the prototype.

Choose one possible solution to develop. Start by making a list of the materials and equipment you will use. Then make a working diagram, or series of diagrams, on paper. This lets you explore and troubleshoot your ideas early on. Your labels should be detailed enough so that other people could build your design. Show your plans to your teacher before you begin construction work.

A simple model of the bridge could be made to show how and where components such as stabilizing wires could be added.

Hint

If things are not working as you planned or imagined, be prepared to modify your plans as you construct your model or prototype.

Construct and test the prototype.

Follow all safety procedures.

If you are working in a group, make sure all members understand tasks before you begin.

Use the appropriate materials and equipment needed to construct your prototype.

Testing lets you see how well your solution works. Testing also lets you know if you need to make modifications. Does your model or prototype meet all the established criteria? Does it solve the problem?

Invite your classmates to try your product.

Hints

- For every successful invention or product, there are thousands of unsuccessful ones. Sometimes it is better to start over from scratch than to follow a design that does not meet its performance criteria.

- Here is an old saying you have probably heard: "If at first you don't succeed, try, try again." Remember, there can be many possible solutions to a practical problem.

Collect, organize, and display data.

With your classmates and your teacher, decide how you will present the data from the test of your prototype. You could use a table, a labelled sketch, notes, or a combination of these.

Identify problems with the prototype. Suggest changes, modify the prototype, and test it again.

Use the feedback from your classmates to help you decide what is and is not working, and how to adjust anything that needs fixing. Perhaps the stabilizing wires on the bridge model could be anchored elsewhere. Maybe more wires could be added.

Determine the solution. Demonstrate the prototype. Communicate the procedure and the results of the design.

Inventors and engineers create things to meet people's needs. When they make something new, they like to show it to other people and explain to them how it works. Sometimes they will use a carefully drawn diagram of the new device and write about how they performed the process for solving a practical problem. Other times, they will show the device to people and explain verbally how it works and how they built it. As a class, you can decide how to prepare your results so you can exhibit the new device you make. If you decide to communicate the results of your design in a written report, you can use the guidelines below to help you.

Tell readers why you did the work.

Under a heading such as "Introduction" or "Purpose," state the purpose of your report and provide background information on the problem to be solved. Give your reasons for designing and making a particular product.

Describe the design challenge.

Use a heading such as "Design Challenge" and list the criteria for success. Describe why you decided to design your product the way you did. Explain how and why you chose your design over other possible designs. You may wish to include a labelled diagram of your design.

List the materials and equipment you used.

Title this section "Materials and Equipment." List all the materials and equipment you used. Include the exact measurements and proper units of the materials used. Remember to include any materials or equipment used for any changes or additions you made.

Describe the steps for constructing and testing the prototype.

Under a heading called "Procedure," include detailed descriptions of the steps you followed when constructing and testing your prototype. If you had to alter your design, describe how you did this.

Show your experimental data.

Use a heading such as "Data" or "Observations" for this section. Show the data you collected when testing your product. Use tables, labelled sketches, and any other visual aids that show the results of your tests.

Analyze and interpret the results of your experiment.

Interpret and analyze your data. Did your prototype meet the criteria for success? Explain what worked and what did not, and how your prototype could be improved.

Form conclusions.

Give this section a heading such as "Conclusions." Explain if your design did what it was supposed to do. If you changed the design of your product, explain why. Describe the practical applications your product might have for the world outside the classroom.

The Decision-Making Process for Analyzing Issues

People can have many different perspectives about issues that may affect society and the environment. This usually means that an issue has more than one possible solution. Scientific and technological information can be used to increase our understanding of an issue and help resolve it.

When people try to make a decision or reach a consensus about an issue, they need to use a decision-making process. Here is one possible process.

Choose and explain the issue.

This involves recognizing that an issue exists. An issue is a controversy that needs to be resolved and it may have more than one possible solution.

For example, suppose you and your friends want some trees in a public park cut down to make space for a playing field. Some members of the community feel the trees should be preserved for birds that nest there. An environmental specialist says that when it rains, the trees protect a nearby stream by reducing runoff, so they should be left alone. Others say that building a playing field is too expensive.

Identify different groups involved in the issue and consider their viewpoints.

The viewpoints in the example above are recreational (you and your friends), ecological (those who wish to leave the trees alone), and economic (those who think that the cost would be too high).

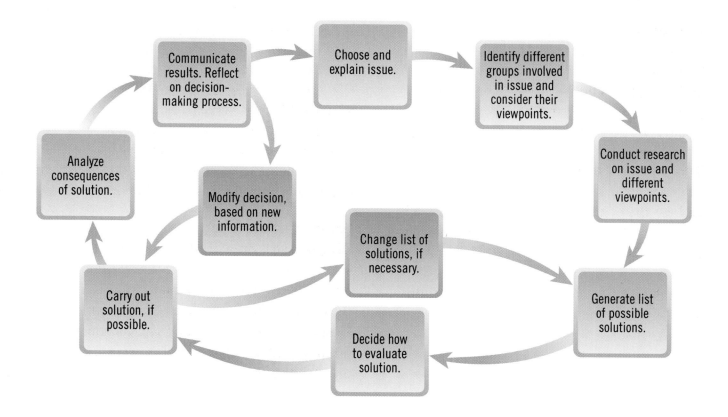

Different groups may have different viewpoints about an issue. Often, people think about issues using one or more viewpoints. Read through the viewpoints below and try to identify the different groups and the likely viewpoints they would have about the example of cutting trees down in a public park.

- Cultural: interest in the customs and practices of a particular group of people
- Ecological: interest in the protection of the natural environment
- Economic: interest in the financial aspects of the situation
- Educational: interest in acquiring and sharing knowledge and skills
- Esthetic: interest in the beauty in art and nature
- Ethical: interest in beliefs about what is right and wrong
- Health and safety: interest in physical and mental well-being
- Historical: interest in knowledge dealing with past events

- Political: interest in the effect of the issue on governments, politicians, and political parties
- Recreational: interest in leisure activities
- Scientific: interest in knowledge based on the inquiry process of science (Toolkit 2)
- Social: interest in human relationships, public welfare, or society
- Technological: interest in the design and use of tools and processes that solve practical problems to satisfy peoples' wants and needs (Toolkit 3)

Conduct research on the issue and the different viewpoints.

You will be able to suggest an appropriate solution to an issue only if you understand the issue and the different viewpoints. It is important to gather unbiased information about the issue itself and then consider the information provided by people with different viewpoints.

Develop specific questions that will help to guide your research. Questions for the playing-field issue might be:

- How many people will use the playing field?
- Is there another more suitable site for the playing field?
- What kind of birds nest in these trees? Could they nest elsewhere in the area?
- What is run-off and why is it a problem?
- What would be the full cost of building the playing field (including the cost of removing the trees)?

Conducting research may involve interviewing people, reading books and magazines, searching the Internet, or making a field trip. It is important to evaluate your sources of information to determine if there is a bias and to separate fact from opinion. You will find tips on how to conduct research in Toolkit 5.

Generate a list of possible solutions.

Examine the background of the issue and the viewpoints in order to generate a list of possible solutions. Brainstorming can be a useful component of this step. Use your research to help guide your thinking.

Examples of possible solutions for the playing-field issue might be as follows:

- Cut down the trees and build the playing field.
- Leave the park as it is.
- Find another more suitable location.
- Modify the plan in the existing park.

Decide how to evaluate the solution.

Decide how you will measure the risks and benefits for the consequences of each alternative solution. You may decide to examine the importance, likelihood, and duration of each possible consequence. The importance of the consequence and the likelihood of its occurrence can be ranked high (3), moderate (2), low (1), or none (0). Duration is considered short term (S) if it is less than 50 years or long term (L) if it is longer than 50 years. Ask how many people will benefit from the alternative and how many will be affected negatively. Make sure to consider health and safety.

For the playing field example, you could analyze the consequences of each possible solution in a table such as the one shown.

Analysis of consequences: Alternative 1— Build the Playing Field in the Park

Consequence	Importance (3, 2, 1, 0)	Likelihood of occurrence (3, 2, 1, 0)	Duration (S, L)
Trees cut down	2	3	L
Run-off	3	3	S
Birds move	2 to 1	3	L
Playing field well used	2	2	possibly L
Development and maintenance cost	2 to 1	3	L

©P

Evaluate your decision-making process to ensure that each step is completed as fully as possible. Consider the consequences of the alternative solutions and how people will respond to each one. Then decide on what you think is the best course of action.

Carry out the solution, if possible.

Whether or not it is practical for you to carry out the solution depends on the issue you are trying to resolve. If you are able to carry out the solution, follow all safety procedures.

If you are working in a group, make sure all members understand tasks before you begin.

Use the appropriate materials and equipment needed to carry out the solution you chose.

Analyze the consequences of the solution.

Use the feedback from different groups of people to help you decide whether your solution is successful. You may have to modify your solution, based on the responses you receive.

Communicate your results. Reflect on your decision-making process.

Communicate your findings in an appropriate way. For example, you may prepare a written report, a verbal presentation, or a position for a debate or a public hearing role-play. Defend your position by clearly stating your case and presenting supporting evidence from a variety of sources.

The guidelines below can help you communicate your findings.

Identify the issue.
Explain the purpose of your report and state the issue. Give some background information to give the issue some context.

Describe the issue from different viewpoints.
Identify the stakeholders and describe the different viewpoints.

Summarize your key findings.
Use only a summary of the essential information needed for a reader to understand the issue and different viewpoints about it. You may wish to include your list of questions that guided your research.

Make conclusions.
Explain how and why you made your decision. Briefly summarize your supporting evidence. Identify the consequences of your solution. If necessary, explain how you have responded to different viewpoints on the issue.

Researching Topics

Research involves finding out something about a topic or subject. That means going to certain resources that will give you accurate information. Information can be found just about anywhere: from your home bookshelves to the public library, from asking experts to looking on the Internet. Here is a process you can follow when you do your research.

Choosing a Topic

In some situations, your teacher may give you the topic to research. Other times, you will select one of your own, such as the issue described in Toolkit 4. If you have trouble coming up with a topic, try brainstorming ideas either by yourself or with a group. Remember, when you brainstorm, there are no right or wrong answers, just "ideas."

Here are some brainstorming suggestions to get you started:

- List two or three general topics about science that interest you.
- For each topic, spend a few minutes writing down as many words or ideas that relate to that topic. They do not have to be directly connected to science.
- Share your list with others and ask them to suggest other possibilities.
- Now you have to filter your idea list to find a topic to research. In other words, go through your ideas until you find two or three that interest you. To help you narrow your idea list, try grouping similar words or ideas, modifying what you have written, or even writing down a new idea. Sometimes, too, working with other people will help to focus your thoughts.

- When you settle on an idea for your topic, write it down. Try to explain it in a couple of sentences or a short paragraph. Do that for each of your two or three topic ideas.
- Have your teacher approve your topic ideas. Now you are ready to go!

Which Topic Should I Choose?

How does product design help sell a product?

How do gears improve the performance of a bicycle?

The next thing you have to do is settle on one topic. (Remember, you should start your research with two or three topic ideas.) One way to help you decide is to determine how easy it will be to find information on your topic.

- Use some of the resources listed under *Finding Information* to do your preliminary research.
- If you cannot easily find at least four good references for a topic, consider dropping it and going on to the next topic.

Hint

Sometimes topics are too broad in scope or too general to make good research reports (for example, "transportation" instead of just "bicycles"). Try rewriting your topic idea to narrow its focus.

If all the topics are easy to research, then you will need some other criteria to help you decide. Think about

- which topic interests you the most
- which topic is not being researched by many students in your class
- which topic interests you the least

How Hard Will It Be to Find Information?

How camera lenses are manufactured

How mirrors are used in some optical devices

Once you have finally chosen your topic, you might want to work with other students and your teacher to

- finalize its wording
- make sure it matches the project or assignment you are doing

Finding Information

There are many resources that you can use to look up information. You will find some of these resources

- in your school
- in your community (such as your public library)
- on the Internet
- in CD-ROM encyclopedias and databases

Here is a suggested list of resources.

Resource	✓	Details
Books		
CD-ROMs		
Community professionals or experts		
Elders and Knowledge Keepers		
Encyclopedias		
Films		
Government agencies (local, provincial, and federal)		
Internet sites		
Journals		
Library catalogue		
Newspapers		
Non-profit organizations		
Posters		
DVDs and videos		

©P

Searching Tips

Finding Information at Your Library

Library computer catalogues can provide a fast way to find books on the subjects you are researching. Most of these electronic catalogues have four ways to search: *subject*, *author*, *title*, and *key words*. If you know the *author* or *title* of a book, just type it in. Otherwise, use the *subject* and *key words* searches to find books on your topic.

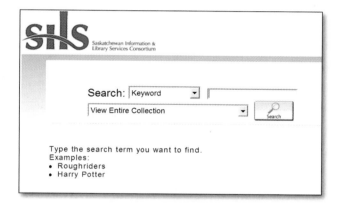

- If you are doing a *subject* search, type in the main topic you are researching. For example, if you are searching for information on solar energy, type in "solar energy." If there are no books on that topic, try using a more general category, such as "renewable resources," or just "energy."

- If you are doing a *key words* search, type in any combination of words that have to do with your topic. For the solar energy example, you could type in words such as: "renewable energy sun solar panels." Using several key words will give you a more specific search. Using only one or two key words, such as "sun" and "energy," will give you a more general search.

Hints

- The library may also have a way to search for magazine articles. This is called a *periodical search*. It is especially useful for searching for information on events and/or discoveries that have taken place recently. Ask your librarian how to do a periodical search.

- Your library will probably have a reference section where all the encyclopedias are kept. There, you may find science and technology, environmental, or even animal encyclopedias, as well as other reference books.

Finding Information on the Internet

On the Internet, you can use searching programs, called *search engines*, to search the Internet on just about any subject. To find a search engine, ask your teacher or click on the search icon found at the top of your Internet browser. Here are some suggestions on how to search the Internet:

- Once you reach a search engine Web page, type in key words or phrases that have to do with your topic. For solar energy, you could type in "solar energy," "solar panels," "renewable resources," or any combination of these and other similar words.

- The search engine will display a list of Web pages it has found that have these words or phrases somewhere in them. Click on any Web page on the list that looks interesting.

- Quite often you will get a long list of possible Web pages to look at. You may need to make your search more specific. This can be done by adding other key words to your search. For example, if you were looking for solar energy examples in Canada and used the key word "solar energy," you may want to do a second search of these results with the key word "Canada" added.

- Do not forget to record the addresses of any interesting Web pages you find. You may wish to save the address as a bookmark for easy future access. Check with your teacher or librarian to find out how to save and organize your bookmarks.
- There is a wide variety of information available on the Internet. How do you know whether the information on a website is valid? Ask your teacher or librarian about guidelines for evaluating the reliability of information on the Internet.

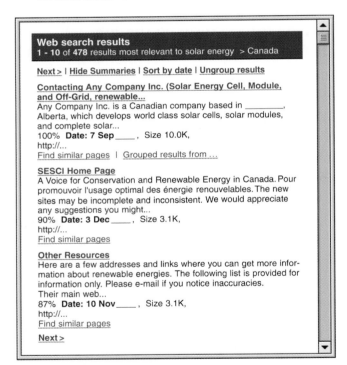

Web search results
1 - 10 of 478 results most relevant to solar energy > Canada

Next > | Hide Summaries | Sort by date | Ungroup results

Contacting Any Company Inc. (Solar Energy Cell, Module, and Off-Grid, renewable...
Any Company Inc. is a Canadian company based in _____, Alberta, which develops world class solar cells, solar modules, and complete solar...
100% **Date: 7 Sep** ____ , Size 10.0K,
http://...
Find similar pages | Grouped results from ...

SESCI Home Page
A Voice for Conservation and Renewable Energy in Canada. Pour promouvoir l'usage optimal des énergie renouvelables. The new sites may be incomplete and inconsistent. We would appreciate any suggestions you might...
90% **Date: 3 Dec** ____ , Size 3.1K,
http://...
Find similar pages

Other Resources
Here are a few addresses and links where you can get more information about renewable energies. The following list is provided for information only. Please e-mail if you notice inaccuracies. Their main web...
87% **Date: 10 Nov** ____ , Size 3.1K,
http://...
Find similar pages

Next >

BEFORE YOU START!

Check with your teacher to find out about your school's policy regarding acceptable use of the Internet. Remember to follow this policy whenever you use the Internet at school. Be aware that some Web sites may be strongly biased toward a specific point of view. If you are looking for scientific or technical information, educational or government websites are generally reliable.

Recording Your Information Sources

An important part of researching a topic is keeping track of where you obtain information. As you do your research, you are reading through or viewing a variety of different sources. Some may be in print, such as magazines and books. Others may be electronic, such as websites and CD-ROMs. And others may be visual, such as videos and photos. No matter what sources you use, you should keep track of them.

With this information, you can easily go back and check details. You can also use it to help you respond to any questions about the accuracy or completeness of your information. Your record of sources should include at least the following basic information:

- title or name of the source (e.g., if you read a chapter of a book, you would write down the book's title; for a website, you would include the address)
- author's name, if known
- publisher (e.g., for a website, this would be the name of the person or the organization that has put up the site)
- date of publication
- pages consulted

Your teacher may want you to list your information sources in a specific format. Check what this format will be before you begin your research so that you can collect the details you need to complete your reference list later. You may want to do your own research on formats for such reference lists or bibliographies.

Reading in Science

You use different skills and strategies when reading different materials such as a novel or a textbook. In a novel, you are mainly reading to enjoy the story. In a science textbook, you are reading for information. A science textbook has terms and concepts that you need to understand.

Using Reading Strategies

You can use the following strategies to help better understand the information presented in this book.

Before Reading

- Skim the section you are going to read. Look at the headings, subheadings, visuals, and boldfaced words to determine the topic.

- Look at how the information is organized. Ask yourself: Is it a cause-and-effect passage? Is it a contrast-and-compare passage? Think about how the organization can help you access the information.

- Think about what you already know about the topic.

- Predict what you will learn.

- List questions that you have about the topic. This will help you to set a purpose for reading.

As You Read

- Rewrite the section headings and subheadings as questions. Look for the answers to the questions as you read.

- Use your answers to the questions to decide on the main idea in each section or subsection.

- Look carefully at any visuals—photographs, illustrations, charts, or graphs. Read the captions and labels that go with the illustrations and photographs, and the titles of any charts or graphs. Think about the information the visuals give you and how this information helps you understand the ideas presented in the text.

- Notice the terms that are boldfaced (dark and heavy type). These are important words that will help you understand and write about the information in the section. Make sure you understand the terms and how they are used. Check the terms in the Glossary to confirm their meanings.

- Use different strategies to help remember what you read. For example, you can make mental pictures, make connections to what you know, or draw a sketch.

After Reading

- Find the information to answer any review questions. Use the headings and boldfaced terms to locate the information needed. Even if you are sure of the answer, reread to confirm that your answer is correct.

- Write brief notes to synthesize what you have learned, or organize the information in a graphic organizer. See below for information about graphic organizers.

- Personalize the information. Think about your opinions on what you have read. Consider if the new information has changed any of your previous ideas. List questions you still have about the topic.

Note-Making Chart

A note-making chart helps you understand how the material you are reading is organized. It also helps you keep track of information as you read.

Suppose your teacher assigns several pages for you to read. Before you begin reading, look at each heading and turn it into a question. Try to use "how," "what," or "why" to begin each question. Write your questions in the left column of your chart. Leave enough space between each question so that you can record information from your reading that answers your question.

You can see an example of a note-making chart below.

Questions from Headings	Answers from Reading
What is the meaning of the word "work"?	— work is done when a force acts on an object to make the object move — If there's no movement, no work is done — just trying to push something isn't work—it's only work if the object moves
How do you calculate work?	
How are energy and work related?	

Graphic Organizers

Graphic organizers can be used to organize information that you read, and to display ideas visually.

Type of Graphic Organizer	Purpose	Method
Concept map or web diagram 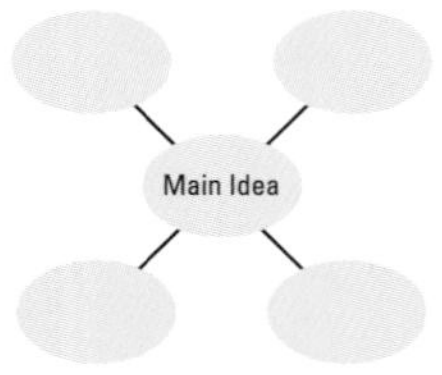 Main Idea	Used to clarify relationships and linkages between concepts, events, or ideas	Brainstorm ideas and link together from "big to small" with arrows or lines linking words. Cluster information around a central concept or idea.
Venn diagram 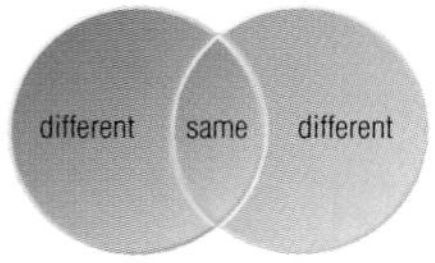 different same different	Used to visualize similarities and differences between two or more ideas, topics, or concepts	Brainstorm similarities, and list these in the overlapping section of the two circles. Then, brainstorm differences, and list these in the non-overlapping sections.
Flowchart or sequence chart 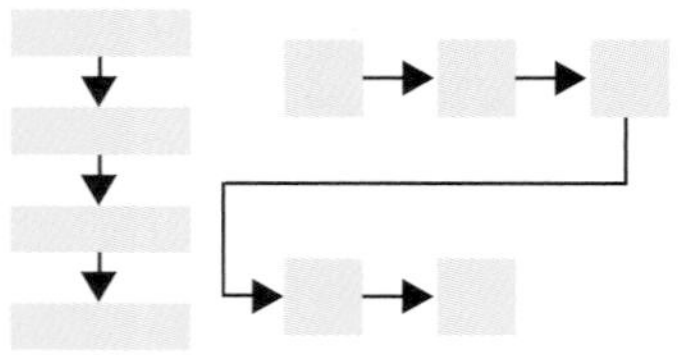	Used to map out your thinking about an issue or to organize ideas for an essay or report	Brainstorm aspects of the whole event or concept. Select important aspects, and put them into sequential order.

©P

Type of Graphic Organizer	Purpose	Method
Comparison matrix	Used to compare the characteristics or properties of a number of things	Brainstorm what you want to compare. Write the characteristics of the things that you will compare and how the things you compare are similar or different.
Fishbone diagram	Used to analyze cause-and-effect relationships	List the effect at the head of the "fish." Brainstorm possible causes, and list them in each "bone." Rank the causes and circle the most probable ones, justifying your choice.
Target diagram	Used to weigh the importance of facts and ideas	Brainstorm facts and ideas. Rank their importance and place the most important facts or ideas centrally and the least important toward the outer ring.
Agree/disagree chart	Used to organize data to support a position for or against an idea or decision	List a series of statements relating to a topic or issue. Survey agreement and disagreement before discussion. Survey again after discussion and research.
Cost/benefit chart	Used to summarize the negative (costs) and positive (benefits) aspects of a topic or issue	List ideas or information relating to the topic or issue. Sort the ideas or information in a chart that includes the headings "Costs" and "Benefits."
Tree diagram	Used to identify and sequence the concepts by placing the main concept at the top of the diagram and all the parts below it	Place the main concept at the top of the page. Then, consider the question "What concepts need to be understood before the concept above can be grasped?" The same question is then asked for each of the parts, and a hierarchy of connected concepts is created.

Communicating in Science

In science, you use your communication skills to clearly show your knowledge, ideas, and understanding. You can use words and visuals, such as diagrams, charts, and tables, to communicate what you know. Some communication may be short, as in answering questions, or long, as in writing reports.

Writing Reports

Toolkit 2 shows you how to plan a science experiment. Toolkit 3 shows you how to design a model or a prototype, and Toolkit 4 shows you how to use a decision-making process for analyzing issues. Guidelines for communicating your results are given in the Toolkits. You can use the list below as a checklist when writing your report.

- Give your report or project a title.
- Tell readers why you did the work.
- State your hypothesis, describe the design challenge, or identify the issue.
- List the materials and equipment you used.
- Describe the steps you took when you did your experiment, designed and made your product, or considered an issue.
- Show your experimental data, the results of testing your product, or the background information on the issue.
- Interpret and analyze the results of your experiment.

- Make conclusions based on the outcome of the experiment, the success of the product you designed, or the research you did on an issue.

Diagrams

Have you heard the saying "a picture is worth a thousand words"? In science, a picture can be worth even more. A carefully drawn diagram can help you express your ideas, record important information, and experiment with designs. Diagrams are an important tool in communicating what you know and your ideas.

One type of diagram you can use is a simple sketch. You may wish to include different views of the object you are drawing. For example, the photo below shows the set-up of an experiment. The sketches show three different views of the set-up.

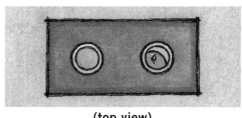
(top view)

(side view)

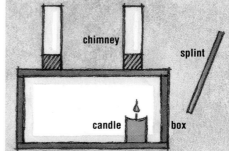
(front view)

©P

Drawing Cell Diagrams

Here are some basic guidelines for drawing what you see through the microscope. Your teacher may have other suggestions as well.

1. Start with a sharp pencil and a blank, unlined piece of paper (or a clean page in your notebook). Use the whole page for your drawing.

2. Using a mathematical compass, draw a circle with a diameter of 10 cm to 12 cm. This represents the view you see through the eyepiece. Scientists call it a *field of view*, or just *field* for short.

3. Draw only what you see. Keep your details simple and straightforward. You do not need to add colour, but you can shade areas, if necessary.

4. Add labels that identify features by name (if you know them) or with brief notes. Always draw your label lines with a ruler. Arrange your labels and label lines clearly and neatly on the page. Record which objective lens you used to observe the image.

5. Give your drawing a title at the top of the page. The title should include information about the object shown.

Remember!

- Give your diagram a title at the top of the page.
- Use the whole page for your diagram.
- Always use a sharp pencil or mechanical pencil for drawing.
- Include only those details that are necessary, keep them simple, and identify them by name.
- If you need labels, use lines, not arrows. Place your labels in line with the feature being labelled, and use a ruler to keep your lines straight. Labels must be accurate, neat and legible, and printed (not written).
- Do not use colour or shading unless your teacher asks you to.
- Include notes and ideas if the sketch is a design for a structure or an invention.

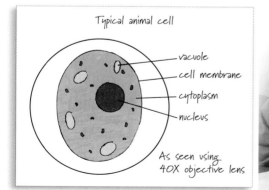

Measurement

Observations from an experiment may be qualitative (descriptive) or quantitative (physical measurements). Quantitative observations help us to describe such things as how far away something is, how massive it is, and how much space it takes up.

Length

The metre is the base unit for measuring length. Long distances are measured in kilometres (km), and small distances are commonly measured in centimetres (cm) or millimetres (mm). The instrument that you use will determine the number of decimal places in your measurement.

When you use a measuring tool such as a ruler, look directly in line with the measurement point, not from an angle. This coin measures 28.0 mm or 2.80 cm.

Hint

When you use a ruler, tape measure, or metre-stick, always start from the 0 measurement point, not the edge of the measuring tool.

Instant Practice

For each of the following, choose the unit of measurement that you think would be used. Explain why.
1. the height of a table
2. the width of a dime
3. the length of a skating rink
4. the distance from Ottawa, Ontario, to Victoria, British Columbia

Volume

Volume indicates the amount of space that something takes up (occupies). Common units used to measure volume include litres (L) for liquids and cubic centimetres (cm^3) for solids. Remember that 1 mL = 1 cm^3.

Graduated cylinders are commonly used in laboratories to accurately measure liquids. Here, "graduated" means a container that has been marked with regular intervals for measuring.

When you add a liquid to a graduated cylinder, the top of the liquid is curved near the sides of the cylinder. This curve is called a *meniscus*. To measure the liquid's volume properly, you need to observe the liquid's surface from eye level so you can see the flat, bottom portion of the curve. Ignore the sides.

Instant Practice

1. Estimate the volume of each of the following objects, using appropriate units.
   (a) soccer ball
   (b) tissue box
   (c) Olympic swimming pool
2. Explain how you could accurately measure 53 mL of water in the school laboratory.

Mass and Weight

The terms mass and weight do not mean the same thing, even though they are often used that way. The mass of something tells you the amount of matter it contains. The weight of an object is a measure of the force of gravity acting on it.

Common units to measure mass include grams (g) and kilograms (kg). Mass is commonly measured using balances, such as an equal arm balance, a triple beam balance, or an electronic scale.

An equal arm balance has two pans. You place the object whose mass you want to measure on one pan. On the other pan, you place standard (known) masses until the two pans are balanced (level). Then, you add up the values of the standard masses. The total is the mass of the object you are measuring.

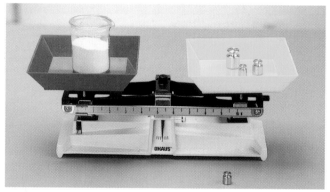
Equal arm balance

A triple beam balance has a single pan. You place the object you are measuring on the pan. You adjust the masses on the beams until the beam assembly is level. Then, you add up the mass equivalent values of the beam masses from the scales on the beam.

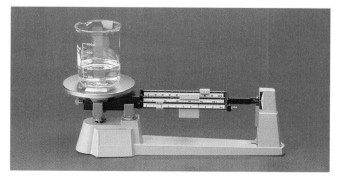
Triple beam balance

Electronic balances allow you to tare (zero) the balance with an object on it. For example, this allows you to ignore the mass of a beaker and measure the mass directly. You do not have to subtract the mass of the beaker.

You can use a spring scale, or force meter, to measure weight, which is the force of gravity acting on an object. A spring scale measures force in newtons.

A spring scale has three main parts: a hook, a spring, and a measuring scale. The hook is used to attach the object to the scale. The spring pulls on the object. As the spring pulls, the pointer moves along the measuring scale.

To measure the weight of an object, hang the object from the hook of the spring scale. Once the pointer stops moving, record the measurement.

Spring scale

Instant Practice

1. The object on the triple beam balance is a water-filled beaker, so the balance is measuring the mass of the water plus the mass of the beaker. Describe, step-by-step, how you would measure just the mass of water in the beaker.
2. How would you measure the mass of an apple? How would this be similar to and different from measuring the mass of a pile of salt?

Temperature

The Celsius temperature scale is commonly used in the metric system, even though the Kelvin degree is the base unit. You will use the Kelvin scale as you learn more about matter in higher grades. Water boils at 100 °C and freezes at 0 °C.

Estimating

It is important to be able to estimate or guess the length, mass, or volume of various objects before you measure. This process will allow you to decide whether your measurements are accurate or if there is instrument error. It will also help you to decide which tool to use. Sometimes, you can estimate by comparing one object with another object that has known measurements. For example, if you are asked to estimate the volume of your drink, you could estimate by comparing it with a large jar of mayonnaise in your fridge, which has its volume marked on the label.

To estimate the volume of your drink, you can compare it with the known volume of a jar of mayonnaise.

Measuring in SI

Most countries and scientific communities have agreed on the use of one system of measurement. This system is called "le Système international d'unités" or SI for short. SI is based on the metric system. Base units are used, and prefixes are added to change the base units by multiples of ten. The table below shows the prefixes, their symbols, and their meanings. A kilometre, for example, is equal to 1000 m, and 1 millimetre is 0.001 m or 1 m = 1000 mm.

SI Base Units

Measurement	Base Unit	Symbol
mass	kilogram	kg
length	metre	m
temperature	Kelvin	K
time	second	s
electric current	ampere	A
amount of substance	mole	mol
intensity of light	candela	cd

Common Metric Prefixes

Prefix	Symbol	Meaning	Exponential Form
giga	G	billion	10^9
mega	M	million	10^6
kilo	k	thousand	10^3
hecto	h	hundred	10^2
deca	da	ten	10
deci	d	one tenth	10^{-1}
centi	c	one hundredth	10^{-2}
milli	m	one thousandth	10^{-3}
micro	μ	one millionth	10^{-6}

Scientific Notation

Scientific notation is often used to express either very large or very small numbers. Numbers written in scientific notation are expressed in the form $x \times 10^n$. x is called the coefficient and is a number between 1 and 10. n is called the exponent and may be positive or negative.

The following steps will help you write a number using scientific notation.

1. Determine the coefficient by placing a decimal after the first digit. Drop all the trailing zeroes. If all the numbers after the decimal are zeroes, keep one zero.

2. Determine the exponent by counting the number of places you moved the decimal place to get the coefficient. If you moved the decimal to the left, the number is positive. If you moved the decimal to the right, the number is negative.

Example 8.1: Write 0.000 15 mm in scientific notation.

The coefficient is 1.5. The decimal is moved four places to the right, so the exponent is -4.

0.000 15 mm is written as 1.5×10^{-4} mm

To convert a number in scientific notation to common notation, move the decimal by the number of places indicated by the exponent. A positive exponent moves the decimal to the right, and a negative exponent moves the decimal to the left.

Example 8.2: Write 2.998×10^8 m/s in common notation.

The power term 10^8 tells you to move the decimal over 8 places to the right.

2.998×10^8 m/s is written as 299 800 000 m/s

Instant Practice

1. 1 AU is approximately 150 000 000 km. Write this number in scientific notation.
2. Write 0.0001 in scientific notation.
3. Write 1.5×10^{-4} in common notation.
4. Write 3.8×10^3 in common notation.

Converting SI Units

Use the following steps to help you convert between SI units.

1. Write the measurement that you want to convert.
2. Multiply by a factor that shows the relationship between the two units you are converting. Write this relationship as a fraction, putting the units you are converting to in the numerator. This will allow you to cancel the given units you started with.
3. The conversion may require two or more steps. This method of solving problems is referred to as unit analysis.

Example 8.3: Express 56 cm in metres.

Multiple the number by its conversion factor, and cancel out any repeated units:

$$56 \text{ cm} \times \frac{1 \text{ m}}{100 \text{ cm}}$$

$$= \frac{56 \text{ m}}{100}$$

$$= 0.56 \text{ m}$$

Example 8.4: Express 3200 cm in kilometres.

Multiple the number by its conversion factor, and cancel out any repeated units:

$$3200 \text{ cm} \times \frac{1 \text{ m}}{100 \text{ cm}} \times \frac{1 \text{ km}}{1000 \text{ m}}$$

$$= \frac{3200 \text{ km}}{100 \times 1000}$$

$$= 0.3200 \text{ km}$$

Graphing

Science and technology often involve collecting a lot of numerical data. This data may be recorded in tables or charts. Sometimes, however, it is difficult to see if there are any patterns in the numbers. That is when it is useful to reorganize the data into graphs. Graphs help to interpret data collected during an experiment by showing how numbers are related to one another. You have probably drawn a lot of graphs over the years in your studies of mathematics, geography, and, of course, science and technology.

Creating Line Graphs

Line graphs are good for exploring data collected for many types of experiments. Using line graphs is a good way to analyze the data that are continually changing. For example, here are some data collected by students investigating temperature changes. They poured hot water into a large container (Container A) and cold water into a smaller container (Container B). After recording the starting temperatures of the water in each container, they placed Container B inside Container A and took measurements every 30 s until there were no more temperature changes.

The data they collected are shown in a table and as a line graph. On the graph, they put the independent variable—time—on the x-axis, and the dependent variable—temperature— on the y-axis. For the scale on the x-axis, they let each interval represent 30 s and for the y-axis, they let each interval represent 5 C°.

Temperature of water in Container A and Container B		
Time (s)	Temperature (°C) of water in Container A	Temperature (°C) of water in Container B
0	51	0
30	45	7
60	38	14
90	33	20
120	30	22
150	29	23
180	28	24
210	27	25
240	26	26
270	26	26
300	26	26

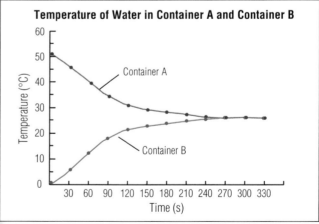

©P

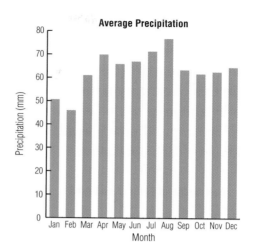

Average Precipitation

Creating Bar Graphs

Bar graphs are useful for showing relationships between separate sets of data. For example, the table below shows the monthly average precipitation (both snow and rain) for a city in Canada. Compare the data in this table with how they "look" when they are reorganized in the form of a bar graph. On the graph, the independent variable—month—is represented on the *x*-axis, and the dependent variable—precipitation—is represented on the *y*-axis.

Hint

Numbers on the axes of bar graphs are often expressed to the nearest whole number.

Instant Practice

1. Why is each bar on a bar graph the same width?
2. Which axis is used for the independent variable? Which is used for the dependent variable?
3. Suppose you were to draw the bar graph for Average Precipitation on a piece of graph paper 32 squares by 24 squares. Describe how you would determine the scale for each axis, keeping in mind that August has the most precipitation of any month, with 76.8 mm.

Month	Average precipitation (mm)
January	50.4
February	46.0
March	61.1
April	70.0
May	66.0
June	67.1
July	71.4
August	76.8
September	63.5
October	61.8
November	62.7
December	64.7

Creating Circle (Pie) Graphs

A circle graph is useful when you want to display data that are part of a whole. For example, in this circle graph, the "whole" is Earth's total land area, which is 100%. The "parts" are the approximate percentages of land made up by each continent.

Percentage of Earth's Land Area

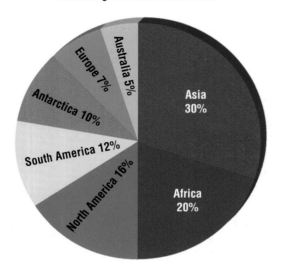

The data from the circle graph are organized into a table below. Which format can you interpret more easily and more quickly?

Continent	Percentage of Earth's land area
Asia	30%
Africa	20%
North America	16%
South America	12%
Antarctica	10%
Europe	7%
Australia	5%

Steps for Drawing a Circle Graph

1. Check that all of the percentage values add up to 100%.

2. Convert each percentage value to an angle of the circle by changing the percentage value to a decimal and multiplying it by 360°. For example, Asia represents 30% of Earth's land area, so the corresponding angle of the circle is $0.30 \times 360° = 108°$.

3. Draw a circle with a compass and use a protractor to measure the angle for each section. For Asia, it is 108°.

4. Use a different colour for each section of the circle.

5. Label each section and add a title to your circle graph.

Hint

You might consider using a computer to draw your circle graphs. Some computer drawing programs allow you to use different colours for the different sections of your graph, making it easier to read.

Instant Practice

1. Which continents, when added together, make up about half of all the land mass on Earth? Why is it easier to determine this from the circle graph than from the table of data?

2. 24 students were asked what they usually eat for breakfast.
   - 12 students usually eat cereal
   - 6 students usually eat toast, waffles, or bread
   - 3 students usually eat eggs
   - 2 students usually eat fruit and yogurt
   - 1 student usually drinks a soy protein shake

   Sketch what this circle graph would look like.

©P

Using a Microscope

A microscope allows us to see an image of an object that is too small to see with the unaided human eye. A light microscope functions by focussing a beam of light through the object into the lens of the microscope. A compound light microscope is any light microscope that contains more than one lens. The compound light microscope you will use in the science classroom contains an eyepiece lens and a number of objective lenses. Each objective lens is a combination of two lenses made of different kinds of glass.

The Parts of the Microscope

It is important to know the location and function of the parts of the microscope in order to use it correctly. These are shown below.

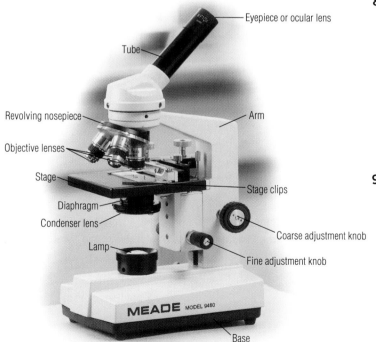

Eyepiece or ocular lens

Tube

Revolving nosepiece

Objective lenses

Stage

Diaphragm

Condenser lens

Lamp

Arm

Stage clips

Coarse adjustment knob

Fine adjustment knob

Base

MEADE MODEL 9480

Using the Microscope

1. Carry the microscope with two hands, grasping the arm of the microscope with one hand and holding the base of the microscope with the other. Place the microscope on the table or bench so that the arm is facing you.
2. Plug in the microscope, and turn on the light.
3. Rotate the nosepiece until the objective lens with the lowest power is in place.
4. Place a microscope slide on the stage, and secure with the stage clips.
5. Watch the stage from one side of the microscope, and slowly raise the stage with the coarse adjustment until it is as close to the obective lens as possible without touching it. Ensure the lens does not touch the slide.
6. Look through the eyepiece. Slowly turn the coarse adjustment so that you move the slide away from the lens. Stop when the image comes into view.
7. Use the fine adjustment to sharpen the focus of the image.
8. If you need to view the object under higher magnification, watch from the side of the microscope and rotate the nosepiece until the next higher power objective lens is in place. Ensure the lens does not touch the slide. Use only the fine adjustment knob to focus the image.

> **CAUTION:** Never use the coarse adjustment knob with the medium-and high-power objective lenses.

9. When you are finished using the microscope, lower the stage using the coarse adjustment knob and remove the slide. Rotate the nosepiece until the lowest power objective lens is in place. Turn off the light and unplug the microscope.

Electricity Backgrounder

Electrical Safety in the Lab

- Handle batteries carefully. They contain acids or bases that can cause corrosive burns.
- Do not connect the two battery terminals with a wire or you will create a short circuit.
- Do not use bare connecting wires.
- Have your teacher check the circuit before you close the switch or connect the power source.
- Disconnect or turn off the power source before you connect wires in a circuit.

Reading an Ammeter

To connect the ammeter, disconnect the circuit at the point where you wish to make a measurement and attach the wires so that the (+) side of the power source connects to the red terminal on the meter and the (–) side of the power source connects to the black terminal on the meter.

A digital ammeter will display the values directly. To read an analog display ammeter, note the position of a pointer on a dial and read the values from it. Many ammeters have two or even three scales. The choice of which scale is used is usually determined by which terminals on the ammeter are used to connect it into the circuit.

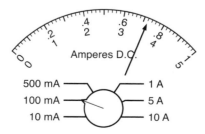

The ammeter above is connected using the 100-mA scale. This means that a full scale deflection of the pointer is 100 mA. Use the scale that has a full scale deflection of 1. This is 100 mA. Since the pointer is at 0.72, the reading is 0.72 mA.

Reading a Voltmeter

Do not disconnect any part of the circuit in order to connect a voltmeter. Connect two wires from the voltmeter to either side of the dry cell or other device where the voltage measurement is to be taken. Attach the wires so that the (+) side of the power source is closest to the wire from the red terminal on the meter and the (–) side of the power source is closest to the wire from the black terminal on the meter.

A digital voltmeter will display the values directly. To read an analog display voltmeter, note the position of a pointer on a dial and read the values from it. Like ammeters, many voltmeters have two or even three scales. The choice of scale used is usually determined by which terminals on the voltmeter are used to connect it into the circuit. Sometimes, a dial is used to select the appropriate scale, as in the example below.

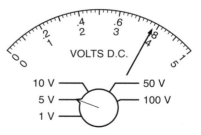

The voltmeter above is connected using the 5-V scale. This means that a full scale deflection of the pointer is 5 V. Use the scale that has a full scale deflection of 5. Since the pointer is at 3.9, the reading is 3.9 V.

Star Charts

The star chart shown here will help you
identify stars in the night sky.

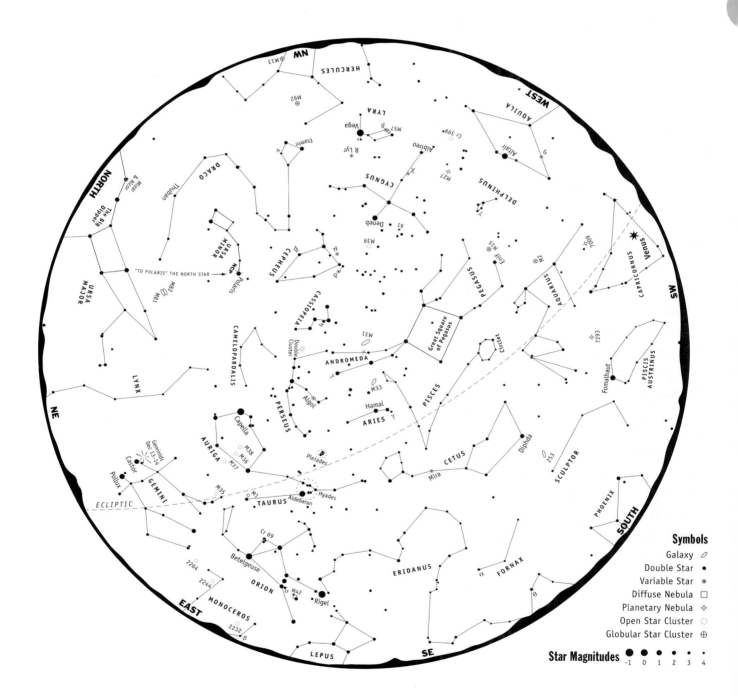

Symbols

Galaxy ⊘
Double Star •
Variable Star ⊛
Diffuse Nebula □
Planetary Nebula ✧
Open Star Cluster ⚬
Globular Star Cluster ⊕

Star Magnitudes ● ● ● • ·
-1 0 1 2 3 4

This star chart shows constellations from some First Nations, including Ojibway, Cree, and Blackfoot. The lighter grey areas represent the Milky Way.

©P

A

adhesion   the property of sticking to other substances; a physical property of water (133)

alkali metals   elements found in Group 1 of the periodic table of elements; these metals have low melting points and react easily with water and air (183)

allele   a possible version of a gene, which codes information for a specific trait, or version of a characteristic (51)

alloy   a solution of two or more metals (159)

alternating current (AC)   the back-and-forth flow of electric current at regular intervals called cycles (239)

altitude   the measurement that describes the vertical position of an object in relation to the horizon; measured in degrees from the horizon to a point directly overhead, known as the zenith (309)

ammeter [A-mee-tuhr]   a device used to measure the current in a circuit (239)

ampere (A) [AM-per]   the SI unit for measuring electric current (239)

analytical   a way of thinking that reduces or compartmentalizes everything into parts and categories; also called a reductionist way of thinking (7)

apparent retrograde motion   the apparent backward motion of a planet's path relative to the background night sky (388)

artificial insemination (AI)   a form of artificial reproductive technology in which sperm are collected from a chosen male and inserted into one or more females (62)

artificial reproductive technology   any artificial method of joining a male and a female gamete (62)

artificial satellite   a human-made device placed in orbit around Earth or another celestial object (407)

asexual reproduction   a form of reproduction that involves only one parent (18)

asterism   a smaller, recognizable star pattern within a larger constellation (306)

asteroid   a metallic, rocky body without atmosphere that orbits the Sun but is too small to be classified as a planet or dwarf planet (336)

asteroid belt   a region of rocky debris that forms a ring all the way around the Sun at a distance of about 3 AU (336)

astronomer   a person who knows and studies astronomy (305)

astronomical body   an object in space, including Earth (305)

astronomical unit (AU)   a unit of measure used to measure distances in space; one AU equals the average distance between the Sun and Earth, about 150 million km (332)

astronomy   the study of objects and phenomena in space (305)

atom   the smallest unit of an element that has all of the element's properties (151)

atomic mass   the average mass of an element's atoms (181)

atomic mass units (amu)   a unit of measure used to measure an atom's mass (181)

atomic number   the number of protons in an atom of an element (180)

atomic theory   the theory that explains the nature of matter; study of the nature of atoms and how they combine to form all types of matter (151)

aurora australis (Southern Lights)   the light displays in the southern hemisphere caused by the solar wind interacting with particles in Earth's atmosphere (323)

aurora borealis (Northern Lights)   the light displays in the northern hemisphere caused by the solar wind interacting with particles in Earth's atmosphere (323)

azimuth   the measurement that describes the horizontal position of a celestial body in relation to due north; measured in degrees along the horizon starting from due north, moving in a clockwise direction (310)

B

battery   a combination of electrochemical cells (243)

Big Bang theory   the theory that states the universe formed when an infinitely dense point suddenly and rapidly expanded in a single moment; all the matter and energy that exists today was created during the early minutes of that hot, rapid expansion (380)

binary fission   a form of asexual reproduction in which single-celled organisms divide into two new individuals that are identical to each other and are clones of the parent cell (20)

binary system   a star-and-planet system with two stars at its centre (352)

biomass   a renewable fuel made of organic material such as plant and animal waste (274)

black hole   a region of space where gravitational forces are so strong that nothing, not even light, can escape (357)

blastocyst   the hollow ball of cells formed by a developing embryo; the inner mass of cells gives rise to the embryo proper, whereas the outer layer of cells help form the amniotic sac and the placenta (95)

bond   the attraction between atoms or ions (170)

budding   a form of asexual reproduction in which a parent produces a small bud or a miniaturized clone that becomes a separate individual (20)

C

cancer   a disease in which a cell divides uncontrollably; develops when a mutation occurs in the cell that affects how that cell divides (12)

carcinogen   a chemical or toxin in the environment that can damage DNA in cells and cause cancer (12)

celestial body   an object that can be observed in the sky; does not include Earth (305)

cell cycle   the process by which the parent cell grows, duplicates itself, and divides to produce new daughter cells, usually two (8)

cervix the lower portion of the uterus that connects the uterus to the vagina (87)

characteristic a feature of an organism such as eye colour or wing shape (41)

charging by contact a form of charging in which a charged object touches a neutral object and transfers electrons to it (216)

charging by induction a form of charging in which a charged object is used to induce a charge in a neutral object and then the newly charged object is grounded so that it retains the charge (216)

chemical change a change in matter that results in the formation of a new substance or substances (136)

chemical family one of 18 vertical columns in the periodic table of elements; classification of elements with certain shared physical and chemical properties; also known as a group (182)

chemical formula a formula that identifies which elements, and how many atoms or ions of each, are in a compound (172)

chemical property a characteristic of a substance that describes its ability to change into a new substance or substances; how a substance interacts with other substances, such as acids, or how it reacts to heat or light (136)

chemical reaction the process in which a chemical change occurs; a reaction that produces a new substance or substances (136)

chromosome a structure in the cell nucleus that contains DNA (9)

circuit a complete path in which electrons can flow; includes energy source, electrical load, and conducting wires (237)

circuit breaker a safety device in which a wire heats up and bends when there is excess current in the circuit, triggering a spring mechanism that turns off the flow of electricity (263)

circuit diagram a model used by engineers and designers in order to design and analyze an electrical circuit (250)

cleavage the process by which a zygote divides into two or more cells to produce an embryo (29)

clone an offspring that is an identical copy of the parent (18)

cohesion the property of sticking together; a physical property of water (133)

combustibility the ability of a substance to react quickly with oxygen to produce heat energy and light (137)

comet a celestial object made of ice and dust that travels in an elliptical orbit around the Sun (338)

compound a pure substance made from two or more elements that are combined together chemically (125)

conduction the movement or transmission of electrons through a substance (210)

conductivity the ability of a material to allow electrons to move freely within it (210)

conductor a material that allows the movement of electrons (210)

constellation a group of stars that, observed from Earth, resembles a form (305)

continuous variation variation in a trait that exists in a range of forms (44)

contraception a technology that prevents pregnancy (103)

corpus luteum the structure formed from a ruptured follicle that produced a mature egg; produces the hormone progesterone (87)

covalent bond the attraction between atoms created by the sharing of a pair of electrons between atoms (171)

cross-pollination the transfer of pollen from one plant to the stigma of another plant (31)

current electrical energy the flow of electric charge in a circuit (237)

cytokinesis the phase of the cell cycle during which the cell contents divide and the cell membrane pinches in to produce two separate daughter cells; in plant cells, the cell wall also grows between the daughter cells to separate them (9)

D

dark matter matter in the universe that is invisible because it does not interact with light or any other kind of radiation (366)

declination (decl) the vertical coordinate measurement that describes the position of a celestial body on the celestial sphere, similar to latitude; measured in units of degrees (310)

diatomic molecule a molecule that contains two atoms of the same element (172)

diploid the characteristic of having a double set of chromosomes (10)

direct current (DC) the flow of electric current in one direction (239)

discrete variation variation in a trait that exists in defined forms (44)

DNA (deoxyribonucleic acid) a long molecule that stores a cell's genetic information, which directs all the cell's functions (9)

dominant allele an allele that codes for a trait that is expressed in the hybrid condition; an allele that is expressed if one or both members of a pair of alleles are dominant (53)

dominant trait a trait that appears if one or both members of a pair of alleles are dominant (53)

dry cell an electrochemical cell that uses a paste instead of a liquid electrolyte; also called a primary cell (243)

dwarf planet an astronomical body that orbits the Sun, has enough mass to form a roughly spherical shape under its own gravitational force, and has an eccentric orbit or orbits in a zone that contains many other objects; protoplanets are a subgroup of dwarf planets; Pluto is a well-known example of a dwarf planet (337)

E

ecliptic the apparent path of the Sun and planets as observed from Earth as they move through the sky during the year (316)

efficiency the ratio of the useful energy that comes out of a device to the total energy that went in (287)

egg (or ovum; plural: ova)   a sex cell from a female (27)

electric charges   charged particles that exert a force on each other (206)

electric current   a measure of the amount of electric charge that passes by a point in an electrical circuit in a given time interval (239)

electrical discharge   the process by which electric charges are transferred very quickly (217)

electrochemical cell   a package of chemicals that converts chemical energy into electrical energy that is stored in charged particles (243)

electrode   a metal strip that reacts with an electrolyte (243)

electrolyte [e-LEK-truh-lite]   a liquid or paste that contains chemicals that form ions and conducts electric charge (243)

electromagnetic radiation   the wave form of light energy that travels in waves of varying lengths; visible light is one form of electromagnetic radiation (382)

electromagnetic spectrum   the full range of electromagnetic radiation, organized by wavelength from very long to very short; examples include radio waves, microwaves, infrared, visible light, ultraviolet radiation, and X rays (382)

electron   a negatively charged particle in an atom, located outside the nucleus of the atom (152, 207)

electron affinity   the tendency of a substance to hold on to electrons (208)

electroscope   an instrument that can detect static electric charges (213)

electrostatics   the study of static electric charges (213)

element   a pure substance that cannot be broken down into simpler substances (125)

embryo   an undeveloped multicellular life form during the earliest stage of its development (29)

endometrium   the lining of the uterus that is produced each month in response to hormones produced during ovulation; helps form the placenta if fertilization and implantation occur (88)

EnerGuide   a label that states how much energy the appliance will use in a year of average use (288)

energy efficiency rating   a rating that indicates how much electrical energy a device consumes during its operation (288)

energy grid   a web of interconnections between generating stations, substations, and users; also called a distribution grid (272)

Energy Star   the symbol identifying the most efficient appliances in each class (288)

epididymis   the structure above each testis in which sperm finish maturing and are stored until ejaculation (83)

equinox   the day of the year when the hours of daylight and the hours of night are of equal length; the vernal equinox occurs around March 21 and the autumnal equinox occurs around September 22 (308)

estrogen   a hormone produced by the ovaries that plays multiple roles in female humans, including developing secondary female characteristics and regulating menstrual cycle; estrogen also plays other roles in both human males and females (85)

F

fallopian tube   the tube that sweep mature eggs up from the ovary and carries them to the uterus (87)

feedback   a system of communication in which signals produce or inhibit a response; if a signal produces a response, it is positive feedback; if a signal inhibits a response, it is negative feedback (88)

fertilization   the union of a sperm cell with an egg cell (27)

fetus   the developing embryo that has been implanted for approximately eight or nine weeks; in mammals, the fetus has all the major structures of an adult (97)

follicle-stimulating hormone (FSH)   a hormone that is produced in the brain and is circulated through the blood in the body to the gonads, where it signals the reproductive system to begin producing mature gametes (78)

fossil fuel   a fuel formed from the organic matter of organisms that lived millions of years ago; includes coal, oil, and natural gas (274)

fragmentation   a form of asexual reproduction by which new individuals are formed from a piece of an existing parent organism (22)

friction   the force that occurs when objects rub against each other (208)

fuse   a safety device in an electric circuit which has a metallic conductor with a low melting point compared to the circuit's wires, and which melts when there is excess current in the circuit (263)

G

galaxy   a collection of hundreds of billions of stars that are held together by gravitational forces (350)

gamete   a sex cell; sex cells from females are called eggs or ova; sex cells from males are called sperm; gametes are haploid (27)

gene   an uninterrupted segment of DNA, which contains coded instructions for a specific characteristic (50)

generator   a device that transforms the energy of motion into an electric current (272)

genetic code   the arrangement of the four chemicals (guanine, cytosine, ademine, thymine) in DNA into instructions that describe how to make any particular organism (49)

genetic engineering   any technological process that directly alters the DNA of an organism (62)

geocentric model   a model of the universe or solar system that places Earth at the centre (387)

geostationary orbit   an orbit in which a satellite orbits Earth at the same rate as Earth rotates, so that the satellite appears to be stationary above Earth when viewed from the ground (408)

geothermal energy   heat or electrical energy generated from water naturally heated by hot rock in the Earth's crust (275)

gonads   the reproductive organs that produce gametes; these are the ovaries in females and the testes in males (78)

grafting   the process of joining a part of one plant to another plant, called the parent tree or the root stock (22)

ground fault circuit interrupter (GFCI)   a safety device that detects a change in current and opens the circuit, stopping the current (264)

grounding   the process of connecting a charged object to Earth's surface (217)

group   one of 18 vertical columns in the periodic table of elements; classification of elements with certain shared physical and chemical properties; also known as a chemical family (182)

H

halogens   elements found in Group 17 of the periodic table of elements; these non-metals are all very reactive (183)

haploid   the characteristic of having a single set of chromosomes; two haploid cells join together in the process of fertilization (11)

heliocentric model   a model of the solar system that places the Sun at the centre of the solar system; Earth and other objects in the solar system revolve around the Sun (388)

heredity   the transmission of traits from one generation to the next (43)

heritable characteristic   a characteristics that are passed from parent to offspring (43)

hermaphrodite   an animal that is able to produce both male and female gametes (30)

holistic [hoh-LIS-tic]   a way of thinking that emphasizes an entire system and a person's connections to the oneness of everything (7)

hormone   a type of molecule that give instructions to cells and cause them to respond in certain ways (78)

hybrid   an individual produced by crossing two purebred parents that differ in a trait (52)

hydroelectrical energy   electrical energy generated from the energy of flowing water (273)

I

implantation   the process in which the blastocyst attaches itself into the endometrium (96)

in vitro fertilization (IVF)   a form of artificial reproductive technology in which sperm from a male and eggs from a female are collected and combined in a Petri dish for fertilization (62)

induction   the movement of electrons within an object caused by a nearby charged object, without direct contact between the two objects (216)

infertility   the inability to reproduce caused by problems in producing suitable gametes, difficulty conceiving, or problems with implantation (106)

insulator (electrical insulator)   a material that resists or blocks the movement of electrons (210)

interphase   the phase of the cell cycle during which a cell performs its normal cell functions, grows, and prepares for cell division (9)

ion   an atom or group of atoms that has an electric charge as the result of losing or gaining electrons (170)

ion charge   an electric charge that an atom or group of joined atoms takes on when it loses or gains electrons (181)

ionic bond   the attraction between ions of opposite charges; e.g., bond in an ionic compound (170)

ionic compound   a pure substance formed when at least one metal and one non-metal combine chemically (169)

isotopes   atoms of the same element that have different atomic masses (180)

K

kilowatt-hour (kW•h)   unit of measure commonly used to measure electrical energy consumption; one kilowatt-hour is equal to a consumption of one kilowatt in one hour (286)

L

lattice   a regular, patterned three-dimensional structure (170)

law   a generalized description of some aspect of the physical world under certain conditions (149)

light-year (ly)   a unit of measure used to measure distances in space; one light-year equals the distance that a beam of light travels through space in one year, equivalent to 63 000 AU or 9000 billion km (332)

load (electrical)   a device that converts electrical energy to another form of energy (237)

lunar eclipse   a celestial event that occurs when Earth blocks all or part of the Sun's light shining on the Moon, making the Moon briefly disappear (320)

M

magnitude   a measure of the brightness of a star (351)

mass   the measurement of the quantity of matter in an object (124)

mass number   the total number of protons and neutrons in the nucleus of an atom (181)

matter   anything that has mass and volume (124)

mechanical mixture   a combination of pure substances in which the different substances are individually visible; a type of heterogeneous mixture (126)

Medicine Wheel (or sacred circle)   a First Nations and Métis way of knowing the physical world; a Medicine Wheel has four quadrants and connects everything in the universe together into one whole (123)

meiosis   the process of cell division that produces gametes, each with half the number of chromosomes of the parent cell (29)

menstrual cycle   the cycle by which a mature egg is produced and released approximately every month (88)

menstruation   the breakdown and shedding of the endometrium from the body, along with the dead, unfertilized egg (88)

metalloids elements with metallic and non-metallic properties; e.g., silicon (160)

metals elements that are malleable and ductile, and conduct electricity and heat; most elements are metals (159)

meteor a meteoroid that enters Earth's atmosphere and burns up as it collides with gas molecules (339)

meteorite a meteor that does not burn up completely and strikes Earth's surface (339)

microgravity an environmental condition in which gravitational forces are greatly reduced to almost zero (418)

mitosis the phase of the cell cycle during which the nucleus divides to produce an exact copy of itself (9)

molecular compound a pure substance formed when non-metals combine chemically (171)

molecule a group of atoms that share electrons; molecular compounds contain molecules (171)

multimeter a multifunctional meter that can function as an ammeter, ohmmeter, or voltmeter (240)

N

nebula (plural: nebulae) a cloud of dust and gases in space, which scientists believe is an area of star formation (330)

nebular theory the theory that explains the formation of the solar system and other star-and-planet systems from nebulae (330)

neutral the property of having no overall electric charge; both the positive and negative charges are equal (170)

neutron a neutral particle in an atom, located in the nucleus of the atom (153, 207)

noble gases elements found in Group 18 of the periodic table of elements; these gases are not chemically reactive except in certain special situations (184)

non-heritable characteristic a characteristic that cannot be passed on to other generations (43)

non-metals elements that do not resemble metals; non-metals are brittle and generally do not conduct electricity or heat; e.g., carbon (160)

non-renewable (non-renewable resource) a resource that cannot be replaced once it is used up (269)

nucleus (atomic) the centre of an atom where all of the atom's positive charge and most of an atom's mass is concentrated (153, 207)

O

ohm (Ω) the SI unit for measuring resistance (240)

Ohm's law the law that establishes the relationships between voltage (V), current (I), and resistance (R); it states that as long as temperature stays the same, $V = IR$ (259)

ohmmeter a device for measuring electrical resistance (240)

orbit the path along which an object, such as a planet, travels around another object, such as a star; Earth travels around the Sun in a slightly elliptical orbit (317)

orbital radius a planet's distance from the Sun (389)

ovaries (singular: ovary) the female gonads that produce eggs (85)

ovulation the release of a mature egg from a follicle in the ovary; usually, one egg is released approximately every 28 days (86)

ovule the female gametes of a plant; found in the pistil, or female structure, of the plant (31)

oxytocin a hormone that makes the uterus contract rhythmically (97)

P

parallel circuit an electric circuit in which the components are arranged in parallel paths; an electric circuit that has multiple paths along which electrons can flow (251)

parthenogenesis a form of asexual reproduction by which unfertilized, haploid eggs mature into new organisms (20)

penis the organ of a male mammal that delivers the sperm to the female during reproduction (83)

period one of seven horizontal rows in the periodic table of elements (182)

periodic law a generalized description stating that elements arranged in order of atomic numbers show a periodic repetition of properties (180)

periodic table of elements a chart that organizes all of the elements in rows and columns; also called periodic table (180)

physical property a characteristic of a substance that can be observed or measured (133)

placenta the organ that connects a developing embryo to the wall of the uterus and allows the exchange of nutrients, oxygen, and carbon dioxide between the mother and the embryo (96)

planet an astronomical body that orbits one or more stars and is capable of forming into a spherical shape under its own gravitational force, or gravity (331)

pollen the male gamete of a plant; found on the stamen, or male structure, of the plant (31)

polyatomic ion a group of atoms of different elements with an overall electric charge, and which acts as a single ion (170)

primary cell an electrochemical cell that uses a paste instead of a liquid electrolyte; also called a dry cell (243)

progesterone a hormone that plays multiple roles in female humans, including developing secondary female characteristics and regulating menstrual cycle; progesterone also plays other roles in both human males and females (85)

property a characteristic that describes a substance (125)

prostate gland the gland that produces a thick, milky fluid called seminal fluid, which combines with sperm to make semen (83)

proton a positively charged particle in an atom, located in the nucleus of the atom (152, 207)

protostar a star in its first stage of formation (353)

puberty the period of growth and development of the final adult form and of sexual maturation (78)

Punnett square   a diagram that is used to show possible combinations of alleles in offspring produced by crossing two parents; can be used predict traits expressed in offspring or trait frequencies (54)

pure substance   a substance made up of only one kind of particle, with a unique set of properties, such as colour, hardness, boiling point, and melting point; an element or compound (125)

Q

quasar   the brightest and most distant objects in the universe, believed by scientists to be supermassive black holes at the centres of distant galaxies (366)

R

recessive allele   an allele that codes for a trait whose expression is masked in the hybrid condition; an allele that is only expressed if both members of a pair of alleles are recessive (54)

recessive trait   a trait that appears only if both members of a pair of alleles are recessive (54)

red-shifted   the increase of a light's wavelength, moving it toward the red end of the visible spectrum (384)

relative mass   the mass of an object in comparison to the mass of another object (154)

renewable (renewable resource)   a resource that can be reused or replaced, such as sunlight or wind (269)

resistance   the degree to which a substance opposes the flow of electric current through it (240)

resistor   a material that can slow current flow in a circuit, such as the filament in a light bulb (241)

revolution   one complete orbit of one object around another; one revolution of Earth around the Sun takes one year (317)

right ascension (RA)   the horizontal coordinate measurement that describes the position of a celestial body on the celestial sphere, similar to longitude; measured in units of hours, minutes, and seconds (310)

rotation   one complete spin of an object, such as a planet, on its axis; one rotation of Earth takes 24 hours (316)

S

satellite   any object that orbits a planet, such as a moon; satellites may be natural or artificial (318)

scrotum   the sac located outside of the body that contains and protects the testes (82)

secondary cell   a dry cell that can be re-energized, and are referred to as "rechargeable" (244)

selective breeding   the process of selecting and breeding individuals with desirable traits to produce offspring that also have the desired traits (61)

self-pollination   the transfer of pollen from a plant to the stigma of the same plant (31)

seminiferous tubules   a type of tissue that makes up the testes and whose cells divide by mitosis to produce diploid cells that develop into sperm (83)

series circuit   an electric circuit in which the components are arranged one after another; an electric circuit that has only one path along which electrons can flow (251)

sexual reproduction   a form of reproduction that involves the union of two sex cells which come together to produce a new individual (27)

short circuit   an accidental low-resistance connection between two points in a circuit, often causing excess current flow (262)

solar eclipse   a celestial event that occurs when the Moon lies directly between Earth and the Sun, blocking all or part of the Sun's light to viewers on Earth (319)

solar flare   a high energy, massive explosion at the surface of the Sun (322)

solar prominence   a large, low energy, curved, bright stream of particles (322)

solar system   the Sun and all the planets and other celestial objects, such as moons, comets, and asteroids, that are held by the Sun's gravity and orbit around it (329)

solar wind   the constant flow of particles streaming out of the Sun's surface in all directions (323)

solstice   the longest period of daylight or night in a year; the summer solstice is the longest day of the year and occurs around June 21 in the northern hemisphere; the winter solstice is the longest night of the year and occurs around December 21 in the northern hemisphere (307)

solution   a combination of pure substances in which the different substances are not individually visible; a homogenous mixture (126)

spectral lines   a series of dark lines that appears across a light spectrum and indicates the chemical elements that make up the material emitting light; the spectral lines across a star's light spectrum indicate that chemical composition of the star (383)

spectral shifting   the change in position of spectral lines to the left or the right of where they normally lie in the spectrum of a light source that is not moving (384)

spectroscope   a device that splits a light sample into its component colours, or spectrum (379)

spectrum (plural: spectra)   the separation of radiation, such as light, into different wavelengths (378)

sperm   a sex cell from a male (27)

spinoff   a secondary effect or product of a thing or an activity (406)

spore   a haploid cell that can develop into a new individual (21)

star   a body of electrically charged gas, or plasma, that emits energy from nuclear reactions taking place in its core (321)

static electric charge   an electric charge that builds up on the surface of an object (207)

subatomic particle   a particle that makes up an atom; includes protons, neutrons, and electrons (154)

sunspot a region on the Sun's surface that is cooler than the surrounding areas (321)

superconductor a type of conductor that has no electrical resistance below a characteristic temperature (241)

supernova the explosion of a high mass star (356)

suspension a cloudy mixture in which tiny particles of one substance are held within another; a type of heterogeneous mixture (126)

sustainable development development that meets the needs of the present without compromising the ability of future generations to meet their own needs (279)

switch a device that turns the circuit on or off by closing or opening the circuit (237)

T

testes (singular: testis) the male gonads that produce sperm (81)

testosterone a hormone that is responsible for developing the secondary male sex characteristics in human males; testosterone also plays other roles in both human males and females (81)

theory a generalized explanation of a set of related observations or events supported by research and good arguments (149)

thermonuclear (thermonuclear generation) the production of electrical energy using heat from nuclear reactions, usually nuclear fission (275)

trait a variation of a characteristic, such as brown eye colour versus blue eye colour, or long wing shape versus round wing shape (41)

transformer a machine that boosts the generator's voltage for long distance transmission (272)

transistor a tiny device that acts as a switch or amplifier in a circuit (249)

transition metals elements in the middle of the periodic table (182)

tumour a clump of cancer cells (12)

turbine a machine that uses the flow of a fluid to turn a shaft; used in generators to generate electricity (272)

two-eyed seeing a way of thinking that respects and combines both holistic and analytical ways of knowing; this idea was developed by Mi'kmaq Elder Albert Marshall from the Eskasoni First Nation in Nova Scotia (60)

U

universe everything that physically exists; the entirety of space and time, and all forms of matter and energy (349)

urethra the tube that carries urine from the bladder to the outside of the body; in male mammals, it is also the tube that carries semen from the vas deferens, through the penis, to the outside the body (84)

uterus the hollow, pear-shaped organ in the female mammal reproductive system that contains and protects a developing baby (87)

V

vagina the long, muscular tube in female mammals that leads from the cervix to the outside of the body; also called the birth canal (87)

vas deferens the tube in the male mammal reproductive system in which sperm travel from the epididymis to the urethra (83)

vegetative reproduction a form of asexual reproduction that produces clones from a parent plant; includes cuttings, runners, rhizomes, tubers, and bulbs (21)

volt (V) the SI unit for measuring voltage (238)

voltage the difference in electrical energy between two points in a circuit (238)

voltmeter a device used to measure voltage (238)

volume the measurement of how big an object is or how much space a fluid takes up (124)

W

wet cell an electrochemical cell that uses a liquid electrolyte (243)

X

X chromosome one of two sex determining chromosomes in many animal species; most female mammals have two X chromosomes whereas male mammals have one X and one Y chromosome (66)

Y

Y chromosome one of two sex determining chromosomes in many animal species; most male mammals have one X and one Y chromosome (66)

Z

zygote a single cell produced from the joining of two gametes (29)

©P

prevention of, 103–105
reproductive technologies, 106, 107
sexual, 27–33
technology-assisted, 101–103
resistance, **240**, 241
in circuits, 252 *table*
in Ohm's law, 259–261
resistor, **241**, 242, 250, 251, 255
retrograde motion, **388**, 389
revolution,
of Earth, **317**
of planets, 334, 335 *table*
of the Moon, 318, 319
rhizomes, 21
right ascension, **310**
rock (*also* earth), 123
rockets, 405
rocky planets, 332, 334
rotation,
of Earth, **316**
of planets, 334, 335 *table*
Russell, Henry Norris, 355
Rutherford, Ernest, 153 *table*

S

Saskatchewan:
Boundary Dam Power Station, 271, 272
Courtney Gress (Environmental Professional), 193
Dawn McGowan (Nurse), 100
Delvin Kanewiyakiho (Traditional Knowledge Keeper), 229
diamond mining, 163 *infoBit*
Dr. Edmond Lemire (Medical Geneticist), 71
Dr. Julia Green-Johnson (Research Microbiologist), 423
Dr. Lee Wilson (Research Chemist), 176
Elder Ann Marie Lemaigre, 108
Elder Julie Pitzel, 138
Elders Alfred and Ernestine Cheecham, 311
Fadiah Parsons (fine baking designer), 145
healing traditions of Indigenous peoples, 140

Indigenous cultural beliefs, 123
mining potash, 127
Kathryn A. Black (Senior Generation Planning Engineer), 281
PotashCorp, 231
renewable energy projects, 269, 270
Rod McEachern (Director R&D), 231
SaskPower, 281
Sheila Flynn (Horticulturist), 26
scientists contributing to genetic study, 69
uranium mining, 275
satellite, **318**
artificial, 407–411, 424, 425
Saturn, 333, 335, 336, 389
scales, 345
Schleiden, Matthias, 8
Schwaan, Theodor, 8
scrotum, **82**
seasons, 317
prediction of by ancient cultures, 308
secondary (rechargeable) cells, **244**
secondary female sex characteristics, 85
secondary male sex characteristics, **81**
seed, 32, 33
selective breeding, **61**
self-fertilization, 31
self-pollination, **31**
semen, 83, 84, 104–106
semiconductors, 160
seminal fluid, 83
seminal vesicle, 83
seminiferous tubules, **83**
sequential hermaphrodites, **30**
series circuit, **251**, 252
sex organs, 77–79, 81–90, 101–107
sex-linked genetic conditions, 66, 67
sextant, 309
sexual reproduction, **27**–33, 50
in humans, 77–79, 81–90, 101–107
short circuit, **262**
silicon, 160
silver, 159, 161
crystal model, 166 *illustr.*
Sirius, 352

Sky World, 328
smart meters, 285
snow line of the solar system, 333
sodium chloride (*also* table salt), 169, 170
solubility, 134 *table*
sodium,
chemistry of, 121
ion, 170
properties of, 164, 169
solar eclipse, **319**, 320
solar energy, 276
solar flares, **322**
solar prominence, **322**
solar radiation, 331
solar system, **329**–339
models of, 387–390
solar wind, 321, **323**, 333
solid, 124
solstices, 307
solubility, 134 *table*
solution, 125, **126**
of metals, 159
Southern Lights (*also* aurora australis), 323
space (*see* universe)
space exploration and research, benefits of, 406–411
challenges of, 415–420
spinoff products, 407
technology for, 402–406
space junk, 424, 425
space probes, 395, 396, 405, 406
space shuttles, 405, 425
disasters, 417
space stations, 405
space weather, 327
spectral lines, **383**–385
spectral shifting, **384**
spectrum (*pl.* spectra), **378**
sperm, **27**, 29, 33, 62, 63, 81, 83 *infoBit*, 93–95, 105, 106
spinoff, **406**, 407
spiral galaxies, 361, 362, 363 *infoBit*, 381
sponges, 33
spontaneous generation, 7
spores, **21**
spray painting, 227
spring equinox, 310
Sputnik 1, 407 *illustr.*
stamen, 31
star charts, 312
star clusters, 365

starfish, 22
stars, 305, 307, **321**, 328–332
birth, 352, 353
brightness (*also* luminosity), 351, 352, 360
classification, 354–356
death, 356–358
life cycles, 353, 354, 359
multiple systems, 352
navigation by, 309
spectral lines, 383–385
supernovas, 356–358
using a Hertzsprung-Russell diagram, 360
states,
of halogens, 183
of molecular compounds, 171
static, 207 *infoBit*
static electric charge (*also* electrostatic charge), **207**–229
uses of 227–229
transfer of, 213–219
Steady State theory, 386
sterilization, 105
style, 31
Styrofoam™, 124, 135 *table*
subatomic particles, **154**
substances (*see* matter classification)
sugar, 125 *illustr.*
sulphur, 160, 161
summer, 317
summer solstice, **307**
Summer Triangle, 306 *illustr.*
Sun, 307, 311, 329–333, 353, 354
distances of planets from, 332
eclipses of, 319, 320
effects on Earth, 323, 324
in ancient Boshongo peoples beliefs, 376
in ancient Egyptian beliefs, 375
in the geocentric model, 387
in the heliocentric model, 388, 389
physical features of, 321, 322
relative to Earth movements, 314–317
sundials, 397
sunspot, **321**
superconductors, **241**

©P

Periodic Table of Elements

1

metal	**C** solid	atomic number — 8 — ion charge (if more than one, first one is the most common)
metalloid	**Br** liquid	symbol — O — 2 –
non-metal	He gas	name — oxygen — atomic mass — 16.00

1
1	1+
H	
hydrogen	
1.01	

2

2
3	1+	4	2+
Li		**Be**	
lithium		beryllium	
6.94		9.01	

3
11	1+	12	2+
Na		**Mg**	
sodium		magnesium	
22.99		24.31	

3	**4**	**5**	**6**	**7**	**8**	**9**

4

19 1+	20 2+	21 3+	22 4+ 3+	23 5+ 4+	24 3+ 2+	25 2+ 4+	26 3+ 2+	27 2+ 3+
K	**Ca**	**Sc**	**Ti**	**V**	**Cr**	**Mn**	**Fe**	**Co**
potassium	calcium	scandium	titanium	vanadium	chromium	manganese	iron	cobalt
39.10	40.08	44.96	47.87	50.94	52.00	54.94	55.85	58.93

5

37 1+	38 2+	39 3+	40 4+	41 5+ 3+	42 6+	43 7+	44 3+ 4+	45 3+
Rb	**Sr**	**Y**	**Zr**	**Nb**	**Mo**	**Tc**	**Ru**	**Rh**
rubidium	strontium	yttrium	zirconium	niobium	molybdenum	technetium	ruthenium	rhodium
85.47	87.62	88.91	91.22	92.91	95.94	(98)	101.07	102.91

6

55 1+	56 2+	57–71	72 4+	73 5+	74 6+	75 7+	76 4+	77 4+
Cs	**Ba**		**Hf**	**Ta**	**W**	**Re**	**Os**	**Ir**
cesium	barium		hafnium	tantalum	tungsten	rhenium	osmium	iridium
132.91	137.33		178.49	180.95	183.84	186.21	190.23	192.22

7

87 1+	88 2+	89–103	104	105	106	107	108	109
Fr	**Ra**		**Rf**	**Db**	**Sg**	**Bh**	**Hs**	**Mt**
francium	radium		rutherfordium	dubnium	seaborgium	bohrium	hassium	meitnerium
(223)	(226)		(261)	(262)	(266)	(264)	(277)	(268)

6

57 3+	58 3+	59 3+	60 3+	61 3+	62 3+ 2+	63 3+ 2+
La	**Ce**	**Pr**	**Nd**	**Pm**	**Sm**	**Eu**
lanthanum	cerium	praseodymium	neodymium	promethium	samarium	europium
138.91	140.12	140.91	144.24	(145)	150.36	151.96

7

89 3+	90 4+	91 5+ 4+	92 6+ 4+	93 5+	94 4+ 6+	95 3+ 4+
Ac	**Th**	**Pa**	**U**	**Np**	**Pu**	**Am**
actinium	thorium	protactinium	uranium	neptunium	plutonium	americium
(227)	232.04	231.04	238.03	(237)	(244)	(243)

©P

						18
13	14	15	16	17		2 He helium 4.00

10	11	12						

Top block:

				5 **B** boron 10.81	6 **C** carbon 12.01	7 N $^{3-}$ nitrogen 14.01	8 O $^{2-}$ oxygen 16.00	9 F $^{1-}$ fluorine 19.00	10 Ne neon 20.18

			13 **Al** $^{3+}$ aluminum 26.98	14 **Si** silicon 28.09	15 **P** $^{3-}$ phosphorus 30.97	16 **S** $^{2-}$ sulphur 32.07	17 Cl $^{1-}$ chlorine 35.45	18 Ar argon 39.95

28 **Ni** $^{2+}_{3+}$ nickel 58.69	29 **Cu** $^{2+}_{1+}$ copper 63.55	30 **Zn** $^{2+}$ zinc 65.41	31 **Ga** $^{3+}$ gallium 69.72	32 **Ge** $^{4+}$ germanium 72.64	33 **As** $^{3-}$ arsenic 74.92	34 **Se** $^{2-}$ selenium 78.96	35 **Br** $^{1-}$ bromine 79.90	36 Kr krypton 83.80
46 **Pd** $^{2+}_{4+}$ palladium 106.42	47 **Ag** $^{1+}$ silver 107.87	48 **Cd** $^{2+}$ cadmium 112.41	49 **In** $^{3+}$ indium 114.82	50 **Sn** $^{4+}_{2+}$ tin 118.71	51 **Sb** $^{3+}_{5+}$ antimony 121.76	52 **Te** $^{2-}$ tellurium 127.60	53 **I** $^{1-}$ iodine 126.90	54 Xe xenon 131.29
78 **Pt** $^{4+}_{2+}$ platinum 195.08	79 **Au** $^{3+}_{1+}$ gold 196.97	80 **Hg** $^{2+}_{1+}$ mercury 200.59	81 **Tl** $^{1+}_{3+}$ thallium 204.38	82 **Pb** $^{2+}_{4+}$ lead 207.21	83 **Bi** $^{3+}_{5+}$ bismuth 208.98	84 **Po** $^{2+}_{4+}$ polonium (209)	85 **At** $^{1-}$ astatine (210)	86 Rn radon (222)
110 **Ds** darmstadtium (271)	111 **Rg** roentgenium (272)	112 **Uub** ununbium (285)	113 **Uut** ununtrium (284)	114 **Uuq** ununquadium (289)	115 **Uup** ununpentium (288)	116 **Uuh** ununhexium (293)	117 **Uus** ununseptium (?)	118 **Uuo** ununoctium (294)

Lanthanide/Actinide block:

64 **Gd** $^{3+}$ gadolinium 157.25	65 **Tb** $^{3+}$ terbium 158.93	66 **Dy** $^{3+}$ dysprosium 162.50	67 **Ho** $^{3+}$ holmium 164.93	68 **Er** $^{3+}$ erbium 167.26	69 **Tm** $^{3+}$ thulium 168.93	70 **Yb** $^{3+}_{2+}$ ytterbium 173.04	71 **Lu** $^{2+}$ lutetium 174.97
96 **Cm** $^{3+}$ curium (247)	97 **Bk** $^{3+}_{4+}$ berkelium (247)	98 **Cf** $^{3+}$ californium (251)	99 **Es** $^{3+}$ einsteinium (252)	100 **Fm** $^{3+}$ fermium (257)	101 **Md** $^{2+}_{3+}$ mendelevium (258)	102 **No** $^{2+}_{3+}$ nobelium (259)	103 **Lr** $^{3+}$ lawrencium (262)